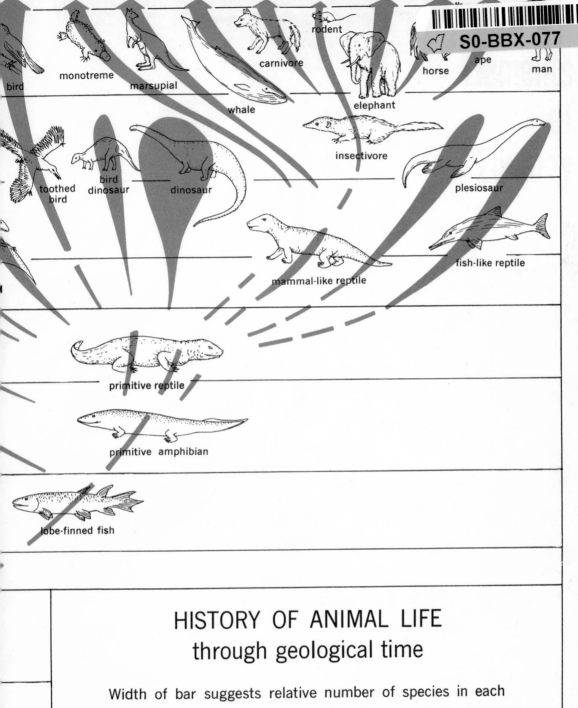

bird
monotreme
marsupial
carnivore
rodent
whale
elephant
horse
ape
man
insectivore

toothed bird
bird dinosaur
dinosaur
plesiosaur
mammal-like reptile
fish-like reptile

primitive reptile

primitive amphibian

lobe-finned fish

HISTORY OF ANIMAL LIFE
through geological time

Width of bar suggests relative number of species in each group during different eras and periods. Broken bars indicate possible origins and also periods when paleontological evidence is lacking.

(invertebrates on back end papers)

Elements of Zoology

THIRD EDITION

Tracy I. Storer
Professor of Zoology, Emeritus
University of California,
Davis

Robert L. Usinger
Professor of Entomology
University of California,
Berkeley

James W. Nybakken
Associate Professor of
Biological Sciences
California State College
at Hayward

McGRAW-HILL BOOK COMPANY

New York
St. Louis
San Francisco
Toronto
London
Sydney

Preface

This book is intended as a text for the elementary course in colleges and universities, particularly for situations where the student takes only one semester of work in zoology. In essential pattern it follows the authors' larger work, "General Zoology" (McGraw-Hill Book Company), in being divided into two major parts: principles of animal biology and an account of the major types and groups of animals—from protozoans to mankind.

The discussion of each animal type includes an account of its structure and bodily processes together with a summary of its habits and reproduction. The relations of animals to their natural environments and their importance to man also receive consideration. The broader aspects of animal biology—heredity and genetics, ecology and distribution, and evolution—are dealt with in special chapters. Throughout the book the subject matter has been arranged to facilitate use by students and instructors for both readings and reference in connection with lectures and laboratory exercises.

A review is provided at the end of each chapter so that students may test their knowledge and understanding of the subject matter. Because of space limitations, the lists of references found in the larger book are omitted.

Further aids for the introductory course in zoology are available in the "Laboratory Manual for Zoology," the "Laboratory Workbook for Zoology," and a series of ten silent filmstrips that deal with animal groups from protozoans to lower chordates. These were prepared by Tracy I. Storer and produced by the McGraw-Hill Book Company.

Technical words in the text are distinguished by different typefaces, as follows: anatomical and other special terms, *vertebra, gamete;* scientific names of genera or species, *Rana pipiens, Mus;* names of families and higher systematic groups, CULICIDAE, PROTOZOA. Names of fossil animals or groups are preceded by a dagger (†).

This third edition includes a revised account of the physical and chemical properties of matter in the animal body. The role of nucleic acids, DNA and RNA, in both cellular functions and heredity are stressed. Electron micrographs have been added to show the finer details of cell structure. The steps in glycolysis and the citric acid cycle for producing metabolic energy are described. Advances in animal physiology and biochemistry are incorporated in the accounts of organ systems. Chapters on the phyla and classes of animals in Part II have been revised to reflect results of new research. The chapter on the history of mankind has been updated with material from recent findings in this rapidly advancing field. On the end papers, the time scale of geological periods and eras shows the results of late determinations. Some text illustrations have been redesigned and some are new. Appropriate pictures at the heads of chapters provide additional illustrations of animal form and function. These are by the senior author except as credited otherwise.

Illustrations supplied through the courtesy of other authors and publishers are credited as to source in the legends. The several artists and kindly critics of the larger work have contributed indirectly to the present book, and their aid is again appreciated. Miss Phoebe Chapman (Mrs. George McNeely) aided in preliminary drafts of several chapters for the present book. The new and reworked figures are all the work of Mrs. Emily E. (Thompson) Reid, who has been a constant help and inspiration to the authors in endeavoring to portray the subject matter of zoology.

Tracy I. Storer
Robert L. Usinger
James W. Nybakken

Contents

Text-films

The following McGraw-Hill Text-Films, all 35-mm. silent filmstrips, are available for use with this book.

Protozoans
Sponges and Coelenterates
Flatworms
Roundworms
Echinoderms
Mollusks
Segmented Worms
Class Crustacea
Class Insecta
Chordates

Part one
Animal Biology

1
Introduction

1-1. The physical world. The earth is formed of nonliving (inanimate) rocks, minerals, soil, and water. Through millions of years its crust has been pushed up and folded by volcanic and other forces and has been worn down by weathering and erosion. These opposing natural agencies have produced the surface relief of mountains, valleys, plains, continents, islands, ocean basins, rivers, and lakes. From the highest mountain to the greatest ocean depth is only 0.3 per cent of the earth's radius, although the differences seem large in human estimation. The soil, rocks, and other features vary in composition, texture, and other characteristics according to the minerals whence they were derived and their geological history. About 72 per cent of the earth's surface is covered by water. The fresh waters of lakes and streams contain small amounts of dissolved chemicals, and the inland brackish or alkaline waters have larger mineral contents. The salt waters of the oceans and connecting inlets and bays average about 3.5 per cent in dissolved salts, chiefly sodium chloride (NaCl).

The daily rotation of the earth on its axis brings the alternations of day and night, and the longer circuit of the earth on its elliptical and inclined orbit around the sun is responsible for the changing seasons. In consequence, the effective solar radiation varies at any one place. This makes for local differences in temperature of the soil, water, and air, in the distribution of water as rain, snow, ice, or water vapor, and in local movements of the atmosphere such as wind. Collectively these influences form what we term *climate,* and different parts of the earth's surface are subjected to various climates, hot or cold, wet or dry, windy or still. The end result of all these differences in surface form (topography), water relations, and climate is a wide variety of physical environments.

BIOLOGY

1-2. The world of life. The earth is populated by living organisms, the plants and animals. These live in a shallow zone on and in the land, in the fresh waters, and in the salt waters. Whether life occurs on other planets or elsewhere in the universe is unknown. Living organisms exist on the earth only under certain physical conditions which include the presence of (1) the chemical substances that go to make up the bodies of animals and plants; (2) water; (3) an atmosphere containing oxygen; (4) energy from the sun as solar radiation necessary for plants to manufacture the organic compounds usable by animals as food; and (5) certain limits of temperature, usually about 0 to 50°C. (32 to 122°F.). Some animals, however, gain their

Illustration at top of page: The study of zoology. Laboratory instructor demonstrating to students.

oxygen indirectly from their food, some do not need sunlight, and many can survive only within narrower temperature limits.

1-3. The Animal Kingdom. The world contains an enormous population of living animals, both kinds (more than 1,000,000) and numbers, and many others have lived during past geological time in the history of the earth. Animals differ in size, structure, internal physiological processes, manner of life, and other ways. The seas and lands, the lakes and streams, the swamps and meadows, the grasslands, the shrubs and trees of natural forests and cultivated places, the deserts, and all other types of environments each have distinctive kinds of animal inhabitants, some abundant and others rare. Most animals are affected by enemies, diseases, and competitors. The total of all these interactions comprises the "web of life" or the "balance of nature," a dynamic complex of forces, physical and biological, that affects every living organism.

All human beings, from primitive natives to the best educated, in country or city, are associated with some sorts of animal life. Certain kinds affect the well-being and health of mankind, for good or evil. The lives and habits of animals provide a highly interesting field of study for many people. There is already a great amount of detailed knowledge about animals—enough in book form to fill a large library—but much more is still to be learned, even about the most familiar animals.

1-4. Science (Latin *scientia*, knowledge) is exact knowledge or tested and verified human experience. A scientist is a person who probes into the unknown, asks questions, and seeks answers by observations and experiments.

The raw materials of science are *facts*, the real state of things in contrast to beliefs or impressions. Accumulated facts or *data* (singular *datum*) are the primary records of science. Simple facts—that fire is hot, or water is wet—are learned by direct experience, but science requires precise methods. By use of calibrated instruments the findings of one scientist may be compared with those of others. A thermometer, for example, measures temperature, the degree of accuracy depending on the type of instrument used. The electron microscope, cyclotron, and electronic computer are instruments that opened new fields and added greater precision to others.

A common observation—that moths are attracted to a candle flame—can be used to illustrate the scientific method. To a scientist this suggests a general proposition, a relation of cause (light) and effect (attraction). As a working explanation or *hypothesis* he assumes that moths react positively to light. Experiments then are planned to test the hypothesis. A trap is devised containing a bright light. A second trap (the control) has no light. In repeated tests moths are attracted to the lighted trap but not to the dark trap. Further experiments show that various kinds of moths react to lights of different wavelengths and intensity. This permits formulating a more definite statement or *theory*—that certain kinds of moths are attracted by blue light but repelled by yellow or red. Finally, after repeated proof connecting cause and effect, a theory may be restated as a *law* or *general principle*. Yet the scientific method accepts nothing as completely infallible. New facts may require change or rejection of a previously accepted law.

1-5. Zoology. The science dealing with animal life is *zoology* (Greek *zoön*, animal + *logos*, discourse). It includes all common knowledge about animals together with more technical data. Zoology deals with the structure and bodily functions of animals, their habits, where and how they live, their relations with one another and with their environments, their classification, and many other features. In short, all the facts, conclusions, theories, and laws relating to animal life make up the science of zoology. Together with botany, the science of plants, it forms *biology* (Gr. *bios*, life), the science of life. These and other fields dealing with the phenomena of nature such as geology (earth structure), physiography (earth-surface features), meteorology (atmosphere), etc., are the natural sciences. They stand in contrast to the physical sciences—physics, the properties of matter, and chemistry, the composition of matter.

Like other sciences, zoology has been subdivided with the great growth of knowledge; a few of the special fields are:

ANATOMY (Gr. *ana,* up + *temno,* cut), structure as revealed by dissection

MORPHOLOGY (Gr. *morphe,* form), structure as a whole (Chaps. 2, 4–10, 16–29)

HISTOLOGY (Gr. *histos,* tissue), microstructure of tissues (Chap. 3)

PHYSIOLOGY (Gr. *physis,* nature), living processes or functions within animals (Chaps. 2–10, 16–29)

NUTRITION (L. *nutrio,* feed), use and conversion of food substances (Chap. 5)

EMBRYOLOGY (Gr. *en,* in + *bryo,* swell), growth and development within the egg (Chap. 11)

GENETICS (Gr. *genesis,* origin), heredity and variation (Chaps. 12, 14)

BEHAVIOR (ethology), study of responses of animals to stimuli as a means of seeking the causative factors involved (Chap. 10)

NATURAL HISTORY, life and habits of animals in their natural surroundings (Chaps. 2, 13, 16–29)

ECOLOGY (Gr. *oikos,* house), relations of animals to their environments (Chaps. 2, 13, 16–29)

ZOOGEOGRAPHY (Gr. *zoön,* animal + geography), distribution of animals in space (Chap. 13)

PALEONTOLOGY (Gr. *palaios,* ancient + *ont,* being),

fossil animals and their distribution in time (Chaps. 13, 14, 16–29)

EVOLUTION (L. *e,* out + *volvo,* roll), origin and differentiation of animal life (Chap. 14)

TAXONOMY (Gr. *taxis,* arrangement + *nomos,* law), classification of animals and principles thereof (Chap. 15)

Zoology is also divided for the study of particular animal groups that are of special interest or importance into such fields as:

PROTOZOOLOGY, study of the one-celled animals, or PROTOZOA (Chap. 16)

ENTOMOLOGY, study of insects; further subdivided into insect taxonomy, economic entomology, etc. (Chap. 23)

1-6. Living things. The average person can distinguish most kinds of living organisms from nonliving or inorganic matter—a tree, or bird, or worm from a rock or some chemical substance—but this is not easy with some lowly forms of life. The seed of a plant or the egg of an insect seems inert, but each, when placed under suitable conditions, will soon reveal its living nature.

Some important basic differences between living and nonliving things are as follows:

1. FORM AND SIZE. Each sort of living thing or organism usually has a definite form and a characteristic size (Figs. 1-1, 1-2). Most of them are also arranged as distinct individuals. A whale or a flea or any common plant is recognized by such features. In contrast nonliv-

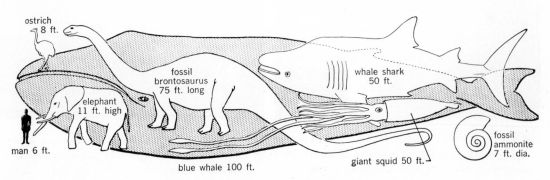

Fig. 1-1. The largest animals as compared with man. (*Adapted from C. R. Knight.*)

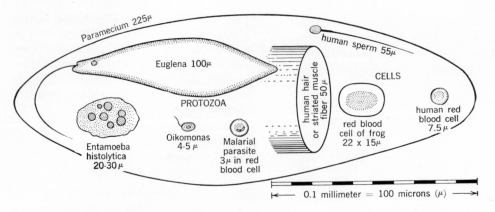

Fig. 1-2. Some of the smallest animals and some animal cells, all included within the outline of a *Paramecium*. Magnified to 500 × natural size.

ing materials usually vary in both size and form, from a sand grain to a rock or a drop of water to an ocean; but many crystals are quite constant in form.

2. CHEMICAL COMPOSITION. Living organisms are composed largely of four chemical elements: carbon (C), hydrogen (H), oxygen (O), and nitrogen (N) in various but definite proportions; these four occur with lesser amounts of calcium (Ca), phosphorus (P), sodium (Na), potassium (K), iron (Fe), copper (Cu), sulfur (S), chlorine (Cl), etc. These

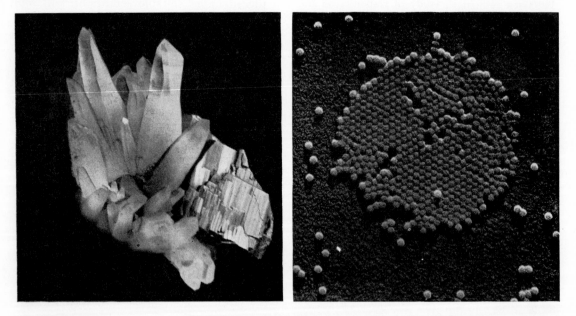

Fig. 1-3. Nonliving vs. living things. *Left.* Crystals of quartz (long, white) and of iron pyrites; ¾ natural size. *Right.* Crystallized form of the poliomyelitis virus that lives and multiplies in cells of animals, including man. 110,000×. (*Electron microscope photo from W. M. Stanley.*)

elements, when bound with one or more atoms of carbon, form complex organic molecules, often of great molecular weight; together they make the living substance or **protoplasm** of the plant or animal. The same and other chemical elements occur in the much smaller molecules that comprise the nonliving minerals, rocks, and soil.

3. ORGANIZATION. Each organism is made up of microscopic cells (and cell products) and these are formed as interrelated systems of organs for performing the various life processes. But in rocks or minerals, any structural arrangement results from the nature of the constituent materials or the manner of formation, as with crystals (Fig. 1-3).

4. METABOLISM. With living organisms various essential processes, collectively termed *metabolism,* are constantly in progress, such as intake and use of food, respiration, secretion, excretion, etc. Nonliving things are relatively stable.

5. IRRITABILITY. Protoplasm and living organisms react to changes (stimuli) in the environment that produce changes (responses) by the organism. Stimuli may be external, such as heat, light, moisture, or contact; or they may be internal. The degree of response often is not proportionate to the stimulus and the organism commonly is not permanently altered by the stimulus. If nonliving materials react, there is definite quantitative relation between the amount of environmental change and the effect produced, as in expansion of a metal by heat.

6. REPRODUCTION. Each sort of living organism has the ability to reproduce itself in kind —pine seeds produce pine trees, not oaks; and the eggs of chickens produce chicks, not ducklings or rabbits. Nonliving things cannot reproduce.

7. GROWTH AND LIFE CYCLE. A living organism grows by development of new parts between or within older ones, and may replace parts during life. Each kind of organism has a definite life cycle: birth, growth, maturity, and death. If nonliving things increase, they do so by external action, as in the case of crystals.

Viruses are, in some ways, intermediate between living and nonliving things (some have been crystallized); but they can grow only in living cells.

1-7. Animals vs. plants. Most living organisms can be easily referred to either the ANIMAL KINGDOM or the PLANT KINGDOM, but some are more difficult to segregate. Animals commonly can move about or move parts of the body, but certain kinds become fixed early in life (sponges, sea anemones, oysters, barnacles), and other fixed forms (hydroids, bryozoans) are of plant-like form. The free-moving green flagellates that contain chlorophyll are considered plants by botanists and animals by zoologists. Some important differences between animals and plants are:

1. FORM AND STRUCTURE. The animal body form is rather invariable, the organs are mostly internal, growth usually produces changes in proportions with age, the cell walls are delicate, and the body fluids contain sodium chloride (NaCl). In plants the form often is variable, organs are added externally, the cells commonly are within thick cellulose walls, and sodium chloride usually is toxic. In plants most growth is at the ends of organs and often continues throughout life, but each kind of plant has a normal growth limit.

2. METABOLISM. Animals require complex organic materials as food, obtained by eating plants or other animals. These foods are broken down (digested) and reorganized chemically within the body. Oxygen (O_2) is needed for respiration. The end products of metabolism are mainly carbon dioxide (CO_2), water (H_2O), and urea ($NH_2)_2CO$. Plants also carry on metabolism but in addition they use water, carbon dioxide from the air, and inorganic chemicals obtained in solution from the soil. By photosynthesis—the action of sunlight on the green pigment known as chlorophyll— these simple materials are formed into vari-

ous organic compounds and oxygen is released as a by-product (Fig. 13-1).

3. IRRITABILITY. Most animals have a nervous system and respond quickly to stimuli; plants have no such system and react slowly.

1-8. Importance of animals to man. The domestic mammals and birds, together with fishes, supply mankind his principal proteins, fats, and oils for food. Oysters, crabs, shrimps, and some other animals also are eaten. Sheep wool and wild furs provide clothing, and bird feathers fill quilts and pillows. Animal hides yield leather and glue, the hair is made into felt, and many medicinal preparations are derived from internal organs and glands. Honey, beeswax, and sponges are other useful animal products. The livestock and meat-packing industries, the commercial fisheries, the fur trade, and beekeeping provide profitable occupations for thousands of persons.

The lower animals aid in understanding human physiology and nutrition. Much useful knowledge comes from research on frogs, rats, rabbits, and dogs. These and other "laboratory animals" serve importantly in studies of hormones, vitamins, and the action of drugs.

Wild animals are of esthetic and recreational interest to man, and certain kinds provide for the healthful outdoor sports of hunting and fishing.

Certain large predatory animals kill useful wild animals and some domestic livestock. Insects and rodents that feed on crop plants, forest trees, and grasslands levy a toll that requires large expenditures for control. Other insects and the "house" rats and mice damage property and stored foods. Some insects, spiders, scorpions, and snakes are dangerously poisonous. Many kinds of parasites—protozoans, worms, insects, and ticks—bring illness and death to man, his livestock, and to desirable wild animals. The protozoan parasites of malaria and the virus of yellow fever carried by mosquitoes, the bacteria of plague transmitted by fleas, the typhus spread by lice and fleas, and other diseases carried by animals

have exercised a dominant role in the history of mankind through the ages.

HISTORY OF ZOOLOGY

1-9. Early zoology. Prehistoric man had a practical interest in animals that provided food, clothing, and other essentials and in the wild beasts that menaced him. Later, animals came to have a part in his religion, medicine, and art. The Cro-Magnon peoples made paintings of animals and some animal statues (Fig. 1-4) in the caves of southwestern Europe. Much later the ancient civilizations about the eastern Mediterranean produced pottery, sculpture, and tapestries that show notable skill in portraying animals. The languages of all primitive races include many terms pertaining to animals; and as these differ from tribe to tribe, they indicate that knowledge of animals is as old as the languages themselves.

The earliest "written" records were cut on stones or marked on clay tablets, later baked for permanency. In Egypt and other Mediterranean countries rolls of papyrus and sheets of animal skin (vellum) were used for preparing manuscripts (L. *manus,* hand + *scribo,* write); these were numerous, as the Greek library at Alexandria (second century B.C.) had over 700,000 scrolls ("books"), and other libraries had large collections. Such manuscripts were copied and recopied through the years, many were lost entirely or in part, and only a limited number survived from early centuries of the Christian era down to the advent of printing (about A.D. 1450). Early records of zoology, like those in other fields of knowledge, therefore are fragmentary.

The first serious attention to biology and zoology, however, is found among the early Greeks. Anaximander (611?–547? B.C.) believed in some sort of evolutionary sequence from lower types to man. Xenophanes (sixth century B.C.) first recognized fossils as animal remains and inferred that their presence on mountains indicated the latter had once been

Fig. 1-4. Animal drawings by prehistoric men in caves of western France and northern Spain—horse, wooly mammoth, ibex, bison, bog elk, and rhinoceros. Some originals were in color. (*After copies by Breuil, far reduced.*)

beneath the sea. Empedocles (fifth century B.C.) reportedly rid a town of malaria by draining nearby swamps. The domestication of animals by early civilizations (Chap. 29) yielded practical information on breeding, growth, and nutrition.

1-10. Greeks and Romans. The first zoologist of record, and one of the greatest, was Aristotle (Greek, 384–322 B.C.). He was a student of Plato and lectured at the Lyceum in Athens. He wrote extensively on philosophy and politics, besides zoology. His manuscripts were copied repeatedly, the oldest surviving being from about the ninth century A.D. His *Historia animalium* of nine "books" (about 500 printed pages in modern translation) deals with the structure and habits of many animals native to Greece, Macedonia, and Asia. Fragments of his *Parts of Animals* and *Reproduction of Animals* also survive. Aristotle learned the daily progress of development of the chick embryo, knew that drone bees develop by parthenogenesis, and that some kinds of sharks bear living young. He

emphasized the value of direct observation, recognized law and order in biological phenomena, and derived conclusions inductively from observed facts. He visualized an evolutionary development from lower to higher forms, ascribed to a supreme "guiding intelligence."

The Romans were mainly practical administrators and soldiers, and made few contributions to zoology. Pliny the Elder (A.D. 23–79) compiled a "natural history" of 37 books covering all natural phenomena, zoology, medicine, and other topics. Containing little that was new, nevertheless it was a major source book for over 1,500 years. Galen (A.D. 130–200), a Greek physician, later of Rome, was the last great biologist of antiquity. He wrote of human anatomy from dissections of lower animals and made some physiological experiments. For 10 centuries his writings comprised the only text on medical anatomy and were considered infallible. A downward trend in scientific inquiry began before the end of the Greek civilization and continued throughout the existence of the Roman Empire and later while barbarians ruled Europe.

1-11. European zoologists. The revival of learning, or the Renaissance, began in the thirteenth century and was stimulated by reports from the travels and voyages of Marco Polo, Vasco da Gama, Columbus, and Magellan. Zoologists of the next three centuries compiled works on the natural history of animals in which there was a gradual increase in records of original observation and less dependence on the writings of Aristotle, Pliny, and Galen. Of note in this respect are Albertus Magnus (Bavarian, 1206–1280), Konrad Gesner (Swiss, 1516–1565), and Rondelet (French, 1507–1566).

Andreas Vesalius (Belgian, 1514–1564) was first to publish a large illustrated text *On the Structure of the Human Body* (1543), figuring carefully the skeleton and muscles as determined by original dissections (Fig. 1-5). William Harvey (English, 1578–1657) introduced into physiology the experimental method and use of deductions from quantitative data. Harvey's book *De motu cordis* (1628) contained convincing proof on the circulation of the blood. From observations on lower animals he described how the chambers of the heart fill and empty in turn by muscular action and how the blood spurts from a cut artery in keeping with contractions of the heart. Finally, by calculations, he showed that so much blood passes through the heart in an hour or day that it must be recirculated constantly, thereby disproving the erroneous speculations of earlier writers. Harvey also described the development of the chick (1651) and inferred that mammals are produced from eggs.

With the invention of the compound microscope, about 1590, an essential tool became available for study of the smaller animals and the minute parts of larger animals (Fig. 1-6). The cellular structure of plants was described in 1665 by Robert Hooke (English, 1635–1703), but the real founder of microanatomy

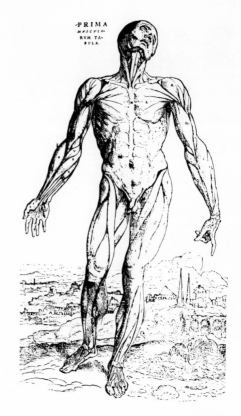

Fig. 1-5. The first accurate portrayal of the human body. Much reduced from a plate in *De fabrica corporis humani* by Andreas Vesalius, 1543.

in both plants and animals was Marcello Malpighi (Italian, 1628–1694), who wrote many papers on the subject. Antony van Leeuwenhoek (Dutch, 1632–1723) discovered and described blood corpuscles, spermatozoa, protozoans, striated muscles, and many other microscopic items.

The first compound microscope with two separated lenses is ascribed to J. and Z. Janssen and Galileo. Prior to this time only hand lenses (and reading spectacles) were known, dating from the thirteenth century or earlier. Today the best compound microscopes magnify about 2,000 times and resolve objects about 1.0 micron (μ) apart. Since 1934 the electron microscope with magnifications to

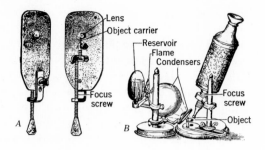

Fig. 1-6. Development of the microscope. (*A*) One of Leeuwenhoek's "microscopes," about 1673, a simple magnifier used in sunlight. (*B*) Robert Hooke's microscope, 1665, with lamp and condenser to concentrate light on the object.

30,000 times or more has been used with extremely thin preparations of animal tissues to reveal the fine structure of cell parts.

For centuries, naturalists listed animals without any particular arrangement or followed a system extracted from Aristotle. Carolus Linnaeus (Swedish, 1707–1778) began in 1735 to publish a *Systema naturae* that passed through 12 editions, the last in 1768. This was a methodical catalogue of plants, animals, and minerals, in larger and subsidiary groups. He gradually perfected his scheme and also developed a binomial system of nomenclature in which each kind of organism was designated by a scientific name of two parts—genus and species. His tenth edition (1758) is the starting point for binomial nomenclature as used in zoology today. Linnaeus stimulated interest in collecting, classifying, and naming organisms, leading to the great natural history museums of today.

From the seventeenth century onward there was an increasing interest in original study of animals as to their embryological development, their structure both gross and microscopic, the physiological processes within their bodies, and various other aspects. The foundations of comparative anatomy and of paleontology, the study of animal fossils, stem from Georges Cuvier (French, 1769–1832). The

"cell theory," that all animals and plants are composed of cells and cell products, began in 1824 with René Dutrochet (French, 1776–1847) but was definitely stated for plants in 1838 by M. J. Schleiden (German, 1804–1881) and for animals in 1839 by Theodor Schwann (German, 1810–1882).

1-12. Evolution. Among the most important and most fruitful concepts of zoology are those dealing with evolution—the origin of species—and heredity and genetics—the manner and mechanism of inheritance. Early writers from Aristotle onward had dealt with evolution, but Charles Darwin (English, 1809–1882) firmly established the theory of evolution based on natural selection (1859) as the guiding principle for all subsequent biological work (see Chap. 14). In like manner, the fundamental researches of Gregor Johann Mendel (Austrian, 1822–1884), which were published in 1866, have provided the basis for all modern investigations in inheritance (see Chap. 12).

MODERN ZOOLOGY

Today zoology is an ever-widening field of study in which rapid strides are being made by a great many investigators. Older subjects, such as comparative anatomy, classification, and embryology, are pursued from increasingly enlightened viewpoints. Experimental zoology, genetics, and the physiology of tissues and cells are explored by refined methods and instruments. New fields have opened and expanded in the study of hormones, vitamins, enzymes, and mineral metabolism. "Tagged" chemical elements made radioactive by one or another means are fed or injected and traced in animal bodies to determine the manner of storage, utilization, and disposal of components in food and body metabolism. The older descriptive natural history of wild animals is being supplanted by quantitative measurements and by the study of individuals and populations, which are yielding clearer

Aristotle
384–322 B.C.

William Harvey
1578–1657

Carolus Linnaeus
1707–1778

Theodor Schwann
1810–1882

Charles Darwin
1809–1882

Gregor Johann Mendel
1822–1884

Fig. 1-7. Some leaders in the development of zoology.

understanding of the events and processes in nature.

1-13. The study of zoology. Many students have some general knowledge about certain kinds of animals gained from everyday experiences in country or city, or from museums and zoological gardens. To expand this knowledge, the beginning course in zoology provides a general outline of the Animal Kingdom, the kinds and numbers of animals, the structure of representatives in different groups, the bodily (physiological) processes, and the ways that animals live. To this is added an understanding of how animals grow and reproduce, the principles of inheritance (heredity), the distribution of animal life over the earth today and in past geological time, and finally how the existing kinds of animals came into being—the theory of organic evolution. Further work in zoology is designed to expand the student's knowledge beyond the limits of an introductory course and to deal with other aspects of the subject.

The requirements for successful study of zoology are simple: (1) ability to observe carefully and to report accurately that which is seen; (2) absolute honesty in all work—a prime requirement in all branches of science; (3) clear thinking to arrive at dependable deductions or inferences from observations; and (4) a judicial attitude to appraise the relative values of conflicting evidence and to arrive at appropriate conclusions—but with a willingness to abandon or alter such conclusions in the presence of evidence pointing in another direction. Skill in attaining all these requirements may be gained even in an elementary course.

The purposes in studying zoology are several. Some knowledge of animals is part of a well-rounded education; it is the basis for specialized education in medicine. Many persons find pleasure in learning about animals, and some develop a special interest in particular groups—birds, insects, fishes, or others—which they follow as a side line of interest beyond the duties of their daily lives. And a knowledge of those animals of practical importance to mankind is essential in our advancing civilization.

REVIEW

1. What physical conditions are necessary for the existence of living organisms on the earth?
2. Distinguish between the natural sciences and the physical sciences; also between biology and zoology.
3. What are the basic differences between living organisms and nonliving objects?
4. What influences contribute to form the various climates at different places on the earth?
5. In what outstanding ways are animals of concern to man?
6. How did each of the following persons contribute to modern biology: Vesalius, Harvey, Malpighi, Leeuwenhoek, Linnaeus, Cuvier, Schleiden, Schwann, Darwin, Mendel?
7. List some important requirements for successful study of zoology. Are these of equal significance in all branches of science and in other walks of life?
8. What is meant by the "scientific method" and how does this differ from other methods of drawing conclusions based on superficial observations or unverified opinions?

2
A representative animal, the frog

The body of any animal has a definite form (morphology) and is composed of various structural parts, both gross and microscopic. These enable it to carry on the activities necessary for life, the *physiological processes* within its body and the *external relations* with its environment. The frog is convenient for an introductory study because of its size and availability and because it shows many resemblances in form and function to the higher vertebrates and man[1] (Chaps. 26 to 29). The details of its structure can be determined easily by dissection, its physiology is well known and readily demonstrated, and its life habits, or *natural history,* are simple and easily observed. The following account will apply to any common species (Fig. 2-1).

2-1. Habits and external relations. Frogs live in water and in moist places on land; thus they are amphibious (Gr. *amphi,* both + *bios,* life). Each kind lives in a particular sort of surroundings, or *habitat,* such as marshes, pools, or streams. On land a frog rests with its short angular forelegs upright and the long

[1] No one kind of animal is "typical" of all vertebrates. As compared with other lower vertebrates, the frog is specialized in having a flat skull with few bones, only four front toes, few vertebrae, and no exoskeleton of scales.

hind legs folded beside the body. When disturbed, it jumps by suddenly extending the hind legs and feet. In the water it swims by alternately flexing and extending the hind legs, the broad webs between the toes pushing against the water and carrying the animal forward. It may float with all legs extended and only the eyes and nostrils above water; from this position it can turn and dive to the bottom by swimming.

The frog does those things which enable it to survive as an individual and to continue as a species. It must find live *food* of proper kind and amount, chiefly insects and worms, which are caught by a quick flip of the sticky mucus-coated tongue and swallowed entire. Motionless animals or objects are ignored, and undesirable food is rejected. The frog seeks *shelter* in the water to escape enemies, to avoid unfavorable weather, to moisten its skin, and to absorb water. In winter it avoids being frozen by burrowing into the mud of a pond for a winter sleep, or hibernation. Frogs seek shallow, quiet water as a *breeding place,* where their jelly-coated eggs are laid and fertilized. The eggs develop into embryos that hatch out as tadpoles or larvae. These feed and grow in the water and later transform into young frogs (Fig. 2-16). Various *enemies* eat frogs, thus reducing their numbers; snakes, turtles, herons, raccoons, and man are the chief ene-

Illustration at top of page: The bullfrog (*Rana catesbeiana*); length to 8 inches.

Fig. 2-1. The leopard or grass frog (*Rana pipiens*), about ½ natural size.

mies. From them frogs try to escape by leaping away, diving into water, and hiding in the bottom debris. Certain internal parasites and some *diseases* tend also to reduce the frog population. The *competitors* of frogs include other animals living in the same habitat that seek insects and similar food.

2-2. Organ systems and physiological processes. The body (like that of most animals) consists of several *organ systems,* each specialized by structure and function to perform some essential physiological process such as digestion, circulation, etc. These systems are integrated to work harmoniously with each other. Each system is composed of several *organs,* to perform some part of the general function; in the digestive system, the mouth is for food taking, the stomach for storage and digestion, and so on. An organ, in turn, is formed of several layers or parts known as *tissues;* and each tissue is composed of many microscopic *cells,* usually of like kind. The wall of the stomach contains four principal tissue layers, including digestive and gland cells, muscle cells, connective tissues, and others. The many substances comprising the cells are known collectively as *protoplasm* (Chap. 3). The frog's body includes the following organ systems (Fig. 2-3):

1. Body covering (skin)
2. Skeletal system
3. Muscular system
4. Digestive system
5. Circulatory system
6. Respiratory system
7. Excretory system
8. Endocrine system
9. Nervous system and sense organs
10. Reproductive system

2-3. External features. The *head* and *trunk* are broadly joined without neck region or tail, and there are two pairs of *legs,* or *limbs.* The entire animal is covered by soft, smooth, moist *skin.* The head (Fig. 2-2) bears a wide transverse *mouth* for taking food, two small *nostrils* (external nares) near the tip of the snout that serve in respiration, two large spherical *eyes* (organs of sight), and behind each eye a flat *eardrum* or *tympanic membrane* that receives sound waves. Each eye has a fleshy opaque upper eyelid and a lesser lower lid. Beneath these is a transparent third eyelid (nictitating membrane) that can move upward over the eyeball to keep it moist in the air and serve as a protection when under water. At the hind end of the body is the *vent,* or *anus,* a small opening through which are discharged undigested food wastes, the liquid excretory waste (urine) from the kidneys, and the sex cells (eggs or sperm) from the reproductive organs.

The short *front leg* (arm) comprises an up-

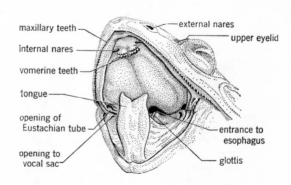

Fig. 2-2. Head and mouth of male bullfrog.

per arm, forearm, wrist, and hand; the latter has a small palm with tubercles beneath, four fingers (digits), and a vestigial "thumb." Each *hind leg* includes a thigh, shank or lower leg, ankle, and the long foot with a narrow sole (metatarsus) and five slender toes joined by broad, thin webs.

A frog is *bilaterally symmetrical,* with equivalent right and left sides. Structures on or toward the central longitudinal axis are termed *medial,* and those toward the sides are said to be *lateral.* The regions of the body are the *anterior end,* which moves forward; the opposite or *posterior end;* the back or *dorsal surface,* which is habitually uppermost; and the lower or *ventral surface* (see Fig. 15-3). The latter comprises the broad *throat* beneath the head; the chest, thorax, or *pectoral region* adjacent to the forelegs; the belly, or *abdo-*

men, behind; and the *pelvic region* between the hind legs.

2-4. Mouth cavity. Within the *upper* and *lower jaws* is the broad *mouth cavity.* This narrows behind as the *pharynx,* connecting to the gullet, or *esophagus.* The flat *tongue* is attached anteriorly to the mouth floor and has taste buds in small papillae on the upper surface. The mucus-coated posterior end can flip forward through the open mouth to capture food. Swallowing is accomplished by raising the mouth floor, in which a flat *hyoid cartilage* is embedded, and is aided by depressing the eyeballs. The upper jaw is margined by fine conical *maxillary teeth,* and the roof of the mouth has two patches of *vomerine teeth.* These all attach to the bone surfaces and are replaced if lost. They serve only to hold food. Near the vomerine teeth are two openings, the

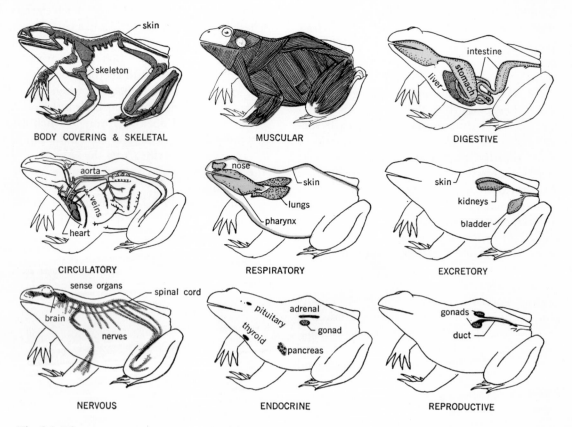

Fig. 2-3. The separate organ systems of a frog (compare Fig. 2-4).

internal nares, connecting with the nostrils, through which air passes to and from the mouth cavity in respiration. The *glottis* is a median ventral slit in the pharynx, behind the tongue, that guards the entrance to the lungs. It is opened for breathing but closes while food is being swallowed. Behind each eyeball and near the corner of the mouth there opens a small *Eustachian tube;* this connects to the middle ear chamber, beneath the eardrum, and allows the air pressure to be equalized on the two surfaces of the eardrum. Male frogs of many species have openings into two *vocal sacs* in the throat; these sacs can be inflated to amplify the croaking notes.

2-5. Internal structure. If the ventral skin and muscular body wall are cut away, the *internal organs* or *viscera* will be found inside the large *body cavity,* or *coelom.* A smooth, transparent membrane, the *peritoneum,* lines the cavity and covers the organs.

Most of the organs are suspended from the middorsal region by double layers of peritoneum, known as *mesenteries,* through which blood vessels and nerves connect to the organs (Figs. 2-4 and 2-5).

Far anterior in the coelom is (1) the reddish pear-shaped *heart* within a tissue sac (pericardium) filled with watery lymph. Beside the heart are (2) the two thin-walled elastic *lungs,* and behind these is (3) the firm brown *liver* of three rounded lobes with (4) the sac-like greenish *gall bladder* between the middle and right lobes. Parts of the digestive tract include (5) the short *esophagus* above the liver, (6) the long whitish *stomach* along the left side, (7) the slender and coiled *small intestine,* and (8) the bigger and dark *large intestine,* or *rectum,* that passes posteriorly. Along the fore part of the small intestine is (9) a slender irregular and whitish *pancreas.* Behind the stomach lies (10) a rounded reddish *spleen.* At

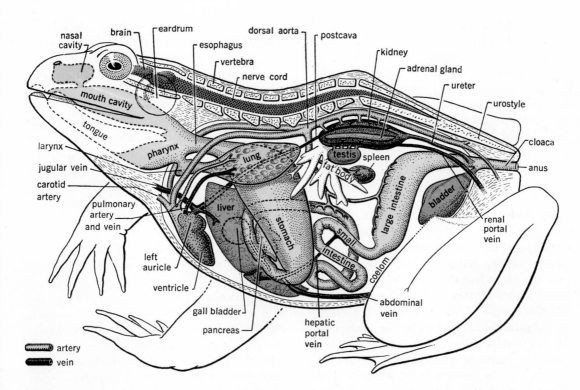

Fig. 2-4. The frog. Internal structure (compare Fig. 2-3).

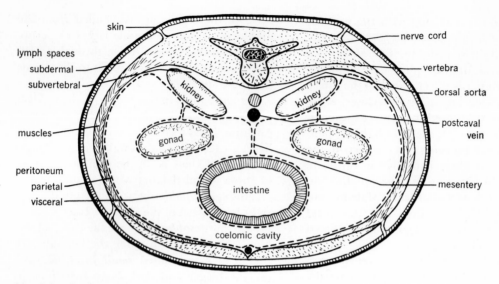

Fig. 2-5. The frog. Diagrammatic cross section of the body to show relations of the peritoneum (broken lines) to internal organs. The skin is multilayered (compare Fig. 2-6).

either side of the middorsal line, above the peritoneum, are (11) two long dark *kidneys.* The *bladder* (12) is a thin-walled sac midventrally at the posterior end of the coelom. Between the intestines and kidneys are (13) the *gonads,* or *sex organs.* A female has two large *ovaries,* containing many small dark spherical eggs, and two convoluted whitish *oviducts* extending along the dorsal wall of the coelom. In a male there are two small dark bean-shaped *testes.* To each sex organ is connected (14) a branched *fat body.* The rectum and the ducts from the kidneys and sex organs all enter (15) the *cloaca,* which opens at the anus.

2-6. Body covering. The thin flexible *skin* over the entire animal provides physical protection, excludes disease organisms, serves in respiration, and is the means of water absorption, because a frog does not drink. As in all land vertebrates, it comprises an outer stratified *epidermis* and a *dermis* beneath, both of several cell layers (Fig. 2-6). In the epidermis, the basal cells (germinative layer) produce successive layers of cells that move outward and flatten, the outermost becoming a thin cornified covering. Every month or so during

the summer, a new layer forms beneath and the old covering is molted, or sloughed off; it splits down the back, is worked off in one piece by the "hands," and usually is swallowed. The dermis is mainly of connective tissue. Its outer spongy portion contains glands and pigment cells over a dark-staining layer of fibers or granules. The deeper part is a compact bed of crossed connective tissue fibers, each layer at about 45 degrees with the body axis, making the skin flexible either along or across the body. In and beneath the dermis are nerves and blood vessels, the latter of importance in cutaneous (skin) respiration. The skin of frogs and toads, unlike that of other vertebrates, is attached to the body only along certain lines (Fig. 2-5).

The glands produce useful fluids, or *secretions,* that pass out on the epidermis through fine ducts. The many small *mucous glands* secrete a colorless watery fluid that keeps the skin moist, glistening, and sticky. If a frog is roughly handled or chloroformed, the scarcer but larger *poison glands* pour out a thick whitish alkaloidal secretion with a burning taste that protects the animal in some degree from enemies. Each gland has a spherical base

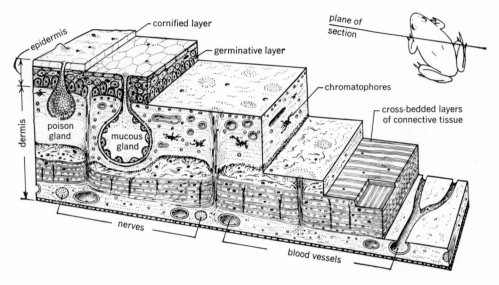

Fig. 2-6. The frog's skin. Enlarged stereogram showing the component cell layers, fibers, and other parts. The section is cut at 45 degrees to the main body axis as indicated in the small outline figure.

of secreting cells discharging into a central cavity, whence the secretion can be forced out of the neck or gland duct by the action of muscle fibers around its base. The loose attachment of the elastic skin and its mucus-covered surface often enable the frog to slip from the grasp of an enemy.

The skin is colored by scattered *pigment granules* in the epidermis and pigment cells, or *chromatophores,* in the dermis—melanophores with black or brown pigment, lipophores with red or yellow, and guanophores that contain whitish crystals. The skin of a tadpole may have over 300 chromatophores per square millimeter. Frogs are usually protectively colored to resemble their surroundings, green on the dorsal and lateral surfaces and pale to whitish beneath. There is no green pigment; the prevailing color results jointly from pigments that absorb some light rays and reflect others (chemical color) and the microscopic structure of the outer layers of the skin that reflects some colors and changes others (physical color due to interference phenomena). Dark spots are due to groupings of

melanophores and golden flecks to yellow lipophores. On most amphibians the patterns are stable, but the colors of some undergo marked changes. Darkening results when the pigment granules in the chromatophores are scattered, and paling occurs when they are concentrated; changes in color result from both external conditions and internal states. Pigment control is due in part to a hormone (intermedin) of the pituitary gland, in part to a hormone of the adrenal glands, and in part to the nervous system.

2-7. Skeletal system. The body framework is a jointed internal *skeleton* that supports the soft parts, protects vital organs, and affords attachments for muscles used in movement and locomotion. In an early frog larva it is entirely of soft gristle or *cartilage,* but many parts later become hard *bone* (Chap. 3). Cartilage persists on the ends of limb bones to form smooth joint surfaces and in parts of the skull and limb girdles. The skull, vertebral column, and sternum comprise the *axial skeleton,* and the limbs and girdles form the *appendicular skelton* (Fig. 2-7; Table 4-1).

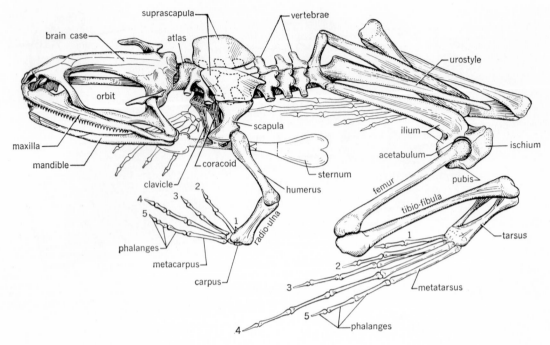

Fig. 2-7. Skeleton of the frog.

The broad, flat *skull* comprises (1) a narrow brain case, or *cranium;* (2) the paired *sense capsules* of the nose and ear and large orbits for the eyes; and (3) the *jaws, hyoid,* and cartilages of the *larynx* (visceral skeleton). Posteriorly each exoccipital bone bears a rounded *occipital condyle.* The two condyles fit depressions in the first vertebra and permit slight movement of the head on the spinal column. Between the condyles is the large opening, or *foramen magnum,* through which the brain and nerve cord connect. Each half of the upper jaw (maxillary arch) includes a premaxilla and maxilla with teeth and a quadratojugal, all fused to the cranium. The lower jaw (mandibular arch) on each side is a rod-like cartilage, encased by the dentary and angulosplenial bones; the latter bone articulates to the quadrate cartilage on the cranium.

The spinal or *vertebral column* supports the body, connects to the head and limbs, and protects the nerve cord. It consists of nine vertebrae and a slender *urostyle.* It is short and scarcely flexible, unlike the column in most vertebrates. Each vertebra is made up of a spool-like *centrum* surmounted by a *neural arch* to house the nerve cord. Above the arch is a low *neural spine,* at either side is a broad *transverse process,* and at either end is a pair of *articular processes* that fit to similar processes on adjacent vertebrae. There are no ribs.

The anterior or *pectoral girdle* is a ᴗ-shaped framework around the thorax that shelters organs within and supports the fore limbs; it is attached to the vertebrae by muscles. Each half includes a broad cartilaginous *suprascapula* dorsally, a narrower *scapula* laterally, and the slender *clavicle* and wider *coracoid* ventrally. The latter join to the midventral breastbone, or *sternum,* which is largely cartilaginous and of several parts. Where the scapula and coracoid meet, there is a shallow depression (glenoid fossa) in which the head of the humerus articulates.

The posterior or *pelvic girdle* is a stout

rigid V-shaped frame that connects the hind limbs to the vertebral column and transmits the power in locomotion from those limbs to the body. It consists of three bones on each side, the long **ilium** anteriorly, the **ischium** posteriorly, and the **pubis** ventrally. Where these join, there is a cup-like socket, the **acetabulum,** in which the head of the femur of the hind limb articulates. Each ilium has a long process, parallel to the urostyle, that attaches to a stout transverse process on the ninth (sacral) vertebra.

The two pairs of limbs differ in size but have comparable bones and parts as follows:

Fore limb (arm):	Hind limb (leg):
Humerus (upper arm)	Femur (thigh)
Radius and ulna (fused) (forearm)	Tibia and fibula (fused) (shank or lower leg)
Carpals (wrist)	Tarsals (ankle)
Metacarpals (palm of hand)	Metatarsals (sole of foot)
Phalanges (fingers)	Phalanges (toes)

The most complete skeletal protection is provided for the brain by the solid skull; the nerve cord is in a bony flexible conduit of neural arches with openings between adjacent vertebrae through which spinal nerves pass; the vertebrae, pectoral girdle, and sternum encircle the thorax; the pelvic girdle shields the abdomen dorsally; and the limb skeleton afford only support.

Each bone is built on good "engineering" principles in both gross and microscopic structure. Those subject to heavy stresses are reinforced within, and where stout muscles or tendons attach the exterior is roughened. Fixed bones of the brain case and pelvic girdle are immovably joined to each other, but most of the bones are movable with smooth **articular surfaces** at the joints where one bone moves on another. At the shoulder and hip there are **ball-and-socket joints** that permit rotation of the movable member (humerus, femur); **hinge joints** that allow movement in one plane occur at the elbow, knee, and elsewhere. Movable bones are attached to one another by **ligaments** of dense connective tissue, besides the muscles and tendons that operate them.

2-8. Muscular system. The body of a frog or any other vertebrate contains three kinds of muscle fibers—smooth, cardiac, and striated—which differ in both microscopic structure and in physiology (Chap. 3). The **skeletal** or **voluntary muscles** (Fig. 2-8) are attached to the bones; under willful control they produce movement and locomotion. Each is made of many parallel striated fibers, bound together by connective tissue. The opposite ends are fastened to separate bones or other parts by extensions of the connective tissue. The more central or less movable end is the **origin,** and that on the more distal or movable part is the **insertion.** Many muscles have the connective tissues extended as a slender **tendon** that inserts at some distance from the muscle itself. On the lower limb segments, feet and toes, some tendons pass under transverse ligaments that serve as pulleys. The **action** of a muscle is to contract, or shorten in length, so that the two structures to which it is attached are brought closer together. Muscles are commonly arranged in opposed groups. The following are the general types, as to mode of action, with an example of each:

FLEXOR, bends one part on another; *biceps,* flexes forearm toward upper arm.

EXTENSOR, straightens or extends a part; *triceps,* extends forearm on upper arm.

ABDUCTOR, draws a part away from axis of body (or of a limb); *deltoid,* draws arm forward.

ADDUCTOR, draws a part toward axis of body (or of a limb); *latissimus dorsi,* draws arm up and back.

DEPRESSOR, lowers a part; *depressor mandibulae,* moves lower jaw down to open mouth.

LEVATOR, elevates or raises a part; *masseter,* raises lower jaw to close mouth.

ROTATOR, rotates a part; *pyriformis,* raises and rotates femur.

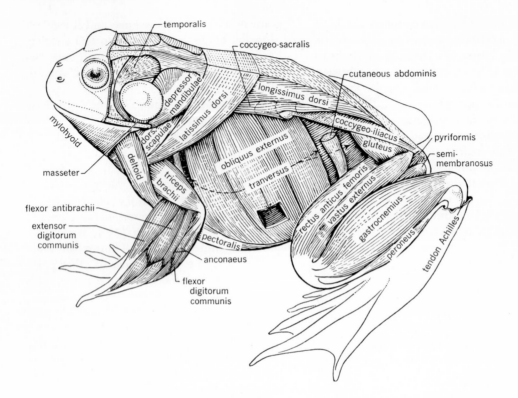

Fig. 2-8. Muscles of the bullfrog.

In many movements of body parts, several muscles act together, some contracting more than others; such coordination is directed by the nervous system. Each fiber or group of fibers has end plates of motor nerves that convey the impulses to stimulate contraction.

2-9. Digestive system. An animal needs food to supply materials for growth and maintenance, for replacement or repair of parts, for energy to move, and for producing sex cells. Plants synthesize the materials they need for life and growth from simple chemical substances in the soil and air. Animals, by contrast, require complex organic substances as food and obtain these by eating plants or other animals. Their food must be subjected to the physical and chemical changes of digestion before it can be absorbed and used in the body. The system serving this function consists of the *digestive tract* and the *digestive glands.* The tract is essentially a tube that extends from the mouth to the anus, being of differing diameter and structure in its several parts.

The small animals taken as food into the frog's mouth are lubricated by mucus secreted there and pass through the *pharynx* to enter the short *esophagus.* This is lined by glands that secrete an alkaline digestive fluid and has muscular walls that move the food to the *stomach,* an organ for storage and digestion. The thick stomach wall is of four layers: (1) the *mucosa,* or inner lining, with many glands; (2) the *submucosa,* a network of connective tissue containing blood and lymph vessels and nerves; (3) the *muscularis* with both circular and longitudinal bundles of smooth muscle fibers; and (4) the *serosa,* or outer covering, which is the peritoneum (Fig. 5-6).

Muscular contractions of the stomach wall crush the food into smaller particles and mix it with the digestive secretions. These secretions contain enzymes or digestive ferments. An *enzyme* is a chemical substance, an organic catalyst, that speeds up certain chemical reactions and converts large amounts of material, without being changed or used up itself in the process. Many kinds of enzymes perform essential vital processes in animal bodies. Each kind of digestive enzyme changes certain classes of food substances into simpler compounds (par. 3-26) that can be absorbed through the wall of the digestive tract and enter the blood. Food is not part of the body until absorbed.

The digestive enzymes in the frog's stomach and intestine include pepsin, trypsin, and erepsin, all of which act on proteins; lipase, which acts on fats; and amylopsin and maltase, which act on starches. Hydrochloric acid secreted in the stomach activates the digestive fluid secreted in the esophagus. The muscular movements that mix and gradually move food along the digestive tract are termed *peristalsis*. Some absorption may occur in the stomach, but most of the mixed and finely divided contents is passed through the *pyloric valve* (a sphincter muscle) at the posterior end and enters the *small intestine*. The intestinal wall is composed of four tissue layers as is the stomach.

Two large *digestive glands,* the liver and pancreas, supply secretions to the small intestine besides those from glands in the intestinal wall. The *liver,* a large multilobed gland, secretes bile that passes through bile capillaries and is stored in the *gall bladder.* It moves through the *bile duct* to the small intestine when food enters the latter. The bile serves to emulsify fats. The *pancreas* is also a multicellular gland. It produces several digestive enzymes that pass into the pancreatic duct joining the common bile duct. Most digestion and absorption takes place in the small intestine. Undigested residues are slowly moved by peristalsis into the *large intestine;* there they are formed into feces and finally pass through the *cloaca* and *anus.* Absorbed materials travel in the blood and lymph to various parts of the body for immediate use in growth or activities or for storage. Much reserve food is stored in the liver as glycogen (animal starch), a carbohydrate that can be converted into glucose for use in the body as needed. Fats may be stored in various places in the body.

2-10. Circulatory system. The transporting of materials within the body is performed by the *circulatory system.* Its principal functions are to carry (1) oxygen and carbon dioxide between the respiratory organs and body tissues; (2) digested foods and water from the digestive tract to other organs; (3) stored foods from place to place as needed; (4) organic wastes and excess minerals in solution, together with water, to the excretory organs; and (5) hormones from the endocrine glands where they are produced to the places where they are used. The system consists of the heart, the arteries, capillaries, veins, and lymph vessels, together with the fluid blood and lymph. The heart is a chambered muscular pump that forces the fluids to circulate constantly through the closed system of tubular elastic vessels.

The *blood* consists of a clear fluid *plasma* containing free cells, or *blood corpuscles* (Fig. 2-9). The plasma comprises water, distinctive blood proteins, and mineral salts, including about 0.65 per cent of sodium chloride; it is the medium that carries soluble materials. The *red blood cells* or *erythrocytes* are elliptical, flattened, and nucleated. They contain a yellow to red respiratory pigment, *hemoglobin,* that serves to carry oxygen to the tissues. Each cell measures about 0.014 by 0.023 mm. (14 by 23 μ), and they number 400,000 or more per cubic millimeter of blood. The *white blood cells* or *leucocytes* are colorless and nucleated; they number about 7,000 per cubic millimeter and are of several kinds (Chap. 6). Most of them can move independently by amoeboid movement. Certain kinds (phagocytes) police the body against invading

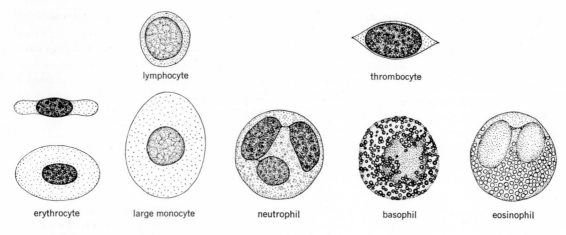

Fig. 2-9. Blood cells of the frog.

bacteria or other foreign organisms and re-move dead or old tissue cells. When a blood vessel is injured, the blood *coagulates,* or forms a *clot,* to stop up the wound and pre-vent loss of blood. The small *thrombocytes* provide the substance thrombin that acts upon the fibrinogen in the plasma to produce clotting. Blood cells are formed chiefly in the *marrow* contained in cavities within the bones. Some are formed in the *spleen,* which also disposes of old cells.

The *heart* is a connected series of chambers enclosed by muscular walls (Fig. 2-10). It con-sists of (1) a conical thick-walled *ventricle* posteriorly; (2) the left and right *auricles* anteriorly, with thin muscular walls; (3) a thin triangular *sinus venosus* dorsally; and (4) a stout tubular *truncus arteriosus* from the anterior base of the ventricle. *Valves* between the chambers prevent backward flow of blood. In the truncus there is a thin, flat, and twisted spiral valve. The heart is covered by a thin

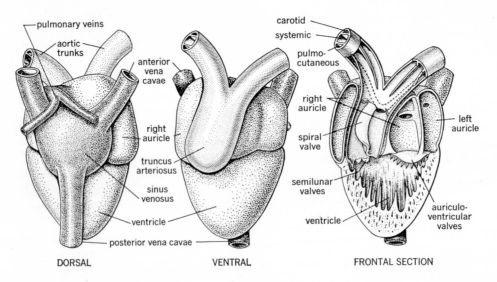

Fig. 2-10. Heart of the bullfrog, enlarged.

membrane, the *pericardium,* and is enclosed in a sac of the same material.

The *arteries* are blood vessels (Fig. 6-3) that carry blood away from the heart. They are lined by a glassy-smooth endothelium and have stout walls containing smooth muscle cells and connective tissue fibers to maintain the *blood pressure* produced by contractions of the heart. The arteries branch again and again into successively smaller vessels, with thinner walls, that extend to all parts of the body. The finest arteries (arterioles) connect to the microscopic *capillaries,* which have walls only of endothelium and are scattered densely among tissue cells of the body. Here food and oxygen are distributed through the capillary walls, some plasma and lymph cells escape, and both carbon dioxide and other wastes are taken into the blood. The capillaries join to form small veins, and these in turn combine into larger *veins* that carry blood toward or to the heart. Their structure is essentially like that of the arteries, but the walls are thinner, with less muscle and connective tissue, since the blood pressure in veins is lower than in arteries.

The course of circulation (Fig. 2-11) is as follows. Blood accumulates in the sinus venosus, which contracts to force it into the right auricle. Blood from the lungs accumulates in the left auricle. The two auricles then contract and force their contents into the ventricle. When the ventricle contracts, the spiral valve deflects more of the unoxygenated blood from the right side into the pulmocutaneous arch and most of the oxygenated blood from the left side into the carotid and systemic arches[1]. Cutaneous respiration, both in water and on land, is thought to compensate for failure of all unoxygenated blood to be pumped to the lungs.

The left and right branches of the truncus subdivide into three major vessels or "arches," the *common carotid* to the head, the *systemic* to the body and viscera, and the *pulmocutaneous* to the lungs and skin. Where the carotid divides, there is a spongy carotid gland to equalize blood pressure in the vessels beyond.

The two systemic arches curve around the esophagus to join as a median *dorsal aorta* extending posteriorly below the vertebrae. Each pulmocutaneous artery divides into a *pulmonary artery* to capillaries in the lungs and a *cutaneous artery* branching on the inner surface of the skin. The arterial system has the pattern of a tree, with repeated branchings (Fig. 2-12).

The venous system is somewhat more complex. Two *precaval veins* return blood to the

[1] Injecting radioactive C[14] into the right (later the left) auricle and then tracing the blood paths with a Geiger counter over each of the arches (carotid, systemic, and pulmocutaneous) has confirmed this routing.

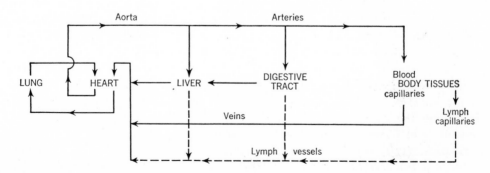

Fig. 2-11. Plan of the circulation in a frog (or other land vertebrate), with both blood vessels (solid lines) and lymph vessels (broken lines); arrows indicate the direction of flow.

Arteries   Veins

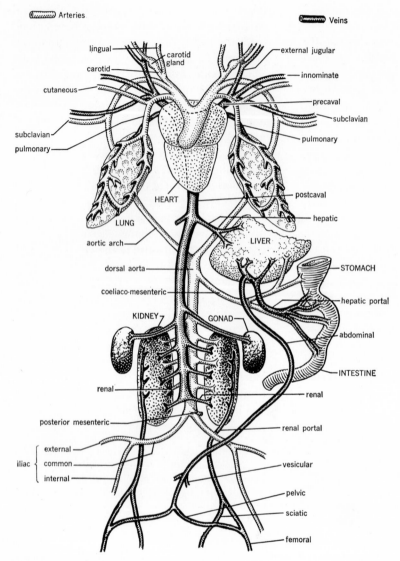

Fig. 2-12. Circulatory system of the bullfrog in ventral view, showing the principal arteries and veins in relation to the internal organs.

sinus venosus from veins in the head, fore limbs, and skin. A median *postcaval vein* collects from the kidneys, gonads, and dorsal musculature. There are also three special venous paths. (1) Two *pulmonary veins* return blood that has been oxygenated in the lungs to the left auricle; all other veins deliver eventually to the sinus venosus and right auricle. (2) The *hepatic portal system* gathers blood from the digestive tract (stomach and intestines) and carries it to the liver. There the veins break up into capillaries, and then the blood is assembled in hepatic veins that enter the postcava. The hepatic portal circulation allows some materials in blood from the digestive tract to be either stored or filtered out during passage through the liver. In the frog the hepatic portal also receives an abdominal vein that collects from the hind limbs (femoral veins), bladder, and ventral body wall. (3) The *renal portal system* gathers blood from the hind limbs (sciatic and femoral veins) and posterior body wall, then divides into capillaries within the kidneys. This blood is collected by the renal veins and returns to the heart in the postcaval vein. (Higher vertebrates lack the renal portal system.)

The *lymphatic system* includes many delicate *lymph vessels* of varied diameter and shape that penetrate the organs and tissues but are difficult to see. Frogs and toads, unlike other vertebrates, also have several large *lymph sacs* or spaces between the skin and body (Fig. 2-5). Behind the shoulder girdle and beside the anus are two pairs of *lymph hearts* that pulsate frequently in a living frog. The watery lymph in these structures contains leucocytes but lacks red cells and some proteins of blood plasma. It filters out from blood capillaries into the tissues, enters the lymph vessels, and later returns to the veins.

2-11. Respiratory system. The energy for life and growth is derived by the oxidation, or "physiological burning," of absorbed food. This is analogous to the burning of coal in the presence of oxygen to yield heat and carbon dioxide ($C + O_2 \rightarrow CO_2 +$ heat). *Respiration* is the process of supplying oxygen to the body; the removal of carbon dioxide that results from metabolism is really a matter of excretion but is commonly discussed as part of respiration. The oxygen–carbon dioxide exchange between the air or water and the blood is termed *external respiration,* and that between the blood and body cells is *internal respiration.*

The *respiratory organs* are the *lungs, skin,* and *lining of the mouth cavity;* all have moist surfaces (epithelium) close over blood vessels. Oxygen from the air dissolves in the surface moisture and diffuses inward to the blood, whereas carbon dioxide passes in the opposite direction. The *hemoglobin* in red blood cells combines with oxygen where plentiful and releases it as the blood passes through body tissues where oxygen is scarcer and needed. The hemoglobin enables the

blood to transport much more oxygen than if the latter were merely dissolved in the plasma. Carbon dioxide, however, is carried mainly by the plasma. The laws of simple diffusion of gases probably account for the exchanges in respiration as the concentration of oxygen in the air (about 20 per cent) is far greater than in blood and that in the blood is greater than in the tissues; the reverse is true for carbon dioxide.

The frog's *lungs* (Fig. 2-13) are two thin elastic sacs with low internal folds that increase the inner surface to form many small chambers, or alveoli. These are lined with pulmonary capillaries. Each lung connects by a short *bronchus* to the voice box or *larynx* behind the glottis. The mechanics of breathing involve *inspiration,* or drawing in air, and *expiration,* or forcing it out, both performed with the mouth closed. At inspiration (1) the glottis closes, the mouth floor is depressed, and air is drawn through the nostrils into the mouth cavity and pharynx; (2) the nostrils close (by valves), and the mouth cavity is compressed to force the air through the opened glottis into the lungs. At expiration the muscles of the body wall contract to force air from the lungs out the mouth cavity and nostrils. Much of the frog's respiration, however, is performed by merely pumping air in and out of the mouth cavity, where the gaseous exchange occurs through the mucous membranes of its lining. The frog's skin contains large blood vessels that also serve in respiration either in air or water and especially during hibernation. The frog tadpole respires by *gills,* which are slender extensions of the epithelium of the pharynx containing many blood capillaries (Fig. 26-2).

The larynx is reinforced by cartilages and contains two elastic bands, the *vocal cords.* When air is forced vigorously from the lungs, the cords vibrate and produce croaking notes.

2-12. Excretory system. The animal body is a delicately balanced system from which excess materials and the wastes, or end products of metabolism, must be removed. The process of removal is termed *excretion.* Some wastes

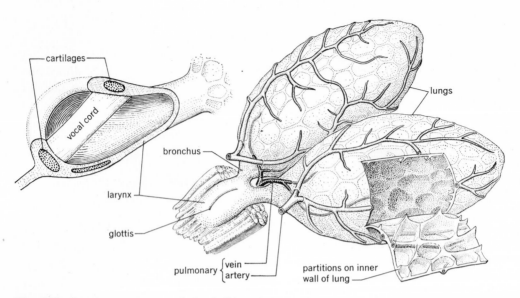

Fig. 2-13. Respiratory organs of the bullfrog in laterodorsal view. *Left*. Larynx opened with right vocal cord in place.

are disposed of by the skin and lungs, others are discharged from the liver in the bile, and some are excreted from the intestine with the feces. The principal *excretory organs* of the frog are the two long brown *kidneys* (Fig. 2-14) dorsal to the coelom and peritoneum.

The kidneys are selective filters that remove soluble organic wastes (especially urea), excess mineral salts, and water gathered from the body cells and fluids by the blood (Chap. 8).

Each kidney is a compact mass of about

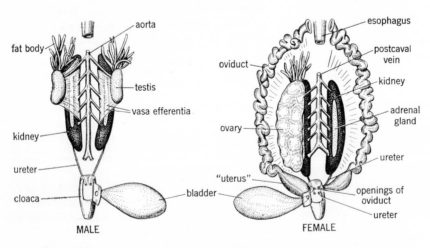

Fig. 2-14. Excretory and reproductive organs (urogenital system) of the frog in ventral view. Cloaca opened ventrally to show entrance of ducts (enlarged) and the bladder turned aside. Aorta and arteries shown in male, and postcaval vein in female; left ovary omitted.

2,000 *renal corpuscles* bound together by connective tissue. A renal corpuscle comprises (1) a coiled knot, or *glomerulus,* of small arteries within (2) a double-walled cup, or *Bowman capsule,* that is connected to (3) a *uriniferous tubule* surrounded by capillaries (Fig. 8-6). The latter joins through collecting tubules to the *ureter,* a fine white tube along the outer margin of the kidney to the dorsal wall of the cloaca. Blood with both oxygen and wastes is brought to the kidneys in the renal arteries, which divide into arterioles in the glomeruli and continue as capillaries about the tubules. The renal portal veins also join to these capillaries. Blood reduced in wastes leaves the kidneys by the renal veins. On the ventral surface of each kidney are many ciliated funnels (nephrostomes) that may drain wastes from the coelom. They connect to uriniferous tubules in frog larvae and later to the renal veins.

The liquid waste collected in the kidneys is the *urine.* It passes down the ureters to the cloaca and may be voided at once through the anus or may be stored temporarily in the thin-walled *bladder* connected to the ventral side of the cloaca. The daily output of urine in summer amounts to about one-third of the frog's weight.

2-13. Endocrine glands. Like other vertebrates, the frog has several *endocrine* or *ductless glands* that produce substances known as *hormones.* The latter are also called internal secretions because they are carried by the blood instead of being passed out through ducts. The hormones regulate various physiological processes (see general discussion in Chap. 9).

At the base of the brain is a minute *pituitary gland* of three lobes. The *anterior lobe,* in larvae and young, secretes a *growth-stimulating hormone* which controls growth, especially of long bones, and also affects the thyroid. Removal of the gland in larvae delays their growth, and they do not change into frogs; replanting the gland restores these functions. Feeding or injecting an extract of the gland produces larvae of greater than normal size. In adult frogs the anterior lobe secretes a *gonad-stimulating hormone* responsible for release of ova or sperm from the reproductive organs. If two or more fresh anterior lobes are implanted on successive days in an adult but nonbreeding female, her eggs will soon mature and be laid. Similar implants into a male will hasten sexual maturity, the clasping reflex, and the discharge of spermatozoa. The *intermediate lobe* produces *intermedin,* which regulates the action of chromatophores in the skin. Its removal is followed by a marked bleaching due to the concentration of the pigment; if then implanted, the pigment spreads and normal coloration results. The *posterior lobe* evidently regulates water intake by the skin; its removal seems to inhibit molt of the cornified epidermis and to cause deposition of pigment there.

The small *thyroid gland* behind the hyoid cartilage produces *thyroxin,* which regulates general metabolism. The gland enlarges and its secretion increases in larvae before they metamorphose into frogs. If this gland is removed, the larvae do not transform. If the gland or its extract is injected into young bullfrog larvae, which normally have a 2-year larval life, their metamorphosis is hastened.

The *pancreas* secretes, besides digestive enzymes, the hormone known as *insulin,* which regulates sugar metabolism. This is produced by special cell groups, the *islets of Langerhans.* Its action is less conspicuous in the cold-blooded frog than in birds and mammals.

Along the ventral surface of each kidney is a slender *adrenal gland* that produces *epinephrine* (adrenalin). This hormone causes increased blood pressure and also contracts the dark pigment in the skin.

2-14. Nervous system. The complex physiological processes of the many organs within the body and the frog's relations with its external environment are controlled and coordinated by the *nervous system* (Fig. 2-15). This is an intricate structure composed of nerve cells, or neurons (par. 3-9). The *central ner-*

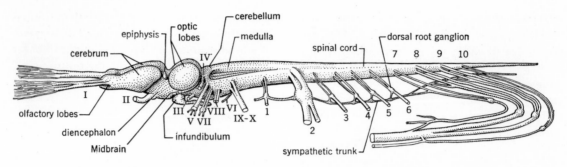

Fig. 2-15. Nervous system of bullfrog in laterodorsal view, with the nerves and sympathetic trunk of the left side. I–X, cranial nerves; 1–10, spinal nerves (see Table 10-1).

vous system comprises the brain and spinal cord, and the *peripheral nervous system* includes all the paired cranial and spinal nerves together with the sympathetic system (Chap. 10).

The *brain* is housed in the "brain box," or cranium. In dorsal view it shows (1) two *olfactory lobes* with nerves to the nasal chambers; (2) two *cerebral hemispheres* closely joined to the preceding and also attached to (3) the median *diencephalon,* or 'tween-brain. Behind this are two rounded *optic lobes,* supported on (4) the *midbrain* below, and followed by (5) a small transverse *cerebellum;* this is over (6) the open-topped *medulla oblongata,* which tapers to join the spinal cord. The diencephalon has a dorsal pineal body or *epiphysis.* Below the diencephalon is the *optic chiasma* (crossing of the optic nerves), followed by the *infundibulum* as a bluntly triangular outgrowth, with the *hypophysis,* or *pituitary gland,* at its posterior end.

The *cavities* within the brain are the first and second *ventricles* in the cerebral hemispheres; these connect to a third ventricle in the diencephalon. From the latter a small aqueduct of Sylvius leads to the fourth ventricle located in the medulla. The fourth ventricle is continuous with a minute central canal through the spinal cord. Cerebrospinal fluid fills the ventricles and other cavities and surrounds the brain. Metabolic exchanges for the brain are performed by arteries and veins over its surface and by two dense networks of blood vessels, the *anterior choroid plexus* over a dorsal opening in the diencephalon and the *posterior choroid plexus* above the medulla. The brain and spinal cord are surrounded by two membranes, a thicker *dura mater* adhering to the enclosing bones and a delicate *pia mater* close over the nervous tissue itself. Ten pairs of *cranial nerves* extend from various parts of the brain to sense organs, muscles, and other structures (Table 10-1).

The functions of the brain have been determined by studying the behavior of frogs after experimentally injuring or removing parts and by stimulation with electric currents. The olfactory lobes serve the sense of smell. The cerebral hemispheres are areas of memory, intelligence, and voluntary control in higher animals, but in the frog their function is less clear. Removal impairs memory; the frog is lethargic, and its movements are more machine-like. The diencephalon is related to vision and balance. The optic lobes inhibit reflexes in the spinal cord, each controlling the opposite side of the body. In higher vertebrates the cerebellum is a center of coordination; in the frog it controls equilibrium in part. The medulla directs most bodily activities. If all the brain but the medulla is removed, the frog can leap, swim, capture and swallow food, recover normal position if inverted, and breathe normally. Death soon follows removal of the medulla.

The *spinal cord* extends backward from the medulla and within the neural arches of the vertebrae, to end as a slender filament in the urostyle. The outer *white matter* is chiefly of nerve fibers, and the inner *gray matter* largely of nerve cells. Ten pairs of *spinal nerves* emerge from the cord, between the vertebrae, as shiny white strands on the dorsal wall of the abdomen above the peritoneum. Each nerve has two roots. The *sensory* or *dorsal root* carries nerve impulses from parts of the body *into* the spinal cord, and on this root is an enlargement or *ganglion* containing nerve cells. The *motor* or *ventral root* comprises fibers that transmit directive impulses *outward* from the cord to the tissues. The two roots of each join outside the cord as a *nerve* that extends to a definite part of the body or limbs. On either side, the large second or brachial nerve joins in a network, or *brachial plexus,* from which nerves run to the fore limb and shoulder region. The seventh to ninth form a *sciatic plexus* that distributes to the hind limb.

The *sympathetic nervous system* shows as two thread-like nerve strands above the dorsal wall of the coelom. Each has 10 ganglia and many fibers connecting to the brain, spinal cord, and viscera. This system directs many internal (vegetative) functions not under conscious or voluntary regulation such as the rate of heartbeat, secretion of digestive juices, muscular movements in the stomach and intestine, and the muscular "tone" of blood vessels (compare Fig. 10-5).

2-15. Sense organs. Changes in either the external or internal environment of an animal act as stimuli that affect *sensory structures,* or *receptors,* in its body. The receptors are connected to sensory nerves and give rise to nerve impulses, which are transmitted to the central nervous system. Each kind of stimulus affects a particular kind of receptor. We know accurately only the sensations of man; from these

we interpret the sensory reactions of lower animals. In the frog, microscopic receptors for *touch* (tactile stimuli) are present under the epidermis. Others probably respond to irritating substances such as strong chemicals and possibly to heat. The tongue bears small papillae containing *taste buds.* The sense of smell is ascribed to endings of the olfactory nerves in the nasal cavities.

The vertebrate *ear* serves two functions: *hearing* and adjusting the *equilibrium* of the body. The latter sense resides in the semicircular canals and ampullae of the inner ear (par. 10-12). The frog has an *eardrum* (tympanic membrane) exposed on either side of the head to receive sound waves from air or water. Vibrations induced in an eardrum are transmitted across the space beneath (middle ear) by a rod (columella) connecting the eardrum and inner ear. The latter lies within the prootic bone and contains a lymph-filled compartment with sensory endings of the auditory nerve (8th cranial) where sound impressions are registered. Frogs are insensitive to most sounds but react to the croaking notes of males during the breeding season.

The *eye* is the most complex of vertebrate sense organs and responds to *light* or electromagnetic radiation of certain frequencies. The frog's eyes are much like those of man (Fig. 10-11). The *eyeball* lies in the orbit, beneath the eyelids; it is moved by six muscles attached to its outer surface. Its structure is analogous to that of a camera, having a transparent biconvex lens that forms an image on the sensitive interior. The outer *sclerotic coat,* of connective tissue, provides a supporting case, with the *cornea* as a transparent front. The next or *choroid coat* includes blood vessels and much black pigment to exclude all light save that entering the front. The innermost layer or *retina* contains the *rods* and *cones,* receptors for vision, that connect to the *optic nerve* (2d cranial). Inside the cornea part of the choroid coat is specialized as the *iris,* a pigmented disc with a central opening, or *pupil,* through which light enters the spherical lens just behind. The pupil contracts or dilates to regulate the amount of light entering the eye. The frog's *lens* does not change in either shape or position. The space before the lens contains a watery *aqueous humor* and that behind, a jelly-like *vitreous humor,* both serving to maintain the form of the eyeball.

2-16. Reproductive system. The organ systems discussed previously are all concerned with the life of the individual animal, whereas the reproductive system serves to maintain the frog as a species. It consists of the *reproductive organs* or *gonads,* which produce sex cells, and the *reproductive ducts* through which these cells leave the body (Fig. 2-14). Frogs are of two *sexes,* the *females,* which lay eggs or *ova* (sing. *ovum*), and the *males,* which produce sperm or *spermatozoa* to fertilize the eggs and cause them to develop into new individuals. Each frog is either female or male, the sexes being separate.

The female's two gonads, or *ovaries,* are attached dorsally in the coelom, near the kidneys, each supported by a mesentery. In early spring the ovaries of an adult contain hundreds of small black eggs that swell out the abdomen, but a summer specimen has only a small mass of grayish ovarian substance. Each ovary is a hollow sac of four to seven lobes with thin double walls, and every egg is enclosed in a delicate follicle formed of cells between the two layers. The ovary is supplied with arteries that bring materials for growth of the ova. Along either side of the middorsal line of the coelom is a whitish convoluted *oviduct;* its anterior end is an open ciliated funnel (ostium), and its posterior end joins dorsally to the cloaca.

When the eggs become mature, in the breeding season, each follicle ruptures (under stimulation of a pituitary hormone) and the eggs escape into the coelom. There they are moved anteriorly by the action of cilia on the peritoneum and enter the oviduct funnels. They are moved down the ducts by cilia on length-wise ridges lining the interior. Between these ridges are gland cells; these secrete albuminous material to form the jelly coatings that swell out around the eggs after laying (Fig. 2-16).

The male has two small bean-shaped *testes* attached near the kidneys by mesenteries. Each testis is a mass of coiled *seminiferous tubules* where spermatozoa are produced. Mature sperm enter several fine ducts, or *vasa efferentia,* that connect to uriniferous tubules in the anterior part of the kidney. The sperm then pass down the tubules and ureter (which are joint urinogenital canals) and may be stored in the dilated posterior end, or *seminal vesicle,* of the ureter. At mating, the sperm are discharged through the cloaca to fertilize the eggs. Mature and functional sperm are present from August to May in the leopard frog, *Rana pipiens.*

The *fat bodies* are paired, finger-like growths in both sexes, anterior to the gonads. They provide reserve nutriment, possibly helping formation of the sex cells, and serve for subsistence during hibernation. They are largest just prior to hibernation and far reduced after breeding, being of special importance to males, which take little food during the breeding season.

Mature females and males differ in most species of frogs and toads in features called *secondary sexual characteristics.* Males have heavier arm muscles, shorter but stouter inner fingers, and roughened "nuptial" pads on the fingers. Male toads and tree toads have a median resonating pouch on the chin, and there are paired pouches in some frogs. The eardrum is larger in the male bullfrog and green frog, and the two sexes of some toads differ in coloration. In birds and mammals such sexual differences are due to endocrines (Fig. 9-4), but this is not clearly so in all amphibians. Implants of testes into female toads produce thick nuptial pads such as occur in males.

2-17. Natural history and life cycle. Frogs need a damp environment so that the soft

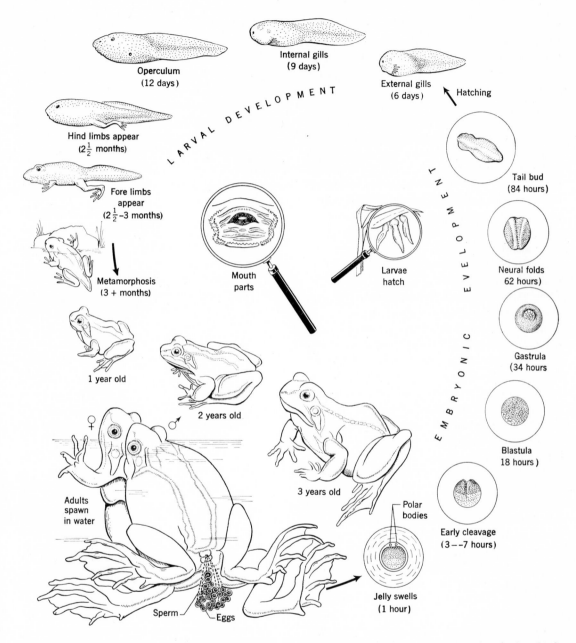

Operculum
(12 days)

Internal gills
(9 days)

External gills
(6 days)   Hatching

L A R V A L   D E V E L O P M E N T

Hind limbs appear
(2½ months)

Fore limbs
appear
(2½–3 months)

Metamorphosis
(3 + months)

Mouth
parts

Larvae
hatch

Tail bud
(84 hours)

Neural folds
62 hours)

Gastrula
(34 hours

Blastula
18 hours)

E M B R Y O N I C   D E V E L O P M E N T

1 year old

2 years old

3 years old

Adults
spawn
in water

Sperm   Eggs

Polar
bodies

Jelly swells
(1 hour)

Early cleavage
(3––7 hours)

Fig. 2-16. Life cycle of the frog. (*After Rosel*, 1758.) Magnified figures show newly hatched tadpoles clinging to vegetation by their adhesive "discs," and the face of an older larva with its dark horny jaws and minute "teeth."

glandular skin will be kept moist, and most species live in or near ponds or streams. They are "cold-blooded," or variable-temperatured (poikilothermous), the body temperature being dependent upon that of the environment. A few live in cold regions but frogs are most abundant in temperate or tropical moist lands. They reproduce, feed, and grow during warm weather, but hibernate where the winter is cold. In this inactive state, all metabolism in the body drops to a low level, and the heartbeat is very slow.

Each species of frog has a definite time of spring emergence, based upon temperature, and most species proceed at once to reproductive activities (Fig. 2-16). Males gather in appropriate waters and croak to attract the females. The latter, when their eggs are "ripe," enter the water, where each is clasped by a male. He mounts her back and grips his forelegs around her thorax. As the female extrudes her eggs, the male discharges milt, or seminal fluid containing spermatozoa, to fertilize them. The jelly coats about the eggs swell and adhere to plant stems, the eggs from each female forming a large, tapioca-like mass. Development starts, and each egg becomes an embryo, which after some days emerges from the jelly as a small "polliwog," tadpole, or larva. It has an ovoid head-and-body, a slender compressed tail, and horny jaws used to scrape green algae from objects in the water for food. The intestine is then long and spirally coiled. The larva has three pairs of external gills on the pharynx, and later these are replaced by three pairs of internal gills within the gill slits. In time the hind legs appear, but the forelegs are hidden under a membrane on the ventral surface of the body. After some weeks or months, depending upon the species and the prevailing temperature, the larva undergoes *metamorphosis.* Its lungs have developed, and it seeks shallow water to gulp down air. The forelegs burst out, and the animal—part larva and part frog —lives at the water's edge as its mouth widens, its gills and tail are reabsorbed, and its intestine shortens. The tadpole thus changes into a frog, and after 1 or more years becomes sexually mature and reproduces.

Each female lays hundreds of eggs, of which some fail to develop and some are eaten by enemies. Many larvae are consumed by fishes, snakes, turtles, or water insects, some larvae die because the water dries up before they transform, and young frogs are victims to these and other enemies. Of the great numbers of eggs laid each season, only a few become adult frogs; but under usual conditions these are enough to maintain the frog as a species.

REVIEW

1. How does the frog capture food, and what kinds does it take?
2. Describe the structure of the frog's skin. As compared with man, what additional functions are performed by the skin of a frog? How does a frog molt?
3. What are the main regions of the frog's skeleton? What is the function of the pectoral girdle? Of the pelvic girdle?
4. What kinds of muscle fibers are found in the frog? List the general types of muscles in respect to their modes of action.
5. Trace a piece of food (insect) through the digestive tract of a frog from mouth to anus, describing the processes that take place in each organ.
6. What are the principal functions of the circulatory system?
7. Trace the course of circulation of the blood. Distinguish between arteries, veins, and capillaries as to both structure and function.
8. Compare the respiration of an adult frog with that of a tadpole.
9. Describe the process of excretion by way of the kidneys.
10. What are the three main divisions of the nervous system? The functions of each? Define: diencephalon, cranial nerve, spinal nerve, medulla, gray matter, brachial plexus.
11. Where are the following endocrine glands located, and what is the effect of the secretion of each: thyroid, pancreas, adrenal, pituitary?
12. By what route do eggs move from the ovary to the exterior? How are they fertilized? What are some changes in a tadpole metamorphosing into a frog?

3
Materials of the animal body

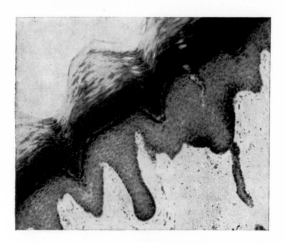

Every animal is an integrated combination of structural parts and systems that perform the various physiological processes essential for life. The larger features of structure and function in the frog are described in Chap. 2. The organ systems are dealt with in greater detail in Chaps. 4 to 10. This chapter discusses the materials and finer components of the animal body.

Biological components

A. CELLS AND PROTOPLASM

3-1. History. The finer structures of living organisms were unknown until after the invention of the compound microscope (about 1591). In 1665 Robert Hooke reported that cork and other plant materials contained many small partitions separating cavities that he named *cells*. In 1824 René Dutrochet stated that ". . . plants are composed entirely of cells, and of organs that are obviously derived from cells . . ." and that the same applied to animals. In 1833 Robert Brown described the nucleus as a central feature in plant cells. In 1838 M. J. Schleiden put forth the thesis that cells were the unit of structure in plants; and in 1839 his coworker Theodor Schwann applied the thesis to animals. This generaliza-

tion is known as the *cell theory*. Greater emphasis was given at first to the cell wall and less to the contents. In 1840 Purkinje named the cell contents protoplasm. Research during the past century has extended the theory and shown that the cell contents are more important than the wall and that intercellular material is produced by certain cells. According to the cell theory *all animals and plants are composed of cells and cell products*. The cell is the fundamental unit, both structural and physiological, in all organisms, and there is a constant exchange of matter and energy within cells in the process of living. In multicellular animals the cells are integrated for proper functioning, whereas in unicellular animals the cell and organism are one. A multicellular animal generally starts life as a single cell that divides repeatedly to form its body.

3-2. Protoplasm. The living substance in the cells of all plants and animals is called *protoplasm*. It is a complex mixture of various materials, including water, mineral salts, and many organic compounds. The latter are known in nature only as components or products of living organisms. In different species and in the parts and organs of any one animal the protoplasm differs in its chemical, physical, and biological properties. It has, however,

Illustration at top of page: A tissue complex—microscopic section through sole of foot of a monkey; cornified layers above, base of epidermis below, with extensions into dermis.

certain common characteristics which are discussed below.

Typically protoplasm is a translucent, often grayish, slimy substance, somewhat viscous, but capable of flowing. Its structure has been variously considered to be (1) granular; (2) foam-like or alveolar; (3) an emulsion; or (4) fibrillar or reticular, of small fibers or threads. Actual differences in kind, difficulties in observing the fine details, and changes incidental to removing protoplasm from living organisms, or the fixing of tissues for study are responsible for some differences in the interpretation of its structure.

Living organisms and the protoplasm of which they are composed are characterized by activity and change. A human being develops as an embryo, is born, grows, lives actively, and dies. Within its protoplasm, as in all animals, many processes are going on constantly. In contrast to nonliving materials, protoplasm is characterized by (1) *metabolism,* the physical and chemical changes by which materials are transformed and used for growth, maintenance and repair, and to yield energy; (2) *irritability,* the response to stimuli from changes in its environment; and (3) *reproduction,* the ability of an organism or its parts to produce new individuals of its own kind. Constructive metabolism (anabolism) includes the synthesis of the products of digestion into compounds, often more complex, which are incorporated into the protoplasm, stored for later use, or formed into essential products such as secretions. By destructive metabolism (catabolism, dissimilation), various components are broken down (oxidized, etc.) to simpler compounds, providing energy for work or heat, with consequent yield of waste products. Both types are occurring simultaneously in living protoplasm, but anabolic processes, leading to growth, predominate during embryonic development and early life. Catabolic processes are in excess in the middle and later years of life.

3-3. The cell. A cell is a mass of protoplasm enclosed in a membrane and containing a nucleus; both nucleus and cytoplasm arise by division of the corresponding elements of a preexisting cell. As exceptions, the red blood cells of mammals lose the nucleus after growth, and cells of striated muscles and a few other kinds have more than one nucleus in each.

Most animal cells are minute (Fig. 3-1). The unit of measure used is 0.001 millimeter (mm.), a *micron* (plural micra, symbol μ). Human red blood cells average 7.5 μ in diameter, and other cells measure 10 to 50 μ, but

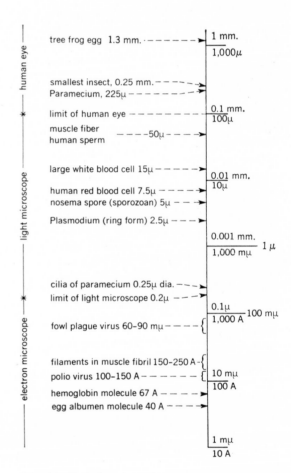

Fig. 3-1. Relative sizes of some animal cells and parts of cells. Each major scale division is $\frac{1}{10}$ of that above. 1 millimeter (mm.) = 1,000 micra; 1 micron (μ) = 1,000 millimicra; 1 millimicron (mμ) = 10 angstrom units (A). Visual microscope magnifies about 10 to 2,000$\times$; electron microscope about 5,000 to 100,000$\times$ or more.

some nerve cells in large animals are several feet in length. The largest cells are the yolks of bird and shark eggs; that of the chicken is about 30 mm. in diameter.

The typical animal cell (Fig. 3-2) is bounded by a very delicate *cell* or *plasma membrane* surrounding the *cytoplasm* (cytosome) that fills the interior of the cell and contains the *nucleus*. The cytoplasm is translucent and viscous. Near the nucleus is a globular *centrosome* (cell center) containing one or two dot-like *centrioles*. The cytoplasm commonly contains various inclusions such as (1) *mitochondria* in the form of fibrils or globules; (2) *Golgi bodies*, small networks or groups of sacs believed to have a part in forming secretions; (3) *ribosomes* (microsomes), minute granules involved in protein synthesis; (4) *fat*, as droplets or as yolk in egg cells;

(5) *vacuoles,* filled with either granular or fluid material; and (6) *secretion granules,* especially in gland cells, later to be transformed and pass out as secretions. These inclusions serve various special purposes in cell physiology, not all understood; some require special techniques to be seen.

The nucleus is commonly oval or spherical, but in some kinds of cells it is long or lobed; it may be centered in the cytoplasm or at one side or end. It is surrounded by a distinct *nuclear membrane* enclosing the nuclear sap. Most important within the nucleus is the *chromatin,* seemingly of isolated granules but actually parts of continuously spiraled filaments, the *chromonemata.* Chromatin is so named because it stains intensely with basic dyes such as hematoxylin. Each nucleus usually contains a spherical *nucleolus* (one or more). The nucleus controls much of cell metabolism; if removed, the cell cannot perform anabolic activities and lives only a short time. An isolated nucleus cannot form cytoplasm.

The study of cell structure and activity is *cytology.* For most such study, cells or pieces of tissue are quickly fixed (killed) in chemical reagents or by freezing, cut in thin sections (10 μ or less), mounted on microscope slides, and stained to differentiate the internal details. Care is necessary that these procedures do not alter the original structures. Living cells may be treated with "vital dyes" that stain and render parts more visible without injury. Apparatus for microdissection permits removal of cell parts or injection of reagents for special studies. Isolated cells and tissues may be kept alive to grow for days (or years) in nutrient solutions. The phase microscope and the electron microscope (Fig. 3-3) are research tools permitting study of the finer details of cell structure.

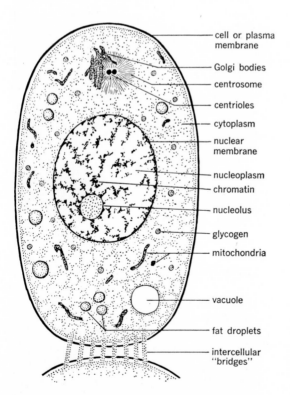

cell or plasma membrane
Golgi bodies
centrosome
centrioles
cytoplasm
nuclear membrane
nucleoplasm
chromatin
nucleolus
glycogen
mitochondria
vacuole
fat droplets
intercellular "bridges"

Fig. 3-2. Diagram of an animal cell. Not all parts shown will be present or evident in any one cell, either living or fixed and stained.

B. CELL DIVISION

Growth in organisms is chiefly by multiplication of cells. In the unicellular PROTOZOA, the animals themselves are multiplied; in

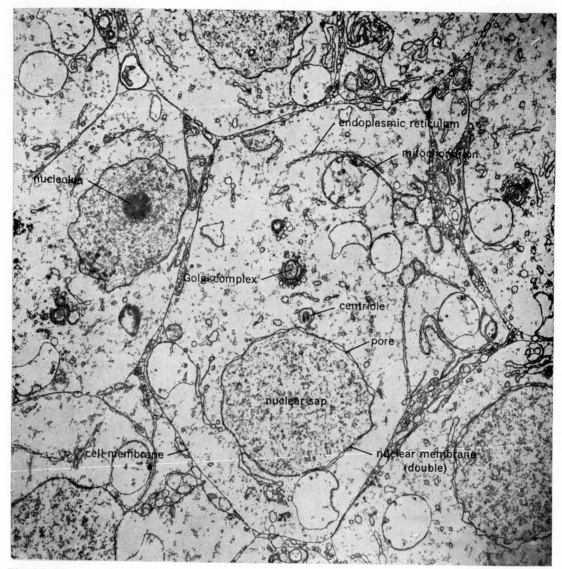

Fig. 3-3. Electron micrograph of an entire cell and cell components. Section of ectoderm from a hydroid medusa (*Aequorea*), × 6,000. A more representative mitochondrion is shown in Fig. 4-8. Nucleolus shows only in nucleus at upper left. (*Micrograph by James H. McAlear, Electron Microscope Laboratory, University of California, Berkeley.*)

other animals the number of cells in the individual is increased. Living cells, when not dividing, are termed metabolic cells, because metabolic processes are going on constantly within them.

3-4. Mitosis. Cells multiply chiefly by *mitosis,* a complex process that involves an equal division of the nuclear chromatin in both kind and amount (Figs. 3-4, 3-5). Mitosis is active during embryonic development, in growth, in repair of injury, and in replacement of body covering at molting. As seen in living cells, it is a continuous dynamic process, but for study purposes is divided into several stages, as follows: (1) prophase, (2) metaphase, (3) anaphase, and (4) telophase. Cells not undergoing mitosis are said to be in the interphase.

PROPHASE. The centrosome usually contains two centrioles (if but one, this divides); the two move to opposite sides of the nucleus. Around each centriole fine short radiating fibers appear in the cytoplasm to form an *aster;* and other longer *spindle fibers* extend between the separating centrioles.

Meanwhile the chromatin within the nucleus becomes evident as distinct chromosomes that shorten, thicken, and stain deeply. Each chromosome is actually composed of two wavy, parallel filaments, the **chromatids** (daughter chromosomes). In the cells of any one species the several chromosomes are of characteristic size and shape—long or short, thick or thin, and shaped like a rod, J, or V. Careful microscopic preparations show a constriction or dot (centromere) where the two arms of a chromosome join; this is the point of attachment by spindle fibers. Toward the end of the prophase the nuclear membrane and nucleolus disappear, and the chromosomes become associated with the spindle fibers and move toward the equatorial plane of the cell.

The total number of chromosomes present at the end of the prophase is the **diploid number.** This is constant and characteristic in any species of animal for all its cells except mature germ cells. In different kinds of animals the chromosome number ranges from 2 to 250 but usually is less than 50.

METAPHASE. The chromosomes lie radially in an equatorial plate across the cell midway between the two asters, each chromosome being connected to the spindle fibers. Other fibers extend continuously between the poles. The two halves of each chromosome become more evident.

ANAPHASE. The halved chromosomes move apart, those of each group toward its respective pole (centriole). In living cells there is an active pulling back and forth of the opposing sets as they separate. Each daughter chromosome consists of an equivalent half of the material formerly in one chromosome.

TELOPHASE. As the groups of daughter chromosomes end their polar movement, they become less conspicuous, a nuclear membrane forms about each group, a nucleolus is produced in each, the centriole divides into two, and the spindle disappears. Finally a cell membrane appears across the former plane of the equatorial plate. When this has ended, mitosis is complete. The chromosomes in each daughter cell revert to the net-like pattern of the interphase or metabolic cell.

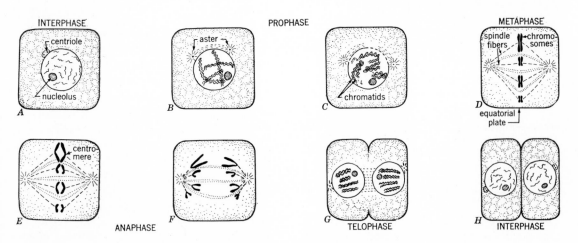

Fig. 3-4. Diagram of stages in mitosis, the division of one cell into two.

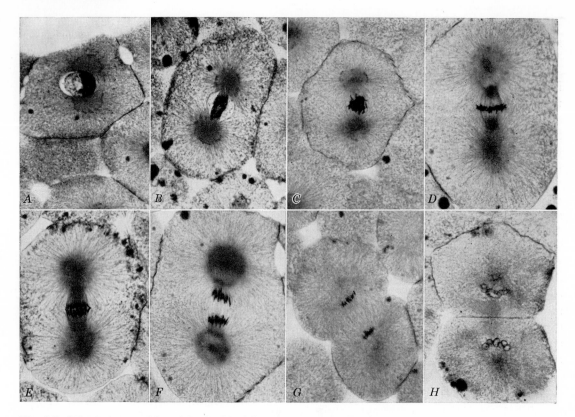

Fig. 3-5. Mitosis in egg (blastula) of whitefish. PROPHASE. (*A*) Centrosome divides. (*B, C*) Centrosomes at opposite poles, chromosomes become evident, nuclear membrane disappears. METAPHASE. (*D, E*) Chromosomes centered on equator of spindle, and (*E*) each divides into two. ANAPHASE. (*F, G*) Chromosomes move toward poles, spindle lengthens, centrosomes less evident. TELOPHASE. (*H*) Nuclear membrane forming around chromosomes; cytoplasm of the two cells separated by cell membrane between. (*Photomicrographs by Dr. Hans Ris.*) Compare Fig. 3-4.

The equal division of chromatin whereby each daughter cell receives half of that in each parent chromosome is of great significance from the standpoint of heredity (Chap. 12), since the genes, or determiners of hereditary characters, are believed to be carried by the chromosomes and to be duplicated with the latter. Such partitioning distributes identical lots of genes to all cells in the body.

C. TISSUES

The parts of any multicellular animal consist of different kinds of cells. Those of similar structure and function are arranged in groups or layers known as *tissues;* hence multicellular animals (METAZOA) are "tissue animals." In each tissue the cells are essentially alike, being of characteristic size, form, and arrangement, and they are specialized or *differentiated* both structurally and physiologically to perform some particular function such as protection, digestion, or contraction, whence a *division of labor* results among different tissues. *Histology,* or microscopic anatomy, is the study of the structure and arrangement of tissues in organs, in contrast to gross anatomy, which deals with organs and organ systems by dissection.

The cells in a multicellular animal may be

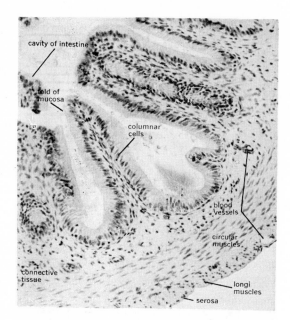

cavity of intestine

fold of mucosa

columnar cells

blood vessels

circular muscles

connective tissue

longi muscles

serosa

Fig. 3-6. Photomicrograph of part of cross section of frog intestine (duodenum), showing how several kinds of cells and tissues are combined to form an organ.

divided into (1) *somatic cells* or *body cells* (and their products), constituting the individual animal throughout its life; and (2) *germ cells,* having to do only with reproduction and continuance of the species (Chap. 11). There are four major groups of somatic tissues: (1) epithelial or covering; (2) connective or supporting (including vascular or cir-

culatory); (3) muscular or contractile; and (4) nervous.

3-5. Epithelial tissues (Fig. 3-7). These cover the body, outside and inside, as in the skin and the lining of the digestive tract (Fig. 3-6). The cells are compactly placed, bonded together by intercellular cement for strength, and often supported beneath on a basement membrane. Structurally the cells may be (1) squamous, or flat; (2) cuboidal; (3) columnar; (4) ciliated; or (5) flagellated. The tissue may be either (6) simple, with the cells in one layer; or (7) stratified, with multiple layers. Functionally, an epithelial tissue may be protective, glandular (secretory), or sensory.

Simple squamous epithelium is of thin, flat cells, like tiles in a floor; such cells form the peritoneum that lines the body cavity and the endothelium lining the inner surface of blood vessels in vertebrates. *Stratified squamous epithelium* forms the outer layers of the human skin (Fig. 4-1) and lines the mouth and nasal cavities. *Cuboidal epithelium,* with cube-like cells, is present in salivary glands, kidney tubules, and the thyroid gland. *Columnar epithelium* consists of cells taller than wide, with their long sides adjacent; this type lines the stomach and intestines of vertebrates.

A *ciliated cell* bears on its exposed surface many short, hair-like protoplasmic processes known as *cilia.* These beat in one direction, the adjacent cilia acting in unison, so that

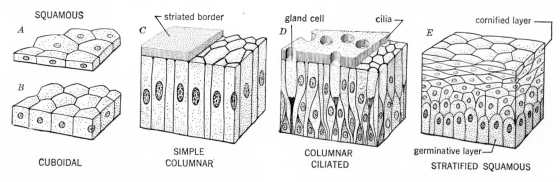

SQUAMOUS

A

B

CUBOIDAL

C striated border

SIMPLE COLUMNAR

D gland cell   cilia

COLUMNAR CILIATED

E   cornified layer

germinative layer

STRATIFIED SQUAMOUS

Fig. 3-7. Types of epithelial tissues.

small particles or materials on the surface are moved along. ***Cuboidal ciliated epithelium*** lines the sperm ducts of earthworms and other animals, and ***columnar ciliated epithelium*** lines the earthworm's intestine and the air passages (trachea, etc.) of land vertebrates. The embryos and young larvae of many aquatic animals are covered with ciliated cells by which they are able to swim about. A ***flagellated cell*** (Fig. 17-2) has one or more slender, whip-like cytoplasmic processes or ***flagella*** on the exposed surface; such cells line the digestive cavities of hydra and sponges.

Protective epithelium guards animals from external injury and from infection. It is one-layered on many invertebrates but stratified on land vertebrates. In the latter case, the basal columnar cells (germinative layer) produce successive layers of cells by mitosis; these pass outward, flatten, and lose their soft protoplasmic texture to become cornified or "horny," as they reach the surface (Fig. 3-7E). The epithelium on the earthworm secretes a thin homogeneous ***cuticle*** over its entire exterior surface, and the body covering on arthropods is similarly produced.

Glandular epithelium (Fig. 3-8) is specialized for secreting products necessary for use by an animal. Individual gland cells of columnar type (goblet cells) that secrete mucus occur on the exterior of the earthworm and in the intestinal epithelium of vertebrates.

Epithelial cells specialized to receive certain kinds of external stimuli are called ***sensory cells.*** Examples are those in the epidermis of the earthworm (Fig. 21-3) and on the tongue and the nasal passages of man (Figs. 10-8, 10-9).

3-6. Connective and supportive tissues. These serve to bind the other tissues and organs together and to support the body (Fig. 3-9). They derive from embryonic mesenchymal cells with fine protoplasmic processes. Tissues of this group later become diverse in form; some produce fibers and other intercellular substance, whereby the cells are less conspicuous.

Reticular tissue is a network of cells with stiff, interconnected protoplasmic fibrils, the spaces between being filled with other types of cells; it makes the framework of blood-forming organs such as lymph glands, red bone marrow, and the spleen. ***Fibrous connective tissue*** consists of scattered cells, rounded or branched in form, with the intercellular spaces occupied by delicate fibers. The ***white fibers*** consist of numerous fine parallel fibrils, pale in color and often wavy in outline, forming bundles that are crossed or interlaced but not branched; they occur commonly in tendons and around muscles and nerves. The ***elastic fibers*** are sharply defined and straight, bent, or branched; they bind the skin to the underlying muscles, attach many other tissues and organs to one another, and are present in walls of the larger blood vessels and elsewhere. Both kinds of fibers occur in the wall of the intestine and in the deeper part (dermis) of

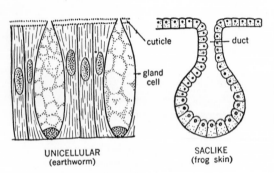

UNICELLULAR
(earthworm)

SACLIKE
(frog skin)

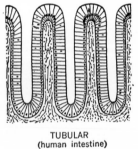

TUBULAR
(human intestine)

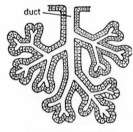

COMPOUND ALVEOLAR
(salivary gland)

Fig. 3-8. Types of glandular tissues.

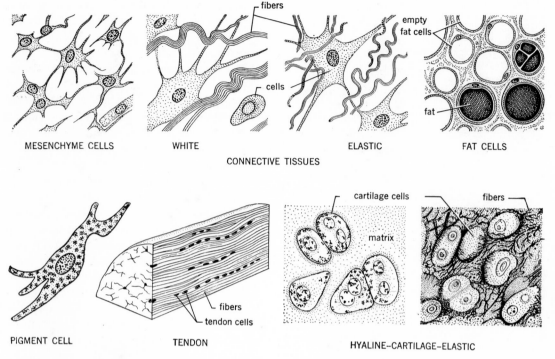

Fig. 3-9. Types of supportive tissues.

vertebrate skin. In *adipose* or *fat tissue* the cells are rounded or polygonal, with thin walls and the nucleus at one side; they contain droplets of fat, which may form larger globules. Fat is usually dissolved out in prepared microscopic sections, leaving a framework of cell outlines.

A *tendon* is a bundle of parallel white fibers surrounded by a sheath of the same material, with inward projections of the sheath that form septa, or partitions. *Cartilage* (gristle) is a firm yet elastic matrix (chondrin) secreted by small groups of rounded cartilage cells embedded within it and covered by a thin fibrous perichondrium. *Hyaline cartilage* is bluish white, translucent, and homogeneous; it covers joint surfaces and rib ends and is present in the nose and in the tracheal rings. It is the skeletal cartilage in the embryos of all vertebrates and in the adults of sharks and rays. It may become impregnated with calcareous salts but as such does not become bone. *Elas-

tic cartilage* containing some yellow fibers is present in the external ears of mammals and in the Eustachian tubes. *Fibrocartilage,* the most resistant type, is largely of fibers, with fewer cells and less matrix. It occurs in the pads between the vertebrae of mammals, in the pubic symphysis, and about joints subject to severe strains.

True *bone* or *osseous tissue* occurs only in the skeletons of bony fishes and land vertebrates (Fig. 3-10); it is unlike the limy skeletons of invertebrates. Bone is a dense organic matrix (chiefly collagen) with mineral deposits, largely tricalcium phosphate, $Ca_3(PO_4)_2$, and calcium carbonate, $CaCO_3$; the mineral part averages about 65 per cent of the total weight. Bone develops either as replacement for previously existing cartilage (cartilage bone) or follows embryonic mesenchymal cells (membrane bone). Both types are produced by *bone cells* (osteoblasts). The cells become separate but retain many minute protoplas-

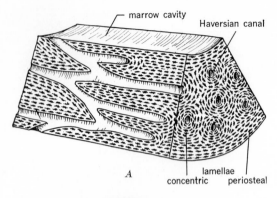

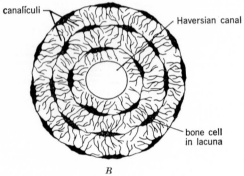

Fig. 3-10. Structure of bone (enlarged, diagrammatic). (*A*) Sector of long bone in longitudinal and cross section. (*B*) Three concentric lamellae around a Haversian canal as seen in a thinly ground cross section. Compare Fig. 4-3.

mic connections with one another and with blood vessels. Bone is, therefore, a living tissue that may be reabsorbed in part or changed in composition. During the life of an individual the proportion of mineral gradually increases and the organic material decreases, so that bones are resilient in early youth and brittle in old age.

A bone (Fig. 4-3) is covered by thin fibrous *periosteum,* to which muscles and tendons attach. Within the periosteum are bone cells that function in growth and repair. The mineral substance is deposited in thin layers, or *lamellae.* Those beneath the periosteum are parallel to the surface. Inside, especially in long bones, are many small tubular *concentric lamellae,* forming cylindrical *Haversian sys-*

tems, the wall of each being of several such lamellae with a central *Haversian canal.* The systems are mainly longitudinal, but cross-connect, providing channels for blood vessels and nerves to pass from the periosteum to the interior marrow cavity of a bone. Individual bone cells occupy small spaces, or *lacunae,* between the lamellae; these connect to one another by many fine radiating canals (canaliculi) occupied by the protoplasmic processes. In flat bones such as those of the skull and in the ends of long bones, the interior lacks regular systems and is more spongy. Cross sections made by sawing such bones show the bone fibers are arranged like beams in arches and trusses to resist compression from the exterior. A slice of bone ground microscopically thin will show the lacunae and canaliculi, which then become filled with air and appear black by refraction. The central cavity in a long bone is filled with soft, spongy *yellow marrow* (containing much fat); the ends and spaces in other bones contain *red marrow,* where blood cells are produced.

Pigment cells or *chromatophores* provide the color of many animals.

3-7. Vascular or circulatory tissues. The blood and lymph that serve to transport and distribute materials in the body consist of a fluid *plasma* containing free cells, or *corpuscles* (Fig. 3-11; Table 6-1). Colorless *white blood cells,* or *leucocytes,* are present in all animals with body fluids; some have the function of "policing" the body by engulfing bacteria and other foreign materials, when they are known as *phagocytes.* Certain white blood cells can move and change shape, hence are called *amoebocytes* (amoeba-like). The leucocytes of vertebrates can pass through the walls of blood vessels and invade other tissues of the body. Vertebrate blood also contains *red blood cells,* or *erythrocytes,* colored red by a pigment, *hemoglobin,* that serves for transport of oxygen. Those in mammals are nonnucleated, biconcave, and usually round, but in other vertebrates they are nucleated, biconvex, and usually oval. The fluid plasma transports most materials carried in the blood stream; it is colorless in vertebrates, but that of some invertebrates is colored either blue or red by dissolved respiratory pigment (hemocyanin, hemoglobin, etc.).

3-8. Muscular or contractile tissues. Movements in most animals are produced by long, slender **muscle cells** (Fig. 3-12) that contain minute fibers or myofibrils. When stimulated, they shorten in length or contract, thus drawing together the parts to which the muscles are attached.

In **striated muscle** the fibrils have alternate dark and light crossbands of different structure or density, producing a distinctly crossbanded or striated appearance; the dark bands shorten and broaden upon contraction. The cells are cylindrical, scarcely 50 μ in diameter; but some measure an inch or more in length. Each cell is surrounded by a delicate membrane (sarcolemma) and contains several to many long nuclei. The vertebrates have groups of striated muscle cells surrounded by

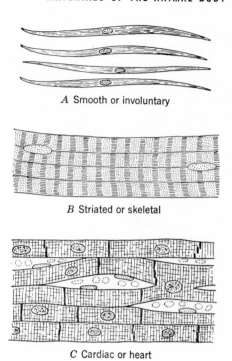

A Smooth or involuntary

B Striated or skeletal

C Cardiac or heart

Fig. 3-12. Types of muscular cells and tissues.

connective tissue sheaths to form **muscles** of various shapes. These sheaths either attach to the periosteum on bones or gather to form tendons by which the muscles are attached to the skeleton (Fig. 4-5). The simultaneous contraction of many fibers causes a muscle to shorten and bulge, as easily seen in the biceps of the upper arm. Striated muscle in vertebrates is attached to the skeleton, hence is called **skeletal muscle;** being under conscious control, it is also termed **voluntary muscle.**

Nonstriated or **smooth muscle** consists of delicate spindle-shaped cells, each with one central oval nucleus and homogeneous fibrils; the cells are arranged in layers, or sheets, held by fibrous connective tissue. Such muscle is found in the internal organs or viscera of the vertebrate body, as in the walls of the digestive tract, blood vessels, respiratory passages, and urinary and genital organs; hence it is also called **visceral muscle;** not being under control of the will, it is also termed **involuntary muscle.** In some lower invertebrates the

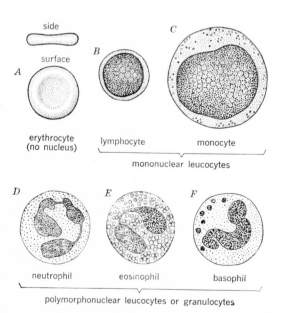

side

surface

A

B

C

erythrocyte (no nucleus)

lymphocyte   monocyte

mononuclear leucocytes

D   *E*   *F*

neutrophil   eosinophil   basophil

polymorphonuclear leucocytes or granulocytes

Fig. 3-11. Human blood cells. Erythrocyte about 7.5 μ in diameter. Nuclei of leucocytes are dark (Table 6-1).

contractile and protoplasmic portions of a muscle cell are of distinct parts, as may be seen in nematodes (Fig. 18-10*B*).

Nonstriated muscle is usually capable of slow but prolonged contraction; in mollusks, it forms the voluntary muscles of the body. Striated muscle can contract rapidly but intermittently and requires frequent rest periods; it occurs in the wing muscles of the swiftest flying insects, in the bodies and viscera of arthropods generally, and throughout the bodies of all vertebrates.

The heart muscle of vertebrates is called *cardiac muscle;* it has delicate cross striations, and the fibers are branched to form an interconnecting network. Cardiac muscle is striated yet involuntary; throughout the life of an individual its only rest period is between successive contractions of the heart.

3-9. Nervous tissues. Nervous systems are composed of nerve cells, or *neurons.* The neurons are of varied form (Fig. 3-13) in the systems of different animals and in the several parts of any one system. The individual neuron usually has a large cell body, a conspicuous nucleus, and two or more protoplasmic processes. The process that transmits stimuli to the cell body is the *dendrite,* and that

carrying impulses away from it is the *axon.* In a large animal an individual neuron may be several feet long. Bipolar cells have one dendrite and one axon; multipolar cells have a multiple dendrite and single axon. The dendrite is often short and commonly much branched (like a tree) near the cell body, whereas the axon may be short or long and is unbranched save for an occasional collateral fiber. A group of nerve-cell bodies, with their conspicuous nuclei, when outside the central nervous system, is termed a *ganglion* (pl. ganglia).

A group of fibers or processes, bound together by connective tissue, is a *nerve.* The central nervous system of animals consists of an aggregation of nerve cells and fibers. Among these is the *neuroglia* (or glia), of several cell types, that seems to serve as delicate packing to hold neurons apart. Nerve fibers without any surrounding sheath are termed *nonmyelinated* (nonmedullated) and are gray in appearance. A *myelinated* fiber has the axon surrounded by a sheath of myelin containing fatty material and appears white. A delicate membrane, or *neurilemma* (Schwann sheath), surrounds both types of fibers. The neurilemma sheath seems to play

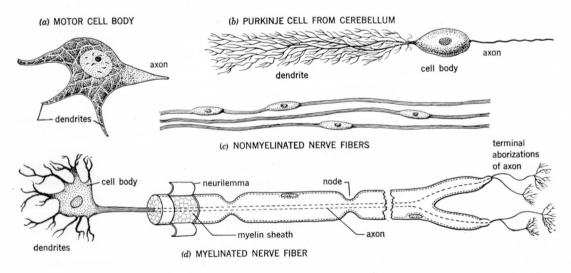

Fig. 3-13. Types of nerve cells.

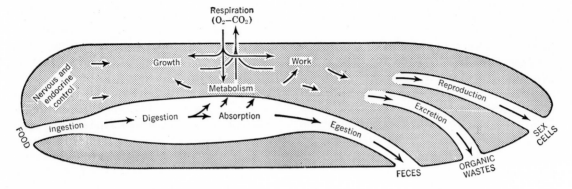

Fig. 3-14. Diagram of the essential functions in an animal.

an important role in the regeneration of damaged nerve fibers. The myelin substance is constricted at intervals, forming the **nodes of Ranvier.** Nonmyelinated fibers are common among invertebrates; and among vertebrates they are found in the sympathetic system and in certain fiber tracts of the spinal cord (internally) and brain (externally). In nerves and on the outside of the spinal cord the myelinated fibers give those parts a whitish appearance.

D. ORGAN SYSTEMS

Every animal, small or large, must carry on a variety of essential functions (Fig. 3-14). Basically these may be reduced to growth, maintenance, and reproduction; all other functions serve these major needs. Actually the bodily operations are complex.

3-10. Organ systems. In the various groups of the Animal Kingdom, from lowest to highest, there is progressive increase in bodily complexity to carry on these functions. A series of bodily systems has evolved to serve the various needs. These and their principal functions are as follows:

1. Body covering or integument—protection from the environment
2. Skeletal system—support (and protection) of the body
3. Muscular system—movement and locomotion
4. Digestive system—reception and preparation of food
5. Circulatory system—transport of materials
6. Respiratory system—exchange of oxygen and carbon dioxide
7. Excretory system—disposal of organic wastes and excess fluid
8. Endocrine glands or system—regulation of internal processes and adjustments to exterior environment
9. Nervous system (and sense organs)—regulation of internal processes and adjustments to exterior environment
10. Reproductive system—production of new individuals

Many of the invertebrates and all the vertebrates have the systems just mentioned. In some cases functions are performed without special structural parts being present. Coelenterates, for example, lack respiratory, circulatory, and excretory organs, and the flatworms and roundworms have no circulatory or respiratory organs. An organ that continues in use maintains its efficiency, but if unused it tends to degenerate. In sedentary animals and many parasites various organs have disappeared. Thus, the tapeworm, which absorbs nutriment directly from its host, has no digestive tract; and insects such as fleas, lice, and others of burrowing or parasitic habits have no wings.

Biochemical aspects

3-11. Chemistry of the animal body. The substances and processes in living matter once were thought to differ from those in rocks, minerals, and other inanimate materials. This was disproved in 1828 when urea, an excretory product of animals, was produced from the inorganic substance, ammonium cyanate. In subsequent years much has been learned of the chemistry of life. Many organic compounds have been synthesized in the laboratory, some exactly like those in plants or animals and many others unknown in nature. The intricate reactions of organic substances have gradually been determined and understood. *Biochemistry* studies the compounds present in living cells and fluids and seeks to understand the phenomena we call *life*. *Molecular biology* is unraveling many of the finer detailed aspects of cellular function (pars. 3-31, 12-19).

E. PHYSICAL PROPERTIES

3-12. Matter, weight, and gravity. The substance of the universe, the earth, and living organisms is termed *matter.* Under different conditions of temperature and pressure, any particular kind of matter may be in one of three physical states—solid, liquid, or gas. Water may be variously solid ice, fluid water, or water vapor. Animal shells and skeletons are mostly of solids, the blood plasma and much of the content of body cells is fluid, and gases are present in lungs or dissolved in body fluids. Almost any animal comprises matter in three states.

The *mass* or quantity of matter in any object or body is a basic attribute. Certain forces attract any two bodies of matter, the degree of attraction being dependent upon their masses and distance apart. The attraction between the earth and that of any animal or other object on or near its surface is termed *gravity,* and the value of this force is its *weight.*

The force of gravity keeps animals against the surface of the earth or any solid object on which they may be. It acts more rapidly in air than in a denser medium such as water where resistance to movement is greater. The weight of any given animal would be less on the moon (small mass) but much greater on Jupiter (larger mass). The volume relation of weight of any object in reference to some standard (such as water) is termed its *specific gravity.* That of a gas is low, whereas that of metals, such as iron or gold is high. Among animals specific gravity, and particularly the weight-surface area relationships, determine their habits and influence the types of environments in which they can live. Bats, birds, and insects are able to fly because of their extensive wing surfaces, and some aquatic invertebrates swim and float readily because they have much surface in relation to weight. The effective specific gravity of any aquatic animal is less than that of a comparable land dweller because the former is buoyed up by the weight of water it displaces.

Because of another property or force, *inertia,* a body at rest tends to remain so, and one in motion tends to continue in motion. Inertia is directly related to mass. A child's wagon requires less force to start into motion (overcoming inertia) than an automobile, but the wagon meets more surface resistance to motion and tends to stop sooner than the heavier vehicle. The same is true of animals. An insect has less inertia than a bear, hence it can start and stop more quickly. In the absence of gravity and friction with the air, water, or ground, a body once set in motion would continue on indefinitely; but on the earth resistance of the surroundings eventually overcomes the inertia of movement. Any animal, large or small, must exert propulsive power to remain in motion.

3-13. Cohesion and adhesion. For particles of matter of submicroscopic size (molecules; see par. 3-15) other forces operate: that of *cohesion* tends to keep particles of the same kind together and that of *adhesion* those of different kinds. Cohesion of molecules at the surface of a body of water (or other fluid) produces an elastic skin-like effect termed *surface tension* that tends to make the surface minimum in extent. This tension has an appreciable elastic strength; it will support a clean needle laid on the surface. Water striders and other insects can "walk" on the surface film because their feet are covered by a nonwettable wax that does not break the cohesive force. Surface tension rounds up rain water as drops, and microscopic amounts of oil within animal cells are formed into spherical droplets by this force. Adhesion and surface tension are responsible for the rise of fluid in a fine capillary tube. An insect that falls with its wings on the surface film of a pool may be unable to rise again because of adhesion between its wings and the water. All the phenomena named—gravity, inertia, cohesion, surface tension, and adhesion—are involved in the structural make-up and bodily processes of animals at both gross and microscopic levels.

3-14. Energy. Another important basic component of our universe is *energy,* "the capacity to do work." All activities of living organisms involve energy; examples are the movements of animals, digestion and use of food, and transmission of nerve impulses. Energy may be manifested in several ways: *motion,* such as the flight of an insect; *heat,* an increase in temperature (due to random movement of particles within matter); *chemical change* or reaction as in the digestion of food; *electric current,* flow of impulses along the course of a nerve; and *light,* transmission of units called photons. All these forms, which are more or less interconvertible, are termed *kinetic energy,* the energy of motion (Gr. *kinein,* to move). A second kind is *potential energy,* the energy of position. An upraised hand or foot has potential energy, but as it swings to throw or kick a ball, this is converted to the kinetic energy of motion. According to the Einstein equation ($e = MC^2$) matter and energy are interconvertible, but this is a phenomenon of nuclear fission, and

such *atomic energy,* a third type, is rare in living organisms.

Two basic laws govern all energy conversion. The law of *conservation of energy* (first law of thermodynamics) states that in any closed system the total quantity of energy remains unchanged. In an animal the total received in food is expended in movements, digestion, and other bodily processes, or lost as heat radiated into the environment. None has actually been "lost" to the system of which the animal is a part. The law of *degradation of energy* (second law of thermodynamics) holds that heat is the end form of all energy transformations and that all forms of energy may be entirely transformed into heat, but that heat may never be transformed completely into the other forms. The energy received by an animal is variously converted in the internal economy of its body, but all that is involved in motion, friction, chemical conversions, or even nerve impulses finally becomes heat that is lost to its environment.

The energy in the world, in the last analysis, all derives from the sun. Solar radiation is responsible for the development and growth of plants, upon which in turn practically all animals depend (Chap. 13).

3-15. Structure of matter. In everyday experience we learn to recognize some of the thousands of kinds of matter or substances to which names are given—water, iron, sugar, etc. Mere inspection, however, will not show whether any particular substance is pure—of one kind—or a mixture of two or more. Ordinary water, for example, usually contains both oxygen (a gas) and salts (solids) in solution. To learn the actual properties of water alone it must be rid of other substances. The science of chemistry deals with the precise nature of different substances in pure form and mixtures and their reactions with one another.

Chemical research has shown that each kind of pure substance consists of ultramicroscopic units called *molecules.* In turn each molecule is made up of one or more *chemical elements.* An element is a material which cannot be broken down into simpler form by ordinary chemical means. The particles of an element are termed *atoms.* A molecule of water consists of two atoms of hydrogen and one of oxygen. For convenience in stating chemical facts and describing chemical reactions the names of elements are represented by symbols: H for hydrogen, O for oxygen, C for carbon, and so on. The formula for the water molecule is therefore H_2O, that of the gas oxygen is O_2, and that of common table sugar is $C_{12}H_{22}O_{11}$. In all, 92 naturally occurring chemical elements have been identified, named, and studied.

By indirect methods we have learned that atoms, in turn, are composed of even smaller particles. No one has been able to see the ultraminute molecules, atoms, or lesser components; but many careful physical experiments and calculations have made it possible to count and determine their weight, learn their electrical charges, and compute their speed of travel. From these and other data the structural make-up of molecules and atoms has been visualized and models of many have been made.

3-16. Atoms. The atom is generally considered as having a spherical outline with a central *nucleus* around which are one or more ultimate particles called *electrons,* each revolving in an orbit (Fig. 3-15). The make-up of an atom thus roughly resembles our solar system with its central sun (nucleus) and revolving planets (electrons). In both there is a vast amount of space between the compo-

nents. If an atom were enlarged to a sphere 100 feet in diameter, the nucleus would be perhaps a half inch through. Around the nucleus electrons would be whirring so fast as to be a faint blur.

The nucleus is composed of *protons,* each of which bears a single positive charge, and also *neutrons* that are uncharged. For every positively charged proton in the nucleus there is an electron, negatively charged, in one of the orbits. The entire atom, therefore, is neutral, as the positive and negative charges are equal.

The atoms of the various chemical elements differ from one another in the number of neutrons, protons, and electrons each contains (Fig. 3-16). The combining of chemical elements (ions) to form compounds (molecules) rests on transfer of electrons from one kind of atom to another (Fig. 3-17).

Different kinds of atoms contain one to seven concentric orbits, each with one or more electrons. The elements can be arranged in a *periodic table* according to the number of electrons (or protons) each contains. Hydrogen has 1 electron (and 1 proton), whereby its atomic number is 1; helium has 2; sodium has 11; and so on. The atomic weight is an arbitrary number assigned to each kind of atom with reference to oxygen (16) as a standard. It is approximately equal to the sum of the number of protons and neutrons in the nucleus. The electrons are practically weightless. Sample atomic weights are: hydrogen 1, carbon 12, sodium 23, uranium 238.

By means of atomic fission isotopes can be made of most elements (many also occur in nature). An *isotope* has essentially the same chemical properties as the original element but differs in atomic weight; some kinds spontaneously release electrons (β radiation) or protons and neutrons (α radiation) and become radioactive. Carbon 14 (atomic weight) so produced is essentially like its "parent," carbon 12, but is radioactive; it can be incorporated into a carbon-containing substance that is fed to or injected into an ani-

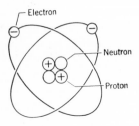

Fig. 3-15. Model of presumed structure of a helium atom.

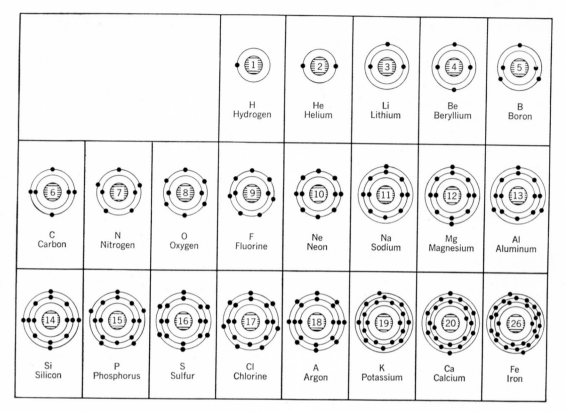

Fig. 3-16. First part of the Periodic Table diagramming the structure of atoms. The central number represents the nucleus and its net positive charge—the atomic number. Small black dots represent planetary electrons, negatively charged, in their respective orbits. The atoms shown include those of elements common (C, H, O, N) or essential (Na, P, etc.) in living matter; still others are present in minute amounts as trace elements (Fe, Si, etc.). Five kinds of atoms are omitted between calcium and iron.

mal, and the course of that type of atom can be traced in its passage in various parts of the body by means of a device to record radioactivity called a Geiger counter. Other isotopes become radioactive through release of nuclear energy (gamma radiation). Research with isotopes in plants and animals is serving to reveal some of the most intimate and fundamental details of their chemical processes.

3-17. Ions, electrolytes, and compounds. When the outer orbit contains fewer than half the total number of electrons that it can hold it may lose one or more; if more than half it may gain electrons. A change in number of electrons changes the electrical nature of the atom—gaining electrons it becomes negative, but losing any it becomes positive. An atom thus changed is termed an *ion;* with an excess of electrons it becomes an *anion* (having a negative charge; in an electric field it moves toward the anode or positive pole); with a deficit it becomes a *cation* (going to the cathode or negative pole). A solution containing ions will conduct an electric current, hence is termed an *electrolyte.*

A substance formed by the joining of two or more different kinds of atoms is a *compound* (Fig. 3-17). Any compound that releases H+ atoms (ions) when dissolved in water is called an *acid.* Common examples are hydrochloric acid, acetic acid (in vinegar), and lactic acid (in sour milk). A *base* or *alkali* is a compound that in solution releases OH⁻ ions. Caustic soda (NaOH) and ammonia water (NH₄OH) are household examples. Both acids and alkalies, in strong concentration, are severe irritants and will "burn" the skin and the delicate coverings of the eyes and mouth.

The strength of an acid or base is indicated by the relative number of hydrogen (H⁺) or hydroxyl (OH⁻) ions present in a given solution. This is represented by an exponential value termed the *pH*, where a value of 7 is

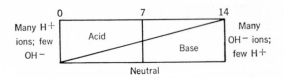

Fig. 3-18. The pH range.

neutral with equal numbers of H⁺ and OH⁻ ions (Fig. 3-18). Most body fluids are close to this value, the pH of human blood being about 7.3 or very slightly alkaline.

Mixing an acid and a base produces a *salt* and water. The H⁺ and OH⁻ ions combine to form water (H_2O), and the remaining ions join as the new compound, the salt. When, for example, hydrochloric acid (HCl) and sodium hydroxide (NaOH) are mixed in solution, the result is the compound sodium chloride (NaCl) and water. The metallic sodium ion has replaced the H⁺ ion of the acid. The process of recombination is a *chemical reaction* and can be expressed in symbols as a *chemical equation,* thus:

$$HCl + NaOH \rightarrow NaCl + H_2O$$

The arrow indicates the course of the reaction. If the reaction is reversible, as is true of many biological reactions in living organisms, a dual symbol $\rightleftharpoons$ is used.

3-18. Mixtures. When a substance is mixed with any fluid the result is variously a solution, suspension, or colloid. In a *solution* the molecules or ions of dissolved substance (the solute) soon become evenly distributed throughout those of the liquid (the solvent). Many acids, bases, salts, and other compounds (e.g., sugars) form true solutions in which the solute soon disappears from view and the solvent becomes clear. One liquid may be dissolved in another, such as alcohol in water, and a gas may be dissolved in a fluid, as oxygen does in water. If, however, the dispersed particles are of larger size (groups of molecules), a *suspension* results; mixing clay or flour in water yields a cloudy product; if al-

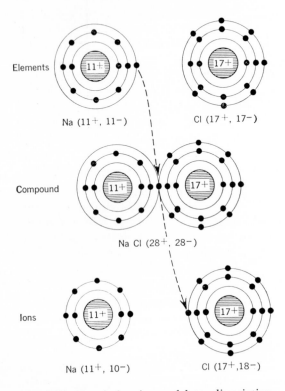

Fig. 3-17. Chemical union and later dissociation. *Elements.* Each with like number of positive and negative charges. Sodium (Na), 1 electron only in outermost orbit; chlorine (Cl), lacking 1 in outermost orbit. *Compound.* Sodium chloride (NaCl, table salt). Single electron shared by both. *Dissociation.* When dissolved in water, the compound dissociates into ions, each with a complete outer orbit; sodium ion has net + charge of 1, chlorine a net − charge of 1.

lowed to stand undisturbed, it will slowly clear as the particles settle to the bottom. An *emulsion* is a mixture of a fluid and fine particles or droplets of another liquid; milk containing droplets of cream (butterfat) and mayonnaise (oil, vinegar, raw egg) are examples.

A *colloid* (Gr. *kolla,* glue) results when the particles are of intermediate size—too large to enter solution but too small to settle out. Glue is a colloid of animal gelatin in water; the particles remain suspended indefinitely. The water is termed the *matrix* (continuous or external phase), and the other material is the *inclusion* (dispersed or internal phase). Colloid particles measure 1/10,000 to 1/1,000,000 mm. in diameter; they are larger than most chemical molecules but cannot be seen with an ordinary microscope. Such division of matter into minute particles results in an enormous increase in ratio of surface to volume. Thus a solid cubic centimeter of any substance has a surface of 6 sq. cm. (about 1 square inch), but when dispersed as particles 1/100,000 mm. in diameter the total surface is about 6,000 sq. meters or 1⅜ acres! The large surfaces provided by colloid dispersion in living matter are important for the chemical changes constantly in progress there. Colloids do not diffuse through membranes (par. 3-19) and when dried usually are masses of indefinite form; by contrast, crystalloids (e.g., salt, sugar) diffuse readily and when dried produce crystals of regular and characteristic structure. A colloid system may be either a semirigid *gel* or a more fluid *sol* (like gelatin in water, when cold, then warmed). In living matter, which is largely colloidal, these states may interchange during metabolic processes.

3-19. Diffusion and osmosis. Molecules in any kind of matter are constantly in motion, and the differences between states of matter—solid, liquid, or gas—result from the relative degree of motion possible. In a solid such as iron or brick the field of motion is extremely small. When more movement is possible the substance is a liquid, and when the limit of

motion is even greater the result is a gas. In a fluid or gas the molecules move out in all directions until they are evenly distributed throughout the available space. Under a high-power microscope a suspension of minute particles shows a dancing "Brownian movement" of the particles resulting from the bombardment of the particles by molecules of the suspension medium.

Movement of molecules from places of higher to lower concentration is termed *diffusion.* If an odoriferous gas (e.g., hydrogen sulfide) is released in one corner of a room, it quickly diffuses and can be smelled in any part of the air. When a solid such as sugar or salt is immersed in water, it quickly *dissolves* and shortly molecules of the compound are uniformly spread throughout the water, as one can confirm by withdrawing a drop in a pipette from any portion and tasting it.

The forces that repel one molecule from another result in a *diffusion pressure* proportional to the number of molecules present per unit volume of space. If two gases are enclosed in a container, each becomes diffused equally, and the total pressure is the sum of the two partial pressures. In like manner there is diffusion pressure in a solution when a quantity of any substance is dissolved in a fluid.

If a vessel containing water is divided in two by a metal partition, then sugar may be dissolved in one compartment and salt in the other, but the two will not mix. If, however, the partition is of collodion, cellophane, or parchment, sugar will diffuse through from the first compartment to the second, and salt in the opposite direction. The thin sheet acts as a *permeable membrane* having submicroscopic pores that permit the molecules of sugar and of salt to pass. Many of the finer structures in animal bodies are surrounded by *semipermeable membranes* that are selective in their action. Such membranes regulate the movement of food substances, respiratory gases, other essential materials, and of wastes between body parts. Some membranes permit passage of larger molecules than others, and the rate of passage varies with the kind of membrane and the kinds and amounts of material on the two sides.

When unequal concentrations of dissolved substances occur on the opposite sides of a permeable membrane, the resulting differences in diffusion pressure bring an exchange of water and of the dissolved substances through the membrane until there is equilibrium (equal diffusion pressure) on the two sides. The diffusion of water through a semipermeable membrane is termed *osmosis* (some authors use this term also for diffusion of dissolved substances). When two fluids contain equal concentrations of dissolved substances they are said to be *isotonic.* Solutions used to immerse living cells or tissues for study are made isotonic with the natural fluids that surrounded them in the body, as to the kinds and amounts of the principal salts (0.9 per cent NaCl for mammalian blood or tissues, etc.). A *hypo*tonic solution has a lower concentration of the dissolved substance than that in the material with which it is being compared, and a *hyper*tonic one has more.

Two experiments with artificial semipermeable membranes (collodion or cellophane) will demonstrate (Fig. 3-19) diffusion and os-mosis. The end of a thistle tube is covered by a semipermeable membrane and inverted in a beaker; the thistle tube contains 10 per cent salt solution (NaCl; molecular weight, 58), and the beaker contains only pure water (*A*). Some salt will diffuse through the membrane from the thistle tube to the beaker and some water from the beaker to the thistle tube until an equilibrium occurs with equal parts of salt and water in each (*B*). When a solution of hemoglobin is placed in the thistle tube (*C*), however, water will move from the beaker to the thistle tube by osmosis, whereby the level of fluid rises in the tube and lowers in the beaker (*D*). This results because hemoglobin molecules are too large (molecular weight, 63,000 to 68,000) to pass through pores in the membrane. These experiments show processes involved in transfer of materials across membranes of living cells in animal bodies.

Although osmosis accounts for the transport of some materials across membranes in the body of the animal, such as the movement of oxygen from the lungs to the blood, it does not account for the transport of all. In many animals certain materials move from regions of low concentration to others of high concen-

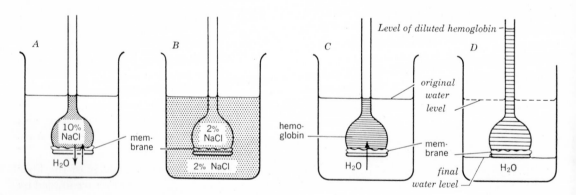

Fig. 3-19. Simple diffusion and osmosis. *Left.* (*A*) End of thistle tube containing 10 per cent salt solution is covered by a permeable membrane and inverted in a beaker of pure water. (*B*) Salt diffuses out through the membrane, and water diffuses in until solution is of same strength on both sides (equilibrium). *Right.* (*C*) Hemoglobin solution in tube, pure water in beaker. (*D*) Molecules of hemoglobin are too large to pass pores in *semi*permeable membrane, but water diffuses inward, diluting hemoglobin solution; level of fluid becomes higher in tube but lower in beaker.

tration. Such movement against a concentration gradient is known as **active transport.** This type of transport requires the expenditure of energy, which is obtained through the process of cell respiration (par. 3-31). The exact mechanism is not fully known.

3-20. Buffers. Protoplasm can "live" only within rather close physical and chemical limits, including (1) temperatures between about 0°C. (32°F.) to 40 or 45°C. (104 or 113°F.); (2) presence of oxygen gas within certain pressures; (3) definite and limited concentrations of salts; and (4) a delicate balance between H^+ and OH^- ions—the **acid-base equilibrium** (regulation of pH). This equilibrium is maintained by **buffers,** which are salts of weak acids that can furnish base (usually Na or K) to form salts of strong acids and release weaker acid. Blood, for example, contains dissociated carbonates of sodium and potassium—salts of carbonic acid. Should a stronger acid (hydrochloric, lactic) appear as a result of metabolism, the protective buffer action replaces it by weaker acid; sample reactions are:

$$NaHCO_3 + HCl \rightarrow NaCl + H_2CO_3$$

sodium   hydrochloric   sodium   carbonic
bicarbonate   acid   chloride   acid

$$H_2CO_3 + NaOH \rightarrow NaHCO_3 + H_2O$$

carbonic   sodium   sodium   water
acid   hydroxide   bicarbonate

Sea water is buffered by bicarbonate to a pH of about 8.1, one of its favorable features as an environment for animals. Isotonic salt solutions (Ringer's and Locke's) used for studies of animal tissues are buffered with bicarbonate.

F. CHEMICAL COMPONENTS OF PROTOPLASM

Protoplasm contains about 20 of the 92 natural chemical elements. The proportions of these and the specific compounds into which they are organized differ in various animals and in the different cells and tissues of any one animal. These elements are among the most common in the rocks, soils, and waters of the earth; they are present in foods taken by animals, in their useful products or secretions, and in the wastes of animal metabolism. An average percentage chemical composition of animal protoplasm (by weight and apart from intercellular substance) is as follows:

Oxygen (O) 76.0
Carbon (C) 10.5
Hydrogen (H) 10.0
Nitrogen (N) 2.5
Phosphorus (P) 0.3
Potassium (K) 0.3
Sulfur (S) 0.2
Chlorine (Cl) 0.10
Sodium (Na) 0.05
Calcium (Ca) 0.02
Magnesium (Mg) 0.02
Iron (Fe) 0.01

Traces of silicon (Si), copper (Cu), aluminum (Al), manganese (Mn), boron (B), cobalt (Co), iodine (I), fluorine (F), and bromine (Br) are also present in many animals. No single element is peculiar to living things, but carbon and nitrogen are more abundant in protoplasm than among inanimate materials.

3-21. Water, salts, and gases. Protoplasm contains much water (H_2O), various salts ($NaCl$, $CaCO_3$, etc.), and some gases, especially oxygen (O_2) and carbon dioxide (CO_2). **Water** makes up 80 to 95 per cent of the weight, being more abundant in young cells or animals than in older ones and in the lower aquatic animals than in the higher terrestrial types. Water (1) is the best solvent for inorganic substances and for many organic compounds; (2) favors the dissociation of electrolytes dissolved in it; (3) has high surface tension; (4) has great fluidity; and (5) has a large capacity to absorb heat. All the necessary processes of protoplasm are dependent upon these characteristics of water, and the life of organisms on this earth would be impossible without it. Watery body fluids (lymph

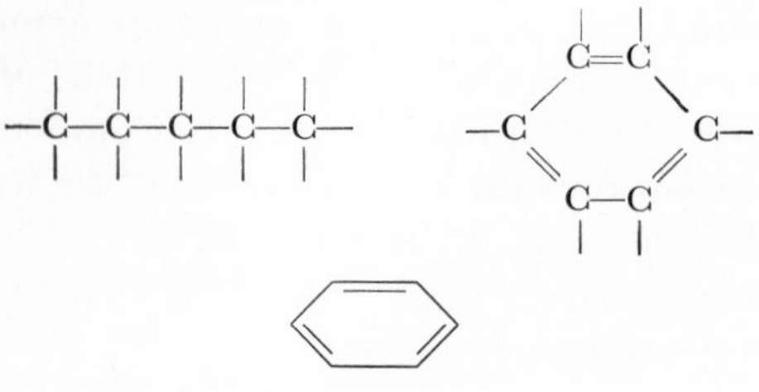

Fig. 3-20. A carbon chain and ring. The latter, a benzene ring, may also be shown in "shorthand," lacking the C's and external bonds (bottom).

and blood plasma), with both inorganic and organic content, surround cells in the animal body and transport materials within it. Terrestrial animals usually have a suitable body covering and other means to restrict undue loss of water.

The ***inorganic salts*** are chiefly those found in sea water, notably sodium chloride ($NaCl$), and are present in small concentrations; the ions of these are important in the composition of protoplasm, its chemical activities and electrical properties, and for growth, maintenance of health, and reproduction. The skeletons or shells of many animals are composed of inorganic salts—especially calcium carbonate, $CaCO_3$, and calcium phosphate, $Ca_3(PO_4)_2$—secreted by specific cells or tissues.

3-22. Organic compounds. Substances that contain carbon (C) in combination with one or more other elements are called organic compounds. Fully half a million kinds are known. Formerly it was believed that they were produced only in protoplasm, but chemists have learned to synthesize a great variety including many unknown in nature. Carbon, with four bonds, becomes grouped in "chains" or rings (Fig. 3-20). The free bonds become joined by hydrogen (H), oxygen (O), hydroxyl (OH), nitrogen (N), phosphorus (P), and sometimes sulfur (S) or other ions or elements. Compounds in the animal body and the changes they undergo often are complex.

Many organic compounds are subdivided by the process of ***hydrolysis*** (Gr. *hydro*, water + *lysis*, to loosen). When a water molecule

(H_2O) is added, a compound A–B splits into two parts:

$$A\text{–}B + H_2O \rightarrow A\text{–}H + B\text{–}OH$$

During digestion complex foods are divided into simpler components by hydrolysis. The reverse process will combine two substances with loss of H_2O. Many essential compounds in the animal body are thus synthesized from simpler materials. These reactions are controlled by substances called enzymes (par. 3-26).

Protoplasm consists mainly of three types of organic compounds: carbohydrates, lipids, and proteins.

3-23. Carbohydrates. These are compounds of carbon, hydrogen, and oxygen, generally with the latter two in a 2 to 1 ratio, as in water. Starches with the formula $(C_6H_{10}O_5)_x$ —where x may be 200 to 300—are common as stored food substances in plants. The cellulose forming the walls of plant cells has the

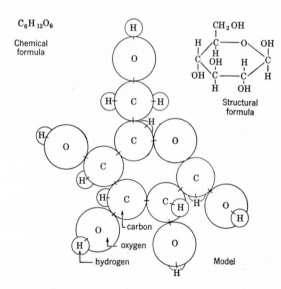

Fig. 3-21. Three ways of picturing the glucose molecule. *Chemical formula,* a shorthand description. *Structural formula,* relative positions of the atoms and the bonds between them. *Model,* "architecture," showing spatial relations.

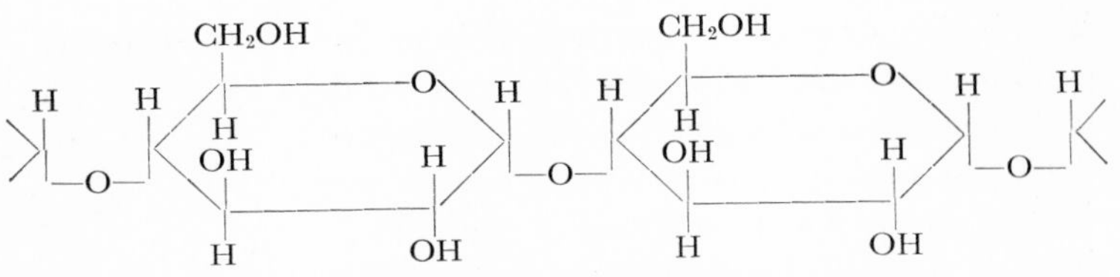

Fig. 3-22. Portion of a glycogen molecule that may be 20 or more units long. Under enzyme action a molecule of H_2O can be added at each junction and separate (individual) glucose molecules will result.

same empirical formula as starch, but x is much larger, and the molecule is of different structure; cellulose is relatively insoluble and can be digested by only a few animals. Starches eaten by animals are broken down (hydrolyzed) into simple sugars by certain digestive enzymes before being absorbed. Glycogen $(C_6H_{10}O_5)_x$—where x is small—is stored in animal tissues and used for energy. For transport in the blood, glycogen is transformed into glucose (Figs. 3-21, 3-22, 5-8; par. 5-10). Lactose, or milk sugar $(C_{12}H_{22}O_{11})$, is a carbohydrate present in the milk secreted by all mammals to nourish their young.

3-24. Lipids. Fatty and related substances that contain carbon and hydrogen, with less oxygen than in carbohydrates, are called lipids. They are all "greasy" and are soluble in organic liquids such as ether, chloroform, or benzene, but rarely in water. Some are fluid at ordinary temperatures, such as cod-liver oil and whale oil; others are solid fats, such as butter, lard, and tallow; and a few are waxes, like that in the human ear or that produced by bees. The true fats, both liquid and solid, are combinations of glycerol (glycerin) and fatty acids (Fig. 3-23), of which oleic acid $(C_{18}H_{34}O_2)$ in olive oil is an example. Fats may be decomposed (saponified) by alkalies such as sodium or potassium hydroxide, yielding glycerol and soaps, which are soluble in water. The compound lipids may contain nitrogen, with or without phosphorus, in addition to carbon, hydrogen, and oxygen; lecithin, abundant in egg yolk, is an example.

The sterols are complex wax-like lipids, with many carbon and hydrogen atoms and at least one OH radical. Cholesterol, vitamin D, some sex hormones, and certain cancer-producing substances belong in this group. The compound lipids and sterols are essential components of all protoplasm. Many fats are received in food of both plant and animal origin and are variously transformed either for immediate use or else for storage in the animal body. They are readily oxidized in protoplasm, yielding energy that is largely transformed into heat.

3-25. Proteins. These are the most abundant organic compounds in animal protoplasm. Besides carbon, hydrogen, oxygen, and *nitrogen*, they contain small amounts of sulfur, sometimes phosphorus, and occasionally

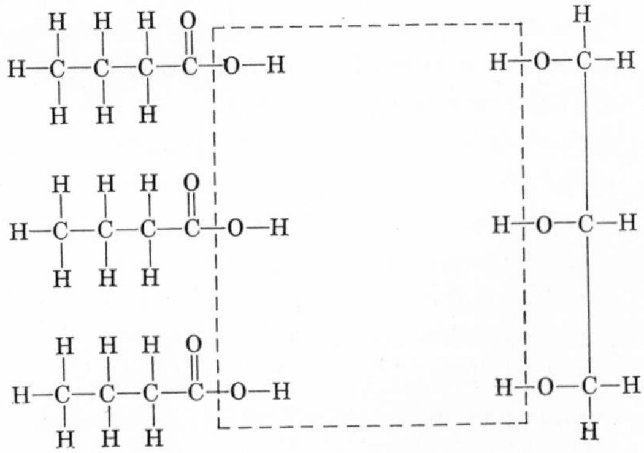

Fig. 3-23. Structure of a fat. Dashed lines enclose symbols for three water molecules lost when fatty acid and glycerol combine.

iron, iodine, or other elements. Protein molecules often are complex and relatively huge with molecular weights of 35,000 (gelatin) to 5,000,000 (hemocyanin) or more. Proteins are infinite in variety, those in each type of tissue in each kind of organism being more or less different from all others. Protein molecules are being built up and broken down constantly in animal cells. Biochemists have yet to create such large molecules in the laboratory but long peptide chains have been synthesized.

The basic structural units or "building blocks" in proteins are called *amino acids,* characterized by nitrogen in an amino radical (NH_2); 23 kinds are known. All have the basic formula ("BF") shown in Fig. 3-24, but the R component is different in each kind.

The simplest, glycine, is "BF" + H with one hydrogen atom in the R position; three other amino acids of common occurrence are shown in Fig. 3-25.

Most animals make 15 amino acids but must derive the other 8 from plants. Amino acids evidently are joined in various ways by the action of enzymes to form peptides. "Simple" proteins consist entirely of amino acid chains; examples are the soluble proteins in blood serum, milk albumen, and egg white and the very insoluble ones known as keratins that form cuticle, hair, and nails. "Conjugated" proteins are those containing other radicals or organic compounds besides amino acids; the hemoglobins in red blood cells and nucleoproteins of cell nuclei are examples with such added or *prosthetic groups.*

3-26. Enzymes. Many reactions between chemical substances in the living body proceed with extreme rapidity; yet the same substances, when removed from the body, react slowly if at all. The difference is due to the presence in animal cells and tissues of organic catalysts, known as *enzymes,* each responsible for a specific type of reaction (Fig. 3-26). A catalyst is a compound that speeds up a chemical reaction without affecting the end point or being combined in the end products. A minute amount of enzyme will transform large amounts of a substance; the enzyme pepsin, in pure form, will digest 50,000 times its weight of boiled egg white in 2 hours.

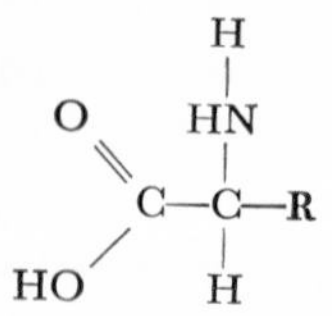

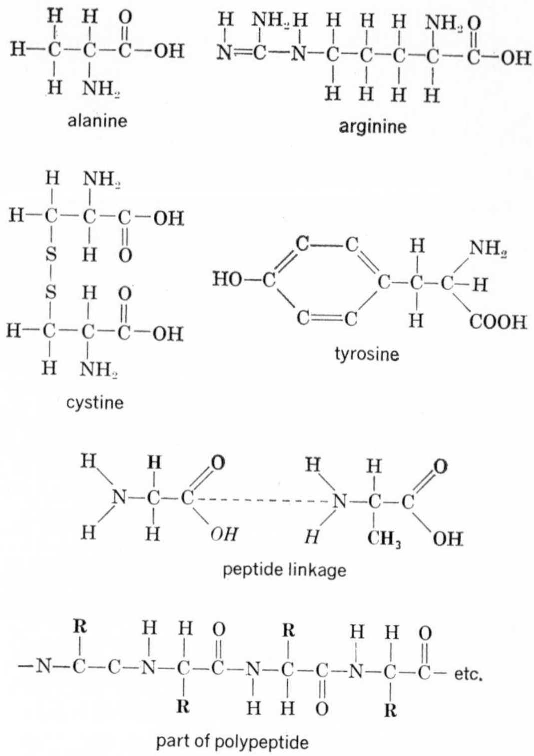

Fig. 3-25. Amino acids and peptide chains. *Top.* Four amino acids; the "BF" ($NH_2 \cdot CH \cdot COOH$) is the same in each but the **R** is not. *Center.* Two amino acids joined by peptide linkage (---) by removal of water ($OH + H$); the **R** components are shown in boldface (**H, CH$_3$**). *Bottom.* Part of a polypeptide linkage. The **R** will differ according to the amino acids present. Bonds at ends connect to other components not shown.

Fig. 3-24. Basic structural formula for an amino acid.

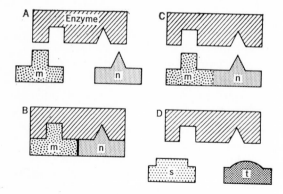

Fig. 3-26. Simplified diagram of the "lock and key" hypothesis (by Emil Fischer) of enzyme and substrate interaction. (*A–C*). Two substrate components (*m, n*) fit together on the enzyme, becoming joined (as by hydrolysis), and separate as a unit molecule. Other *m* and *n* components then may follow the same sequence. Alternatively the *mn* compound may be divided by the *C* to *A* sequence. (*D*). Two other nonfitting components (*s, t*) cannot be joined by an enzyme of the type shown.

Most enzymes are named for the reactions they promote; the dehydrogenases remove hydrogen from compounds, and the decarboxylases remove carbon dioxide. Other enzymes are named for the substrate upon which they act; lactase splits lactose (milk sugar) into two simple sugars, and sucrase divides sucrose (table sugar) into glucose and fructose.

Digestion, respiration, secretion, excretion, and other vital processes depend upon enzymes. Some biologists believe there may be a thousand kinds in one animal cell. Each enzyme acts in a particular constructive or destructive type of reaction (Chap. 5). Many enzymes bring about hydrolysis: by action of the enzyme a molecule of water is added to the molecule acted upon, and the combination then separates into two molecules. Other enzymes may carry the breakdown still farther. During digestion, for example, carbohydrates are ultimately reduced to simple sugars, fats to fatty acids and glycerol, and proteins to amino acids. Many enzyme reactions are reversible—under one set of conditions a substance is split into two products, but under other circumstances the two will be synthesized into the original material.

Enzymes are protein in nature. Many lose their catalytic power when heated to 40 or 50°C., and this may be one reason many animals die at such temperatures. Each kind does best at some particular temperature and at a certain pH, for example, pepsin at pH 1.5 (HCl, in the stomach), but trypsin at 7 to 8.6 (mildly alkaline, in the intestine). Some 20 to 30 enzymes have been crystallized, but none synthesized. Many enzymes are formed as inactive **zymogens** in the cells where they are produced but require the presence of another substance, an **activator,** to become functional. Thus the inactive trypsinogen, secreted in the pancreas, becomes the active protein-splitting enzyme, trypsin, only after it has passed through the pancreatic duct into the small intestine and been activated there by enterokinase secreted by cells in the intestinal wall. With some enzymes a second substance, or **coenzyme,** is necessary for their functioning. Several vitamins (B_1, B_2, B_6; Table 5-1) are involved in certain enzyme systems.

3-27. Nucleic acids. These large complex organic molecules have fundamental roles in cellular metabolism and in heredity. First identified in 1870 in the sperm of salmon, their detailed chemical make-up and their basic biological significance have only recently been learned. Two classes are known, **ribonucleic acid (RNA),** present in both the nuclei and cytoplasm of cells (par. 3-3) and **deoxyribonucleic acid (DNA),** found only in nuclei.

Nucleic acids contain three types of molecules: a 5-carbon sugar, deoxyribose or ribose; nitrogenous organic bases, purines and pyrimidines (ring compounds with one or more carbon atoms replaced by nitrogen); and a phosphate (Fig. 3-27). These parts are joined as follows: sugar + base + phosphate = nucleotide; many nucleotides joined by the sugar of one nucleotide to the phosphate of

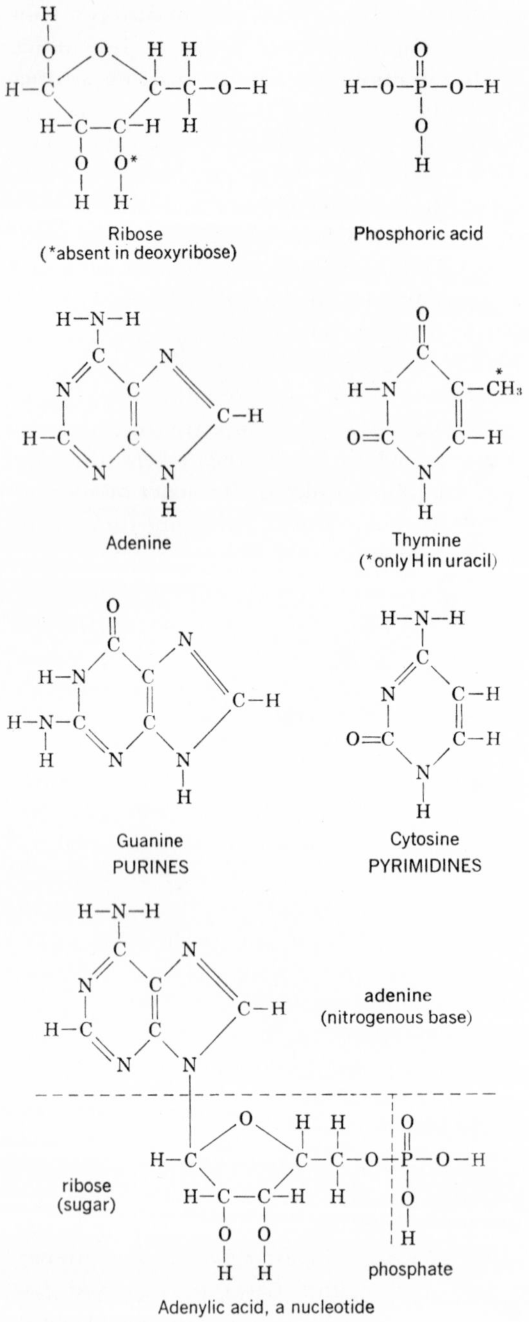

Ribose
(*absent in deoxyribose)

Phosphoric acid

Adenine

Thymine
(*only H in uracil)

Guanine
PURINES

Cytosine
PYRIMIDINES

adenine
(nitrogenous base)

ribose
(sugar)

phosphate

Adenylic acid, a nucleotide

Fig. 3-27. Components of nucleic acids.

another nucleotide = nucleic acid; and nucleic acid + protein = nucleoprotein. In DNA the purine bases are adenine (A) and guanine (G), and the pyrimidines are cytosine (C) and thymine (T). In RNA thymine is replaced by uracil (U) and the sugar is ribose. It is believed that the DNA molecule consists of two chains of nucleic acids arranged in a twisted double helix or spiral. The two chains are coiled in such a manner that the adenine of one chain always joins a thymine (in RNA adenine joins uracil) of the other, and the guanine of one to the cytosine of the other. The huge nucleic acid molecule thus resembles a spiral staircase: the rails of alternate sugar and phosphate molecules and the steps of nitrogenous bases between the sugar molecules, each pair of opposing bases joined centrally by hydrogen bonds (Fig. 3-28).

DNA in the cell chromosomes is the genetic material that controls heredity (par. 12-19) and is capable of reproducing itself in kind (duplication of chromosomes); in this duplication, the DNA strands are assumed to uncoil and separate; because the bases of each strand must pair only with certain other bases (A with T, G with C) each single strand is capable of producing an exact duplicate of the separated strand.

DNA is probably responsible for the production of RNA, which directs the synthesis of proteins in the cell. In RNA production the DNA serves as a template, each base taking on its appropriate opposite by complementary pairing (A joins to U, C to G, U to A, G to C); and the free ends of the bases become connected in a new ribose–phosphate–etc. sequence. The single strand of RNA so produced separates from the DNA template in the nucleus and passes into the cytoplasm. There are three forms of RNA (messenger RNA, transfer RNA, and ribosomal RNA) which differ slightly among themselves, but all probably are produced in a similar manner. Through the interaction of the three forms of RNA, proteins are constructed in the cell from constituent amino acids. In the synthesis of these proteins the sequence of bases along the RNA molecules is the likely means for directing the alignment of the amino acids in protein synthesis. To code each of the 20 amino acids found in proteins it is assumed

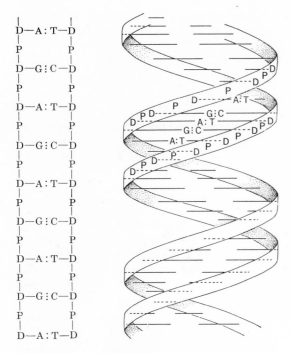

```
|         |
D—A : T—D
|         |
P         P
|         |
D—G : C—D
|         |
P         P
|         |
D—A : T—D
|         |
P         P
|         |
D—G : C—D
|         |
P         P
|         |
D—A : T—D
|         |
P         P
|         |
D—G : C—D
|         |
P         P
|         |
D—A : T—D
|         |
P         P
|         |
D—G : C—D
|         |
P         P
|         |
D—A : T—D
```

Fig. 3-28. *Left.* Diagram of part of DNA double chain. D, deoxyribose sugar; P, phosphoric acid; A, adenine; G, guanine; C, cytosine; T, thymine. In RNA the D is replaced by R (ribose) and T by U (uracil). Dots (:) are hydrogen bonds between nitrogenous bases. *Right.* Part of helix (diagrammatic). Actually the components are closely compacted.

that a unit sequence of at least 3 bases is necessary.

The chemical make-up of nucleic acids varies widely according to the assortment of their components. Many kinds of both RNA and DNA already are known. There are reasons for believing that each kind of protoplasm has its own specific nucleic acids.

The chromatin of cell nuclei (par. 3-3) is rich in these acids, which makes possible staining the chromatin with basic dyes. Nucleic acids also are basic components of viruses. In animals a succession of digestive enzymes serves to reduce nucleic acids to their derivatives for absorption or elimination.

Protoplasm contains additional organic substances, some of unknown composition, that either direct the activities of individual

cells or tissues or else control and coordinate the activities of the entire animal. These regulatory substances include enzymes (par. 3-26), vitamins (par. 5-12), respiratory pigments (par. 7-8), and hormones (Chap. 9).

G. CELLULAR METABOLISM

All living processes require supplies of chemical substances and energy. Because the many reactions involved in synthesis and breakdown of materials all take place within living cells of plants and animals, this subject is called *cellular metabolism.* During recent decades studies by an ever-increasing number of biochemists and physiologists have revealed many of the fascinating details. Refined research methods such as use of radioactive isotopes, chromatography, and microchemical analyses have made known many of the chemical components, enzymes, and processes involved. Since molecules and their reactions are invisible, all the evidence is indirect, based on complex physical and chemical tests. There is reasonable proof for some parts, but others remain in the realm of hypothesis. This section outlines the simpler aspects of cell metabolism.

3-28. Metabolism and energy. In essence, the entire living world depends on a series of reversible reactions summarized by:

$$6CO_2 + 6H_2O + energy \rightleftharpoons C_6H_{12}O_6 + 6O_2$$

The energy derives from sunlight. Plants combine CO_2 and H_2O with energy from solar radiation—by the photosynthetic action of chlorophyll—to produce organic compounds (glucose and others) and release oxygen. Certain chemical bonds in the organic molecules represent stored or potential energy. Some of this is used by the plants themselves in synthesizing other of their own necessary components. The energy needed by animals is obtained either directly by feeding on plants or secondarily by eating other plant-consuming animals. Animals use glucose and oxygen—by respiration—to derive their energy, giving off

CO_2 and H_2O as by-products. The processes in both plants and animals actually are complex, and various other intermediate compounds are involved; some of the reactions are very rapid.

The syntheses of compounds in organisms are called **endothermal** reactions because they require energy from a source outside the reacting substances, as in photosynthesis. All other life processes are **exothermal** because they liberate energy from potential sources in physiological fuels. Growth, maintenance and repair, muscular contraction, secretion, etc., are all of the latter type. Physiological oxidations are the most important exothermal reactions. Such oxidations are the basis of life; death results when they cease.

3-29. Oxidation and reduction. In simple combustion or burning of coal, fat, or sugar in the presence of oxygen, there result CO_2, H_2O, and energy as heat—but the reaction requires high temperature. By contrast, physiological oxidation of material in an animal proceeds at moderate temperature ($40°C$. or lower). The by-products again are CO_2 and H_2O, but little of the energy becomes heat and most of it is available for vital processes. This is because there is an orderly series of enzyme-controlled reactions that step by step releases the potential energy, making more efficient use of the fuel. Typically **oxidation** is the chemical union of oxygen with another substance. Other kinds of reactions also are termed oxidation, including that of the removal of hydrogen (even when the hydrogen combines with something other than oxygen). Oxidation of a substance includes the loss or transfer of one or more electrons (e^-) to another material. The latter undergoes **reduction** because it gains an electron with a minus charge.

In living organisms, many metabolic oxidations, by transfer of hydrogen, are the work of enzymes known collectively as **dehydrogenases.** Some, the **flavoproteins** or yellow enzymes, are conjugated proteins containing riboflavin (vitamin B_2) as the prosthetic group. Still others, the **cytochromes** or cell pigments, have iron-containing groups. By gaining an electron (e^-), the iron is reduced ($Fe^{+++} + e^- \rightarrow Fe^{++}$). It then transfers its electron to another cytochrome and is itself regenerated. The final cytochrome transfers its electron to oxygen, which then unites with hydrogen to form water. A succession of such transfers occurs in cellular respiration, the Krebs cycle (par. 3-33). Each removal of hydrogen is accompanied by transfer of some chemical energy that can do useful work—not dissipated as heat as in the burst of a flame.

3-30. Role of phosphorus. In many vital processes of plants and animals phosphorus (P) is an essential constituent in either inorganic or organic combination. Human bones contain about 60 per cent of tricalcium phosphate, $Ca_3(PO_4)_2$; a normal adult excretes 3 to 4 grams of phosphoric acid daily, which must be replaced by the food. The calcium-phosphorus ratio in diet of grazing animals influences their rate of gain. At the cellular level, simple fermentation of sugar by yeast is speeded by adding phosphate, which becomes organically combined in the reaction. In animals many enzyme-controlled reactions require phosphate compounds in synthesizing body components, in providing energy for muscle contraction, and other activities. Special enzymes control the addition or removal (phosphorylation or dephosphorylation) of phosphoric acid groups.

Adenosine triphosphate (ATP) and diphosphate (ADP) are complex molecules containing energy-rich phosphate bonds ($\sim$) that participate in many of these reactions. The ATP molecule (Fig. 3-29) comprises adenine ($C_5H_4N_5$, a nitrogenous base), a sugar ($C_5H_8O_3$), and 3 phosphoric acid groups ($—HPO_3$), 2 attached by high-energy bonds. ADP contains 2 acid groups and 1 high-energy bond. ATP appears in many biological reactions. It also is involved in the fermentation of sugar and the metabolism of glucose in the Krebs cycle (par. 3-33); also it is required in muscle contraction (par. 4-12). Synthesis of compounds by cells usually requires the pres-

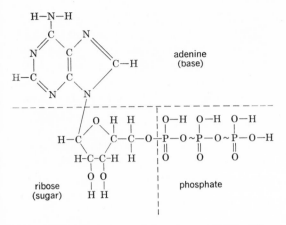

Fig. 3-29. Adenosine triphosphate (ATP). The symbol ~ indicates an energy-rich bond. Loss of the outermost —PO_3H results in the diphosphate (ADP), with release of much energy; loss of the second phosphate unit leaves the monophosphate (AMP), yielding further energy.

ence of ATP or ADP. The linkage of simple sugars to produce disaccharides or starch requires the presence of glucose phosphate. The same is true in forming polypeptides from amino acids and for the synthesis of DNA from its nucleotides—they must be present as triphosphates.

3-31. Cellular respiration. The energy necessary for life processes in the cell and organism is obtained by breaking down (degradation) the simple organic molecules absorbed in the digestive system—sugars, fatty acids, glycerol, and amino acids (Fig. 3-31). These substances enter the sequence of energy derivation at different places. Amino acids are deaminated (—NH_2 removed) and the resulting keto acids enter at several points. Fatty acids are broken down by a series of enzymatic reactions into acetyl coenzyme A and enter the cycle in that form. Sugars, especially glucose and fructose, are used more directly but if not needed they are converted to glycogen in the liver and stored. Glycogen is a large molecule made of glucose molecules joined together (Fig. 3-22). It also may be formed from nonsugar precursors such as amino acids, fatty acids, or glycerol. Glycogen, therefore, is the energy reservoir for the organism.

The process of obtaining energy from glucose results eventually in the oxidation of glucose to CO_2 and H_2O. This is the process of *cellular respiration.* Oxidation results from either the addition of oxygen to a molecule or the removal of hydrogen. These transformations are considered to occur in the mitochondria (Figs. 3-2, 4-8).

Each of the several phases of the entire process is controlled by one or more enzymes and most of the reactions are reversible. The two major phases of cellular respiration are glycolysis and the Krebs, or citric acid, cycle.

3-32. Glycolysis (Fig. 3-30). The first step is conversion of glycogen to glucose and activation of the latter molecule. These processes are accomplished simultaneously by enzyme action with addition of a phosphate group, —H_2PO_3 (phosphorylation).

The latter is furnished by adenosine triphosphate (ATP; Fig. 3-29) if glucose is the precursor. If glycogen is the precursor, it comes from inorganic phosphate (H_3PO_4). In the phosphorylation of glucose, the ATP transfers its third phosphate group to the glucose molecule to form glucose phosphate, whereby it becomes adenosine diphosphate (ADP), with one remaining high-energy bond. Glucose phosphate is the activated form of glucose.

After the initial activation, a series of reactions and addition of one more phosphate group from another molecule of ATP yield fructose diphosphate. The latter is then split into two parts, each with 3 carbon atoms and a phosphate group. The two are slightly different in structure, but interconvertible, the major one being glyceraldehyde phosphate. The fate of each half is the same so that it is necessary to follow only one. Since two molecules were produced from fructose diphosphate, all reactants and products are doubled through the remainder of the process.

Each glyceraldehyde phosphate molecule is next phosphorylated by adding another phosphate group derived from inorganic phosphoric acid (H_3PO_4), not from ATP. Simul-

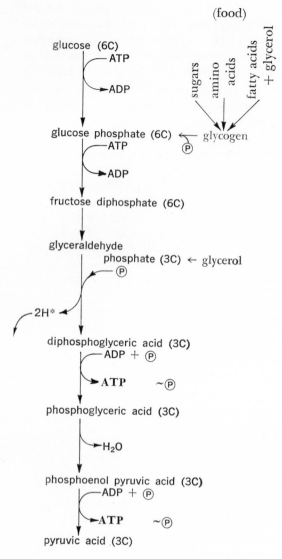

Fig. 3-30. Glycolysis. Starting with the products of digestion (glucose, fatty acids, glycerol, and amino acids) or with stored glycogen, the process of glycolysis proceeds through a series of intermediate compounds to end with pyruvic acid. The number of carbon atoms (C) in each stage is indicated. Points of direct energy production are marked by the symbol $\sim \circledP$. Derived products are shown in boldface (**ATP**). Splitting of fructose diphosphate results in 2 molecules of glyceraldehyde phosphate, whereby all products thenceforth are doubled—but only one sequence is shown. 2H* atoms go to the cytochrome system in Fig. 3-31. For ATP vs. ADP see Fig. 3-29.

taneously the glyceraldehyde is oxidized by removal of 2 H ions; the resulting molecule of diphosphoglyceric acid then includes one phosphate group with a high-energy bond ($\sim \circledP$).

The remaining steps leading to pyruvic acid involve (1) transfer of the one high-energy phosphate bond of the phosphoglyceric acid to a molecule of ADP to form ATP; (2) internal rearrangement of the molecule to transform the remaining phosphate group into a high-energy bond; and (3) transfer of this last bond to ADP to form ATP. The resulting molecule is pyruvic acid. A similar sequence occurs in muscle except that pyruvic acid is converted (reduced) to lactic acid by the addition of hydrogen.

With the formation of either pyruvic or lactic acid, the first part of the energy production sequence (glycolysis) is completed. It is an anaerobic process, which does not require the presence of oxygen. Further degradation of pyruvic or lactic acid proceeds aerobically.

As a result of the above events, some of the energy originally in the glucose molecule has been made available for use, stored in the high-energy bonds of ATP. Energy in the form of 2 ATP molecules was needed to start the sequence when glucose was the source—but only 1 molecule each of ATP and inorganic phosphate if glycogen was the precursor. In glycolysis 4 ATP molecules are produced (2 from each glyceraldehyde phosphate molecule). Hence there is a net gain of 2 with each glucose molecule and 3 with each glycogen unit. This is the total amount of energy obtainable in the absence of oxygen.

The preceding phase is not normally isolated from the next part, which requires oxygen. Further energy, 6 more molecules of ATP, may be obtained under aerobic conditions. In the change from glyceraldehyde phosphate to diphosphoglyceric acid 2 H atoms were removed; these are transferred by a special system of coupled molecules called the **cytochrome system.** At the end of this system the two hydrogen atoms are united with oxygen to form water. The process of transfer is accomplished by successive reductions and oxidations of the component molecules whereby more energy is captured in ATP molecules; 3 of the latter are formed for every 2 hydrogen atoms transferred to water. Thus, in addition to the 2 (or 3) ATP molecules derived anaerobically, 6 more are obtained, 3 for each glyceraldehyde phosphate molecule. The overall results from glycolysis may be summed thus:

$$\text{Glucose} + 8\text{ ADP} + 8\text{ phosphate}$$
$$\downarrow$$
$$2\text{ pyruvic acid} + 8\text{ ATP}$$

3-33. The Krebs cycle. Only part of the energy in each glucose molecule becomes available through glycolysis. More results from complete oxidation of pyruvic acid to CO_2 and H_2O, a sequence that requires oxygen. This series of enzyme-controlled reactions is called the *citric acid cycle* or *Krebs cycle* (Fig. 3-31).

The first step in oxidation of pyruvic acid is the removal of CO_2 and activation of the remaining 2-carbon units with coenzyme A, an organic molecule. The resulting complex is called acetyl coenzyme A (acetyl CoA). In the process two more H atoms are removed and transferred by the cytochrome system to join one O and form a molecule of water.

Next acetyl CoA is condensed with oxaloacetic acid, CoA is freed, and a molecule of citric acid is formed. The latter then undergoes changes that form, in turn, a succession of organic acids. During this sequence 2 molecules of CO_2 are given off and 4 pairs of H atoms are removed through the cytochrome system generating 11 ATP molecules; 1 additional molecule is formed directly preceding the formation of succinic acid, one of the organic acids formed. (The 4 pairs of H atoms yield 11 ATPs instead of 12 because in one case the cytochrome system is shortened and only 2 result from an H pair.) The final step in the Krebs cycle yields oxaloacetic acid, which is then available to join acetyl CoA and start again.

Pyruvic acid thus is completely oxidized to CO_2 and H_2O. The cycle generates 5 molecules of H_2O (in the cytochrome system) and 3 of CO_2. Of the 5 H_2O, 3 are used in the cycle, so the net output is only 2. From each pyruvic acid molecule, 15 ATP molecules are formed; a glucose molecule yields 2 molecules of pyruvic acid, so that each molecule of glucose forms 30 ATP molecules. The Krebs cycle may be summarized thus:

$$\text{Pyruvic acid} + 5\text{ oxygen} + 15\text{ ADP}$$
$$+ 15\text{ phosphate}$$
$$\downarrow$$
$$3\text{ }CO_2 + 2\text{ }H_2O + 15\text{ ATP}$$

The significance of this complex series of reactions lies in the fact that the energy obtained is stored in high-energy bonds of ATP which then serve in all life processes of the cell requiring energy. Complete burning of 1 mole (180 grams) of glucose produces 690,000 calories of energy. One mole of ATP holds about 10,000 calories. Since 38 moles of ATP are formed in cell respiration from 1 mole of glucose, 380,000 calories have been stored; the rest is lost as heat. The efficiency of the reaction is thus 55 per cent, far higher than any of man's engines.

REVIEW

1. Where is energy for animals obtained, and in what ways is it used?
2. Define diffusion, semipermeable membrane, osmosis. Why is osmosis such a vital process in living cells?
3. What are the principal inorganic and organic constituents of protoplasm? What are its physical characteristics?
4. What is an enzyme, and what does it do?
5. Describe a typical animal cell. What are the functions of the principal parts?
6. Define mitosis, and explain the various stages. What is the significance of mitosis from the standpoint of heredity?
7. What is a tissue? Are there tissues in unicellular animals? Where in the animal body would you expect to find the following tissues: epithelial, connective, supportive?
8. Name the principal organ systems, and de-

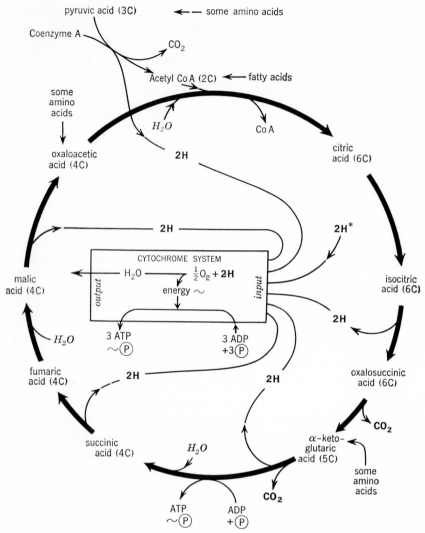

Fig. 3-31. Krebs cycle. Pyruvic acid (derived by glycolysis; Fig. 3-30) is oxidized to CO_2 and H_2O to yield energy. Most of the energy is obtained by passage of the H atoms through the cytochrome system to join with O and form water. For every 2H transferred, 3 ATP molecules are generated, each with a high-energy bond (* = 2H from glycolysis). Points of energy production are marked by the symbol ∼; trapping of this energy in ATP is indicated by ∼Ⓟ. The number of carbon atoms (C) in each compound is shown. Places where fatty acids and amino acids may enter the cycle are marked.

scribe the major functions of each. Are any of these lacking in particular groups of animals?

9. What are the functions of DNA and RNA in the cell?

10. What is meant by "base pairing" and what is its importance in protein synthesis?

11. What are the essential steps in the production of energy from glucose?

12. What is the importance of the cytochrome system?

13. How is the energy which is produced in glycolysis and the Krebs cycle stored for use in the animal body?

4
Body covering, skeleton, and body muscles

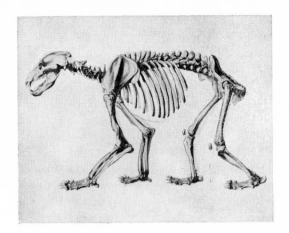

In all but the lowest animals the external body covering, the supporting framework or skeleton, and the muscles that serve for movements and locomotion are variously interrelated. The kind of covering, the type of skeleton, and the arrangement of muscles in each animal group depend on its ancestry, the sort of environment it inhabits, and its mode of life. Among invertebrates the functions of protection and support are often combined in a firm external exoskeleton with the muscles inside. The most efficient designs are among the insects and other arthropods which have jointed body segments and appendages, with many individual muscles attached to inward projections of parts of the covering skeleton. By contrast, the vertebrates, almost from their beginning, have had a separate body covering or integument and an internal jointed framework or skeleton with muscles on its outer surfaces; both hinge and ball-and-socket joints are present. The muscles on vertebrates, by their size and arrangement, are partly responsible for bodily shape.

A. BODY COVERING

4-1. Invertebrates. The body in all animals has some covering to conserve the protoplasm within, to give physical protection, and to exclude disease organisms. Many protozoans (e.g., *Amoeba*) are covered only by the delicate cell membrane, whereas others (*Paramecium*) also have a firm elastic pellicle. All multicellular animals are covered by a tissue, the *epidermis.* On many soft-bodied invertebrates of the water or moist environments on land, such as coelenterates, flatworms, and slugs, this is a single layer of cells. The epidermis on many worms secretes an external, noncellular *cuticle* as additional covering; this is delicate on earthworms but resistant on flukes, tapeworms, and roundworms. On insects, snails, and some other animals the epidermis secretes a protective external skeleton or shell.

The coverings of terrestrial arthropods include a cuticle and usually a thin layer of wax as well; therefore they resist the loss of body fluids. This arrangement, with other adaptations to life in air, enables the insects, spiders, and relatives to inhabit dry environments.

4-2. Vertebrates. The body covering is a *skin,* or *integument,* consisting of an outer *epidermis* over an underlying *dermis* that contains blood vessels, nerves, and pigment. On fishes the thin epidermis contains many

Illustration at top of page: Skeleton of a grizzly bear.

glands that provide mucus to lubricate the exterior of the body. Sharks and rays have enamel-covered exposed scales, and most bony fishes are protected by dermal scales that sheathe the body. The land vertebrates (amphibians to mammals) have a *stratified epidermis* of several cell layers (Figs. 2-6, 4-1). The outermost layer becomes hardened, or *cornified,* as a more resistant covering and is continually renewed by growth of new layers from the base of the epidermis. Amphibian skin is glandular and moist, as in the frog. On reptiles, birds, and mammals the cornified part is dry and tougher, to resist wear in dry environments. It also limits the loss of moisture by evaporation and thus conserves body fluids. The skin of reptiles usually contains dermal *scales* that afford added physical protection, and on lizards and snakes the cornified exterior is molted at intervals. Birds are covered by *feathers;* these are dry, nonliving cornified products of the epidermis that insulate the body, provide streamlined exterior contours of bodily form, and make the broad surfaces of the wings and tail used for flight. The skin of mammals is covered by *hairs,* another type of cornified epidermal product, also serving for insulation. Both feathers and hair are replaced periodically by molt of the old and growth of new coverings.

Only the birds and mammals with their heat-conserving body coverings are "warm-blooded" (homoiothermous), with regulated body temperatures. All other animals are "cold-blooded" (poikilothermous) like the frog, their body temperatures following closely those of the environments in which they live. Seals, whales, and other aquatic mammals have deep layers of fat (blubber) under the skin that insulate their bodies from heat loss in the water. The human skin (Fig. 4-1) resembles that of other mammals but is scantily haired on most parts. Evaporation of the watery perspiration secreted by the *sweat glands* helps to cool and regulate the body temperature in hot environments (par. 8-5).

Other cornified epidermal products include

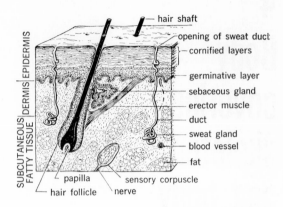

Fig. 4-1. Section through human skin; enlarged and diagrammatic.

the horns of cattle and sheep (but not the calcareous antlers of deer), the claws, nails, hoofs, and horny pads on the feet of various land vertebrates, the beak and shank coverings on birds, and the outer scutes on turtle shells. Cornified materials are all highly insoluble proteins (keratins) that are quite resistant to wear and to chemical disintegration. Some other keratins are the horny coverings on fish eggs and the horny skeletons of bath sponges and sea fans (coelenterates).

4-3. Pigment and coloration. An important protective device in the body covering of many animals is the presence of *coloring matter* or *pigment.* Protection is gained by the pattern of pigment (camouflage, see Chaps. 2, 14) or by the density and extent of pigment (for protection from the rays of the sun; par. 12-9).

B. SKELETAL SYSTEMS

All animals in some phyla and some in most others have a firm framework or *skeleton,* that gives physical support and protection for the body and often provides surfaces for the attachment of muscles. A skeleton is not absolutely necessary, however, since many aquatic invertebrates and a few land animals have none. Parts of the skeleton in arthropods and vertebrates form jointed appendages that serve as levers for locomotion. In such cases there is a close mutual relation of structure and function between the skeletal parts and muscles, whereby their interaction is more efficient.

The skeleton (Fig. 4-2) may be a shell or other *external* covering (exoskeleton), as on corals, mollusks, and arthropods, or *internal* (endoskeleton), as in vertebrates. It is *rigid* on corals, many mollusks, and others, but variously *jointed* and movable in echinoderms, arthropods, and vertebrates. Exoskeletons serving as defensive armor were present on fossil animals such as the trilobites, primitive fish-like ostracoderms, early amphibians (labyrinthodonts), and some ancient reptiles (dinosaurs); they occur also on living brachiopods, most mollusks, barnacles, some fishes, the turtles, and the armadillo.

An exoskeleton limits the ultimate size of an animal and may become so heavy that the organism must remain fixed. This is because the internal muscles cannot be large and powerful enough to move the heavy framework. The internal skeleton of a vertebrate involves far less limitation, and some vertebrates have attained to huge size; these include the brontosaurs and other fossil reptiles and the living elephants and rhinoceroses. Certain sharks and whales, whose weight is partly supported by the water, are even larger (Fig. 1-1).

4-4. Invertebrate skeletons. Some protozoans (Sarcodina, Mastigophora) secrete or otherwise form skeletons of calcareous (limy), siliceous (glassy), or organic substances, often of intricate pattern. Sponges secrete microscopic internal rods (spicules) or fibers of the same kinds of materials. The skeletons of corals, brachiopods, echinoderms, and mollusks are mainly of lime ($CaCO_3$) and are retained throughout the life of the individual, growing at the margins and becoming thicker

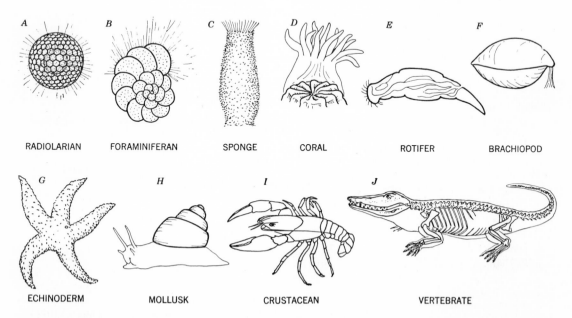

RADIOLARIAN   FORAMINIFERAN   SPONGE   CORAL   ROTIFER   BRACHIOPOD

ECHINODERM   MOLLUSK   CRUSTACEAN   VERTEBRATE

Fig. 4-2. Skeletons in animals; diagrammatic. (*A, B*) Protozoans. (*A*) Radiolarian, framework of silica. (*B*) Foraminiferan, limy shell. (*C*) Sponge, many minute limy spicules. (*D*) Coral, solid calcareous (limy) cup with partitions. (*E*) Rotifer, firm "glassy" cuticle. (*F*) Brachiopod, 2 limy shells. (*G*) Echinoderm, internal jointed skeleton of limy plates. (*H*) Mollusk, limy shell. (*I*) Crustacean, complete exoskeleton with chitin. (*J*) Vertebrate, skull, vertebrae, limb girdles, and limb skeleton of bone.

with age. All arthropods—crustaceans, insects, and others—are covered completely by jointed exoskeletons of organic materials containing chitin (par. 22-2). These are flexible at the joints between segments of the body and appendages but more rigid elsewhere. On crabs and related crustaceans the external covering is reinforced by internal deposits of limy salts that produce a hard "crust."

The appendages number one pair per body segment (somite) or fewer and are variously developed as sensory antennae, jaws or other mouth parts, and legs for walking or swimming. Since the skeletons of arthropods when once hardened cannot expand, these animals undergo complete molt of the old covering at intervals to permit growth; the body parts enlarge immediately after a molt, before the new covering has hardened. The secreted tubes in which some aquatic worms live, the cases built of bottom debris by some protozoans and certain insect larvae, and the empty snail shells used by hermit crabs all serve as protective exoskeletons.

4-5. Vertebrate skeletons. The internal skeleton has a common basic pattern with the fundamental features seen in a frog (par. 2-7). From the cyclostomes to the mammals a progressive sequence may be traced, although there are many differences in the size and form of component parts and in the presence or absence of certain elements. The essential features in a land vertebrate are given in Table 4-1. The skeleton supports the body, provides for attachment of muscles, and houses the brain and nerve cord. In all but the cyclostomes it includes framework for the jaws and the paired fins or limbs. The skeleton is of hyaline cartilage in adult cyclostomes and sharks and in the embryos of all higher vertebrates, but in the adults of bony fishes to mammals it is largely of bone with cartilage over joint surfaces and in a few other places. The skeletal parts increase gradually in size by growth at the ends or margins (Fig. 4-3).

4-6. Vertebral column. In all chordates the first skeletal element to appear in the embryo is a slender unsegmented and gelatinous rod, the *notochord,* that extends along the body axis between the digestive tract and the nerve cord. It persists thus in amphioxus and cyclostomes but in fishes and higher types is later

Table 4-1. General divisions of the skeleton in a land vertebrate

Axial skeleton (*median*)			Appendicular skeleton (*lateral, paired*)	
Skull	Vertebral column	Thoracic basket	Pectoral (*anterior*)	Pelvic (*posterior*)
Cranium (brain box) Sense capsules (nose, eye, ear) Visceral arches (jaws, hyoid, larynx)	Vertebrae Cervical (*neck*) Thoracic (*chest*) Lumbar (*lower back*) Sacral (*hip*) Caudal (*tail*)	Ribs (*paired; bony or cartilaginous*) Sternum (*breastbone*)	Shoulder girdle Scapula (*dorsal*) Clavicle (*anterior*) Coracoid (*posterior*) Fore limb	Hip girdle Ilium Pubis Ischium Hind limb
			Humerus (*upper arm*) Radius and ulna (*forearm*) Carpals (*wrist*) Metacarpals (*palm*) Phalanges (*fingers*)	Femur (*thigh*) Tibia and fibula (*shank*) Tarsals (*ankle*) Metatarsals (*sole*) Phalanges (*toes*)

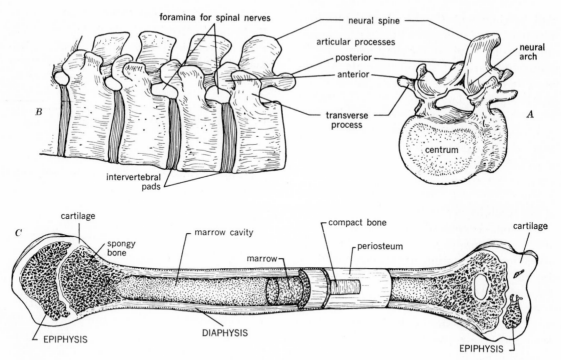

Fig. 4-3. Gross structure of bones. (*A*) One human lumbar vertebra. (*B*) Part of vertebral column (lumbar region in man) showing way in which vertebrae articulate and also the pads between the centra and the foramina for spinal nerves connecting to nerve cord. (*C*) Section of a long bone: the shaft (diaphysis) with cap (epiphysis) at each end. Growth in length occurs in cartilage area between shaft and ends. Ends covered with smooth articular cartilage. (*C, after Woerderman.*)

surrounded and supplanted by the backbone, or **spinal column,** of separate vertebrae (Fig. 4-3). The spool-like **centrum** of each vertebra has a dorsal **neural arch** to enclose the nerve cord. In the tails of fishes each vertebra has also a ventral **hemal arch** around the main artery and vein; this arch is spread open in the body or trunk region and forms rib-like structures shielding the internal organs. In land vertebrates the centrum bears a pair of **transverse processes** as points of attachment for the true ribs of these animals (except frogs). At either end of the centrum are two **articular processes** by which one vertebra may turn slightly on those directly before and behind. The vertebral column of fishes comprises only **trunk** and **tail** regions, but in salamanders, reptiles, and mammals there are five regions: neck, or **cervical;** chest, or **thoracic,**

with ribs; lower back, or **lumbar;** pelvic, or **sacral,** joining the hind-limb girdle; and tail, or **caudal.** The caudal vertebrae are few in man and birds. Long-bodied swimming vertebrates have the vertebrae numerous and much alike, as seen in eels and similar fishes, in some salamanders (*Siren*), in certain fossil reptiles, and in whales. The living snakes that literally swim on land have many vertebrae (Fig. 26-8). The ribs of land vertebrates usually join ventrally to a breastbone, or **sternum,** but this is lacking in snakes. The sternum of birds has a large median keel for attachment of the stout flight muscles.

4-7. Skull. This structure, which frames the vertebrate head, begins in the embryo as cartilage and consists of (1) the **cranium,** or brain box, which houses the brain; (2) three pairs of **sense capsules** for the organs of smell, sight, and hearing; and (3) the *visceral skeleton,* which is a series of paired arches providing the jaws, the support for the tongue (hyoid apparatus), and the supports for the gill region. It continues in this state in adults of sharks and rays, but in bony fishes and higher forms the cartilaginous cranium is replaced by numerous bones; also the capsules and upper jaw become more completely joined to the cranium. In land vertebrates parts of the visceral arches are put to other uses. Both the general form and detailed structure of the skull in adults of various vertebrates are diverse, and a comparative study from fishes to mammals shows many differences, including reduction in the number of bones; yet there is an underlying continuity in pattern throughout the entire series.

4-8. Limbs. Cyclostomes have no lateral appendages, but the sharks and bony fishes have two pairs, the *pectoral* and *pelvic fins,* with skeletal elements consisting of fin rays. Each pair is supported on a framework, or girdle. Land vertebrates have two pairs of **limbs** in place of the fins, and these are supported by the *pectoral* and *pelvic girdles,* respectively, as in the frog. Each limb characteristically ends in five *toes,* or *digits.* The component bones of the girdles and limbs are homologous from amphibians to mammals, although variously modified in adaptation to special modes of life (Fig. 14-2). Loss of digits, fusion of other bones, and reduction or complete loss of fins, limbs, and girdles have occurred in various vertebrates. Some salamanders have only four or three toes on each foot, and no living bird has more than three "fingers" or four toes. Reduction in number of toes occurs in many mammals, the horse being an extreme case, with only one functional toe on each foot (Fig. 14-9). The radius and ulna and the tibia and fibula are fused in many species that have slight rotational movement of the limbs. The limbs and digits are far reduced in some salamanders and lizards and are absent in a few lizards and all snakes. Whales and sirenians have no hind limbs, and among fishes the eels lack pelvic fins. Vestiges of the limbs or girdles in whales, boas, and other limbless vertebrates indicate that these animals have descended from ancestors with limbs.

C. MUSCULAR SYSTEMS

The ability to contract is a fundamental property of protoplasm, but in most animals the contractions that bring about changes in shape or form and locomotion are produced by special fibrils or muscular tissues (par. 3-8). Most multicellular animals that are capable of locomotion have opposed sets of muscles to perform these movements.

4-9. Invertebrates. Simple protozoans such as *Amoeba* can contract or extend the one-celled body in any direction (Fig. 16-3). Others of more specialized structure such as the stalked *Vorticella* have special contractile fibrils (myonemes). The body wall of coelenterates contains T-shaped epitheliomuscular cells with contractile fibers in the basal part; these cells lie in opposed sets in the body wall (Fig. 17-8), whereby the body can be reduced in either length or diameter. Flatworms usually have muscle fibers in three directions—longitudinal, transverse, and dorsoventral (Fig. 18-3); contraction of those in any one plane will force the soft but fluid-filled body to extend in the others, much as the human tongue can be moved. In roundworms the muscle cells somewhat resemble those of coelenterates, but all are aligned against the body wall and parallel to the main body axis (Fig. 18-10). The alternate contraction of fibers along opposite sides of the body enables the worm to bend and straighten, but it can neither twist freely nor extend the body in length. In an earthworm the body wall includes two layers of muscles, an outer circular and an inner longitudinal layer (Fig. 21-3). Contraction of the outer layer causes the fluid-filled body to lengthen, and action of the longitudinal muscles shortens it. The crustaceans, insects, and other arthropods are the

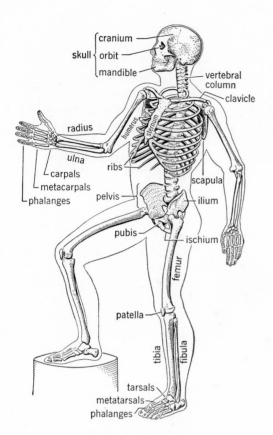

Fig. 4-4. The human skeleton.

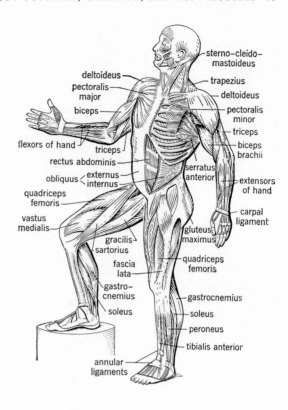

Fig. 4-5. Superficial muscles of the human body (pectoralis major and external oblique removed on left side).

only invertebrates that depart from the "layer" arrangement of muscles; they have many separate muscles, varied in size, arrangement, and attachments, that move the body segments and the parts of the jointed legs and other appendages. These muscles are fastened to the internal surfaces of the exoskeleton and act over hinge joints between adjacent parts. A caterpillar may have 2,000 separate muscles.

4-10. Vertebrates. The muscles of vertebrates attach to parts of the skeleton. In the fish-like forms—cyclostomes to permanently gilled amphibians—and the limbless reptiles the muscles are predominantly segmental (Fig. 25-10). They alternate with the vertebrae and provide the undulating movements by which the animals travel. In land vertebrates, from frogs to mammals, the nonsegmented muscles that move the limbs and head are larger and more important (Figs. 2-8, 4-5). In the higher forms some segmental muscles persist, however, between the vertebrae and the ribs and in the rectus abdominis muscles of the ventral body wall. The contraction of muscles is controlled by end plates of motor nerve fibers that attach to the muscle fibers (Fig. 10-7E).

4-11. Muscle and nerve. In a living animal the contraction (shortening) of a muscle results from impulses passing from the central nervous system along a nerve. This may be demonstrated with a nerve-muscle preparation such as the sciatic nerve and gastrocnemius muscle dissected out together from a frog (Fig. 4-6A). One end of the muscle is attached immovably and the opposite end is tied to a lever that will magnify or record any change in length of the muscle. Impulses, in the form of brief electric shocks, are applied to the nerve. Beginning with one too weak to produce any result and gradually increasing the intensity, a threshold of stimulation is reached at which slight contraction results. Further increase will produce a greater contraction, but finally still stronger impulses have no further effect. If all fibers but one in the nerve are cut and the remaining one is stimulated at increasing intensities, nothing happens until the threshold is reached, when the response is at once a maximum. This is the **all-or-none effect.** The graded increase in action of an entire nerve-muscle preparation results from different fibers having slightly unlike thresholds.

An individual muscle contraction follows a characteristic pattern (Fig. 4-6B) lasting about 0.1 second. The interval between the initial stimulus and shortening, about 0.01 second, is known as the **latent period.** Although no mechanical change occurs during this phase, reactions are taking place within the muscle which liberate the energy required for contraction. The second phase, the **period of contraction,** lasts about 0.04 second. Finally in the period of **relaxation,** about 0.05 second, the muscle returns to its original length and physiological state. When the individual shocks are well spaced in time, the muscle relaxes completely to its original length between them. But if shocks are repeated at close intervals, the muscle does not relax; this state is called **clonus.** With still higher frequency of stimulus there is no relaxation but a smoothly maintained contraction, termed **tetanus.** Normal movements of the entire animal and also the maintained tensions or **tonus** of the body —as when a person is seated or standing—all result from tetanic contractions.

4-12. Muscular contraction. Many striated muscles can contract with extreme speed (as in an insect wing) and do so repeatedly for a time. In a 100-yard dash the runner's leg muscles may contract 30 times within 10 seconds; at the end he has an "oxygen debt" that is repaid by quick, heavy breathing for several minutes. In rapidly contracting muscle oxygen is used, carbon dioxide is given off, the glycogen content is reduced, lactic acid accumulates, and much heat is involved (see Krebs cycle, par. 3-33).

Special studies by x-ray diffraction and electron micrographs help to visualize the process of contraction. A muscle is composed of many fibers to which end plates of motor nerves are attached (Fig. 10-8). Each fiber consists of myofibrils about 1 μ in diameter and shows a repeating pattern of light and dark bands. Between two narrow dark Z lines are two light I bands and a dark A band, the last crossed at the middle by a lighter H zone (Fig. 4-7). At contraction the A band remains constant but both the I band and the H zone decrease. These facts can be explained by assuming a model with a myofibril consisting of individual filaments sliding on one another. The electron microscope shows two kinds of filaments, one twice as thick as the other. The filaments are linked together by cross bridges, one thick filament being joined to each of six adjacent thin filaments. The thick filaments contain myosin, the thin ones actin. If these proteins are extracted, purified, and placed in solution they combine to form actomyosin, a substance that, when artificially formed into fibers and treated with ATP, contracts like living muscle. Returning to the model, it seems that the myosin bridges make contact with the actin filaments, hooking up at different places to cause the sliding (contraction) with energy supplied by ATP (par. 3-30). The exact means of utilizing energy to move the filaments is still unknown. The energy for muscle contraction is derived ultimately from breakdown of glucose (par. 3-33). The immediate sources, however, are two high-energy compounds: (1) adenosine triphosphate, ATP, and (2) phosphocreatine,

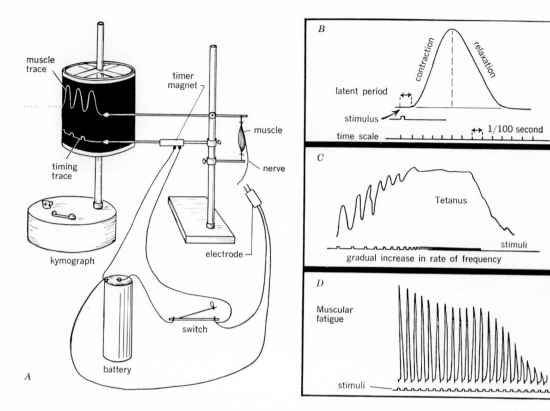

Fig. 4-6. Contraction of voluntary muscle. (*A*) Nerve-muscle preparation attached to kymograph for recording contraction when nerve is stimulated by electric impulse from battery. (*B*) Diagram of normal contraction and relaxation after a single stimulus. Kymograph records. (*C*) Tetanus (maintained contraction) with higher frequency of stimuli. (*D*) Fatigue resulting from repeated stimuli over a long period.

PC. With contraction each undergoes chemical change, and *each reaction releases much energy*. Chemical analyses show that:

1. ATP is cleaved to adenosine diphosphate (ADP).
2. Phosphocreatine (PC) is broken down into creatine and phosphate.
3. Glycogen is converted into lactic acid.

The energy of the three reactions above is utilized as follows:

1. Breakdown of ATP provides the actual energy for muscular contraction; the other reactions are all involved in recovery.

2. Division of PC supplies the energy to resynthesize ATP.
3. The glycolysis converts glycogen to lactic acid and affords energy for reforming PC from P and C, and ATP from ADP.
4. Oxygen reacts with about one-fifth of the lactic acid to provide energy for reconverting the remaining four-fifths to glycogen.

Cleavage of both ATP and PC is by hydrolysis (addition of water) and involves no oxidation so that it can proceed under anaerobic conditions (absence of oxygen). In contrast, the reconversion of lactic acid to glycogen is aerobic, involving use of some of the

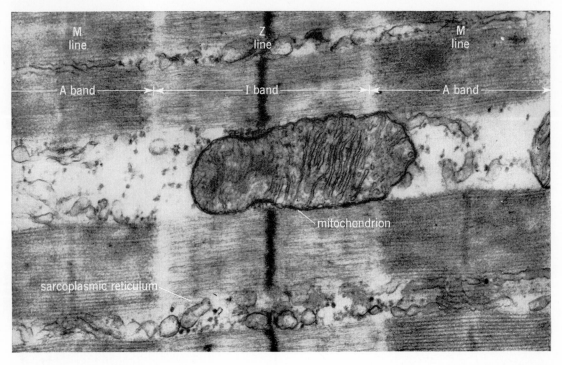

Fig. 4-7. Electron micrographs of striated muscle fibers from frog muscle (compare par. 4-12) in longisection (X33,000). I-band (pale) of single filaments only; A-bands (dark) of thicker filaments. *(Original micrograph by Dr. Lee D. Peachey, Columbia University.)*

oxygen always present in muscle. The "oxygen debt" is built up by the breakdown reactions of ATP and PC, then is repaid by the lactic acid–glycogen reaction.

4-13. Muscles and bodily movements. In locomotion each pair of opposed muscles shows a rhythm of alternate activity. If more than one such pair is involved, their action shows a regular sequence. The primitive pattern, as in an eel, snake, or other slender animal, is a series of waves of contraction passing alternately along either side of the body. The movement of limbs in land forms is also alternate, in both vertebrates and insects. In lower vertebrates the stimulus for movement comes mainly from the environment and is controlled by nerve centers in the medulla oblongata but is modified by sensory stimuli from the eyes, nose, or other special receptors.

Among invertebrates such as earthworms, crustaceans, and insects, destruction of the "brain" does not seriously disturb the normal pattern of locomotion, which depends upon stimuli from contact with the ground or other surfaces.

4-14. Cilia and flagella. Certain movable processes on cells (see par. 3-5) serve in locomotion and in many vital processes in the bodies of animals. A *flagellum* is a beating, whip-like process arising from a granule (blepharoplast) within a cell. When many short processes are present they are termed *cilia.* Cilia are moved by a fibrillar or neuromotor system (par. 16-14). Electron micrographs show that all flagella and cilia have the same internal structure. In cross section there are 11 very fine filaments, 2 in the center surrounded by 9 double filaments. Flagella occur on some protozoans, on the collar cells of sponges, and on internal cells of hydra (Chaps. 16, 17).

External cilia provide for the locomotion of ciliate protozoans, ctenophores, rotifers, some flatworms, and aquatic larvae of many invertebrates. Cilia occur on the tentacles of bryozoans, some marine worms, and certain coelenterates, on the exterior of starfishes, and on gills of bivalve mollusks. They line parts of the respiratory and genital tracts of vertebrates, the intestines of mollusks and earthworms, the feeding groove (endostyle) of lower chordates, and the excretory organs of many invertebrates. Some rates of beat, per second, for cilia are: *Vorticella,* 6 to 8; *Stentor,* up to 42; gills of a mussel, 10; and for flagella in a sponge, 20.

In multicellular animals *mucus* is often secreted by gland cells adjacent to those bearing cilia, and materials trapped in the mucus are carried in one direction by the continual beating of many cilia. Cilia and mucus carry food to the mouth on anemones, bivalves, and bryozoans, and foreign particles trapped by mucus in the respiratory passages of land vertebrates are carried outward by ciliary action. The cilia in egg and sperm ducts aid in carrying sex cells to the exterior.

REVIEW

1. What are the functions of epidermis?
2. What are the body coverings of an amoeba, a flatworm, an earthworm, an insect, and a vertebrate? How does the epidermis of man differ from that of a frog?
3. Which of the following are cornified epidermal products: snail shell, toenails of a land vertebrate, human tooth, hair, deer antlers, the beak covering in a bird?
4. Compare an exoskeleton with an internal skeleton. What are the advantages and disadvantages of each?
5. Outline the common basic pattern of the vertebrate skeleton.
6. What is the relationship of the notochord to the spinal column? Describe the various parts of a vertebra.
7. Compare the fore and hind limbs of man, part by part. Are limbs completely absent in any vertebrate group?
8. How do muscles accomplish movement of an animal?
9. From the demonstration of a muscle preparation on the kymograph describe the response when a muscle receives: one short stimulus; many stimuli at progressively shorter intervals; repeated stimuli over a long period.

5
Digestive
systems
and
metabolism

Green plants build their tissues from inorganic materials by the photosynthetic process, using energy from the sun (pars. 1-7, 13-1; Fig. 13-1). The food of animals is obtained by eating plants or other animals. It serves two purposes, as a fuel to supply bodily energy and as a source of materials for growth and repair. After being obtained (feeding), it is broken down into simpler chemical substances (digestion) and then is taken into the cells and tissues of the body (absorption) where it is utilized (metabolism).

5-1. Feeding. Animals differ widely in their food habits. Some insects feed on the tissues or juices of a single species of plant or the blood of one kind of animal, but most animals take several or many kinds of food. Cattle, deer, rodents, and insects that eat leaves and stems of plants are said to be *herbivorous;* cats, sharks, flesh flies, and many marine animals whose food is entirely or largely of other animals are termed *carnivorous;* and man, bears, rats, and others that eat various plant and animal materials are called general feeders, or *omnivorous.*

Paramecium, some sea anemones, and certain fishes that feed on small particles, living or dead, such as plankton, are termed microphagous feeders. In contrast, most higher animals, including man, that use larger materials

are macrophagous feeders. Still other animals are fluid feeders, like the mosquitoes that suck blood and the aphids that pump in plant juices.

The digestive mechanism or system in various animals (Fig. 5-1) differs in general form, structural details, and physiological processes according to the nature of the food, manner of life, and other factors. All means for taking and using food are essentially alike in that materials from the external environment are brought into intimate contact with internal membranous surfaces where digestion and absorption can take place.

5-2. Invertebrates. Many protozoans have no permanent structures for taking or digesting food. An amoeba pushes out lobes of protoplasm (pseudopodia) at any part of its one-celled body to surround an item of food; the latter is taken into a fluid-filled *food vacuole* within the cytoplasm for digestion (Fig. 16-4). In paramecium and other ciliate protozoans a permanent external *oral groove* lined by beating cilia carries food particles to a definite "cell mouth," where they pass into food vacuoles and are digested (Fig. 16-11). Drawing food to the mouth in a current of water by use of cilia is done by many animals from protozoans to lower chordates.

The microscopic food of sponges is cap-

Illustration at top of page: Feeding, the prelude to digestion. Cone-nose bug (*Triatoma*) sucking blood from a rabbit. (*Photo by R. L. Usinger.*)

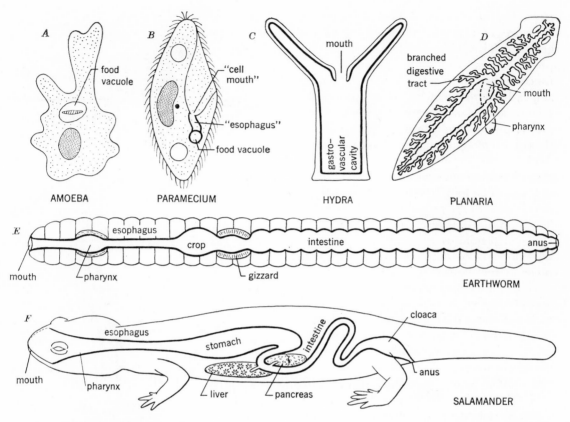

Fig. 5-1. Types of digestive systems in animals; diagrammatic. (*A*) Amoeba, food enters at any place on cell surface. (*B*) Paramecium, with definite cell mouth. (*C*) Hydra, mouth and sac-like digestive cavity. (*D*) Planaria, mouth and branched digestive tract, but no anus. (*E*) Earthworm, tubular digestive tract having specialized sections, complete with terminal mouth and anus. (*F*) Vertebrate, complete and partly coiled tract with specialized parts and digestive glands, anus at base of tail.

tured by and digested in flagellated *collar cells* that line certain interior canals of the animal; digestion is thus intracellular, as in protozoans. Coelenterates have a definite **mouth** connected to a sac-like *digestive* (gastro-vascular) *cavity* within the body that is lined by a tissue layer of special digestive cells (Fig. 17-8). The flatworms (except tapeworms) have a mouth and a branched *digestive tract* extending to all parts of the body (Fig. 18-1). In both the latter groups the tract is *incomplete* in that foods enter and undigested residues pass out the same opening, the mouth. In the coelenterates and flatworms, food that has entered the digestive tract is acted upon by

enzymes secreted from gland cells in the interior lining. This is intercellular digestion, in a digestive cavity, such as occurs in all higher animals; some partly digested food, however, is taken into cells lining the cavity for intracellular digestion.

In most other invertebrates the digestive tract is essentially a tube within the body. It is external in the sense of being open to the outside (mouth, anus) and separated from the interior body spaces by semipermeable membranes. It is termed *complete* because food enters the mouth and passes through various organs for storage, digestion, or absorption and any residues pass out the anus at the opposite end of the system. The parts differ in structure in animals belonging to various groups (Chaps. 18 to 23), but the names applied to them give some indication of the function of each part. An earthworm, for example, has a *mouth* with fleshy lips to grasp food, a muscular *pharynx* that sucks in the food and lubricates it by mucous secretions, a slender *esophagus* to carry food on to the dilated *crop* for storage, a muscular-walled *gizzard,* where food is ground against particles of sand, and a long *intestine* with pouch-like lateral extensions providing a large surface for absorption of digested portions (Fig. 21-3). Undigested residues pass out the anus at the posterior end of the body. Jaws with teeth occur in the mouths of some other annelid worms, in squids and octopuses, in sea urchins, and in many arthropods. The mouth in all mollusks except the bivalves has a radula (Fig. 20-10) bearing many fine horny teeth that serve to rasp off particles of food. The mouth parts of arthropods are modified appendages; those of insects are adapted for either chewing or sucking (Chap. 23; Table 23-2).

5-3. Vertebrates.[1] The digestive system of almost every vertebrate has the following essential parts (Figs. 5-2, 5-3): (1) The *mouth* and *mouth cavity* commonly have *teeth* to grasp, tear, or chew food and a *tongue* that may help in capturing or manipulating it; in most land vertebrates the *salivary glands* se-

[1] For a comparison of the digestive and other organ systems in the various classes of vertebrates see the figures on "general structure" in Chaps. 2, 25 to 28.

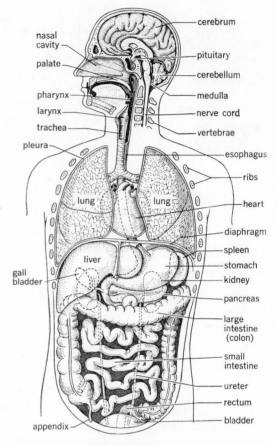

Fig. 5-3. The human digestive system and other internal organs. Greater omentum supporting organs at front of abdomen removed; reproductive organs omitted.

crete saliva to lubricate the food and start digestion. (2) The *pharynx* contains gill slits in fishes and aquatic amphibians but has no

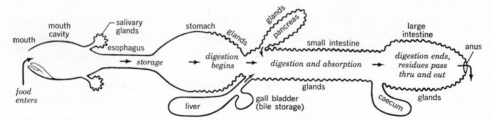

Fig. 5-2. Diagram of structure and activities in the digestive tract of a vertebrate. Wavy lines indicate glandular areas.

direct digestive function. (3) The *esophagus* (gullet) is an elastic tube carrying food past the region of the heart and lungs. (4) The *stomach* is a large pouch where food is stored and some digestion occurs. (5) The *small intestine,* a long slender tube, folded or coiled, is the principal region for digestion and absorption. (6) The *large intestine* (colon) is the portion where absorption is completed and undigested residues are formed into masses (feces) for expulsion through (7) the *cloaca,* which ends with (8) the *anus.* The cloaca is also an exit for excretory wastes and sex cells in sharks, amphibians, reptiles, and birds, but these pass out separate openings in most mammals. All vertebrates have two large digestive glands, the *liver* and *pancreas,* connected by ducts to the small intestine; cyclostomes have no pancreas. Typically all vertebrates have teeth except the living birds, although a few in other classes are toothless. Teeth in some fishes and reptiles and in most mammals are differentiated for piercing, shearing, crushing, or grinding, according to food habits (Fig. 28-8).

5-4. Food and digestion. The plant and animal foods taken by animals consist of protoplasm (Chap. 3), which is made up of proteins, carbohydrates, and fats, together with vitamins, minerals, and water. The water and inorganic salts can be absorbed from the digestive tract without change, but the protoplasmic materials must be altered before they can be utilized. The digestive system is a "laboratory" where these changes occur.

The processes of digestion, absorption, and utilization of food may, by analogy, be likened to a miscellany of large and small buildings (food), which are taken apart, the wooden portions into boards, the plumbing into pipes and fittings, and so on (digestion). Each part must be of such size as to pass through a series of holes in a great wall (absorption). On the other side the various parts may be stored or recombined into new structures of different kinds from the original ones, and some are burned to supply energy (utilization).

Some foods are subjected only to chemical alteration, as with the microscopic organisms taken as food by protozoans and other small animals, the fluids of plants sucked up by bees and aphids, the blood pumped in by parasitic worms, leeches, or insects, and the larger prey taken by coelenterates and starfishes. Many other animals use food that must be reduced physically before chemical digestion can proceed effectively. This is accomplished by teeth in the mouth or elsewhere (pharynx of some fishes, stomach of crayfishes) and by grinding in the gizzard of earthworms and birds. Flesh eaters such as the sharks, large fishes, snakes, hawks, owls, cats, and others bolt down their food entire or in large pieces, and its physical reduction is accomplished by muscular action in the stomach. Other fishes and the herbivorous mammals that subsist upon plant materials chew their food thoroughly before it can be digested.

5-5. Digestive enzymes. The chemical aspects of digestion involve reduction of complex organic substances in the food into simpler molecules that can be passed through the cells of the digestive epithelium to enter the fluids and cells of the body. Proteins are broken down into amino acids, fats to fatty acids and glycerol, and carbohydrates to simple sugars (monosaccharides) such as glucose. These changes are performed by the digestive ferments, or *enzymes* (par. 3-26).

In general these enzymes can act only on dead protoplasm and are unable to penetrate living cells, whereby the digestive epithelium is protected. They are produced by all animals from protozoans to mammals, but the same kinds or numbers of enzymes are not present in every sort of animal. The food in a vacuole within a protozoan can be seen to change gradually in form and size as it is acted upon by enzymes. The reaction of the vacuole changes from acid to alkaline during the process, as can be shown by indicator dyes. The cytoplasm therefore has the ability to secrete enzymes and also substances to change the reaction (pH). Among the lower invertebrates, enzymes are secreted by cells in some or all parts of the digestive tract, but in higher animals only by glands or cells in certain portions of it. In the vertebrates, some are produced in the salivary glands and others regularly in the stomach, small intestine, and pancreas (Fig. 5-8).

5-6. The digestive process in man. The taking of food into the mouth cavity is a joint action of the lips, tongue, and teeth. The flexible lips are delicately sensitive to the physical character and temperature of the food, but not to taste. The tongue, having muscles in three planes, has great ability in movement and change of shape to handle the food; on its surface the taste buds (Fig. 10-8) are concentrated. The teeth are specialized to cut and grind the food. (In many lower vertebrates the teeth, in the absence of flexible lips, serve merely to grasp food; see Chaps. 2, 25, 26.) Structurally a tooth has a hard outside enamel, a filling of softer dentine, and a central living pulp, supplied with nerves; the root is set in a socket of the jaw (Figs. 5-4, 28-9, 28-10).

In the mouth cavity the food is lubricated by *saliva* secreted by three pairs of *salivary glands,* the submaxillary, sublingual, and parotid (Fig. 5-5*A*). About 1,000 cc. of saliva is produced per day, mostly at mealtimes. This secretion is a reflex act (par. 10-15) stimulated

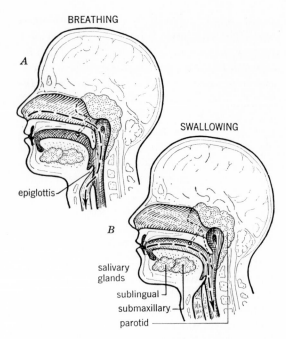

Fig. 5-5. (*A*) The respiratory path, trachea open. (*B*) Route of food when swallowed—larynx raised against epiglottis, closing trachea.

by savory tastes in the food or even by the sight or smell of food that literally "makes your mouth water." The intensity of the stimulus seemingly is related to the water content of the food—dry bread in the mouth stimulates a copious flow, wet bread much less, and water none at all.

Saliva contains a protein, mucin, serving as a lubricant, and an enzyme, *ptyalin* (salivary amylase); the latter, in the normal alkaline medium of the mouth, reduces starches first to dextrins and then to the double sugar, maltose (malt sugar). The action is more rapid on cooked starch but, at best, is slight because food is in the mouth only a short time. Chewing aids starch digestion by breaking up the food, mixing in the enzyme, and lengthening the time of exposure to ptyalin. Starch requires about an hour for digestion. The action of ptyalin continues within the food mass in the stomach until penetrated by the acid gastric juice.

After a mouthful of food has been ground

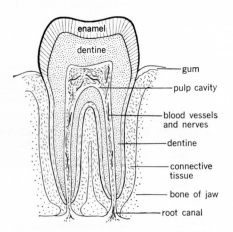

Fig. 5-4. Enlarged section of human tooth in the jaw. Compare Fig. 28-10.

by the teeth and mixed with saliva, the tongue, by voluntary action, moves it backward into the pharynx and there presses it into a compact bolus. The remainder of the process of swallowing is involuntary, guided by a sequence of reflex movements. These result first in closing the respiratory passages and opening the esophagus (Fig. 5-5*B*, *A*). Failure in any of these reflexes results in "swallowing the wrong way"—the bolus of food enters the glottis and choking is followed by a convulsive cough to remove the obstacle. The normal passage of a bolus through the esophagus results from a slow wave of muscular contraction down the walls of the gullet until the food passes the cardiac valve and enters the stomach.

All the movements and kneading of food in the digestive tract below the pharynx are by slow rhythmic contraction and relaxation of involuntary muscles, longitudinal and circular, in the wall of the tract. This process is known as *peristalsis.* By alternate action of the muscles, the diameter of the tract at any one place is first enlarged, then reduced. A wave of contraction moving down the esophagus carries a food bolus from esophagus to stomach. In the latter organ the alternate action kneads and mixes the food with secretions. In the intestine this movement, long continued, serves to divide and redivide the contents, to mix it thoroughly, to bring new portions against the inner wall, and to move the contents slowly along.

5-7. The stomach. This structure is a storage chamber that receives the food of a meal. Here the contents are given both physical and chemical treatment, then are passed, a little at a time, to the small intestine. Storage is mainly in the upper part (fundus) of the stomach and muscular action chiefly in the middle (body) portion. The lower part (pyloric) ends with the pyloric valve, a circular muscle at the junction with the intestine. The stomach is important because its secretion has an antiseptic effect on bacteria in the food and because there is partial digestion by the gastric juice. Yet surgical removal of the stomach is

not necessarily fatal in man, because food can be completely digested in the intestine.

Gastric glands in the stomach wall secrete the *gastric juice.* This results from reflexes initiated by the smell or taste of food plus action of a hormone (gastrin). The gastric secretions include mucin, which further lubricates the food mass, hydrochloric acid (about 0.2 per cent), and enzymes. The acid reaction of gastric juice (pH about 1.0) is well known from the unpleasant experience of vomiting. Of the gastric enzymes, *pepsin* splits proteins partly (to polypeptides such as proteoses and peptones), and *rennin* causes the casein in milk to coagulate. (Rennin extracted from the stomachs of calves is used to form the "curd" in cheese making.) There is possibly a third enzyme, *gastric lipase,* having slight action on emulsified fats. An average person secretes an estimated 2,000 to 3,000 cc. of gastric juice daily.

5-8. The intestines. The small intestine is a slender tube about 25 feet long. The first 10 inches or so are the duodenum, the long central part is the jejunum, and the remaining 4 or 5 feet the ileum. When food in semifluid state (chyme) has passed through the pyloric valve into the duodenum, it stimulates secretions of the "intestinal juice" from tubular glands in the much-folded wall (Fig. 5-6). This alkaline fluid contains several enzymes. *Erepsin* continues the gastric digestion of proteins, splitting the proteoses and peptones into amino acids. The three carbohydrate-splitting enzymes are: *maltase,* which converts maltose into glucose; *sucrase,* which changes sucrose (cane sugar) to glucose and fructose; and *lactase,* which divides lactose (milk sugar) into glucose and galactose.

The acid (HCl) in the chyme, upon entering the intestine, stimulates cells in the wall to release *secretin* from prosecretin (Fig. 5-7). This is a hormone (Chap. 9) carried in the blood stream through the heart and to the pancreas. There, independent of the nervous system, it initiates discharge into the intestine of the clear yellowish *pancreatic juice;* the daily secretion is 500 to 1,000 cc. Carbonates

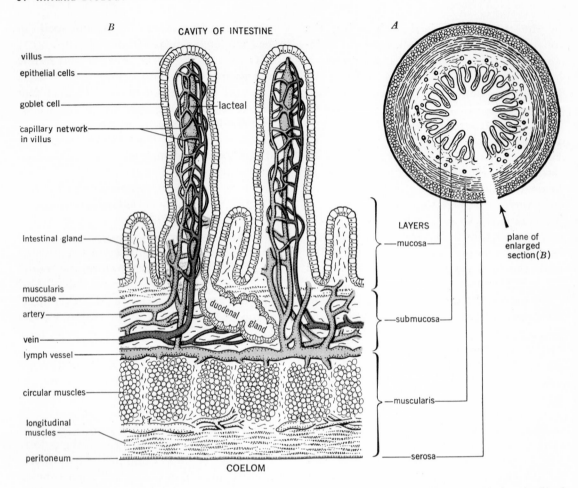

Fig. 5-6. Structure of the small intestine (duodenum). (*A*) Cross section. (*B*) Diagrammatic longitudinal section, enlarged.

in this fluid neutralize the hydrochloric acid in the chyme making the intestinal contents mildly alkaline in reaction. Enzymes in the pancreatic juice are: ***trypsin*** (activated from trypsinogen), which splits intact or partly divided proteins into amino acids; ***lipase,*** which converts fats to fatty acids and glycerol; and ***amylopsin,*** which reduces entire or partly digested starches to sugars.

A third fluid, ***bile*** (not an enzyme), is added from the liver through the bile duct. This greenish-yellow liquid contains bile salts that facilitate digestion by physically reducing fats to small droplets (emulsification). Bile is stored in the gall bladder, whence 500 to 1,000 cc. per day flow to the intestine. If the flow

of bile is interrupted mechanically, as by gallstones or infection of the bile duct, certain bile pigments are diverted into the blood stream and produce jaundice, with yellowing of the skin.

The ***liver,*** the largest "gland" in the body, besides the secretion of bile, performs several other functions related to the digestive tract and other parts of the body (Fig. 5-8). Briefly it (1) stores glucose (as glycogen) and provides a regulated supply to the body as needed; (2) converts other sugars, amino acids, and fats to glucose; (3) serves in protein synthesis and also in the formulation and disposal of waste nitrogenous products; (4) helps dispose of poisons; and (5) forms a substance (antiane-

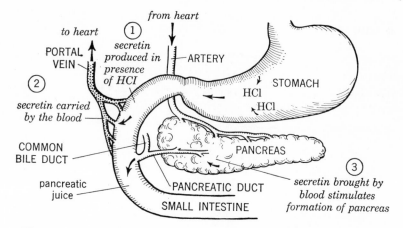

Fig. 5-7. The path and action of secretin in stimulating production of pancreatic juice.

mia factor) aiding in red blood cell production—but also breaks down old red cells.

The *large intestine,* or *colon,* serves principally to dispose of undigested and indigestible residues by way of the rectum and anus and to conserve water by absorption from the mass. The food residues, bacteria, mucus, and dead cells from the intestinal wall make up the feces that are expelled at intervals. The feces are characteristically colored by pigments from the bile (bilirubin and biliverdin) that are breakdown products of hemoglobin. Food usually passes from the mouth to the end of the small intestine in about 4½ hours; but residues may continue for a longer time, even beyond 24 hours, in the colon. During this time there is much bacterial action. Bacteria that survive the stomach acidity multiply rapidly, and some bring about more or less putrefaction, especially in the colon, where various toxic products and foul-smelling gases result. Bacteria comprise up to 50 per cent of the dry weight of the feces.

5-9. Absorption. The small intestine is the principal area for absorption, the process that fulfills the purpose of digestion. Through the intestinal wall the chemical substances derived from food enter the body proper to be built into living tissues or used for energy. The wall acts as a semipermeable membrane. Its absorbing surface is increased about ten-fold (to about 5 sq. meters) by upward of 4,000,000 minute projections, or *villi,* each containing blood capillaries and a central *lacteal vessel* (Fig. 5-6). The end products of protein and carbohydrate digestion (amino acids, simple sugars) pass through cells of the intestinal mucosa and into blood capillaries connecting to the hepatic portal vein, whence they are carried to the liver. End products of fat digestion enter the lacteals which connect to the lymphatic system. Lymph vessels from the intestine join those from elsewhere in the body to form a large trunk, the thoracic duct, that in turn enters the venous system close to the heart (par. 6-10, Fig. 6-4).

5-10. Metabolism. When the products of digestion reach their ultimate destinations by way of the blood they are variously (1) broken down chemically to supply energy (catabolism); (2) built into new protoplasm (anabolism); or (3) stored as glycogen—animal starch —or as depot fat. Synthesis and breakdown are going on simultaneously in every living cell. The two processes are in dynamic equilibrium, with one or the other dominating at various times or places (Figs. 5-8, 5-10).

The liver plays a central role in carbohydrate metabolism, receiving glucose in blood from the intestine and converting it into glycogen. The latter is (1) stored in the liver for use between meals when it is reconverted into

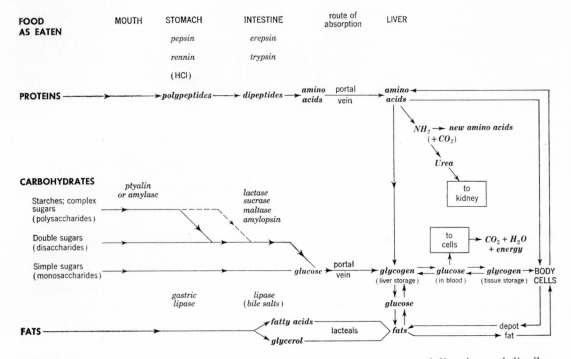

Fig. 5-8. History of food in the body—from the mouth through the processes of digestion and distribution, including some functions of the liver. Enzymes named in italics. (*Adapted from Weisz, 1954.*)

glucose; (2) released into the blood stream gradually so as to maintain a rather constant glucose (blood sugar) level of about 0.1 per cent; and (3) carried to all parts of the body. The blood sugar level is largely controlled by the hormone insulin, formed by the islets of Langerhans in the pancreas (Chap. 9). Some of the lactic acid produced in the muscles is also carried by the blood to the liver where it is converted to liver glycogen. Thus there is a constant circulation of carbohydrate within the body (Fig. 5-9).

When carbohydrates are taken in excess, they can be converted into fats by several steps—breakdown into 2-carbon units by the series of glycolytic reactions (par. 3-32) followed by resynthesis of the latter into fatty acids and finally fats. Other fats form from fatty acids and glycerol absorbed into the lacteals and transported by lymphatic vessels. They can also be derived from amino acids after the amino radical (—NH₂) is removed (deamination). Whatever the source,

fats are stored in special fat cells among the muscles, under the skin, and elsewhere.

Anabolism, the synthesis of new tissues, is one of the remarkable processes that characterize living organisms. This constructive process is essential for replacement of old tissues and for growth and reproduction. No less

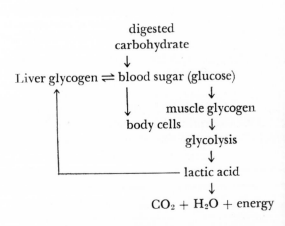

Fig. 5-9. Routes of carbohydrate.

INPUT   OUTPUT

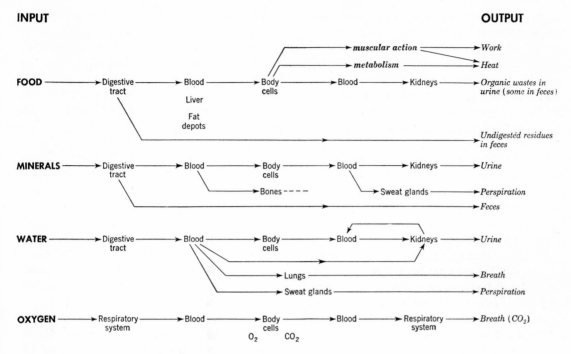

Fig. 5-10. Flow chart of input and output from the body.

important is the synthesis of secretions by living cells. The principal substances involved in synthesis are the proteins (Chap. 3).

Protein is in a dynamic state in the body, with constant turnover in the amino acid content. This cycling is through a "metabolic pool" of nitrogen believed to consist primarily of amino acids. Relations between the several components are as follows:

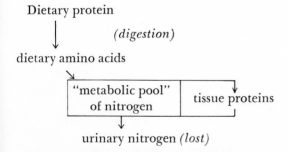

Because of this cycling, the animal requires a continuing intake of nitrogen. When the dietary intake equals the urinary loss, the organism is said to be in nitrogen balance. If the loss is greater than the intake, it is in negative balance, but if the opposite is true it is in positive balance.

5-11. Utilization. The percentage of food actually absorbed of the total amount ingested is an indication of the degree or efficiency of utilization. This varies widely depending on the composition of the foodstuff and on the specific needs of each kind of animal. Meat and other materials of animal origin are almost completely utilized, 95 per cent or more being absorbed. Foods from plant sources are less efficient, depending on the extent to which each is digested. Seeds yield more usable food than leaf or stem materials.

A daily account of the intake and output for each group of substances shows that the animal body is in a state of balance or fluctuates around an equilibrium. Demands are greater in growing individuals or in those at hard manual labor as compared with adults in sedentary activities. The equilibrium is maintained by the selective utilization of various substances in the diet. It is upset if any essential and irreplaceable element is lacking, and also if the total of foodstuffs is not sufficient for the minimum requirements of the organism. A diet, therefore, should be both qualitatively and quantitatively adequate.

The metabolic decomposition of food in the body to yield energy or heat is an oxidative process, corresponding to the combustion of a fuel. The heat of combustion for organic compounds is recorded in calories. One kilogram-calorie is the heat needed to raise one kilogram of water one degree centigrade (at fifteen degrees centigrade). Laboratory experiments show the fuel value for the three main classes of foodstuffs in Calories, per kilogram, to be as follows: carbohydrate, 4.1; protein, 5.5; fat, 9.3. Fat thus has high "fuel value" in the animal body. The amount of energy needed to maintain the vital functions of an animal is essentially constant and is termed the standard or basal metabolism. This is the metabolic rate when the organism is at rest and no food is being digested or absorbed. For a 25-year human male of 155 pounds it is about 1 (kilo) Calorie per kilogram of weight per hours at 37°C., or 1,700 calories per day (155 pounds or 70 kg. × 24 = 1,680). In active life the daily energy requirement is about twice the basal rate. The rate depends to a large extent on the functioning of the thyroid gland (Chap. 9) and can be altered by feeding thyroid extract or by removing part of the gland.

5-12. Kinds of food. The preceding discussion shows that the amount of food is not the only criterion for an adequate diet. A "balanced diet" is a mixture of foods containing all of the substances essential for the development, growth, and maintenance of the individual. Foremost of these are the carbohydrates, fats, and proteins. Furthermore, the proteins must include most or all of the amino acids to provide the body with the building materials to synthesize its own proteins.

Certain additional substances, the *inorganic elements* (minerals) and the *vitamins,* are essential in a balanced diet. Most diets contain adequate amounts of these substances; so their need was not suspected until recent years. Experiments have shown that minute amounts of iron, copper, zinc, manganese, cobalt, and iodine are essential micronutrients for animals; and a number of vitamins (Table 5-1) are necessary for normal health, growth, and reproduction.

Iodine is an example of an essential "trace element." For several hundred years it has been known that iodine deficiency produces a disease called goiter, with a tumor-like bulge in the neck region. We now know that goiter results from malfunction of the thyroid gland, which, in the absence of iodine, cannot produce the essential metabolism-regulating hormone, thyroxin. Iodine comprises 65 per cent by weight of the thyroxin molecule, but not more than one part per million is needed in the blood stream because the thyroid gland can accumulate and store iodine until the necessary level is reached. The required minute amounts of iodine are now generally provided, in areas where it does not occur naturally in food or water, by use of "iodized salt."

Another deficiency disease is anemia, caused by insufficient iron. Most (66 per cent) of this element in the body is contained in the hemoglobin of the blood; additional iron occurs in the liver, spleen, and bone marrow, where red blood cells are formed.

Vitamins are organic substances, mostly of plant origin, that regulate many vital processes in animal bodies. The effects they produce are out of all proportion to the quantities needed; hence their contribution is not as an energy supply but as catalysts. Each vitamin evidently regulates or is involved in one or more particular biochemical or enzymatic process and a certain minimal amount must be present in the food; the requirement varies with different vitamins and different animals. A lesser amount or complete absence leads to a deficiency disease. Well-balanced diets usually provide enough of all vitamins. For example, the normal daily requirement of vita-

Table 5-1. The vitamins and their characteristics

Name, formula, and principal effect	Important sources	Physiological functions	Result of deficiency or absence (in man, except as noted)
A ($C_{20}H_{30}O$) antixerophthalmic (fat-soluble)	*Plant form* (carotene, $C_{40}H_{56}$) in green leaves, carrots, etc.; in liver becomes *animal form*, in fish-liver oil, egg yolk, milk	Maintains integrity of epithelium and capillaries Needed to regenerate visual purple in retina of eye	Xerophthalmia (dry cornea, no tear secretion) Night blindness "Nutritional roup" in birds
B "complex" (water-soluble) B_1 or thiamine ($C_{12}H_{17}ON_4S$) antineuritic	Yeast, germ of cereals, especially wheat, peanuts, other leguminous seeds, egg yolk, liver, and lean pork	Needed in pyruvic acid metabolism (Stimulates root growth in plants)	Beriberi (on diet high in polished rice) Loss of appetite, reduced digestive motility; cessation of growth Polyneuritis in birds (Fig. 5-11)
Riboflavin ($C_{17}H_{20}O_6N_4$)	Green leaves, milk, eggs, liver, yeast	Needed in cytochrome system; an active part in enzymes affecting food metabolism	Cheilosis (cracking at corners of mouth); "yellow liver" of dogs; "curl toe" of chicks
Nicotinic acid or niacin ($C_6H_5NO_2$) antipellagric	Green leaves, wheat germ, egg yolk, meat, liver, yeast	Forms substances essential to cytochrome system	Pellagra in man (Fig. 5-12), monkeys, pigs; blacktongue in dogs; perosis in birds
Folic acid ($C_{19}H_{19}O_6N_7$)	Green leaves, liver, soybeans, yeast, egg yolk	Essential for nucleic acid synthesis and blood cell formation	Anemia and sprue in man; slow growth and anemia in chicks and rats
Pyridoxine (B_6) ($C_8H_{12}O_3N$)	Yeast, cereal grains, milk, liver	Needed in amino acid reactions	Anemia in dogs and pigs; dermatitis in rats; paralysis in pigs, rats, and chicks
Pantothenic acid ($C_9H_{17}O_5N$)	Yeast, cane molasses, peanuts, egg yolk, milk, liver	Forms "coenzyme A" in choline reactions and in Krebs cycle	Dermatitis in chicks and rats; gray fur in black rats; "goose stepping" in pigs
Biotin ($C_{10}H_{16}O_3N_2S$)	Yeast, cereal grains, cane molasses, egg yolk, vegetables, fresh fruits	Needed in amino acid synthesis and CO_2 fixation	Dermatitis and thick skin in rats and chicks; perosis in birds
B_{12} ($C_{63}H_{90}N_{14}O_{14}PCo$)	Liver, fish, meat, milk, egg yolk	Needed in biosynthesis of methyl groups and thymidine	Pernicious anemia; slow growth and paralysis in young pigs Slow growth in chicks
C or ascorbic acid ($C_6H_8O_6$)	Citrus fruits; tomatoes Most animals produce vitamin C (except primates and guinea pigs)	Maintains integrity of capillary walls; involved in formation of "intercellular cement"	Scurvy (bleeding in mucous membranes, under skin, and into joints) in man (Fig. 5-13) and guinea pigs
D ($C_{28}H_{44}O$) antirachitic (fat-soluble)	Fish-liver oils (tuna, cod); ultraviolet radiation	Regulates calcium and phosphorus metabolism; needed for normal bone growth	Rickets in young (bones soft, yielding, often deformed, Fig. 5-14)
E or tocopherol ($C_{29}H_{50}O_2$) antisterility (fat-soluble)	Green leaves, wheat-germ oil, other vegetable fats	Regulates tissue respiration; has antioxidant activity	Sterility in male fowls and rats Death of embryos "Suckling paralysis" in young
K ($C_{31}H_{46}O_2$) antihemorrhagic (fat-soluble)	Green leaves; also in some intestinal bacteria	Production of prothrombin in liver; for blood clotting	Blood fails to clot

min B_1 is about 0.5 mg. per 1,000 calories, usually supplied by the bread or cereal eaten; that for vitamin C (100 mg. ascorbic acid) is contained in a glass of orange juice or the usual serving of tomatoes. Taking excessive amounts of some vitamins (A, D) may be poisonous.

Fads in eating and the restricted diets of some races of people (also domestic birds and mammals) lead to deficiency diseases (Figs. 5-11 to 5-14). Scurvy (vitamin C deficiency) was common on long sea voyages in past centuries; the British sea captains who later learned to carry limes as a food accessory to prevent scurvy were known as "lime-juicers." Beriberi (B_1 deficiency) is a disease prevalent among Oriental peoples who live largely on polished rice; and pellagra occurs among persons living on diets largely of corn that is deficient in niacin.

Water and inorganic salts also are necessary in the diet since they are essential elements in protoplasm (Chap. 3). Aquatic species obtain both from their environments. Land dwellers may take them in part or entirely with their

Fig. 5-11. Vitamin B_1 deficiency—polyneuritis. (A) Pigeon fed 12 to 24 days on polished rice lacking vitamin B_1. (B) Same bird, completely normal, a few hours after receiving B_1 concentrate or food high in B_1 content. (*After Harris, Vitamins, J. & A. Churchill, Ltd.*)

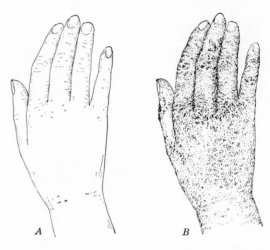

Fig. 5-12. Pellagra. (A) Normal hand. (B) Hand of person on diet lacking niacin of vitamin B complex: skin thickened, sloughing, cracking, and with extra pigment. (*After Harris, Vitamins, J. & A. Churchill, Ltd.*)

food, but many drink to obtain an adequate amount of water. Some desert reptiles and mammals have no access to water except that contained in their food; and they do not drink if water is offered. Many desert mammals conserve water by being active only at night. The normal oxidation of food in all animals yields "metabolic water"; for insects living in wood or dry cereals this is the chief source of water supply.

5-13. Other digestive processes. There are many differences in the digestive mechanisms and processes among animals. In many birds and some insects the lower end of the esopha-

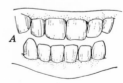 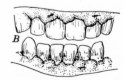

Fig. 5-13. Scurvy, from vitamin C deficiency. (A) Normal gums of person receiving adequate supply of vitamin C in citrus, tomato juice, etc. (B) Gums of severe scurvy, swollen and bleeding.

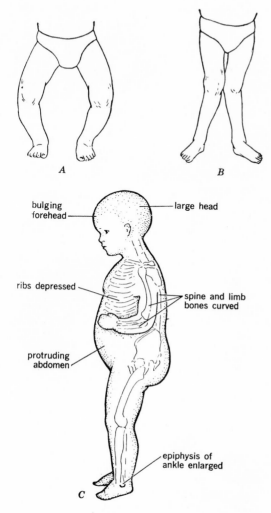

Fig. 5-14. Rickets, result of vitamin D deficiency in diet. (*A, B*) Leg deformities. (*C*) Other deformities, not all to be seen in any one individual. (*After Harris, Vitamins, J. & A. Churchill, Ltd.*)

specializations of the esophagus and have rough cornified linings where food is abraded and worked on by bacteria (Fig. 28-11). Rodents, horses, and some other herbivores have a large, thin-walled caecum at the junction of the small and large intestines; there is some bacterial digestion of cellulose in this chamber. Man has a short caecum (Fig. 5-3), to which the vermiform appendix attaches (the latter has no known useful function and may become infected, requiring surgical removal).

Microorganisms are essential for the digestion of cellulose by certain termites and a few other wood-eating invertebrates. If the bacteria and protozoans normally in the digestive system of a termite are eliminated (by high temperature), the insect starves because it cannot produce enzymes to digest the cellulose in its diet of wood. Blood-sucking animals commonly have a special anticoagulant in the saliva that keeps the blood in a fluid state during ingestion. In scale insects and their relatives, which suck plant fluids, the terminal part of the intestine is bent back into a loop fitting into a dilated pouch of the esophagus; this "filter chamber" eliminates excess water from the highly diluted foodstuffs.

A few animals partly digest their food outside the body. The protozoan *Vampyrella* secretes an enzyme, cellulase, to dissolve the cell walls of an alga, *Spirogyra,* on which it feeds. A starfish extrudes its stomach to envelop and digest large prey. Larvae of some beetles (*Dytiscus, Lampyris,* etc.) inject a protease into their prey—tadpoles, slugs, and snails—that predigests parts of these animals, the softened food then being ingested.

REVIEW

1. What are the types of feeding mechanisms among invertebrate animals?
2. Distinguish between intracellular and extracellular digestion; also between an incomplete and a complete digestive system.
3. What is the purpose of a digestive tract, and what are its main processes?

gus is dilated into a crop for temporary storage of food. Most birds also have a stomach of two parts, a slender, soft glandular proventriculus, and a larger thick-walled muscular gizzard, lined by hardened secretion, where food is ground up by grit swallowed for the purpose. The cattle, deer, and other cud-chewing mammals (ruminants) have a stomach of four compartments: the first three are

4. How do enzymes operate?

5. Why can a man or horse drink from a creek when the mouth is lower than the body?

6. If the stomach fails to secrete hydrochloric acid, what enzymes and types of food are affected, and how?

7. What structures serve to increase the area of the inner surface of the gut? What purpose does the enlarged area serve?

8. Name the principal functions of the liver.

9. Outline the means by which a steady level of sugar is maintained in the blood.

10. Describe the effects that would follow surgical removal of the stomach; the liver; the pancreas.

11. What are some trace elements in human diet? What happens when they are lacking?

12. For vitamins A and D state the sources, the specific functions of each in the body, and the effect of insufficient intake.

13. Trace the course of a particle of carbohydrate from the human mouth to its arrival in a voluntary muscle, naming each organ or structure through which it passes and describing the chemical transformations which it undergoes; mention the enzymes involved at appropriate places. Do the same for fat and for protein.

14. What is meant by the phrase "dynamic state of protein in the body"?

6
Circulatory systems

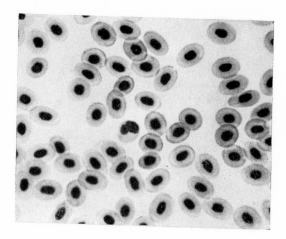

The life processes of an animal require that food and oxygen be available continually for metabolism in all parts of its body and that wastes be removed promptly. In protozoans these interchanges are aided by streaming movements of the cytoplasm within the one-celled body; and in the simple multicellular types the exchanges occur by diffusion between the epidermal cells and adjacent body parts. More complex animals, with organs and tissues well removed from the exterior or gut, have a *circulatory system* for internal transport (Fig. 6-1). Its essential parts are (1) the *blood,* consisting of fluid plasma and free cells or blood corpuscles; (2) the *heart* (or an equivalent structure) with muscular walls that contract periodically to pump the blood through the body; and (3) a system of tubular *blood vessels* through which the fluid is moved. The system is *closed* in vertebrates and annelids, where the vessels convey blood from the heart in various circuits among the tissues and back to the heart. Mollusks and arthropods have an *open* (lacunar) system, blood being pumped from the heart through blood vessels to various organs but returning partly or entirely through body spaces (hemocoel) to the heart.

6-1. Invertebrates. Sponges, coelenterates, ctenophores, flatworms, roundworms, and bryozoans have no circulatory system. It is only slightly developed in the ribbon worms,

brachiopods, and echinoderms but is more elaborate in the mollusks, annelids, and arthropods. The blood plasma is colorless in some invertebrates and in others is colored by dissolved respiratory pigments that carry oxygen (see Chap. 7). The red plasma in earthworms and some insect larvae (e.g., *Chironomus*) contains a hemoglobin-like substance, erythrocruorin; and in the "blue" blood of many mollusks and crustaceans hemocyanin is present. Invertebrate blood has limited numbers of amoeboid corpuscles, or "white blood cells."

The heart of invertebrates is dorsal to the digestive tract except in earthworms which have 5 pairs of lateral hearts. In mollusks it is short, lies within a thin pericardial sac, and consists of one or two thin-walled *auricles* that receive blood from the body and deliver it to a single muscular-walled *ventricle.* The latter contracts to force the blood through the vessels, or *arteries,* that distribute to various organs (Fig. 20-6).

Insects and many other arthropods have the heart as a slender tube with segmentally placed lateral openings (ostia) that receive blood from the body spaces and pump it through a median aorta to organs and tissues (Figs. 22-4, 23-4). The earthworm has several lengthwise vessels through the body, with paired transverse connecting vessels in most

Illustration at top of page: Blood cells of a frog; many red cells, a few white (with lobed nuclei).

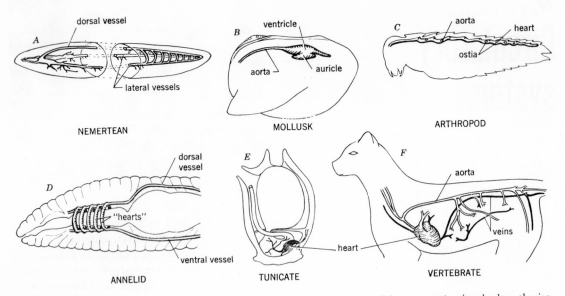

Fig. 6-1. Types of circulatory systems in animals. (*A*) Nemertean (ribbon worm), simple lengthwise dorsal and lateral vessels with cross-connectives. (*B*) Mollusk (bivalve), dorsal heart with auricle (1 or 2) and ventricle, anterior and posterior aortas, blood returns through body spaces (hemocoel)—open system. (*C*) Arthropod (insect), dorsal tubular heart and aorta, blood returns through body spaces (hemocoel)—open system. (*D*) Annelid (earthworm), dorsal and ventral vessels (and others) with cross-connectives—closed system. (*E*) Tunicate (sea squirt), a heart and aortas, vessels obscure; blood flow reverses. (*F*) Vertebrate (mammal), chambered heart, definite aorta, arteries, and veins, with connections to respiratory organs—closed system.

body segments. The circulation is produced by contractions of the middorsal vessel and by the 5 pairs of hearts far anterior in the body (Fig. 21-2).

6-2. Vertebrate blood.[1] In all vertebrates the *blood* comprises (1) a nearly colorless plasma; (2) white blood cells or leucocytes of several kinds; (3) red cells or erythrocytes colored by the contained hemoglobin which

[1] Functions of the circulatory system and the structure of the blood, heart, and vessels of vertebrates are much as described for the frog (Chap. 2; Figs. 2-9 to 2-11). Human blood cells are shown in Fig. 3-11, and their characteristics in Table 6-1; structure and action of the human heart are illustrated in Fig. 6-2, and the principal vessels of the human circulatory system in Fig. 6-4; microanatomy of arteries, capillaries, and veins is indicated in Fig. 6-3; progressive differences in the heart and aortic arches of vertebrates are illustrated in Fig. 14-3; the general plan of vertebrate circulation is diagrammed in Fig. 2-11.

serves to transport oxygen; and (4) smaller cells (platelets or thrombocytes) (Fig. 3-11). The *plasma* carries dissolved foods, wastes, internal secretions, and some gases. Human blood plasma consists of about 92 per cent water plus proteins and other organic compounds and about 0.9 per cent of inorganic salts, chiefly sodium chloride; in health, these vary but slightly in amount. Physiological salt solution containing the same kinds and amounts of these salts can be used to dilute blood without injuring the corpuscles. An average person (155 pounds) contains 5 to 6 quarts of blood, about equally plasma and cells.

6-3. Erythrocytes. The *red cells* are nucleated and oval in all vertebrates but mammals, where they are nonnucleated, biconcave, and circular (oval in camels). Mammalian red cells are nucleated, however, during their develop-

Table 6-1. Average characteristics of human blood cells

Kinds of cells and average number per cubic millimeter of blood	Structure; color with Wright's blood stain*; diameter (μ = 0.001 mm.)	Source	Function
Erythrocytes (red blood cells): 5,000,000 (in males) 4,500,000 (in females)	Nonnucleated, circular, biconcave; orange-buff; 7.5 to 7.7 μ (8.6 μ in fresh blood)	Endothelium of capillaries in bone marrow	Transport oxygen; remain in blood vessels
Leucocytes (white blood cells): 5,000 to 10,000 1. GRANULOCYTES	Colorless in life Nucleus of lobes joined by thread, stains dark lilac; cytoplasm granular, pale blue, 10 to 12 μ	Reticulo-endothelial cells outside capillaries of bone marrow	Amoeboid; can leave blood vessels and enter tissues Defend against infection
a. *Neutrophils*, 65 to 75%	Granules stain weakly		
b. *Eosinophils*, 2 to 5%	Granules few, (red)		
c. *Basophils*, 0.5%	Granules deep blue		
2. LYMPHOCYTES, 20 to 25%	Nucleus single, large, round, deep blue; scant cytoplasm, clear blue; 6 to 10 μ	Lymphoid tissue, spleen and lymph glands	Nonmotile; related to immunity
3. MONOCYTES, 2 to 6%	Nucleus single, large, round, deep blue; much cytoplasm, muddy blue; 12 to 15 μ	Spleen and bone marrow	Very motile; phagocytic
Platelets: about 250,000 (150,000 to 400,000)	Small, refractile, no nucleus; dark blue to lilac; 2 to 4 μ	Cytoplasmic fragments of megakaryocytes in bone marrow	Provide substance needed in clotting

* A stain containing two special kinds of dyes, methylene blue and eosin, together with sodium bicarbonate and methyl alcohol.

ment. The red cells total about 30 trillion (3×10^{12}) in a human being; each may live to 120 days and make 50,000 circuits in the blood stream. Red cells are more numerous in infants and in persons living at high altitudes; their numbers are altered in some diseases, being reduced in anemia. Red cells are produced chiefly in red bone marrow, and an excess supply is often stored in the spleen. Old cells are destroyed chiefly in the spleen, whence much of the hemoglobin passes to the liver; its pigment is excreted in the bile and its iron content largely returned to the marrow.

6-4. Leucocytes. The several kinds of *white cells* have their principal activities in the tissues, and those seen in the blood stream are but a part of the "passing parade" on their way from their origins in the marrow, spleen, or lymphoid structures to the tissues or to their death. The lymphocytes, with a single rounded nucleus, are commonest in lymph vessels and in the lymph nodes along those vessels; the granulocytes, with lobed nuclei, are in the blood stream and also around tissues. The estimated life of a white cell is 12 to 13 days. Most white cells of both types can perform amoeboid movements and can crawl out between the endothelial cells lining capillaries into spaces between tissue cells. There many of them can act as *phagocytes* (Gr. *phagos,* eat) to protect the body by consuming bacteria that invade wounds. In an acute infection such as appendicitis or pneumonia the neutrophils and small lymphocytes increase markedly; the total leucocyte count will rise from the normal (5,000–10,000) to 20,000 or 30,000 per cubic millimeter, to battle the infection. The whitish pus of an infected area consists of dead leucocytes, tissue cells, and blood serum.

The *blood platelets* or *thrombocytes* are an obscure but essential element of the blood. They are more or less disc-shaped, much smaller than red cells, and without nuclei. When injured, they disintegrate releasing thromboplastin which initiates the clotting process.

6-5. Functions of the blood. The blood performs a variety of duties for the many parts of the body. Some were listed previously, but all may be mentioned here to show the importance of this fluid-circulating medium. It serves to carry (1) oxygen and carbon dioxide between respiratory organs and body tissues (pars. 7-8, 7-9); (2) water and digested foods from the digestive tract to other organs (par. 5-10); (3) stored foods from one organ or tissue to another as needed (par. 5-11); (4) organic wastes, excess minerals in solution, and water to the excretory organs (par. 8-2); and (5) hormones from the glands where produced to the places of use (Chap. 9). Besides these miscellaneous transport functions the blood acts to regulate the pH of tissues within narrow limits by means of buffers such as phosphates and carbonates; the blood is slightly alkaline with a pH relatively constant at 7.4. Its role in water balance between the tissues and excretory structures is all-important, and it does this at such a rate that the water content of the blood does not vary appreciably in a normal individual. In the "warm-blooded" birds and mammals the blood, by differential distribution between the internal organs and the body surface, serves to maintain the temperature of the entire body within close limits. Finally, the blood is the defense mechanism against foreign organisms, having therefore a major role in maintaining normal health and opposing the effects of infection.

6-6. Clotting. When a blood vessel is cut, the issuing blood is soon stopped by a protective *clot.* The injured tissues and disintegrating *blood platelets* release *thromboplastin,* which, in combination with *calcium ions* always present in the plasma, acts upon *prothrombin,* also in the blood, to produce *thrombin.* The latter converts a soluble blood protein, *fibrinogen,* into *fibrin* which becomes a mass of fine fibers entangling corpuscles to form the clot. The fluid residue from a clot is the *blood serum.* A further substance, *heparin,* prevents the formation of thrombin in blood flowing normally within blood vessels. Decrease in the number of platelets lengthens the clotting time. Blood withdrawn for transfusion or for laboratory use is kept from clotting by addition of sodium citrate which makes the calcium ions unavailable. In certain male persons known as "bleeders" clotting is long delayed or fails; a slight cut or tooth extraction may result in death by loss of blood (hemorrhage). This condition is caused by a sex-linked hereditary disease (hemophilia) transmitted by females but manifested chiefly in males; among females only those rare individuals homozygous for the defect experience the disease.

6-7. Antibodies. When a "foreign protein" (i.e., not naturally in the body) is injected into the blood of an animal, a specific protective substance, or *antibody,* usually is formed. Thus, if a small (sublethal) dose of rattlesnake venom is injected into a pigeon, the bird's plasma, after several days, will contain antibodies capable of neutralizing a much larger dose of venom. The venom has served as an *antigen* stimulating some tissues to produce an antibody which is carried mainly in the blood plasma. Bacteria and other organisms may serve as antigens. Recovery from any germ-caused disease results from the production of antibodies, which often confer a degree of *immunity,* transient or permanent, to further attack by the organism in question. Human beings and domestic animals are now rendered immune to certain diseases by injecting the dead or attenuated organisms (vaccine) of a particular disease or the immune serum (antitoxin) from a horse or other animal that has previously been immunized. Examples are vaccines for smallpox and typhoid fever and antitoxins for diphtheria, tetanus, and snake bite.

6-8. Human blood groups. If red blood cells from one person are mixed with blood plasma of another individual, the cells remain separate in some cases but become clumped, or agglutinated, in others. This is a matter of great practical importance when blood from a healthy donor is sought for transfusion into the veins of a sick or wounded person; should clumping occur, the patient may die instead of being helped. The blood of donor and patient must be "compatible." Extensive tests show that two types of *antigens* (agglutinogens) called *A* and *B* occur in the red cells of different persons, and the plasma contains two kinds of *antibodies* (agglutinins) known as *a* (anti-*A*) and *b* (anti-*B*). There are four *blood groups* among human beings: Group O, having antibodies *a* and *b* but no antigens; Group A, antibody *b* and antigen *A*; Group B, antibody *a* and antigen *B*; and Group AB, antigens *A* and *B* but not antibodies. The results of mixing cells of any one group with plasma of another are summarized in Table 6-2. Blood-group characteristics are inherited and

Table 6-2. Results of mixing cells and serum of human blood groups

−, *compatible; no agglutination*
+, *not compatible; agglutinates*

			Blood group			
			O	**A**	**B**	**AB**
			Antigen in red cells			
			None	*A*	*B*	*AB*
Blood group	**O**	*a, b*	−	+	+	+
	A	*b*	−	−	+	+
	B	*a*	−	+	−	+
	AB	None	−	−	−	−

(left side label: Antibodies in serum)

remain constant throughout life. Blood of any anthropoid ape is like one or another human group; monkeys and lower mammals also have blood groups but not identical with those of man.

Sterile dried plasma, without corpuscles, now serves extensively for blood transfusion. It keeps indefinitely under varied climatic conditions, needs only to be mixed with sterile water before injection, and involves no problem of agglutination.

6-9. The Rh factor. About 85 per cent of white persons have another antigen in their red blood cells, and their blood is known as Rh+ (Rh positive); those lacking this substance are termed Rh− (Rh negative), the difference being due to heredity. If Rh+ blood is repeatedly transfused into an Rh− individual, the antigen stimulates production of anti-Rh agglutinin. This is called *isoimmunization,* since both the antigen (Rh) and antibody (anti-Rh) are in the same species.

An Rh− individual receiving blood from

Rh+ donors shows no reaction at first but later becomes iso-immunized; if then transfused with Rh+ blood there is a severe reaction, usually fatal. The anti-Rh agglutinins cause hemolysis of the Rh+ transfused blood.

An Rh− mother bearing an Rh+ fetus (that received the Rh+ factor from the father) may become immunized by Rh+ fetal erythrocytes entering the maternal circulation. Then in second or later pregnancies the maternal anti-Rh agglutinins cross the placenta, enter the fetal circulation, and hemolyze the fetal red cells, commonly with fatal results. This disease (erythroblastosis) in the fetus or newborn results in loss of about 1 pregnancy in 50 among the white women of the United States. The disease rarely develops with the first child. Once immunized, such a mother, with a homozygous father (par. 12-4), is unlikely to bear a living child.

6-10. The lymphatic system. Within the tissues of the body there is a fluid in contact with individual cells and with the blood capillaries, known as the *tissue fluid* or *lymph.* Essentially it is a plasma filtrate, a fluid which originates from seepage or percolation of water plus solutes through capillary walls. The lymph plays a vital role in transport between cells, as also in diffusion and in immunity. It is primarily extracellular but may return to the blood through the lymphatic system. Between the cells in all tissues there are minute channels where fluid collects. These channels converge to form fine, thin-walled *lymph vessels* with valves. Most lymph vessels are so delicate as not to be seen in anatomical preparations. They become larger in the thorax and there unite to form the *thoracic duct,* which empties into the venous system near the heart (Fig. 6-4). The lymphatic system carries fluid in only one direction, from the tissues to the blood and heart (Fig. 2-11). Scattered along the system are many *lymph nodes.* Besides producing lymphocytes, the nodes defend the body from infection by intercepting disease organisms. Throat infections,

for example, may be accompanied by swelling of lymph nodes in the neck, and severe infections of the feet or hands may result in swelling of lymph nodes in the groin or armpits.

The *spleen* is a part of the lymphatic and circulatory systems, capable of acting as a reservoir to hold a fifth to a third of all blood; it serves to regulate the volume of blood elsewhere in circulation. In addition it produces white cells (lymphocytes) and destroys old red cells.

6-11. The heart. The entire circulatory system in any vertebrate is composed of the heart, the blood vessels (arteries, arterioles, capillaries, and veins), and the lymphatic channels and nodes (Fig. 6-4). The heart comprises a series of chambers with slight or heavy muscular walls that receive blood from the veins and pump it through the arteries. In the two-chambered heart of fishes (1 auricle, 1 ventricle) all blood passing through the heart is unoxygenated; amphibians and most reptiles have two auricles that receive blood from the body and lungs, respectively, and a single ventricle; crocodiles have a four-chambered heart. In birds and mammals the four-chambered heart (2 auricles, 2 ventricles) is really a dual structure, the right side pumping only from the body to the lungs and the left side from the lungs to the body (Figs. 6-2, 14-3).

Action of the heart is under involuntary nervous control, but the heart will continue to beat after all nervous connections have been severed experimentally. The remarkable independence of heart muscle may be demonstrated by removing the heart of an amphibian and suspending it in physiological saline solution (0.7 per cent NaCl), where the rhythmical contractions will continue. Primary regulation of heartbeat is by the *"pacemaker"* (sino-auricular node, high in wall of right auricle), which excites the *bundle of His,* a network of fibers on the ventricles causing the latter to contract in unison.

The sequence of heart action is as follows (Fig. 6-2*A* to *D*): First the auricle fills and

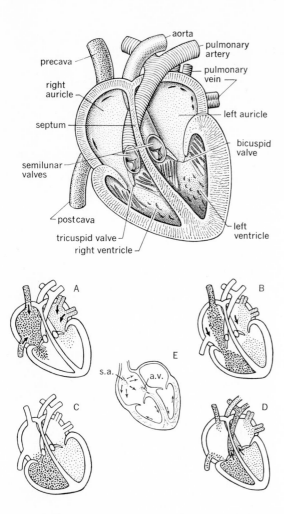

Fig. 6-2. *Above.* The mammalian (human) heart opened in frontal plane, ventral view. *Below.* Its mode of action (*A-D*). Arrows indicate paths of blood flow. Heavy stipple, unoxygenated blood; light stipple, oxygenated blood. *A.* Auricles filling from veins. *B.* Blood entering relaxed ventricles. *C.* Auricles contracting, valves closing. *D.* Ventricles contracting, blood forced into aorta and pulmonary arteries. *E.* Location of sino-auricular (s.a.) and auriculo-ventricular (a.v.) nodes. Arrows indicate spread of control. The aorta and pulmonary artery actually emerge from the dorsal side (rear) but are shown here to aid in tracing the flow of blood. (*Modified from Best and Taylor, The human body and its functions, Henry Holt and Co., Inc.*)

contracts, then the ventricle fills and contracts. The short intervals while the chambers are filling provide the only rest for the heart muscle throughout life. The human heart in a quiet normal adult contracts, or "beats," about 72 times per minute; the rate is increased by exercise, emotional excitement, and certain diseases. In some small birds and mammals the heart beats 200 to 400 times per minute. Blood moves from the heart in a series of spurts, which in an exposed artery as on the wrist or temple may be felt as the "pulse," greatest as the heart is contracted (systole) and least when filling (diastole). The pressure declines at progressive distances from the heart because of frictional losses, especially in the arterioles; and the returning flow in the veins is practically smooth. Typical pressures for man in millimeters of mercury are: arteries, 120/80 (systolic/diastolic); capillaries, 30/10; veins, 10/0.

6-12. Blood vessels. The heart and all vessels are lined throughout with a glassy-smooth endothelium. The walls of the aorta and larger arteries contain heavy layers of elastic tissue and muscle fibers (Fig. 6-3), but the small arterioles are covered by smooth muscle fibers only. The capillary walls, where all exchanges of nutrients, gases, and wastes occur between the blood stream and tissues, have no muscle fibers but possess many contractile cells on their outer surfaces. Frog muscle shows about 400 capillaries per square millimeter in cross section, and 1 cc. of blood in passing has contact with about 2,700 sq. mm. of capillary surface. In a dog the comparable figures (by Krogh) are 2,600 capillaries and 5,600 sq. mm. Veins are thin-walled, with connective tissue fibers but few muscles; unlike the arteries, they collapse when empty. The walls of all blood vessels are elastic, and vasomotor nerve fibers control the muscle fibers, causing arterioles to dilate or contract so as to alter the amount of blood passing to any region. The veins are provided with a series of valves which help to maintain the flow of

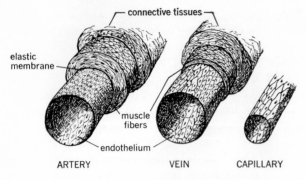

elastic membrane

connective tissues

muscle fibers

endothelium

ARTERY   VEIN   CAPILLARY

Fig. 6-3. Structure of blood vessels (not to scale). An artery has a thicker muscular layer than a vein, and a vein is usually larger than its corresponding artery. The wall of a capillary consists only of endothelium.

blood back to the heart. The blood in man helps to control the body temperature by regulating the loss of heat. Excess heat acts through a nerve center in the medulla to permit dilation of superficial blood vessels in the skin where heat may be lost; chilling results in contraction of such vessels. In a resting dog the rate of blood flow per second is 300 to 500 mm. in large arteries and 0.5 mm. in capillaries.

6-13. Blood circulation in vertebrates. The paths of blood circulation are similar in principle in all vertebrates but differ in details depending on the complexity of the heart (1 or 2 auricles and ventricles), status of the renal portal system (none above amphibians), and the type of respiration (gills or lungs). The circulation of the blood in man was first demonstrated by William Harvey (1578–1657), an English physician, early in the seventeenth century. Harvey tied a ligature above the elbow and noted enlargements at the location of valves in the veins of the forearm. When he held his finger on a vein and pressed the blood out above that point, he noticed that the vein remained empty. By this and other experiments he deduced that blood flows along the veins toward the heart. Harvey reasoned that the blood must enter the extremities through the arteries and pass somehow to

the veins, but it remained for the Italian anatomist, Marcello Malpighi, to discover the capillaries 33 years later.

In man, the *path of circulation* is essentially as follows: The blood arriving from various parts of the body passes into the precaval and postcaval veins to enter the right auricle; it is poor in oxygen, dark bluish red in color (blue, Fig. 6-4), and carries carbon dioxide. From the right auricle it flows through the tricuspid valve (Fig. 6-2) to the right ventricle and thence, as the result of a strong contraction of the heart muscle (systole), through the semilunar valve and along the pulmonary artery to the lungs.

In the lungs the blood courses through many small capillaries in membranes covering the alveoli (Fig. 7-3C), where it becomes reoxygenated (red, Fig. 6-4) and gives up its carbon dioxide (see par. 7-9). Thence it flows to larger vessels and to the pulmonary veins entering the left auricle. Through the bicuspid valve it reaches the left ventricle, where, by powerful muscular contraction (systole), it is forced into the aorta, the largest and most stout-walled vessel in the body.

The aorta divides first into several large arteries that in turn branch and subdivide to supply all parts of the body. The blood travels along the arteries to microscopic arterioles and thence to the nonmuscular capillaries in the tissues. Diffusion through the capillary walls and active transport are the means for interchange of water, gases, salts, and soluble organic materials between the blood and the cells composing the body.

The most direct route for return of blood to the heart is through the systemic part of the venous system. Capillaries join to form venules, and these merge to form veins, finally collecting in the two great veins, precaval and postcaval, first named.

In addition to the complete cycle outlined there are several vital side paths. Arterial blood in the abdomen enters a system of capillaries lining the walls of the stomach and intestines, where digested food is absorbed; then

VEINS

ARTERIES

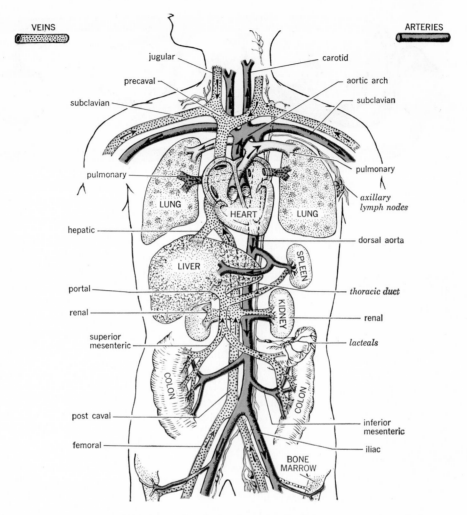

jugular

carotid

precaval

aortic arch

subclavian

subclavian

pulmonary

pulmonary

axillary lymph nodes

LUNG

HEART

LUNG

hepatic

dorsal aorta

SPLEEN

LIVER

portal

thoracic duct

renal

KIDNEY

renal

superior mesenteric

lacteals

COLON

COLON

post caval

inferior mesenteric

femoral

iliac

BONE MARROW

Fig. 6-4. Principal blood vessels of the human circulatory system in relation to internal organs; stomach, small intestine, bladder, and sex organs omitted. Arrows indicate paths of blood flow; blue, blood low in oxygen; red, blood richer in oxygen. The veins are stippled and labeled on the left side and the arteries are unstippled and labeled on the right side. Of the pulmonary vessels, the arteries (blue) carry blood *to* the lungs and the veins (red) *return* oxygenated blood to the heart. The thoracic duct of the lymphatic system and a few lymph nodes are shown in yellow and labeled in italics.

the blood passes into the portal vein to the liver. There it spreads through another system of capillaries, where food substances may be stored in liver cells and other essential processes take place as described in par. 5-10. To complete this important side route, blood

from the liver gathers in the hepatic vein and flows to the postcaval vein.

An equally essential path takes arterial blood through a double system of capillaries in the kidneys (par. 8-3; Fig. 8-5), whence it returns to the heart. The blood is the chief

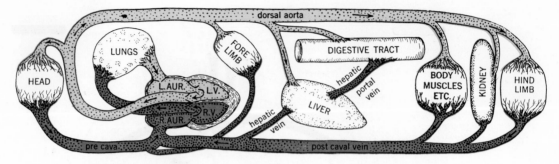

Fig. 6-5. Blood circulation in birds and mammals. Arrows indicate paths of flow. Blue, unoxygenated blood; red, oxygenated blood.

regulatory mechanism of the body. During its passage through the kidneys excess water and wastes are removed to maintain a relatively uniform condition (steady state) in the body as a whole.

Other activities of the circulatory system include that of the bone marrow in formation of red cells, that of the spleen in storing blood, and of the spleen and liver in destroying old red cells.

6-14. Integration of the circulatory system. The heart and blood vessels are controlled by the nervous system and also by certain substances in the blood. The circulatory system is sensitive to slight changes in the body, and its performance is complex because so many organs and functions are involved. The simple act of walking, for example, brings adjustments in heartbeat, blood pressure, and distribution of blood. Muscular activity requires oxygen and produces carbon dioxide. By chemical and nervous stimulation, the oxygen demand increases arterial pressure and dilates the capillaries, making for a greater flow of blood. The rate of heartbeat quickens from a reflex stimulated by increased pressure in the right auricle. Other reflexes stimulate constrictor and dilator centers in the medulla (Fig. 10-3), decreasing blood flow to inactive areas and hastening it where needed. Meanwhile the hypothalamus is activated and epinephrine (adrenalin) is secreted, resulting

in constriction of blood vessels in the skin and viscera and dilation of those in the muscles. All these changes tend in one direction and, unless checked, would lead to excessive heartbeat and a blood pressure so high it would endanger fine blood vessels of the brain. But sensory elements in the aortic arch and carotid sinuses, acting through the medulla, cause a relaxation of arterial muscles and decrease in heart rate. The various parts of the circulatory system thus are integrated and operate with sensitive checks and balances.

6-15. Aortic arches (Fig. 14-3). Six pairs of aortic arches appear in the embryos of all vertebrates, proceeding from a ventral aorta at the anterior end of the heart and passing between the gill slits that develop in the sides of the pharynx. The first and second pairs soon disappear. In adult fishes, arches 3 to 6 lead to the gills, where respiratory exchanges occur, and then all join above to form the dorsal aorta; similarly, arches 4 to 6 supply the gills in permanently gilled salamanders. Among land vertebrates, arch 3 forms the common carotid artery on each side, arch 5 disappears, and arch 6 becomes the pulmonary artery to the lungs. In frogs, toads, and reptiles the two parts of arch 4 become the systemic arches of the dorsal aorta; in birds only the right half persists; and in mammals only the left half, the opposite in each forming a subclavian artery.

REVIEW

1. What are the essential structural parts of a circulatory system? In what groups of animals is the system closed? What groups have no circulatory system?

2. What are the principal components of blood in a vertebrate? Review the function of each.

3. Describe the process of blood clotting. What substance is used to prevent clotting when blood is stored for laboratory use?

4. How does blood serve in developing and maintaining immunity? Define antigen, antibody.

5. Name the four blood groups among human beings. Why are these groups important in modern medical practice?

6. What hazard is involved when a woman with Rh− blood marries a man with Rh+ blood?

7. Describe the basic features of the lymphatic system. What are its functions? What are the principal components of lymph?

8. Describe in detail the action of the human heart.

9. Trace the main paths and important side paths of blood circulation in man. What exchanges occur when the blood is in the lungs? The liver? The kidneys? The spleen?

10. What is the fate of each of the 6 pairs of embryonic aortic arches in adult fishes and land vertebrates? (See also Chap. 14.)

7
Respiratory systems

Normal metabolism in living cells requires oxygen; and the end product, carbon dioxide, must be removed from the body. The exchange of these gases is termed *respiration.* The air contains 21 per cent of oxygen (210 ml. per liter), but water holds only 0.7 per cent or less (7 ml. per liter).

The essentials of a respiratory system are: a moist and permeable membrane, body fluids containing a relatively high percentage of carbon dioxide on one side, and air or fluid with high oxygen content on the other. In accordance with physical laws each gas acts independently of others. When a difference in diffusion pressure exists on two sides of a membrane (par. 3-19, Fig. 3-19), more molecules pass toward the region of lower pressure than in the opposite direction. The partial pressure of oxygen in the air or water is greater than within an animal body, where it is constantly being used up, so that oxygen tends to enter any suitable membrane surface. The partial pressure of carbon dioxide is greater within the animal, so that it tends to pass outward. These changes occur simultaneously.

In many small animals the exchange of gases is direct, from air or water through membranes to tissue cells; but it is more complex in larger species and those with dry or nonpermeable exteriors. In the latter respiration consists of two stages: *external respiration,* the exchange between environment and the respiratory organs; and *internal respiration,* the exchange between the body fluids and the tissue cells. A third stage, the utilization of oxygen in the cells, or cell respiration, is a part of metabolism (pars. 3-31 to 3-33).

The term "respiration" is normally associated with free oxygen but, for convenience, may apply to metabolic processes in the few animals such as some intestinal parasites and muck-inhabiting invertebrates that live where there is little or no oxygen in the air or water. These anaerobic animals may obtain energy in the absence of free oxygen by the metabolism of foods (glycogen; fats) in their bodies.

7-1. Respiratory mechanisms. Animals obtain oxygen by one or another of five principal methods: (1) simple diffusion from water or air through a moist surface into the body (amoeba, flatworm); (2) diffusion from air or water through thin body tissues to blood vessels (earthworms, etc.); (3) from air (through spiracles) or from water (through tracheal gills) to a system of air ducts (tracheae) to the tissues (insects); (4) from water through gill surfaces to blood vessels (fishes, amphibians); (5) from air through moist lung surfaces to

Illustration at top of page: Gills, the respiratory organs of a larval salamander, *Taricha. (Photo by Victor C. Twitty.)*

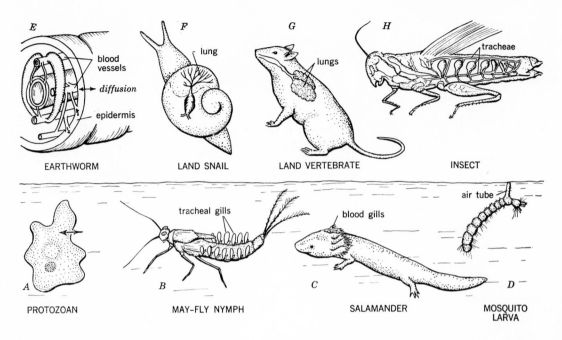

Fig. 7-1. Types of respiratory mechanisms in animals. IN WATER (*below*). (*A*) Protozoan, diffusion through cell wall. (*B*) May-fly nymph (insect), tracheal gills. (*C*) Salamander, blood gills. (*D*) Mosquito larvae, aquatic, with tube for breathing free air. IN AIR (*above*). (*E*) Earthworm, diffusion through moist body wall to blood vessels. (*F*) Land snail, moist lung inside body. (*G*) Land vertebrate, pair of moist lungs inside body. (*H*) Insect, system of air ducts (tracheae) throughout body.

blood vessels (land snails, land vertebrates) (Figs. 7-1, 7-2).

7-2. Simple diffusion. Many aquatic animals obtain air directly from their environments. In a protozoan, gaseous exchange takes place through the cell membrane to and from the surrounding water. In sponges, coelenterates and other lower soft-bodied invertebrates, the gases diffuse through epithelial cells and thence to those deeper in the body. Some endoparasites are bathed in the body fluids of their hosts from which they absorb oxygen and to which they give up carbon dioxide. Terrestrial flatworms can live in damp places where respiratory diffusion is possible through the moist epidermis. Direct diffusion would be inadequate for large animals because their internal organs are distant from the outer surface. Terrestrial species must conserve bodily

water and cannot afford a large moist exterior for respiration by diffusion.

7-3. Tracheae. Insects, isopods, millipedes, some arachnids, and *Peripatus* have fine tubes branching in from the body surface to all the interior organs. These are known as *tracheae.* They develop as ingrowths of the body wall and are lined with chitin. Each ends in microscopic tracheal cells that extend as intracellular *tracheoles,* sometimes forming a capillary network in the tissues. The end of a tracheole is filled with fluid through which oxygen and carbon dioxide diffuse to and from the adjacent tissue cells. Diffusion of gases through the tracheal system is aided by movements of the thoracic and abdominal segments of the body. The efficiency of this scheme depends on the rapid diffusion rate of oxygen in air (45,000 times that in water) and

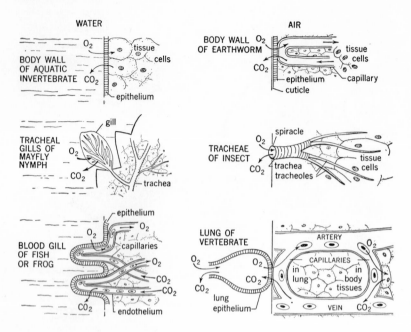

Fig. 7-2. Equivalent nature of various respiratory mechanisms in different animals living in water or air; diagrammatic.

on the relatively small size of tracheate animals. In many insects the exterior openings or *spiracles* of the tracheal system have valves (lids) which can close to limit loss of water.

Larvae of dragonflies, May-flies, stone-flies, midges, and certain other tracheate arthropods are aquatic. Their respiration is by diffusion from the water either through the cuticle to the tracheal system or through specialized *tracheal gills* which provide more surface for diffusion. Adult water beetles and bugs swim to the surface and take down a silvery bubble of air under the wings from which oxygen diffuses into the tracheal system. For a while, oxygen in the bubble is replaced by diffusion from the water.

7-4. Blood gills. In most higher animals respiration is aided by a blood transport system. Its simplest form is seen in the earthworm, where oxygen diffuses through the body wall into superficial blood vessels and then passes to the tissue cells. In the frog the

moist skin and the lining of the mouth cavity serve similarly. Many aquatic animals, however, have a more efficient mechanism—*blood gills*—of many slender filaments covered by delicate epidermis and containing capillary networks. The O_2–CO_2 exchange occurs between the surrounding water and the blood within. Only free dissolved oxygen diffuses inward from the water, the oxygen in the water molecule (H_2O) being unavailable. Cold water holds more oxygen than warm water, and the "white water" of fast-flowing streams has more than the still water of ponds or stagnant swamps. The small amount of oxygen dissolved in water limits the density of animal populations, but aquatic plants partly offset this by releasing oxygen during photosynthesis.

The gill filaments of salamander larvae (Fig. 26-2) and those of some marine worms are merely exposed to the water, but tube-dwelling annelids, aquatic crustaceans such as

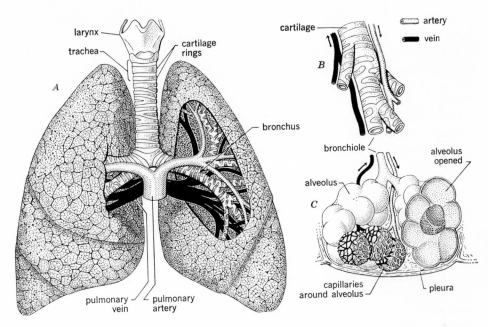

Fig. 7-3. Human respiratory system. (*A*) Larynx, trachea, and lungs in ventral view; left lung opened. (*B*) Part of a bronchiole, with cartilages; small blood vessels adjacent. (*C*) Alveoli and capillaries; diagrammatic.

the crayfish (Fig. 22-5), and many aquatic mollusks have special means to force water over the gills. The gills of lower vertebrates are in chambers at the sides of the pharynx, and water taken into the mouth (nostrils in amphibians) is forced out over the filaments (Fig. 25-13).

7-5. Lungs. All "land vertebrates," including the aquatic reptiles, birds, and mammals, have *lungs* essentially like those of a frog. A lung is a chamber lined by moist epithelium underlaid by a network of blood capillaries, where atmospheric air can be used. Basically, a lung is like a blood gill but invaginated rather than evaginated. The reptile lung contains many interior partitions, and those of mammals are elaborately subdivided, affording large internal respiratory surfaces. The finer lung branches or *bronchioles* end in microscopic compartments, the *alveoli,* surrounded by many blood capillaries (Fig. 7-3*C*), where respiratory exchanges occur. Bird lungs

are dense, and air is forced through the bronchioles to and from a series of thin-walled *air sacs* (Fig. 27-5); these occupy spaces between internal organs and around or in some bones. The air sacs serve mainly to dissipate excess body heat and are not entirely essential for respiration.

7-6. The human respiratory system. The mouth and nose communicate with the lungs through a series of special structures. The *glottis* is an opening in the floor of the pharynx, protected above by a lid or *epiglottis,* and supported by a cartilaginous framework, the *larynx.* The latter connects to a flexible tube, the *trachea,* or windpipe, that extends into the thorax and forks into two *bronchi,* one to each *lung* (Fig. 7-3).

In the nose the entering air is filtered, warmed, and moistened. This is accomplished by a thick layer of mucous membrane lining the nasal cavities. The mouth serves as an alternate route for air, and the pharynx is a passage for air from either the nose or the mouth to the larynx (Fig. 5-5*B*).

The larynx, or voice organ (Fig. 7-4), is in the front part of the neck. It is broad above, triangular in shape, and consists of nine cartilages moved by muscles; it contains two folds of mucous membrane with embedded fibrous, elastic ligaments, the *vocal cords.*

The voice is produced by air forced from the lungs to vibrate the vocal cords, and the positioning of the cords is changed to produce various sounds. The sound waves so created pass through the pharynx, mouth, and nasal cavities, which act as resonating chambers; these parts, together with the tongue and lips, are important in speech. The size of the larynx varies in different individuals; at the time of puberty it grows more rapidly in males than in females, resulting in change to a deeper and lower-pitched voice.

The trachea and bronchi are reinforced against collapse by rings of cartilage. In the lungs the bronchi branch into many bronchial tubes and *bronchioles* (Fig. 7-3*C*), with successively thinner walls. Each bronchiole ends in a sac-like atrium, having on its surface many small irregular chambers, the *alveoli* or air sacs. The latter are surrounded by blood capillaries where the respiratory exchanges occur. The human lungs have 700,000,000 or more alveoli. The entire inner surface is estimated as about 90 sq. meters, more than one hundred times the skin area of an average adult.

The substance of the lungs is porous and spongy. The right lung is larger, broader, and 1 inch shorter than the left, owing to the asymmetrical positions of heart and liver. The *diaphragm* is a dome-shaped muscular partition separating the thorax, containing the heart and lungs, from the abdominal cavity. Under normal conditions the lungs occupy fully the airtight thoracic cavity because the atmospheric pressure of air in the alveoli keeps them expanded against the inner surface of that cavity. If air enters the thoracic cavity, by accident or in the treatment of pulmonary disease, the lung collapses.

7-7. Breathing. This essential process consists of movements, partly voluntary, that alter the size of the thoracic cavity and therefore the lung capacity. At inspiration the ribs are raised, and muscles in the diaphragm contract to flatten the latter; the thoracic space is thus enlarged, and pressure about the lung is lessened, whereupon air passes down the trachea and into the lungs. Expiration results from lessening the volume of the thorax by relaxing the muscles controlling the ribs and diaphragm (Fig. 7-5).

Only about one-tenth of the total amount of air flows in and out of the lungs with each quiet respiratory movement (Fig. 7-6). The average composition is, of course, different for

Fig. 7-4. Human larynx and vocal cords and their action; the opening is the glottis. (*A*) Larynx viewed from base of tongue—vocal cords as in normal breathing. (*B*) In deep inhalation. (*C*) When singing a high note. (*Kimber et al., Textbook of anatomy and physiology, The Macmillan Co.*)

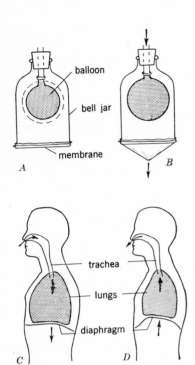

Fig. 7-5. Mechanism of breathing. (*A*) Semifirm rubber balloon in bell jar covered at bottom with flexible membrane. (*B*) When membrane is pulled down, space inside is increased and pressure of air through tube causes balloon to expand. (*C*) When chest box is expanded and diaphragm drawn down, air enters through nose and trachea, expanding lungs to fill chest cavity. (*D*) When ribs and diaphragm relax, air is forced out.

atmospheric air (20.96 per cent oxygen) and expired air (16.02 per cent oxygen). There is a net loss of 4.94 per cent oxygen and a gain of 4.34 per cent carbon dioxide. The nitrogen in air (79 per cent) is inert and has no part in respiration. In the lungs there is a gradient, owing to diffusion through the residual air, so that the alveolar air contains only 14 per cent oxygen. The rate of breathing is controlled mainly by a respiratory center in the medulla of the brain, and this in turn is stimulated by an excess of carbon dioxide in the blood. The respiratory rate increases during vigorous ex-

ercise because of the greater production of carbon dioxide in muscular metabolism. A person may "hold his breath" for a limited time, but as the carbon dioxide concentration increases in the blood, the stimulus eventually becomes too strong to be resisted. The respiratory rate is also subject to nervous control of other sorts, as seen in emotional states of anger or excitement. If breathing stops owing to suffocation, death soon follows unless respiratory movements are restored artificially by alternately applying and releasing pressure on the ribs to simulate breathing and bring about gaseous exchange. The lungs of a newborn baby are inflated with the first breath following the interruption of the placental circulation.

The air at high altitudes is rarefied (lesser barometric pressure), and a given volume contains less oxygen than at sea level. This affects the normal respiratory needs of men and animals. A mountain climber or person in an airplane must use a tank of oxygen and a face mask to obtain adequate oxygen. Planes operating above 10,000 feet usually have the air pressure inside raised (pressurized) to facilitate breathing.

A person who enters the water without an

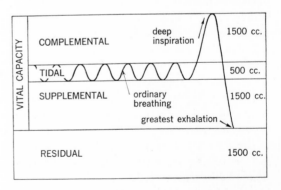

Fig. 7-6. Lung capacity and breathing in man. Ordinary respiration exchanges only the tidal air (10%); deep breathing flushes most of the lung (3,500 cc. or 70%); the residual air changes only by diffusion. (*Winton & Bayliss, Human physiology, J. & A. Churchill, Ltd.*)

artificial supply of air can hold his breath and remain submerged about 2 minutes, then must come up to breathe and repay the oxygen debt incurred. For continued submergence commercial divers wear a metal helmet connected to a hose supplying air under pressure. "Skin divers" use a tank of compressed air (aqualung) and a face mask for the same purpose. In both cases the air provides oxygen and also serves to keep the lungs inflated. The maximum safe limit for experienced divers is toward 200 feet. Deep submergence and the consequent heavy pressure act to force some nitrogen into solution in the blood plasma; a diver must rise slowly, stopping at intervals, else the bubbling release of nitrogen causes painful decompression sickness or "the bends."

7-8. Respiratory function of the blood. After oxygen has crossed the alveolar membrane, it must be delivered to the tissue cells where needed. In man and most higher animals this transport is accomplished by the blood. The process is complicated because mere diffusion is not adequate to meet the needs of large active animals. Human blood plasma carries in solution only 2 or 3 per cent of the total oxygen. The remainder is transported by the red pigment, *hemoglobin*, with which it enters into combination in the erythrocytes or red corpuscles. The process is as follows: After diffusion into the alveolar capillaries, the oxygen unites with the hemoglobin because the tension of the gas is lower in the blood than in the alveoli. The combined oxyhemoglobin then travels in the circulation to the tissues, where oxygen tension is lower than in the arterial blood. There oxygen is freed to diffuse to the cells, and the deoxygenated hemoglobin returns to the lungs in the venous blood. The total oxygen capacity of the human blood averages about 1,200 ml., and 100 to 350 ml. of oxygen passes into the tissues at each circuit. In an hour the body at rest uses about 15 liters (4 gallons) of oxygen and in strenuous exercise up to 280 liters (75 gallons).

Hemoglobin itself is a so-called "respiratory pigment," formed by the union of red *heme,* which contains iron, with a colorless protein, *globin.* The unique feature of hemoglobin is that a given amount may combine with different amounts of oxygen, depending on the tension of the gas in contact with the system. Thus the reaction is reversible and may be represented by the generalized equation $Hb_4 + 4O_2 \rightleftharpoons Hb_4O_8$, where Hb stands for a molecule of hemoglobin. Hb_4O_8 is oxyhemoglobin, of bright red color, in contrast to the duller hemoglobin. The respiratory pigment in most mollusks and arthropods is *hemocyanin* (with copper instead of iron). When oxygenated, hemocyanin is blue rather than red.

7-9. Carbon dioxide. Respiration involves the exchange of two gases and it might be inferred that disposal of carbon dioxide is a reversal of the inward flow of oxygen. Actually the mechanism of carbon dioxide transport is quite different. Some carbon dioxide is necessary to maintain the buffer system of the blood and tissues. Excess carbon dioxide is eliminated mainly in the plasma as bicarbonate. The exact mechanism is complicated and involves the so-called "chloride shift" by which chloride ions pass into the red cells and bicarbonate ions pass out to maintain the necessary acid-base equilibrium of the blood at a pH of about 7.4.

7-10. Ventilation. It has long been assumed that "fresh" air must be provided for human respiration. This appears logical at first thought, but experiments seem to prove that air in a poorly ventilated room does not differ appreciably in oxygen and carbon dioxide content from that in one well ventilated. The injurious effects of poor ventilation actually are due to interference with the heat-regulating mechanism of the body. The combination of accumulated body odors plus an increase in temperature and moisture leads to a feeling of inertia or fatigue. For greatest comfort the air in a room should be moderately cool, should contain some moisture, and should be undergoing slight movement.

REVIEW

1. What are the essential purposes of a respiratory system? Distinguish between external and internal respiration.
2. What are the five principal methods by which animals obtain oxygen? Name an example of each.
3. Could an animal as large as a horse depend on a tracheal system for its oxygen? Explain.
4. Understand the relationship between the vocal cords and the respiratory system in man. How is sound produced?
5. Describe the fine structures of the human lungs. In what ways are they specially adapted to meet man's respiratory needs?
6. What is meant by expired air? Residual air? Alveolar air? What is the role of carbon dioxide in the breathing process? Of nitrogen?
7. What is hemoglobin? How does it function in the respiratory process?
8. How is carbon dioxide carried in the blood?
9. Trace the path of oxygen from the atmospheric air to a muscle cell in the body. Trace the path of carbon dioxide from a muscle cell to the outside air.
10. What are the primary considerations in planning adequate ventilation in a house?

8
Excretory systems and regulation

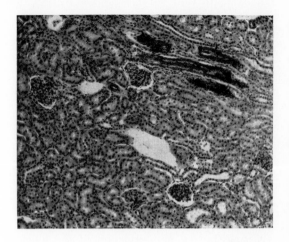

A. EXCRETION

Excretion is the process of ridding the body of wastes resulting from metabolism. The protoplasm and fluids of an animal, be it protozoan or human, comprise a delicately balanced physicochemical system, and it is the function of the excretory system (Fig. 8-1) to maintain this constant internal environment. Excess water, gases, salts, and organic materials, including metabolic wastes, are excreted, whereas substances essential for normal functions are conserved. As the materials to be disposed of are usually in solution, excretion is essentially a process of selective filtering. Some excretion takes place by physical forces alone, but most of the process results from the work of cells with expenditure of energy.

8-1. Excretion in invertebrates. The simplest-appearing method of excretion is to pass wastes through the cell membrane into the surrounding water, as occurs in many protozoans. *Amoeba, Paramecium,* and various other fresh-water protozoans have one or more **contractile vacuoles** that accumulate excess water from within the cytoplasm and periodically discharge it to the exterior so as to maintain the normal fluid balance within the cell body. The means of disposal of excretions

(chiefly ammonia) by protozoans is obscure. Excretions of sponges and coelenterates diffuse from body cells into the epidermis and thence into the water.

Among insects and a few other arthropods the principal excretory organs are slender *Malpighian tubules* (Fig. 8-2*A, B*), attached to the anterior end of the hind-gut and closed at their inner ends; these tubules collect wastes from the body fluids and discharge them into the hind-gut. Both urates and carbon dioxide are received from the blood in solution; water and other materials are reabsorbed in the lower parts of the tubules. The final excretions, including uric acid crystals, carbonates, oxalates, and in some cases urea or ammonia, pass out with the feces. The fat body of insects is also a depository for organic wastes and is the chief excretory mechanism in the springtails (Collembola), which lack Malpighian tubules. The exoskeleton renders excretory service in some invertebrates, including insects, since nitrogenous materials are deposited in it and eliminated when the animal molts. The white substance in wings of cabbage butterflies, formed from uric acid, is clearly an excretory product.

The commonest excretory organs in many animals are tubular structures, the *nephridia*

Illustration at top of page: Section through mammalian kidney (photomicrograph), showing small, rounded, dark glomeruli and tubules in both cross and longitudinal section.

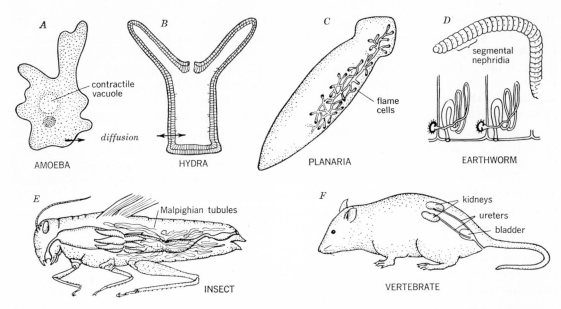

Fig. 8-1. Types of excretory mechanisms in animals. (*A*) Amoeba, contractile vacuole and diffusion from cell surface. (*B*) Hydra, diffusion from cells. (*C*) Planaria, many flame cells connecting to ducts ending in common excretory pore(s). (*D*) Earthworm, 2 nephridia in each body somite, emptying separately through body wall. (*E*) Grasshopper, series of fine Malpighian tubules connected to end of midgut. (*F*) Vertebrate, 2 kidneys with ducts to a single bladder discharging to exterior.

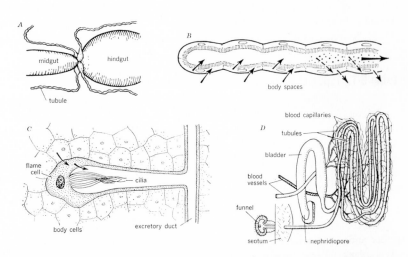

Fig. 8-2. (*A*) Malpighian tubules of insect attached to gut. (*B*) Section of one tubule, showing entry of excretions from body spaces (→), reabsorption routes for water and some other materials (– – →), and exit route of wastes (→). (*C*) Planarian flame cell draws fluid wastes from surrounding body cells; bundle of cilia drives fluid into excretory duct. (*D*) Earthworm nephridium receives fluid wastes from coelom through funnel and also by diffusion from surrounding blood vessels.

and *coelomoducts.* Primitively these were arranged one pair to a body somite, but they have become variously modified in the course of evolution. Flatworms, ribbon worms, and rotifers have many *flame cells* (protonephridia with inner ends closed) scattered among the body cells from which wastes are drawn to pass out in a branched system of ducts (Figs. 8-2C, 18-2). In the earthworm, each somite contains a pair of fine tubular nephridia with inner ends open (Fig. 8-2D). The inner end of each has a ciliated funnel, or *nephrostome,* draining from the coelom, and about the long tubule are blood vessels whence wastes are also drawn; the tubule ends externally as a minute ventral *nephridiopore.*

In some annelids, mollusks, arthropods, and in the chordates the principal excretory organs are coelomoducts, probably derived from genital ducts, but now variously modified to remove wastes from the body cavity. Crustaceans have two pairs, the "antennal" (green) and "maxillary" glands; each has an end sac with a duct opening at the base of an appendage. Only rarely are both developed in the same stage of a single species.

8-2. Nitrogenous wastes and urea formation. The metabolism of amino acids in the body leads to production of nitrogenous wastes, the elimination of which is one major task of an excretory system. The first step is the removal of the amino group ($-NH_2$) from the molecule in a process called *deamination.* This results in the formation of ammonia (NH_3), a highly toxic material that must be removed from the organism. Among the vertebrates, only the bony fishes excrete waste nitrogen as ammonia. The cartilaginous fishes and all terrestrial vertebrates transform the ammonia into other nitrogenous excretion products that can be tolerated in some concentration until removed by the kidneys. Amphibians and mammals excrete the waste as urea; in reptiles and birds it becomes uric acid.

The principal site for urea formation is in the liver, which is also an important place for deamination of amino acids.

Urea is formed from ammonia by a cyclical system of carriers and enzymes called the *ornithine cycle* (Fig. 8-3). First ammonia and carbon dioxide (CO_2) are condensed with the organic compound ornithine to form another organic substance, citrulline. The latter then condenses with another molecule of ammonia

Table 8-1. Types of Kidneys in the Vertebrates

	Pronephros or head kidney	Mesonephros or midkidney	Metanephros or hind kidney
Embryonic history and adult structure	First to appear in embryo; develops segmentally, far forward in body cavity; each unit with a nephrostome opening from the coelom; no glomeruli	Develops segmentally in middle part of body cavity; some nephrostomes open to coelom, but excretion chiefly by glomeruli	Last to develop; not segmental; posterior in body cavity; no nephrostomes; many glomeruli; all excretion from blood stream
Fishes and amphibians	*Functions in larva;* disappears in adult (persists in hagfish)	*Becomes functional kidney of adult*	(Not developed)
Reptiles, birds, and mammals	Appears transiently in embryo and soon disappears	Appears after pronephros; *functions during embryonic life,* disappearing before hatching or birth; duct persists as vas deferens in male	Last to appear; *becomes functional kidney throughout life*

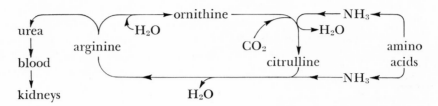

Fig. 8-3. The ornithine cycle.

to form the amino acid arginine. In the final step arginine is cleaved by water into urea and ornithine, whereupon the cycle begins again. Urea so formed is carried in the blood to the kidneys and thence eliminated from the body.

8-3. The vertebrate kidney. The principal excretory organs in a vertebrate are two *kidneys.* They are short and posterior in all but the fishes and salamanders, where they extend along most of the body cavity. The kidneys of lower vertebrates—cyclostomes to amphibians—and the embryonic renal corpuscles of the higher groups develop segmentally, a pair per body somite (pronephros, mesonephros); some tubules have nephrostomes opening to the coelom, thus somewhat resembling the nephridia of earthworms (Figs. 8-4, 8-5; Table 8-1). The adult kidneys of reptiles, birds, and mammals (metanephros) are nonsegmental and drain wastes only from the blood.

From each kidney, of whatever type, a common collecting duct, the **ureter,** carries the waste posteriorly. In amphibians, reptiles, and birds the two ureters discharge into the **cloaca,** to which a **urinary bladder** connects in amphibians and some reptiles. The waste, or **urine,** is always fluid except in reptiles and birds, where the semisolid excretions (uric acid) are voided as a white paste (guano) with the feces. In most mammals the ureters connect directly to the bladder, whence a median duct, the **urethra,** discharges to the exterior; that of males passes through the penis. The interrelated excretory and reproductive systems of vertebrates are commonly termed the **urogenital system.**

The human kidney (Fig. 8-6) is a bean-shaped organ, at the back of the abdominal cavity, one on each side of the spinal column. Each kidney consists of an inner **medulla** and an outer **cortex,** the latter containing about a million excretory units, or **nephrons.** A neph-

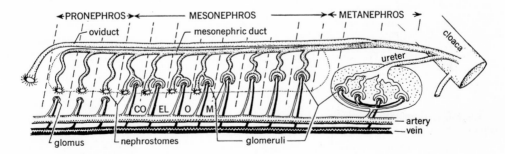

Fig. 8-4. Basic patterns of vertebrate excretory systems in relation to circulatory system and coelom; diagrammatic (see Table 8-1). *Pronephros.* Segmental. Ciliated ducts gather fluid waste from coelom; a knot (glomus) of blood capillaries adjacent. *Mesonephros.* Segmental. Some with open ciliated ducts, others without; branch from duct around knot of blood capillaries forming a glomerulus. *Metanephros.* Nonsegmental. Concentrated groups of glomeruli draining to one large duct; no opening to coelom (compare Fig. 8-5).

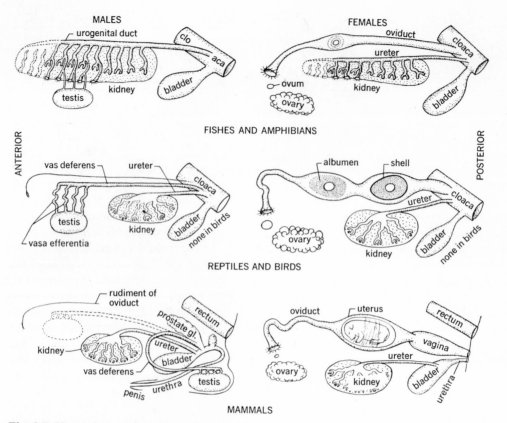

Fig. 8-5. Urogenital systems of vertebrates; only one side or half of each is shown. For the male mammal the primitive (embryonic) positions of testis and vas deferens are shown by broken lines.

ron is made up of (1) a *Malpighian* or *renal corpuscle* composed of a globular double-walled *Bowman capsule* around a clump of arterioles, or *glomerulus;* and (2) a *tubule,* both convoluted and straight, surrounded by blood capillaries. The corpuscle is about 0.2 mm. in diameter, and the tubule is 0.015 to 0.025 mm. in diameter by 50 to 60 mm. long.

The 2 million nephrons in a man, put end to end, would extend for nearly 50 miles. All the tubules discharge into a central cavity (pelvis) of the kidney that connects to the ureter.

8-4. Kidney function. The first step in urine formation is filtration. Wastes and other materials are brought in the blood stream by the renal arteries to the arterioles. According to

Table 8-2. Concentrating action of the human kidney

	Water	Sodium (Na)	Chloride (Cl)	Potassium (K)	Phosphate (PO_4)	Sulfate (SO_4)	Uric acid	Urea
Blood plasma, %	92	0.30	0.37	0.02	0.009	0.002	0.004	0.03
Urine, %	95	0.35	0.60	0.15	0.150	0.180	0.050	2.00
Concentration by the kidney, number of times	...	1	2	7	16	90	12	60

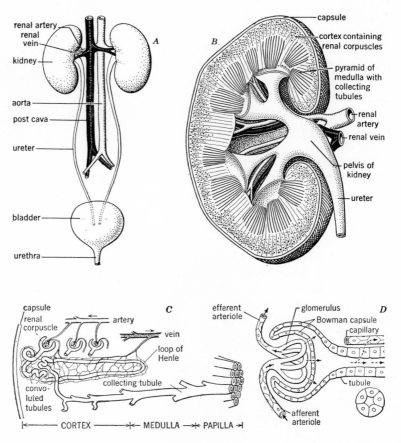

Fig. 8-6. The human excretory system. (*A*) Entire system, ventral view. (*B*) One kidney in median section. (*C*) Relations of renal corpuscles, tubules, and blood vessels. (*D*) One renal corpuscle and adjacent tubule (shown also in cross section)—solid arrows show flow of blood, broken arrows the excretory path. (*C, D* diagrammatic and much enlarged.)

the generally accepted theory of kidney function (by Cushny), protein-free fluid passes from the arterioles in the glomerulus through the Bowman capsule. This process takes place because of the pressure of the blood; the fluid in the **capsule** has the same percentage composition as blood plasma minus the colloids to which the membranes are impermeable. The second step is differential reabsorption by cells of the tubules—mostly in the proximal convoluted tubule but also in the loop of Henle and the distal convoluted tubule. Reabsorption involves active transport with the use of oxygen and the expenditure of energy,

because materials pass from a region of high concentration against a gradient.

The most remarkable feature of reabsorption by the tubules is its selectivity. For example, about 1,140 grams (2½ pounds) of salt (NaCl) passes from the glomeruli into the tubules each day—but normally only 4 to 8 grams (0.14 to 0.28 ounces) of this leaves the body in the urine. The rest is reabsorbed into the blood stream. Urea, on the other hand, is constantly being removed; it is about half (30 grams daily) of all solids in the urine, where it is in much higher concentration than in the blood plasma (Table 8-2). Materials like glucose, sodium, and calcium are called "high-threshold substances" because they are reabsorbed in considerable quantities; those reabsorbed in small quantities (urea, uric acid, etc.) are termed "low-threshold substances." In addition to glomerular filtration and reabsorption, there is some direct tubular excretion of waste products difficult to metabolize in the body.

The capacity of the human kidneys is truly remarkable. They comprise scarcely $\frac{1}{200}$ (0.5 per cent) of the total body weight, yet receive 20 per cent of the blood volume pumped by the heart. About 1,700 quarts of blood flows through the kidneys each day, but only about 180 quarts is filtered, and of this fluid 178 quarts is reabsorbed; thus only 1 or 2 quarts passes off as urine. In other words, an amount equal to the entire volume of blood is filtered by the tubules about 30 to 36 times per day.

Normal kidney function is essential to health, and any irregularity or disease in the kidney is serious. Certain salts, especially oxalates, may crystallize to form kidney stones in the pelvis of the kidney and sometimes require removal by surgery. The content of the urine may be altered by other abnormal conditions. Urinalysis, therefore, may give useful clues to the general state of bodily function, healthy or otherwise. Abnormal constituents of the urine may be albumin, excess glucose, acetone bodies, cell casts, pus, blood, or bile pigments. It is a remarkable fact that removal of one kidney, and even part of the second kidney, does not entirely hinder the total excretory process in man.

An artificial kidney has been devised and is now available in many hospitals for cases of acute kidney failure or blood poisoning. Blood is diverted from an artery through cellophane tubing set in a circulating bath fluid and thence back to a vein. The cellophane has pores of about the same size as the glomerular capillaries so substances will diffuse in or out depending on the concentration of each in the bath and in the blood. By adjusting the concentration of substances in the bath, it is possible to add or to remove elements from the blood as desired.

8-5. The bladder and urination. The urine forms at a fairly constant rate, about 1 ml. per minute. It passes down the ureters to accumulate in the urinary bladder, whence it is expelled at intervals through the urethra. The bladder is a hollow, pear-shaped organ low in the front of the abdominal cavity. It, like the stomach, can adapt to change in volume without altering the internal pressure. The smooth muscle of the bladder wall accommodates to increase in volume until about 300 ml. of urine has accumulated; then a sensation of fullness develops. The desire to urinate may, however, be suppressed by voluntary control of the external urethral sphincter until the total content is 700 to 800 ml. Urination, or emptying of the bladder, is controlled by several reflex mechanisms which involve stretching followed by contraction of the bladder wall with simultaneous relaxation of the sphincters. Even small amounts of urine can be passed by straining, which increases the pressure in the abdomen and compresses the bladder. When the urine reaches the urethra, urination continues by reflex action, even though pressure is discontinued.

8-6. Other means of excretion. In higher animals, including man, some wastes are eliminated other than by the principal excretory organs. Metabolic CO_2 is disposed of by routes described in Chap. 7. Water is eliminated as vapor through the lungs, up to 240 ml. (8 ounces) per day in man. Some other excretory products are voided with the feces, including wastes of heavy metals (iron and calcium), bile pigments excreted by the liver during the breakdown of hemoglobin, and more or less water.

The skin of man, by its 2½ million sweat glands (Fig. 4-1), also serves for the elimination of water, together with salts, traces of CO_2, and some nitrogenous waste. The loss through perspiration is usually small, but during active sweating as much as 3 gallons of water may be lost in a day. Under such circumstances salt (NaCl) needed in the body's economy must be replaced by eating foods with sufficient salt; also the supply of vitamin C must be adequate. Perspiration is only incidentally excretory, its primary function being temperature regulation. It is also influenced by fright and emergency situations in which a "cold sweat" occurs.

B. REGULATION IN THE BODY

8-7. Homeostasis. The famous French physiologist Claude Bernard said, "All the vital mechanisms, varied as they are, have only one object, that of preserving constant the conditions of life in the internal environment." All living organisms maintain a more or less *steady internal state,* known as homeostasis, regardless of extremes in their external environment. In general the degree to which a particular group has achieved independence of its environment is a measure of its evolutionary progress; some generalized protozoans are affected by nearly every factor in the medium around them, whereas man is variously independent, by one means or another.

Several mechanisms exist for regulating the internal environment, but reflex activity of the nervous system and the hormone-producing endocrine system are the bases of all steady-state control. Every part of the animal body during all stages of growth and reproduction is under the influence of these systems. The situation of even the simplest animal is so intricate and little understood that regulatory processes generally are considered piecemeal, in terms of a few readily measurable criteria, rather than as an integrated whole. Osmotic pressure, hydrogen ion concentration, and temperature are three of these criteria, and each is intimately connected with water.

8-8. Water regulation. Water is taken in with food and also to some extent by absorption in aquatic forms. It is the universal solvent and carrier in protoplasm, and no organism can be independent of this essential fluid. Because of its property of diffusing across membranes, water is the vehicle for maintenance of the steady state.

Osmotic pressure is the force produced by different concentrations of solvent and solute on two sides of a semipermeable membrane (par. 3-19). In most marine invertebrates the body fluids are more or less in equilibrium with sea water; that is, the osmotic pressures on the inside and outside are the same. The body fluids of all fresh-water animals tend to absorb water because of the higher salt content of the body fluids, and these creatures therefore have developed various means for disposing of the excess water. Protozoans do this by means of the contractile vacuole, which usually is absent in marine forms. Most other animals regulate osmotic pressure by their excretory organs. The differential selectivity of the human kidney is an example.

Cormorants, gulls, and other marine birds drink sea water for their internal needs. The water is absorbed by the gut wall and the excess of salts passes in the blood stream to a pair of salt-secreting glands located near the eyes, with ducts to the nostrils. The secretion that pours out has higher salt content than sea water. Marine reptiles also excrete salt by nasal glands, and marine iguanas squirt the fluid in two streams for a distance of a foot or more. The rectal gland of sharks serves the same function.

The excretion or retention of water depends on the state of hydration of the body as a whole. In man, excessive sweating decreases the volume of fluid that passes out in the urine, whereas drinking quantities of fluid increases the urinary output. Water balance is controlled to a certain extent by thirst, which varies remarkably with the state of hydration, and by kidney action, which is influenced by the antidiuretic hormone secreted by the posterior lobe of the pituitary. In the absence of this hormone, reabsorption by the kidney tubules decreases. The control mechanism is automatic, because an increase of osmotic pressure in the blood causes increased secretion of the hormone. This, in turn, stimulates reabsorption and thus conserves water. Alcohol inhibits secretion of the antidiuretic hormone and thus has a dehydrating effect. Caffeine acts as a diuretic by increasing the glomerular filtration rate and by reducing reabsorption of water by the tubule cells.

8-9. Regulation of pH. The hydrogen ion concentration of most body fluids varies, but it is usually between pH 7 and 8. The regulatory mechanism by the blood in this case is the buffering action of such inorganic ions as carbonates and phosphates. Ion pairs, like $=HPO_4$ and $-H_2PO_4$, and $=CO_3$ and $-HCO_3$, act as buffers by combining with excess H^+. For example, the $=CO_3$ forms $-HCO_3$, resulting in a decrease of carbonate, an increase in bicarbonate, and the elimination of free H^+ ions. When the blood becomes too alkaline, this reaction is reversed. A considerable amount of acid or base thus may be absorbed without altering the pH of body fluids.

8-10. Heat regulation. The metabolism in an animal produces heat (which can be measured and stated in calories; see par. 5-11). The body temperature at any given time, however, is a function of the heat produced, conserved, and lost. In most animals metabolism is low and the body temperature does not differ much from that of the environment. Such animals are called cold-blooded, though actually their body fluids may be comparatively warm or cold, following the fluctuations in outside temperature. Birds and mammals are warm-blooded, or even-temperatured (homoiothermous); to maintain this condition, their energy production goes up as the outside temperature goes down, and thus the body temperature remains nearly constant. The normal temperature by mouth in man is about 37°C. (98.6°F.). This varies within a few degrees for various reasons, of which the most important is infection. Regulation is effected by the nervous system, which acts literally as a thermostat. In cold weather metabolism is increased through muscular activity, including the involuntary act of shivering, and some of this

energy is in the form of heat. During warm weather, excess heat is lost in two ways. Blood vessels in the skin are dilated so that heat is taken to the surface more rapidly, and the activity of the sweat glands is increased. The actual loss of heat is largely through radiation from the body surface and utilization of heat in the process of evaporating water. Excessive humidity hinders evaporation and is the cause of discomfort on hot, moist days. Clothing produces no heat but holds a layer of warm moist air between it and the skin and thus reduces the loss of heat due to evaporation and radiation. Evaporation through increased respiration is an important means of regulating temperature in animals such as dogs that do not perspire.

8-11. Hibernation. Many cold-blooded animals hide away in sheltered places during the low temperatures of winter to avoid death by heat loss or by freezing. Their temperature becomes practically that of the surroundings, and metabolism drops to a very low level when they are thus in "winter sleep," or hibernation. Some warm-blooded animals such as ground squirrels, chipmunks, and certain bats also hibernate during the colder parts of the year, when their food is scarce. The body temperature then follows that of the surroundings. During this period normal heat regulation is interrupted, and the whole physiology of the animal becomes modified—rate of heartbeat, oxygen consumption, and metabolism all are far reduced.

8-12. Hormonal control. Ultimately it appears that the various parts of the pituitary gland (Chap. 9) are primarily responsible for control of specific hormones which, in turn, maintain particular equilibria in the body's steady state. Thus thyroxin, secreted by the thyroid, regulates general metabolism, the parathyroid glands control calcium metabolism, and insulin, secreted by the islets of Langerhans in the pancreas, maintains the blood glucose level. Reduced production of insulin causes the well-known disease diabetes mellitus.

8-13. The blood in regulation. In higher animals the circulating blood is the vehicle for maintenance of the steady state. Besides carrying the raw materials and waste products of metabolism, it transports water, hormones, and enzymes, and it also serves as a defense mechanism against the invasion of harmful organisms. Blood cells have a direct phagocytic action, but the blood also plays a vital role in the immunity of the body against infection. When a foreign protein (bacterial or toxin) is introduced into the blood and threatens to upset the "steady state," antibodies usually are formed. These are very specific and confer immunity for periods of a few months or several years to the total length of life of the individual (see par. 6-7). Some individuals become hypersensitive to particular proteins, such as certain kinds of pollens that cause hay fever or asthma. The body fluids of every animal are in a more or less steady state of equilibrium with all the materials and infectious agents in its environment. This intricate system breaks down occasionally, with serious and even fatal results.

8-14. Organizational levels. The so-called "steady state" is not a single, static condition but a dynamic equilibrium of many systems which change in successive stages of development. Furthermore, it exists at all levels. There is the cellular steady state by which individual cells are maintained in equilibrium with their cellular environment; there is regulation at the tissue level, at the organ level, and finally at the level of the whole organism. Regulation and the steady state are at the basis of life.

REVIEW

1. Compare the following methods of excretion in invertebrates: direct diffusion, contractile vacuoles, Malpighian tubules, nephridia, coelomoducts.
2. Describe the probable origin and evolution of vertebrate kidneys.
3. Explain in detail the functioning of the human kidney. Is the process a simple filtration?
4. What waste materials are eliminated from the body elsewhere than by the kidneys in man? What processes are involved?
5. Define Bowman capsule, glomerulus, loop of Henle, cortex, medulla.
6. What is the normal composition of urine? How would you expect this to change on a very hot day?
7. Where is the urine stored in the human body, and how is it expelled at intervals?
8. What is meant by homeostasis? How has its degree of development been used as a measure of evolutionary progress among animals?
9. What are the two basic mechanisms responsible for maintenance of the "steady state" in man?
10. How does the body regulate water balance, salts, and temperature?
11. What is the role of the pituitary gland with respect to the steady state?
12. In what ways does the blood help to maintain the steady state?
13. How is urea formed?

9
The
endocrine
glands
or systems

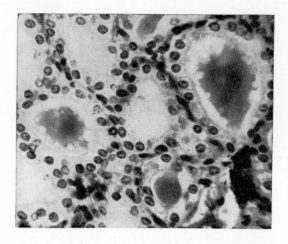

Glands are cells or groups of cells specialized in structure and function to produce substances needed in bodily processes; these are synthesized from ingredients obtained in the blood or lymph. Most glands discharge their products through ducts and are called glands of external secretion (exocrine). The salivary glands and liver, for example, have ducts carrying secretions to parts of the digestive tract, whereas the mammary and sweat glands discharge through openings on the body surface. In addition there are other glands, without ducts, whose secretions are carried by the blood stream to various parts of the body. These are the *glands of internal secretion, ductless glands,* or *endocrine glands,* and their products are called *internal secretions, hormones,* or *endocrines.* Minute amounts of these endocrine substances exercise profound regulatory control over many bodily functions, stimulating or inhibiting the development, growth, and activities of various tissues, and influencing the behavior of the individual and various aspects of reproduction.

9-1. Control by endocrines. Most or all endocrine activities are interrelated and work together so that we may speak of an endocrine system. It acts in conjunction with the nervous system to regulate bodily functions. This situation is like that in a factory where rapid decisions are made on the spot by workers and foremen (analogous to nerve impulses in the body), whereas long-term adjustments and general policies are laid down by top management (endocrines in cooperation with parts of the nervous system).

The exact mechanism by which endocrines influence physiological processes is unknown. Some evidence indicates that hormones act to accelerate or inhibit metabolism in "target" tissues rather than starting or stopping physiological activities. Knowledge of hormone chemistry has advanced by synthesis of two hormones, thyroxin and epinephrine (adrenalin); the molecules are rather simple. Experiments show that hormones are not specific for the animals in which they are produced but will influence bodily processes in many others. Adrenalin, for example, has an effect in protozoans and various crustaceans besides man and other vertebrates. Cross effects even have been found between plants and animals. Auxin, the growth hormone of plants, will stimulate the protozoan *Euglena viridis;* and some animal hormones stimulate growth in root tips of plants which by decapitation have been deprived of a supply of their own growth hormone. It appears, therefore, that hormones are fundamental substances that probably appeared early in biochemical evolution. The

Illustration at top of page: Photomicrograph of thyroid gland with colloid in the rounded follicles.

extent of their occurrence in organisms is still unknown, but they or similar undiscovered substances must be widespread. There is some evidence that physiological activities of individual cells are regulated by intracellular hormones; and hormones may be the chemical messengers by which genes determine bodily form and function.

9-2. Invertebrate hormones. There is evidence of hormones in flatworms, annelids, some other worms, mollusks, and arthropods. In crustaceans a substance produced in the **sinus gland** on the eyestalk influences the chromatophores. The pigments—white, red, and yellow (also black, brown, and blue)—are variously spread or condensed so that the body color comes to resemble the environment.

Molting and metamorphosis in insects are controlled by internal secretions. In bugs (*Rhodnius*) a hormone from the **corpus allatum** behind the brain inhibits metamorphosis (see par. 23-27), whereas another from neurosecretory cells in the **pars intercerebralis** of the brain induces molting and differentiation. Metamorphosis of the overwintering pupa into an adult in the silkworm moth (*Platy-*

samia cecropia) results from interaction of two hormones (Fig. 9-1). In nature, the cold of winter is necessary to end the rest period (diapause) that precedes metamorphosis. After chilling, a growth and differentiation hormone, ecdysone (GDH:$C_{18}H_{30}O_4$) is secreted by **prothoracic glands** anterior in the thorax. Its production is triggered by another hormone (NSH) produced in neurosecretory cells of the pars intercerebralis in the brain. NSH is carried in nerve axons to the **corpora cardiaca** behind the brain, is released there into the blood, and travels thence to the prothoracic glands. Experiments demonstrating these endocrine activities are as follows: (1) A normal pupa does not transform if kept over winter at room temperature but does so after being stored at 5°C. (2) If a chilled and an unchilled larva are joined surgically (parabiosis) so their blood streams mingle, both will transform; hormone from the one circulates in the other. (3) If a chilled pupa is dissected into two parts, head-thorax and abdomen, the first transforms into normal fore parts of an adult, but the second does not. If, however, brain and prothoracic glands are

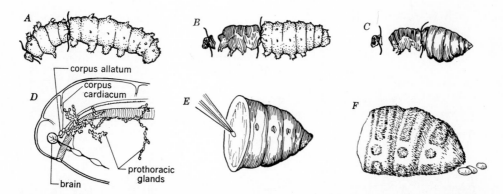

Fig. 9-1. Endocrine control of metamorphosis in larvae of the Cecropia moth. (*A*) Ligatures tied behind head and thorax before NSH is secreted; no metamorphosis. (*B*) Ligatures tied after NSH reached thorax; GDH activated, head and thorax transform. (*C*) Ligatures applied still later; GDH throughout body, metamorphosis complete. (*D*) Position of corpora allata and prothoracic glands in head of larva. (*E*) Brain and prothoracic glands from chilled larva implanted in isolated abdomen of pupa. (*F*) Hormones produce metamorphosis to adult form, and eggs laid! Stipple, larva; lines, pupa; hairy, adult. (*After C. M. Williams, Biological Bull., 1952, 1948.*)

then implanted in the second, it becomes a normal abdomen, which may lay eggs! (4) If the brain is removed from eight chilled larvae, the larvae then grafted to one another in a chain, and a brain transplanted into the first, the whole series will transform in sequence.

In early larval life the corpora allata secrete an inhibitory or status quo hormone (SQH). Removal of corpora allata in a young larva is followed by premature pupation, metamorphosis, and emergence of a miniature adult. Evidently SQH suppresses action of GDH in early larval life; prior to pupation, however, secretion of SQH lessens, whereupon GDH can act.

9-3. Vertebrate hormones.[1] In the higher

[1] See also endocrines of the frog (par. 2-13), control of secretory activities in digestion (par. 5-8), iodine and the thyroid (par. 5-12), and regulation of excretion (pars. 8-6, 8-7, 8-11).

vertebrates and man (Fig. 9-2) the endocrine glands include the pituitary, thyroid, parathyroids, islets of Langerhans, adrenals, gonads, parts of the gastric and intestinal mucosa, and, in some mammals, the placenta. The pineal and thymus were earlier thought to produce internal secretions, but there is no clearcut evidence to support this view. The location, structure, and functions of the endocrine glands are enough alike throughout the vertebrates to suggest a homologous series, differing as to details.

Knowledge of vertebrate endocrines has advanced enormously through experimental research since about 1920. Endocrine functions are studied by (1) removing the glands from either young or adult animals; (2) implanting them into subjects of various ages; (3) feeding the gland substance or an extract of it; (4) injecting the extract into the body; and (5) ob-

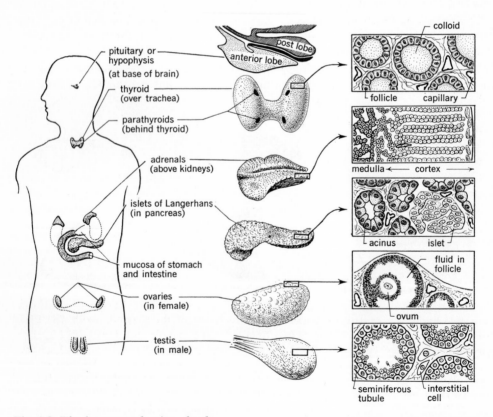

Fig. 9-2. The human endocrine glands.

serving individuals with diseased glands. Deficiency of a particular secretion is termed *hypo-*, and an excess *hyper-*. With the thyroid, for example, a scant supply is referred to as hypothyroidism, and an excess results in hyperthyroidism. The science of endocrinology has important applications in human medicine and some bearing on the production of domesticated animals. The structure and function of the endocrines are described here with particular reference to man.

9-4. Thyroid. This gland, of two lobes joined by an isthmus, lies on either side of the trachea below the larynx. It consists of many spherical closed sacs or follicles of microscopic size that are lined with cuboidal cells and surrounded by blood vessels and nerves. The follicles are filled with a colloid protein (thyroglobulin) containing the active principle, ***thyroxin*** ($C_{15}H_{11}O_4NI_4$; about 65 per cent of iodine by weight), which regulates the general metabolism of the body, oxygen consumption in tissues, and growth and sexual development. Normal function produces a varying amount of thyroxin depending on age, sex, and other factors. Control is by a thyroid-stimulating hormone (TSH) regulated by the hypothalamus. The thyroid in turn influences other endocrine glands including the adrenal cortex and the gonads. With decreased production of thyroxin the person is less active, is listless, and feels "cold" because of lowered general metabolism. This condition may be overcome by a daily dose of a few milligrams of thyroid extract (prepared from beef thyroid). Unlike other hormones, thyroxin is not easily digested, and so it can be given by mouth. Overgrowth or overfunction in man speeds up bodily activities (basal metabolism), increasing both heat production and heartbeat. This condition is usually relieved by removing part of the gland surgically to reduce the amount of thyroxin in the body. Extreme cases of hyperthyroidism often exhibit nervous excitability and exophthalmic goiter or protrusion of the eyeballs (Fig. 9-3A). If the thyroid is removed in a young animal, skeletal growth is arrested and sexual maturity fails; if removed from tadpoles, they do not transform into frogs. Normal development is restored, however, if thyroid is implanted or fed or an extract of it is injected.

A deficiency of iodine in the soil and water occurs in glaciated areas and in other places far from the sea, such as the Great Lakes region, the Alps, and the Himalayas. Chronic enlargement of the thyroid, known as **goiter**, often occurs to compensate for the deficiency (Fig. 9-3C). If there is malfunction of the thyroid, **cretinism** results among children. Cretins (Fig. 9-3B) are dwarfed in size, with thick, puffy skin and coarse facial features, the basal metabolism is decreased, and the sexual organs do not develop; mental growth is seriously retarded, many are imbeciles or idiots, and deaf-mutes are common. Comparable dysfunction in adults causes **myxedema**, charac-

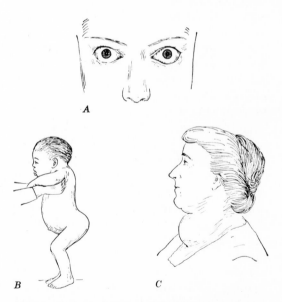

Fig. 9-3. Disorders of the thyroid. HYPERTHYROIDISM. (*A*) Exophthalmia, protrusion of the eyeballs. (*C*) Goiter, overgrowth of the thyroid gland. HYPOTHYROIDISM. (*B*) Cretin child, result of deficient thyroid secretion. (*B, after Hoskins, The tides of life, W. W. Norton & Company, Inc.; C, after Robinson, Our mysterious life glands, Eugenics Publishing Co.*)

terized by thick, puffy skin, scant, dry hair, lowered metabolism, disturbance of sexual function, and mental lethargy. Treatment with thyroid extract, if commenced early, stimulates young cretins to normal development and commonly restores myxedematous adults. In regions of deficiency the addition of iodine to the diet, as iodized salt, prevents the occurrence of such defects.

9-5. Parathyroids. Behind or partly embedded in the thyroid are two pairs of small oval *parathyroids.* Their secretion regulates the calcium-phosphorus balance in the blood plasma and affects the calcium metabolism in the body. Removal of the glands is followed by muscular twitchings and spasmodic contractions of increasing violence, leading to severe convulsions (parathyroid tetany) and death. Injection of parathyroid extract stops these effects. Overproduction of parathyroid secretion raises the level of calcium in the blood, and calcium may be withdrawn from the bones.

9-6. Gastric and intestinal mucosa. There is evidence of several hormones produced in cells lining the stomach and small intestine that control secretion of digestive enzymes. Secretin (Fig. 5-7) from the intestinal wall stimulates secretion of the pancreatic juice, and gastrin from the mucosa of the stomach serves similarly for gastric juice.

9-7. Islets of Langerhans. Within the substance of the pancreas, in addition to the glandular tissue providing digestive enzymes that pass through the pancreatic duct to the intestine, there are many small groups of cells, of different form and staining reaction, not connected to the duct. These *islets of Langerhans* produce the endocrine *insulin,* which regulates the metabolism of carbohydrates, including sugars, and of fats. Disease in the islets or removal of the pancreas is followed by an increase of sugar in the blood and urine, a condition known as *diabetes mellitus.* Formerly this was fatal in children and young adults and a considerable cause of death in older people, but its effects can now largely

be prevented by daily intake of insulin or by dieting to restrict the intake of sugar.

In some diseases an excess of insulin is produced, resulting in a drastic reduction in the level of blood sugar. This is comparable to the condition caused by injecting an overdose of insulin into a diabetic. The resulting insulin shock is not unlike some forms of drunkenness and can be overcome by eating sugar and thus raising the level of sugar in the blood. Insulin is extracted from the pancreas of cattle and sheep obtained in slaughterhouses.

The islets of Langerhans also produce a hormone called **glucagon** that accelerates breakdown of glycogen to glucose and hence raises the glucose level in the blood.

9-8. Adrenals. These two glands lie adjacent to the anterior or upper end of the kidneys and have an unusually rich blood supply. Each consists of an outer **cortex** and inner **medulla,** of different microscopic structure. In frogs the adrenal lies along the ventral surface of the kidney, and in sharks the cortex and medulla are separate structures.

The medulla produces **epinephrine** (adrenalin), which, injected into an animal, causes contraction of smooth muscle fibers in some arterioles, chiefly in the abdomen and skin, with consequent rise in blood pressure, while arterioles in skeletal muscle are relaxed and the heart is stimulated. Epinephrine relaxes smooth muscle on the bronchioles of the lung (hence relieves attacks of asthma) and retards muscular movements in the intestine; it also hastens the transformation of glycogen into glucose. One or two parts per billion of epinephrine are normal in the blood stream of man; but under emotional stress, such as fear or anger, additional amounts are suddenly secreted, and blood is shifted from the viscera to the muscles and the brain, so that the individual is ready for "fight or flight." This hormone is also produced in many invertebrates and has been synthesized in the laboratory.

Unlike other endocrine glands, removal of the adrenal medulla by surgery, which stops the secretion of epinephrine, results in no significant disturbance. Possibly the autonomic nervous system can take over in the absence of epinephrine so that this hormone may have a strictly emergency function. Epinephrine is unique in another respect: its secretion is under nervous control.

The cortex or outer part of the adrenal gland produces about seven endocrine substances. Chemically these are steroids, some of the more important being deoxycorticosterone, corticosterone, and cortisone. The last named is beneficial in treating some types of arthritis.

Cortical hormones are involved in a wide variety of biochemical and physiological functions in the body. These include metabolism of electrolytes and water; protein, carbohydrate, and lipid metabolism; maintenance of homeostasis in the circulatory system; and immunity and resistance to infection.

Complete removal of both adrenals is followed by death in 10 to 15 days. Earlier symptoms are loss of appetite, vomiting, weakness, and prostration, reduction in bodily temperature and metabolism, and loss of water and sodium chloride from the blood. Destruction of the adrenal cortex (Addison's disease) in man results in bronzing of the skin, gradual decline, and finally death.

9-9. Gonads, or sex glands. The testes of the male and ovaries of the female are the *gonads,* or *primary sex organs.* The sperm ducts, associated glands, and penis of the male and the oviducts, uterus, and vagina in the female are the *accessory sex organs;* these are related in various ways to reproduction (Chap. 11). External differences between the sexes, or *secondary sexual characteristics,* appear in many animals upon attaining sexual maturity. The gonads, or primary sex organs, besides producing eggs and sperm, respectively, secrete hormones that affect the accessory sex organs and secondary sexual characteristics. Other endocrine glands, especially the pituitary and thyroid, also influence the sexual structures and functions.

The thick neck, deeper voice, and belliger-

ent manner of bulls, the antlers of male deer, and the larger comb, wattles, and spurs and crowing habits of roosters are some familiar secondary sexual characteristics. Castration, or removal of the gonads, before sexual maturity produces striking changes in the form and temperament of these animals. The steer (castrated bull) has a smaller neck and more cow-like voice and is docile; the castrated deer grows no antlers; and the capon (castrated rooster) has smaller comb and spurs and does not crow (Fig. 9-4). In all such castrates the secondary characters are lacking, the accessory sex organs are reduced, sexual behavior is slight or absent, and the individuals tend to accumulate fat.

The endocrine of the testis responsible for these changes is **testosterone,** $C_{19}H_{30}O_2$ (and related androgenic hormones), evidently produced by the **Leydig** or **interstitial cells** be-

Fig. 9-4. Effect of sex hormone in fowls. (*A*) Normal male, long comb and wattles, slender body. (*B*) Castrated male (capon), scant comb and wattles, heavier body, resembles female. (*C*) Normal female. (*D*) Castrated male later receiving engrafted ovary—bigger size, larger comb and wattles, longer feathers on neck. (*After Finlay,* 1925.)

tween the seminiferous tubules. If this hormone is injected into a castrated individual, the accessory sex organs enlarge, the secondary sexual characters develop, and the behavior becomes that of a normal (uncastrated) animal.

Follicles of the ovary produce a female sex hormone *estradiol* (and related estrogenic hormones), responsible for the phenomenon of estrus, or "heat," in female mammals. Removing the ovaries from an immature female prevents her from becoming sexually mature, the accessory sex organs remain infantile, and the sex instincts are not shown. Injecting estradiol into a castrated female corrects these effects. If injected into a normal (uncastrated) but immature female, sexual maturity is quickly brought about, the accessory organs develop, but the ovaries remain infantile.

The accessory reproductive organs of females, especially after estrus, are controlled by another ovarian hormone, *progesterone* (progestin); this is produced by the corpus luteum that forms in a Graafian follicle of the ovary after discharge of the ovum. Progesterone, together with estradiol, prepares the uterus for receiving a fertilized ovum. Both hormones, directly or indirectly, induce enlargement of the mammary glands for their subsequent function; later the lactogenic hormone of the pituitary stimulates milk secretion. A third ovarian hormone, *relaxin,* facilitates birth by relaxing ligaments of the pelvic girdle. A similar set of hormones is produced by the placenta.

9-10. Pituitary. At the base of the brain is the *pituitary gland,* or *hypophysis,* formed during embryonic development of (1) an anterior lobe from a pouch (Rathke's pocket) on the roof of the mouth and (2) a posterior lobe from the infundibulum of the brain. In an adult human being it weighs about 0.5 gram, but it has an enormous influence on the growth and functioning of the body. It consists of four parts: anterior, intermedia, posterior (nervosa), and tuberalis.

An extract of the posterior lobe affects smooth muscle, causing a rise in arterial blood pressure by contraction of all blood vessels (thus being unlike epinephrine); it also contracts smooth muscle in the intestine, gall bladder, ureters, urinary bladder, and uterus. The former effect can be attributed to the hormone *vasopressin,* the latter to the hormone *oxytocin.* Vasopressin also has an important effect on the kidneys where it has the function of accelerating water reabsorption. Loss of function of the posterior lobe in man leads to a clinical condition called *diabetes insipidus* in which enormous amounts of water are excreted and the patient is terribly thirsty. This condition is mitigated by feeding vasopressin. A commercial extract, *pituitrin,* produces all these effects. In cold-blooded vertebrates *intermedin* from the intermediate lobe causes extension of the melanophores, or pigment cells.

The anterior lobe of the pituitary produces several distinct hormones that affect other endocrine glands and also various parts of the body. Thus, the rate of production of thyroid hormone depends on the supply of thyrotropic hormone from the anterior pituitary. The principal anterior pituitary hormones and their effects are as follows:

1. GROWTH STIMULATING. Excessive secretion of this hormone or overgrowth of the gland causes **gigantism.** If this occurs during early youth, it results in lengthening of the long bones; human giants 8 to 9 feet tall are produced by extreme overfunction. An excess later in life causes *acromegaly,* in which the forehead, nose, and lower jaw become massive and the facial skin is thick and coarse (Fig. 9-5). Deficiency of this hormone results in *dwarfing,* the individual retaining the proportions of a child.

2. GONADOTROPIC. In female mammals this hormone (one or more) causes normal growth of the Graafian follicle in the ovary. When injected into immature females, it causes precocious sexual maturity within a few days; overdoses in rats cause a doubling or trebling of the number of eggs (up to 33) released

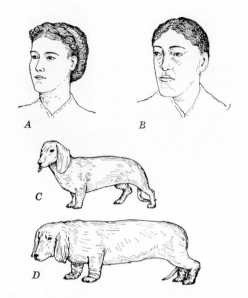

Fig. 9-5. Disturbances due to unbalance in growth hormone of anterior pituitary gland. (*A*) Normal woman, age 25 years. (*B*) Same individual, age 42, advanced acromegaly—heavy brow ridges, nose, and lips, and lengthening of jaw. (*After Robinson, Our mysterious life glands, Eugenics Publishing Co.*) (*C*) Normal dachshund. (*D*) Litter mate that received hypophysis implants for 35 weeks. (*After Evans et al., 1933.*)

from the ovaries at one time. In male mammals it stimulates growth of both the seminiferous tubules and interstitial tissue. Implantation of pituitary gland into amphibians results in rapid maturing and laying of eggs within a few days. Removal of the pituitary is followed by atrophy of the gonads and the accessory sex organs.

3. LACTOGENIC. This hormone stimulates milk secretion in the mammary glands of mammals and secretion of "crop milk" in pigeons; it is present in birds when they are "broody."

4. ADRENOCORTICOTROPIC. Growth and secretory activity of the adrenal glands are stimulated. One of these products is the adrenocortico-

tropic hormone, ACTH, which in turn stimulates the secretion of other hormones including cortisone.

5. THYROTROPIC. The growth and the secretory activity of the thyroid gland are regulated by this hormone.

9-11. The endocrine glands as a system. The several glands of internal secretion, located at different places in the body, thus constitute a somewhat loose "system." The products of the anterior pituitary exercise the important role of integrating the function of other endocrine glands and of various organs and tissues in the body.

REVIEW

1. Why are the endocrine glands also called ductless glands or glands of internal secretion?
2. What functions among arthropods are known to be controlled by hormones?
3. What are some results of inadequate secretion and of oversecretion of thyroxin?
4. What is diabetes mellitus? How is it caused? What treatment is possible?
5. Name the endocrines produced by the adrenal glands and their functions.
6. Why are the gonads included as glands of internal secretion?
7. What happens as to structure, function, and behavior when a rooster is castrated?
8. Where is hormone produced in the testis?
9. What hormones are derived from the pituitary, and what is the function of each?
10. How and where are hormones obtained for use in human medicine?
11. What hormone(s) regulates each of the following bodily processes: general metabolism; calcium metabolism; metamorphosis of tadpoles; sugar metabolism; contraction of smooth muscle; contraction of capillaries in visceral muscle; sexual maturity in a female?

10
Nervous systems, sense organs, and animal behavior

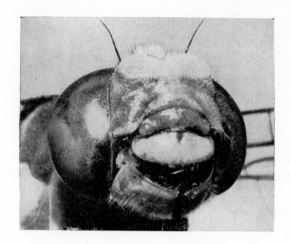

stimuli act directly upon cells or tissues and elicit a direct response (e.g., sunburn), but most animals have various kinds of specialized receptors (sense organs) to receive stimuli.

A *receptor* is a cell or organ having an especial sensitivity (lowered threshold) to some particular kind or kinds of stimulus, as the eye to light and the ear to sound. *Exteroceptors* receive stimuli from the external environment, and *interoceptors* from within the body, as with hunger or thirst. (See also Proprioceptors, par. 10-15.) Receptors induce the transmission of nerve impulses through the nervous system; the impulses, in turn, excite terminal structures, or *effectors,* to bring about responses.

Some stimuli are gradual, and response is slow, as in the chilling that precedes a sneeze; others are abrupt and produce a quick response, like the jab of a pin. Beyond a certain minimum there may be no quantitative relation between the intensity of a stimulus and the kind or magnitude of the responses that it produces (the all-or-none effect); this depends upon the kinds of cells or organs excited and their physiological condition. Several weak stimuli in rapid succession may bring a response although each individually is too slight to do so; this is called the summation effect. Upon being excited, muscles contract to pro-

All living protoplasm is excitable or irritable. Because of this, every organism is sensitive to changes of stimuli from both its external and its internal environments; to these it responds or reacts in various ways. Every type of organic response, from the simplest action of an amoeba to the most complex bodily function or mental process in man, results from this fundamental characteristic of excitability. To perceive stimuli, to transmit these to various body parts, and to effect responses, most animals have sense organs and a *nervous system* (Fig. 10-1). This system (together with endocrine glands in some) serves also to coordinate and integrate the functions of cells, tissues, and organ systems so that they act harmoniously as a unit, resulting in what we see as the behavior of animals.

Any physical or chemical change capable of exciting an organism or its parts is a *stimulus.* Common external stimuli derive from temperature, moisture, light, gravity, contact, pressure, oxygen supply, salt concentrations, and odors (chemical emanations). Internal stimuli result from the quantity of food, water, oxygen, or wastes in the body and from fatigue, pain, disease, or other conditions. Some

Illustration at top of page: Sense organs of a dragonfly—short antennae, huge compound eyes, and sensory hairs around mouth.

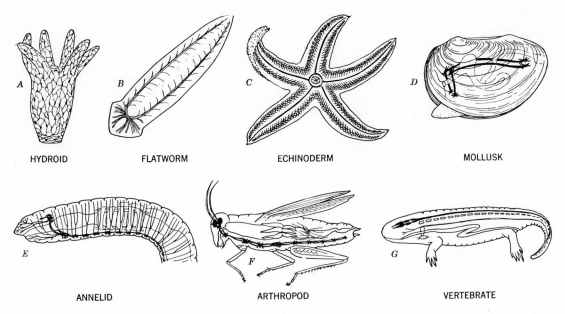

HYDROID   FLATWORM   ECHINODERM   MOLLUSK

ANNELID   ARTHROPOD   VERTEBRATE

Fig. 10-1. Nervous systems in animals (heavy black). (*A*) Hydroid, nerve net throughout body. (*B*) Flatworm, ganglia in "head" region, 2 nerve cords. (*C*) Echinodern, nerve ring around mouth, median nerve in each arm. (*D*) Bivalve mollusk, 3 pairs of ganglia and connectives. (*E*) Annelid, a "brain" of ganglia in anterior end, double solid ventral nerve cord, segmental ganglia and nerves. (*F*) Arthropod, similar to earthworm. (*G*) Vertebrate, brain in head, single hollow dorsal nerve cord with paired segmental nerves.

duce movements, and gland cells pour forth the secretions previously synthesized within them.

A. NERVOUS SYSTEMS

10-1. Neurons and nerves. Nervous systems are composed of nerve cells, or *neurons,* with cell processes known as *dendrites* and *axons.* Dendrites transmit impulses toward the cell body and axons away. The neurons are of varied form (Fig. 3-13) in the systems of different animals and in the several parts of any one nervous system. According to the "neuron theory" each neuron is a distinct anatomical unit, having no protoplasmic continuity with other neurons, and also is physiologically distinct. Injury to the nucleus or cell body destroys a neuron but does not always affect adjacent neurons. The neuron is the functional unit of the nervous system, which consists solely of neurons in orderly arrangement, they alone performing the nervous functions. Between any two neurons related in function there is a delicate contact, or *synapse;* this is a "physiological valve" that passes nerve impulses in only one direction, from the axon of one neuron to the dendrite of the other. A *nerve* consists of one to many *nerve fibers* (axons or dendrites) bound together by connective tissue and including blood vessels to supply nutrients and oxygen.

10-2. The nerve impulse. The *impulse* that passes along a nerve fiber involves both chemical and electrical change. It requires the presence of oxygen, and produces a minute but measurable amount of carbon dioxide, and also a rise in temperature. The impulse moves like the burning of a trail of gunpowder; once ignited (stimulated), it travels at a uniform speed with the same intensity throughout. A wave of electrical change accompanies the impulse. In the resting nerve fiber the exterior of the semipermeable membrane has a positive charge (excess of Na^+ ions) and the interior a negative one (fewer K^+ ions)—hence the fiber is "polarized." The impulse is started by stimulation of a sense organ with resulting change of ion permeability. As the impulse passes along the nerve fiber, the charges on the plasma membrane are neutralized or even reversed. This occurs because the resistance of the membrane to permeability by ions drops, permitting some ions to move in and others to move out. Sodium ions move inward, leaving a negative charge relative to other parts of the surface and creating a positive charge in the interior. The changes in permeability affect adjacent parts of the fiber, so the impulse is "propagated" or moves along. The current flow (called the action potential) can be measured by connecting a galvanometer to an exposed nerve (Fig. 4-6). As the impulse passes, an abrupt peak (spike) occurs, followed by a slower drop in potential. After the peak there is a refractory period (0.001 to 0.005 second) during which the depolarized fiber cannot carry another stimulus. Movement of potassium and sodium ions at this time reestablishes polarization and the fiber again can conduct. The interchange of sodium and potassium ions, due to shifts in permeability, explains the local change in potential. The ultimate source of energy for entry of sodium is thought to be metabolism involving the splitting of thyamine and recovery by glycolysis.

A nerve impulse travels 6 to 12 meters per second in a lobster, 28 to 30 meters per second in a frog, and up to 120 meters per second in some mammalian fibers. There is a short delay in passage at each synapse. An impulse, upon reaching the finely branched ends of an axon, causes the latter to produce a chemical **neurohumor** which sets up an impulse in the next neuron. Acetylcholine is produced in most synapses including those at effectors on skeletal muscle. The presence of acetylcholine would continue to stimulate the next neuron but for the fact that an enzyme, cholinesterase, quickly inactivates it.

Sensory or **afferent neurons** are those which conduct impulses from receptors to or toward the central nervous system; and **motor** or **efferent neurons** conduct from the central nervous system to various effectors. Still other **adjustor neurons** in the brain and nerve cord join variously between sensory and motor neurons. Some nerves contain only sensory fibers, others only motor fibers, and many are mixed nerves including both types. A **ganglion** is a unit containing the cell bodies of few or many neurons, and certain ganglia in the brain are known as **centers**.

10-3. Invertebrate nervous systems (Fig. 10-1). Most protozoans show no structures for coordination, but some ciliates such as *Paramecium* have a definite system of fibrils or a **neuromotor apparatus** (Fig. 16-12*B*); this evidently receives stimuli, conducts impulses, and coordinates movements of the cell body. In sponges the cells about the openings (oscula) in the body wall contract slowly if touched, and these reactions may be communicated to nearby cells, but there are no definite nerve cells or structures. Hydra and other coelenterates have a diffuse **nerve net** around the body in or under the epithelium, but no central ganglion. The net is composed of nerve cells, which are unlike typical neurons in being joined to one another by protoplasmic processes. They connect to both receptors (modified epithelial cells) in the epidermis and to the bases of epitheliomuscular cells that contract slowly to alter the body shape. Nerve nets occur in some other animals and even on the blood vessels of vertebrates.

In bilaterally symmetrical animals the nervous system is linear, usually comprising one or more pairs of **ganglia** or a **brain** in the anterior end joined to one or more **nerve cords** that extend posteriorly through the body. The nerve cords of invertebrates are all ventral and solid, and nerves pass from the ganglia and cords to various organs. Flatworms (Fig. 18-1) have two anterior ganglia, with nerves to the head region, and two separated nerve cords which are joined by cross-connectives. In mollusks, annelids, and arthropods the paired anterior ganglia (supraesophageal, subesophageal) lie above and below the esophagus and are joined by connectives. The more specialized mollusks lack ventral nerve cords but have large ganglia joined by connectives in the head, foot, and viscera. In annelid worms and the more primitive arthropods, including some insects and their larvae, the two ventral nerve cords have a pair of ganglia and a pair or more of nerves in each body segment. In the higher crustaceans, insects, and arachnoids the ventral ganglia are concentrated anteriorly. The starfishes and other echinoderms have a radially arranged nervous system in keeping with their symmetry.

10-4. Vertebrate nervous systems. In all vertebrates the nervous system has a comparable embryonic origin (par. 11-17) and is always single, hollow, and dorsal to the digestive tract. In basic pattern it is like that of the frog (Fig. 2-15) and consists of (1) the *central nervous system* with a large anterior *brain* (Fig. 10-2) connected to a spinal or *nerve cord* and (2) the *peripheral nervous system* of 10 or 12 pairs of *cranial nerves* from the brain (Table 10-1), a pair of *spinal nerves* from the cord for each primitive body segment, and the *autonomic* (or sympathetic) *nervous system* (Fig. 10-5). The description of the frog's nervous system will suffice for almost any vertebrate save for proportional differences in the brain, the length of the spinal cord, and the number of cranial and spinal nerves.

10-5. Brain. In the adult shark and frog the parts of the brain are in linear arrangement. In higher vertebrates this primitive *brain stem* becomes folded or flexed, and the *cerebrum* and the *cerebellum* become progressively enlarged (Fig. 10-2) until in mammals and especially in man (Fig. 10-3) the cerebrum overlies all other parts. Furthermore, the outermost gray matter, or *cortex,* of the cerebrum is both thickened and increased in area, so that it becomes folded or convoluted. In

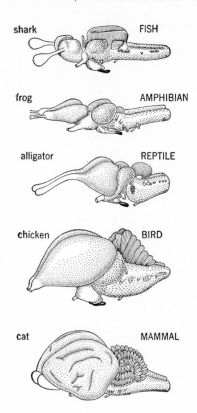

Fig. 10-2. The brains of representative vertebrates, showing progressive increase, especially in the cerebral hemispheres and cerebellum. *Olfactory lobes,* clear; *cerebrum,* lightly stippled; *optic tracts and lobes,* coarsely stippled; *base of midbrain,* wavy lines; *cerebellum,* vertical lines; *medulla oblongata,* horizontal dashes; *pituitary body,* black. Stubs of cranial nerves are outlined.

man it contains several billion neurons and their synapses. The cortex is the seat of all conscious sensations and actions, memory, the will, and intelligence; its increase in bulk among the higher vertebrates is in keeping with their greater mental abilities. The cerebellum is concerned with muscular coordinations and shows especial development in fishes and birds whose movements are quick and well balanced.

10-6. Spinal cord and nerves (Fig. 10-4). The outer or *white matter* of the spinal cord is of bundles of myelinated fibers connecting

Table 10-1. The paired cranial nerves of vertebrates

Number and name of nerve	Origin (in brain)	Distribution (external connections)	Function (chiefly as in man)
I Olfactory	Olfactory lobe (or bulb)	Olfactory epithelium in nasal cavity	*Sensory:* smell
II Optic	Optic lobe on midbrain	Retina of eye	*Sensory:* sight
III Oculomotor	Floor of midbrain	Eye: 4 muscles of eyeball; also iris, lens, upper lid	*Motor:* movements of eyeball, iris, lens, and eyelid
IV Trochlear	Floor of midbrain (emerges dorsally)	Eye: superior oblique muscle of eyeball	*Motor:* rotation of eyeball
V Trigeminal	Side of medulla	Top and sides of head, face, jaws, and teeth	*Sensory:* feeling on forehead, scalp, upper eyelid, side of nose, in teeth *Motor:* movement of tongue and of muscles used in chewing
VI Abducens	Side of medulla	Eye: external rectus muscle of eyeball	*Motor:* rotation of eyeball
VII Facial	Side and floor of medulla	Tongue (anterior ⅔), muscles of face, of mastication, and of neck	*Sensory:* taste *Motor:* facial expression, chewing, movement of neck
VIII Auditory (acoustic)	Side of medulla	Inner ear: (1) Organ of Corti in cochlea (2) Semicircular canals	*Sensory:* (1) Hearing (2) Equilibrium
IX Glossopharyngeal	Side of medulla	Tongue (posterior ⅓); mucous membrane and muscles of pharynx	*Sensory:* taste and touch *Motor:* movements in pharynx
X Vagus (pneumogastric)	Side and floor of medulla	Pharynx, vocal cords, lungs, heart, esophagus, stomach, and intestine	*Sensory:* vocal cords, lungs *Motor:* pharynx, vocal cords, lungs, esophagus, stomach, heart; inhibits heartbeat
XI * Spinal accessory	Floor of medulla	Muscles of palate, larynx, vocal cords, and neck	*Motor:* muscles of pharynx, larynx, and neck
XII * Hypoglossal	Floor of medulla	Muscles of tongue (and neck)	*Motor:* movements of tongue

* Nos. XI, XII are lacking in amphibians, fishes, and cyclostomes.

between various parts of the brain and the nuclei of spinal nerves and adjustor neurons. The inner **gray matter** contains adjustor neurons and the nuclei of motor neurons; nuclei of sensory neurons are in the **dorsal root gan-** *glia* of spinal nerves. If the dorsal root of a spinal nerve is cut, any sensory impulses from the entering fibers fail to reach the cord and brain. Destruction of the ventral root blocks all motor control by fibers in that nerve. The

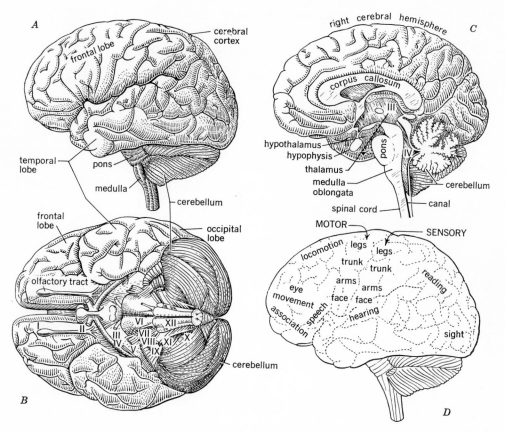

Fig. 10-3. The humain brain. (*A*) Left side. (*B*) Ventral surface; I-XII, cranial nerves. (*C*) Median section; III, IV, ventricles. (*D*) Left side, showing localization of certain functions on the surface of the cerebral cortex.

ventral roots are variously injured or destroyed in poliomyelitis, leading to impairment of muscular function.

10-7. Sensory pathways. After an impulse reaches the spinal cord it follows specific sensory pathways to higher centers. These differ for various kinds of stimuli. Injury to the spinal column results in loss of sensitivity on the afflicted side in the case of touch and pressure but on the opposite side in the case of pain and temperature. In the first, the afferent neurons for touch and pressure enter the spinal cord and immediately turn upward on the same side to the medulla oblongata. There the impulse is transmitted across a synapse and activates a secondary neuron, axons of which cross the medulla and turn up to end in

the *thalamus.* This structure, in the brain stem, acts as the sensory relay station; from there the impulse is relayed to the cerebral cortex for conscious appreciation and integration.

The pathway for pain and temperature is quite different. Impulses enter the spinal cord through the dorsal roots and pass to afferent neurons ending in the dorsal horn of the gray matter. Passing a synapse, the impulse enters the secondary neuron which crosses the spinal cord at the same level and then turns upward on the side opposite the original sensory receptor and ascends past the medulla directly to the thalamus. From there the impulse follows a course similar to that described for touch and pressure, ending in the cerebral

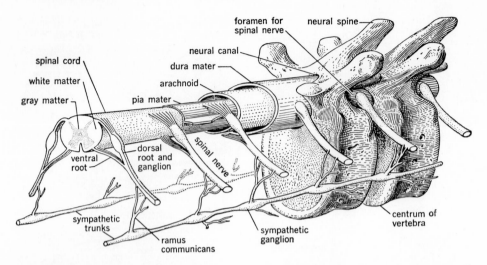

Fig. 10-4. The human spinal cord, spinal nerves, and sympathetic nervous system and their relation to the vertebrae and the membranes (meninges) about the cord.

cortex. It will be seen that in both cases there is a crossing over between sensory receptor and cerebral cortex, though at different levels. Thus injury to one side of the cerebral cortex, as in cerebral hemorrhage, results in a loss of sensation on the opposite side of the body. All the neurons ever to be present develop early in the life of an individual, but new associations and pathways are established throughout life according to the kinds and intensity of stimuli received and the patterns of behavior developed. There is a functional localization for certain kinds of sensory and motor phenomena in the cortex; these have been ascertained (Fig. 10-3D) partly by experiment and partly by study of the effects of brain injuries.

10-8. Autonomic nervous system (Fig. 10-5). The somatic nerves (cranial, spinal) connect mainly to skeletal muscles and direct the adjustment of an animal to its surroundings. By contrast, the *autonomic nervous system,* of ganglia and fibers connecting to all smooth muscles, glands, and the viscera, deals with the internal environment of the body. It controls routine (vegetative) functions such as the rate of metabolism, the action and tone of internal muscles, and the maintaining of a constant state (homeostasis) of components in the blood, lymph, and tissue fluids. In birds

and mammals it closely regulates the body temperature by increasing metabolism and fluffing out the feathers or fur in cold weather or by promoting loss of heat in a warm environment.

The thoracolumbar portion, or *sympathetic system,* includes two lengthwise chains of connected ganglia along the trunk vertebrae and aorta. Efferent fibers from the spinal cord pass in spinal nerves to enter the sympathetic ganglia as preganglionic fibers. Upon leaving, as postganglionic fibers, those of each group unite as a *plexus,* then distribute to various organs, as with the nerves from the coeliac plexus to the stomach, liver, etc. Afferent sympathetic fibers pass directly from organs to the dorsal roots of spinal nerves and into the spinal cord. Still other fibers connect to the erector muscles of the hairs, to sweat glands, and small blood vessels. The craniosacral portion, or *parasympathetic system,* includes fibers in certain cranial nerves, to the iris of the eye (III), the glands and mucous membranes of the mouth (V, VII), and the heart, lungs, stomach, and upper small intestine (X or vagus); and other fibers from sacral nerves connect to organs in the lower abdomen.

Most visceral organs and some others are

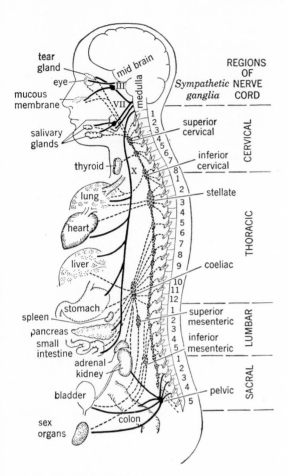

Fig. 10-5. The autonomic nervous system of man and its connections with the central nervous system and the internal organs; diagrammatic and simplified. *Sympathetic trunk and main ganglia* (coeliac, etc.), heavy stipple; *sympathetic nerves,* broken lines; *parasympathetic nerves,* heavy solid lines; *cranial nerves,* III, VII, (IX), X; *spinal nerves* numbered for each region of spinal cord.

innervated by both systems, and the two have more or less opposite effects. The parasympathetic promotes secretion of saliva and digestive juices, increases muscular activity of the intestine, constricts bronchioles in the lungs, slows the heartbeat, and constricts the pupil and adjusts the eye for near vision. In contrast, the sympathetic increases heartbeat, slows gastro-intestinal action, dilates the

bronchioles, etc. By increasing secretion of epinephrine from the adrenal glands (par. 9-8) it also mobilizes bodily resources for emergencies—fright, flight or fight, and injury. The epinephrine constricts blood vessels of the skin and viscera, dilates those of the heart and skeletal muscle, releases glucose from the liver for muscle metabolism, and shortens the clotting time of the blood.

B. SENSE ORGANS

Receptors that yield conscious sensations are called *sense organs* (Fig. 10-6). The functions of these are well known only in man; we cannot always determine their functions with certainty in other animals. The human "special senses" are as follows: *touch,* including contact, pressure, heat, and cold; *taste,* for certain substances in solution; *smell,* for volatile chemicals and gases in the air; *hearing,* for vibrations in air, water, or solids; and *sight,* for light waves. Compared with man, the dog has a more delicate sense of smell, the cat hears sounds of higher pitch, the eagle has keener sight, and the honeybee responds to light farther into the violet but less of the red. Sensory structures are located so as to meet the environment, being around the body in sessile animals but more numerous anteriorly in bilaterally symmetrical species.

10-9. Touch. Tactile receptors are common on the tentacles of coelenterates and annelid worms and on the antennae of arthropods; the latter commonly have tactile hairs on the body (Fig. 23-3D). On vertebrates, tactile receptors occur over most of the exterior surface. Some are *free nerve endings,* and others are special *corpuscles* that contain the sensory nerve terminations (Fig. 10-7). In man these are most sensitive and closely spaced on the lips, face, and the palmar surfaces of the fingers. At the finger tip a pressure of only 3 grams per square millimeter is detected and two points 2.3 mm. apart (2-point threshold) will receive separate sensations, whereas on the back of the body the minima are 48 grams and 67 mm.

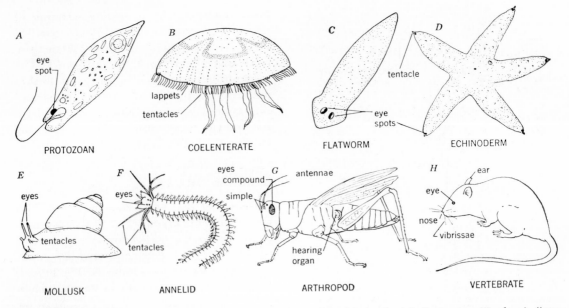

Fig. 10-6. Sensory devices and sense organs in various types of animals. (*A*) Protozoan (*Euglena*), "eye-spot." (*B*) Coelenterate (jellyfish), lappets and tentacles. (*C*) Flatworm (*Euplanaria*), eyespots. (*D*) Echinoderm (starfish), eyespots on ends of arms. (*E*) Mollusk (land snail), eyes and tentacles on head. (*F*) Annelid worm (sandworm), eyes and tentacles on head. (*G*) Arthropod (grasshopper), both compound and simple eyes and antennae on head; hearing organ on thorax. (*H*) Vertebrate (mammal), eyes, ears, and nose, also sensory hairs on tip of head.

10-10. Taste and smell. A common *chemical sense* to irritating chemicals is present in the human mouth and nasal cavities and over all the body in amphibians, fishes, and many other aquatic animals. *Taste,* or gustation, is the perception of dissolved materials by taste buds. These are groups of narrow receptors with fine tips in a small external pore (Fig. 10-8). They are usually in or about the mouth but occur over the body in catfishes and carp and on the tarsi of butterflies. Human taste buds distinguish sweets, salts, acids, and bitter (alkaloidal) substances but differ in sensitivity as to the concentrations of various materials that can be detected: cane sugar, 1 part in 200; table salt, 1 in 400; hydrochloric acid, 1 in 15,000; and strychnine, 1 in 2,500,000. The olfactory organs of fishes and other aquatic animals respond like taste buds to substances dissolved in the water.

Besides their ordinary service, the taste buds may help in maintaining the constancy of the body's internal environment. Rats suffering from experimental dietary or endocrine deficiencies, when offered a choice of foods or solutions, chose those containing the needed substances.

Smell, or olfaction—"taste at a distance"—depends in man on slender neurons with directly exposed tips that lie in mucous membranes high in the nasal cavity (Fig. 10-9). Eddy currents of air carry volatile substances directly to these cell endings, which have much greater sensitivity than taste buds. Man can detect oil of peppermint at 0.024 mg. per liter of air and artificial musk at 0.0004 mg. per liter. Much of our "taste" for food depends upon smell, as shown by the fact that when a cold congests the nasal membranes all food tastes much alike. The sense of smell

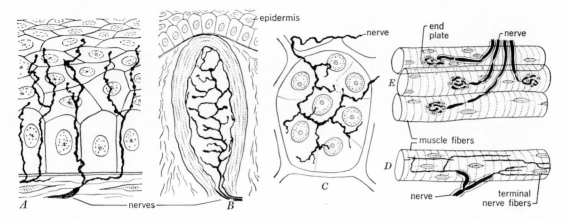

Fig. 10-7. Receptors and effectors, the end organs related to sensory and motor nerves. (*A*) Free sensory nerve endings in cornea of eye. (*B*) Meissner corpuscle (sensory) under human epidermis. (*C*) Nerve endings on gland cell in pancreas. (*D*) Motor fibers on muscles in frog. (*E*) Motor end plates on muscle fibers in rabbit. (*Adapted from Cajal, Histology, The Williams & Wilkins Co.*)

is vastly more delicate among wild mammals and insects and serves them variously in finding food and mates and sometimes in avoiding enemies. In some moths the odor of a female may attract a male for a mile or more.

10-11. Equilibration. A *statocyst* is a small organ of equilibration in which a particle rests among hair-like projections on sensory cells. A change in position of the animal brings the particle, or *statolith*, against one or another of the receptors, which transmits an impulse indicating the body position in respect to gravity. In mollusks the statolith is a small limy concretion, whereas in the crayfish (par.

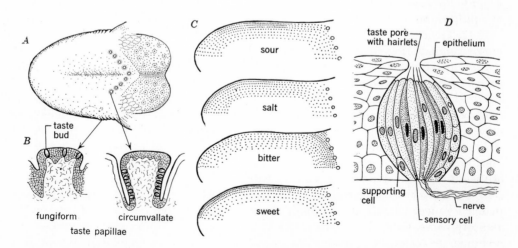

Fig. 10-8. The mechanism of taste in man. (*A*) Dorsal surface of tongue. (*B*) Two types of taste papillae in section and enlarged. (*C*) Relative sensitivity on the tongue for the four tastes. (*D*) Section of a taste bud; enlarged and diagrammatic. (*Partly after Parker, Smell, taste and allied senses in the vertebrates, J. B. Lippincott Co.*)

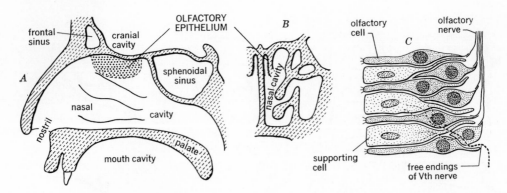

Fig. 10-9. The mechanism of smell (olfaction) in man; diagrammatic. (*A*) Section of the head, showing olfactory epithelium on lateral wall of right nasal cavity. (*B*) Transverse section of nasal cavity. (*C*) Enlarged microscopic section of the olfactory epithelium. (*Adapted from Parker, Smell, taste and allied senses in the vertebrates, J. B. Lippincott Co.*)

22-10) a particle of sand serves this purpose. Some aquatic animals have hydrostatic organs which aid in equilibration by their sensitivity to small differences in pressure. Air bladders and air bubbles serve a hydrostatic function in many fishes and aquatic insects.

The inner ear of most vertebrates has three fluid-filled semicircular canals (Fig. 10-10*A*), in three separate planes, each with a swelling, or *ampulla,* containing a statocyst-like organ of *equilibrium.*

10-12. Hearing. The organ of hearing in most mammals (Fig. 10-10) has an external sound-collecting shell (pinna) around a tubular *external auditory canal.* At the end of the canal, sound waves act to set the eardrum, or *tympanic membrane,* into vibration. These movements pass through three *auditory ossicles* (malleus, incus, stapes) to produce vibrations in the fluid that fills the spiral *cochlea* of the inner ear. In the latter are many *hair cells,* each evidently the receptor for a particular frequency, that induce stimuli in the auditory nerve. Other land vertebrates have no pinna, the cochlea is represented by a small outgrowth (lagena), and one bone (columella) replaces the three ossicles. The human ear responds to sound frequencies of about 30 to 15,000, or higher, per second. Among inverte-

brates sound receptors are known only in certain insects (Fig. 23-1; par. 23-9).

10-13. Light and sight. Photoreceptors sensitive to light are present in earthworms, and there are "eyespots" on various coelenterates and mollusks. From such simple structures various types of eyes have been developed. Among arthropods there are both simple and compound eyes (Figs. 22-6, 22-12, 23-1). The latter consist of many separate eyes with lenses arranged as a mosaic. The cephalopod mollusks have eyes much like those of vertebrates, but they are derived differently.

The *eye* in all vertebrates (Fig. 10-11) is much as described for the frog. It is of the "camera" type, with a lens that focuses images of external objects on the receptors in the *retina,* as on a photographic film. The receptors consist of *rods* (about 115 million in a human eye), which form colorless sensations in dim light, and the *cones* (6.5 million), which are active in bright light and are sensitive to both white and colored light. Cones are lacking in many vertebrates that are active only at night, such as most mammals.

After exposure to bright light, some time is needed for dark adaptation (vision in very dim light). The rods contain a protein pigment, visual purple or rhodopsin, that is

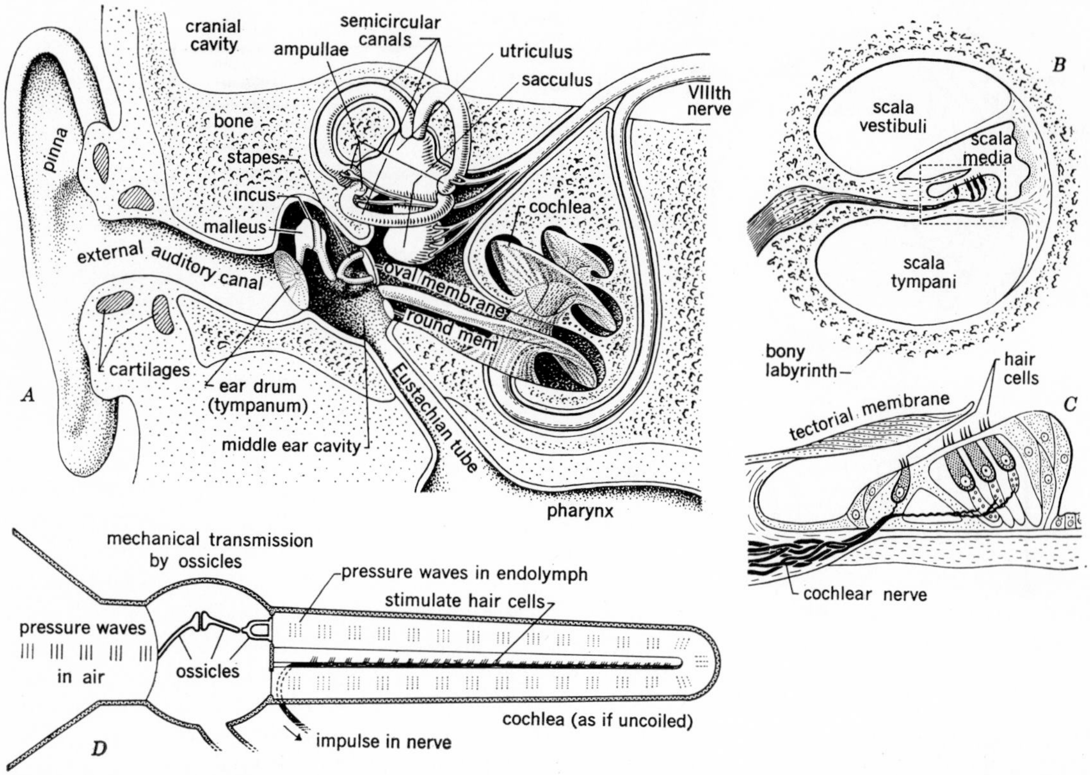

Fig. 10-10. The mechanism of hearing and equilibrium in man. (*A*) General structure of the ear. (*B*) Cross section of one part of cochlea (area of *C* in dotted lines). (*C*) Enlarged section through spiral organ of Corti with sensory hair cells. (*D*) Diagram of sound transmission from the air to an impulse in the auditory nerve.

bleached by light and must be present for vision in the dark. Rhodopsin is related to carotene compounds, and vitamin A is considered a stage in its regeneration; severe vitamin A deficiency interferes with dark adaptation, producing "night blindness."

The human eye is sensitive to a visible spectrum from violet to red (397 to 723 mμ, and most acute at 510 mμ = yellow); it cannot perceive vibrations of other wavelengths. Focusing in mammals is accomplished by change in curvature of the lens through action of the ciliary muscle, whereas in birds the lens moves to and fro as in a camera. The size of the opening or pupil in the iris diaphragm, which admits light to the interior, is changed reflexly according to the intensity of the light. Many mammals, some birds, and a few other vertebrates have **binocular vision** in that both eyes can focus on an object in part of the visual field. Such vision facilitates detecting movements in the line of sight and enables man and some animals to judge distances accurately.

10-14. Proprioceptors. There are a number of "sense organs" in muscles, tendons, connective tissues, and skeletal tissues which do not produce well-defined sensations but help coordinate the position of the limbs and are generally concerned with the so-called "kinesthetic sense." These are the **proprioceptors.** The simple act of touching a particular part of the body when the eyes are shut is learned by practice and involves unconscious memory of the exact tensions and displacements of

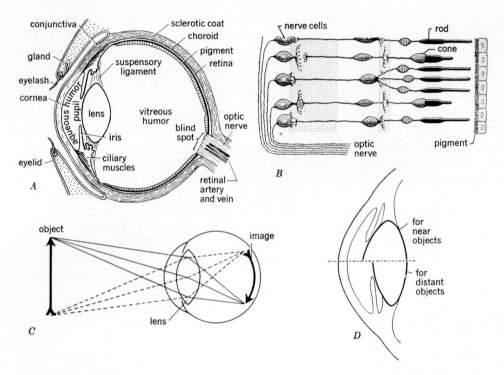

Fig. 10-11. The mechanism of sight in man. (*A*) Median vertical section of the eye. (*B*) Enlarged diagram of the structure of the retina. (*C*) Changes in shape of the lens (accommodation) to focus on near and distant objects. (*D*) Manner in which lens serves to form an image on the retina. (*A, modified from Dakin, Elements of general zoology, Oxford University Press.*)

muscles required to place the finger in the right spot. The same mechanism is involved in more complicated acts which, once learned, are carried out unconsciously, as in piano playing, skating, or typewriting. To a certain extent the proprioceptors are responsible for maintenance of posture.

C. ANIMAL BEHAVIOR

Much of animal behavior can be explained in terms of stimuli and responses as discussed in previous pages, but the subject becomes complex when dealing with higher animals and man. Physiologists, ecologists, and especially psychologists have done much to advance knowledge in this field and students of evolution recognize that the behavior of an

animal is just as characteristic as its structure and has evolved in the same way.

10-15. Types of response. Certain responses in animals can be classified readily, but many cannot, because they differ from one another in degree and not in kind. Among lower animals many are invariable, whereas in higher forms the variable responses predominate. The amoeba exhibits many fixed responses; yet it can learn in a simple way. Man's behavior is highly variable, but he has many constant and involuntary responses.

The essentially unvarying type of response by which an animal orients itself toward or away from a given stimulus is termed a ***taxis***. (The term "tropism" now is reserved for the turning movements of plants.) A fish that heads into a current so that the two sides of its body are stimulated equally by flowing water exhibits positive **rheotaxis** (Gr. *rheos,* current), and an insect that climbs directly upward in opposition to gravity is said to show **negative geotaxis** (Gr. *geos,* earth). The moth that flies directly to a light is **photo-positive** or shows positive phototaxis (Gr. *photos,* light), whereas a cockroach that scuttles for cover when spotted by a light at night is **photo-negative** (negative phototaxis). These several types of response are considered to depend upon reflexes.

10-16. Reflexes. The simplest invariable coordinated response involving a nervous system is a **reflex act** and occurs in animals with nerve cords and nerves, such as annelid worms, arthropods, and vertebrates. When the human leg is bent and suspended freely and the knee tendon is tapped, the leg jerks forward. This knee-jerk reflex is an automatic, unlearned, and involuntary response to the stimulus. The **reflex arc** (Fig. 10-12*A*) (1) involves a receptor excited by the stimulus and (2) induces a nerve impulse in the dendrite of a sensory neuron, which passes through the nerve-cell body (in the dorsal root ganglion) and along the sensory axon into the gray matter of the spinal cord. There the impulse (3) crosses a synapse, or center of correlation, to (4) a second conductor, the motor (efferent) neuron, and continues out its axon in the ventral root to (5) the end organ in contact with an effector; if the latter is a muscle, it is excited to contract. Other simple reflexes are winking of the eyelids when an object is thrust before the eyes and the sudden secretion of tears by the tear glands when a bit of dust lodges on the cornea. A reflex may or may not evoke a conscious sensation.

Few if any reflexes in vertebrates are really simple. The majority are **compound reflexes** wherein an impulse entering on one sensory neuron influences several motor neurons through intermediate or **adjustor neurons** (Fig. 10-12*B, C*); or impulses from several sensory neurons are compounded to act on one motor neuron. **Allied reflexes** are combined to produce a harmonious effect, such as the muscular movements in a person when walking or in an earthworm or caterpillar when crawling. These actions may be modified or inhibited through **association neurons** ex-

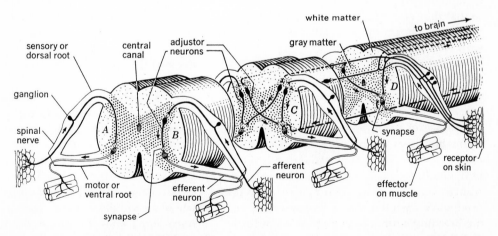

Fig. 10-12. Simplified stereogram of the vertebrate spinal cord and nerves to show relations of neurons involved in reflex arcs. *Afferent neurons,* solid; *efferent neurons,* outlined; *association neurons,* broken lines; *receptors,* as in skin; *effectors,* as on muscles. Arrows show paths of nerve impulses. Each nerve contains many fibers. (*A*) Simple reflex arc. (*B*) Reflex arc with one adjustor neuron. (*C*) Reflex arc with cross connections. (*D*) Reflex arc with cross connections and also others to and from the brain.

tending to other portions of the nerve cord and to the brain (Fig. 10-12D). *Chain reflexes* act in sequence, the response of one becoming the stimulus for the next. A frog reacts to a nearby moving insect by opening its mouth and flipping its tongue forward and back; the captured prey in the mouth stimulates receptors there to bring about closing of the mouth and to start swallowing reflexes in the pharynx and esophagus.

By training, a reflex may be conditioned to follow upon some environmental stimulus other than the original one that evoked it. In a dog the sight of food induces reflexly a flow of saliva, whereas the ringing of a bell does not. The Russian physiologist Pavlov rang a bell whenever food was offered to a dog. After some repetitions the mere sound of the bell, without food, induced salivary secretion in the animal. This Pavlov termed a *conditioned reflex.* Many human acts become conditioned reflexes, often of complex character. Repeated performance of a particular act or procedure becomes a *habit* by some more or less enduring change in the mode of response to a stimulus. Many of the routine activities of human beings are thus reduced to habits so that they are induced by particular stimuli without the intervention of conscious control, such as dressing oneself.

10-17. Instinct. An *instinct* is a complex and invariable form of behavior. Most instincts serve to maintain the individual or the species. In many kinds of animals the choice of and means of using food are instinctive acts throughout life, whereas instincts pertaining to reproduction are manifested only when the individuals become sexually mature. Among animals that live more than one year the reproductive instincts are active only during the breeding season. The migrations of birds and fishes and the manner of making nests and caring for young among insects and vertebrates are governed entirely or largely by instinct. The mud dauber wasp exemplifies a complex cycle of instincts. Each female makes a tube of mud; then just before it is sealed, she captures and paralyzes spiders with her sting, lays an egg on each, and seals them in the tube. The wasp larvae hatch and feed on the living prey, and when mature the young wasps cut their way out. The parent female never sees her offspring, but her instinctive behavior and later that of the young serve to maintain the species. In social insects such as the honeybee (par. 23-13) each caste has separate instincts that function together for the well-being of the colony.

Beyond hereditary taxes, reflexes, and instincts are the higher aspects of nervous functions by which these innate *patterns of behavior* become modified in adaptations to special needs. These grade upward to the display of *intelligence* among the higher vertebrates and man, in which the brain contains a greater number and more intricate arrangement of conduction paths and larger numbers of association neurons in the cerebral cortex.

10-18. Learning and intelligence. For a short-lived spider there is no time to learn how to spin a complicated web by trial and error. This instinctive act undoubtedly evolved by natural selection over a long period (Fig. 10-13). Higher vertebrates have a longer time to learn patterns of behavior from their parents. Mammals in particular have a more or less prolonged attachment to the mother during the period when they are being nursed.

Some types of learning that have been studied experimentally are (1) classical conditioning as in the Pavlov salivating-dog experiment; (2) instrumental learning, in which a rat or other animal, through trial and error, learns to manipulate mechanical devices to obtain food; and (3) perceptual learning, where an animal bypasses the trial-and-error stage and comes to the correct answer after analyzing the problem. A tortoise, for example, is stopped by a barrier, while a dog observes the barrier and then walks around it. *Imprinting* is a special type of learning in which a young duck, for example, follows the first moving object it sees shortly after hatch-

Fig. 10-13. Orb-weaving spider web. Young spiders spin a perfect web the first time they try. A horizontal bridge is established by letting a thread drift freely until it catches a branch or other support. A Y structure is next achieved by the spider dropping from the middle of the bridge. Then the radii are built and meet in the hub. Finally the spiral is spun, working inwards. The spider then settles in a retreat but is alerted when its prey is caught by movements of the radii or by a signal thread. Blinded spiders spin normal webs, thus vision is not important in the instinctive behavior pattern.

ing. This is usually its mother, but Konrad Lorenz, the pioneer Austrian behaviorist, successfully taught three goslings to accept him as their "mother." Imprinting may be the method by which some homing migrations are accomplished. *Intelligence* or the ability to learn is best developed among the higher vertebrates and man, in which the brain contains a greater number and more intricate arrangement of conduction paths and larger numbers of association neurons in the cerebral cortex. A discussion of the nature of consciousness, memory, and the will is beyond the scope of this text.

REVIEW

1. Define: stimulus, response, effector, proprioceptor, reflex arc, reflex act, efferent nerve pathway, dorsal root ganglion, conditioned reflex, instinct, statocyst, semicircular canal, retina.
2. Distinguish between axon and dendrite; between ganglion and nerve; between myelinated and nonmyelinated fibers.
3. State the essentials of the neuron theory.
4. What is the lowest group of animals containing a nerve cord or cords?
5. How do the nerve cords of invertebrates and vertebrates differ?
6. Name the major divisions of the vertebrate brain and the function of each.
7. What services are performed by the autonomic nervous system? Of what advantage is this system in a human being?
8. Describe the differences between taste and smell in man as to kind and degree.
9. If an older person cannot hear a frequency of 10,000 cycles per second, what structures may be involved?
10. What vitamin influences night vision? Why do many people wear glasses?
11. Trace the results from suddenly sitting down on a sharply pointed object; indicate some of the major routes from stimulus to response and the principal body structures involved.
12. How do an instinct and a conditioned reflex differ? What are examples of each in mankind?

11 Reproduction and development

comes only from preexisting life (*omne vivum ex vivo*); this is the process of **biogenesis,** or **reproduction.**

The ability to produce new living individuals is a basic characteristic of all plants and animals. Early biologists understood correctly how the higher animals reproduce, but for centuries it was believed that many forms of life arose from nonliving materials by **spontaneous generation**—worms and tadpoles from mud and flies from the carcasses of dead animals. These erroneous ideas were gradually abandoned after Francesco Redi (Italian, 1626?–1697) showed in 1668 that maggots and flies are produced from meat only if living flies have laid eggs on such material. Only a century ago it was thought that bacteria and other microorganisms could develop spontaneously. In 1861, Louis Pasteur (French, 1822–1895) proved that, when such cultures were heated enough to kill the organisms and properly stoppered to prevent reinvasion by germs or their spores from the air, they would remain without life. The principle of **sterilization** that he demonstrated is the basis for destroying microorganisms by heat or chemicals. It is used in present-day surgery and medicine, in preserving food by canning, in the keeping of *pasteur*ized milk, in safeguarding public water supplies, and in other aspects of modern life.

All reliable evidence indicates that new life

A. REPRODUCTION

11-1. Asexual reproduction. Reproduction involving only one "parent" and no special reproductive structures is termed **asexual reproduction.** It occurs in many plants and many lower animals. Protozoans such as *Paramecium* multiply by **binary fission,** in which an individual divides into two halves, usually equal, after which each grows to the original form. The nucleus divides, and then the cytoplasm. Multiple fission, or **sporulation,** occurs in the sporozoans (*Plasmodium,* etc.), where the nucleus divides repeatedly and then the cytoplasm subdivides so that a part of it surrounds each of the many daughter nuclei (Fig. 16-10). **Budding** is a type of reproduction in which a new individual arises as an outgrowth, or **bud,** on an older animal; it grows to the form and size of the latter. Budding of sponges, coelenterates, bryozoans, and tunicates results in colonies of many individuals. Fresh-water sponges also produce internal buds, or **gemmules** (Chap. 17), each of several cells, within a common dense covering. These escape, and later each gemmule produces a new individual.

Illustration at top of page: New life—emergence of a mosquito (*Culex*) from the pupal skin at surface of water. (*Photo by R. L. Usinger.*)

Fragmentation occurs in some flatworms (TURBELLARIA) and ribbon worms (NEMERTINEA), an individual breaking into two or more parts, each capable of growing to be a complete animal (Fig. 11-1).

11-2. Regeneration. The capacity to replace or *regenerate* parts lost by injury or otherwise is allied to growth after fragmentation. Young animals and species low in the evolutionary scale usually have greater regenerative powers than older or higher animals. A cutting of willow or geranium in moist soil will grow into a complete plant, and pieces of some hydroid coelenterates if put in sand under sea water will form complete animals. When a flatworm (*Euplanaria* or *Dugesia*) is cut into pieces, each will usually regenerate to form a complete but smaller individual. Starfishes and brittle stars regenerate lost arms, and sea cucumbers can regenerate all their internal organs. Appendages of crabs and other crustaceans and the tails of some salamanders and lizards may be cast off under stress, a process termed *autotomy* (Gr. *auto,* self + *toma,* to cut). Then the animal regenerates the lost part.

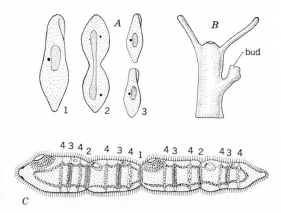

Fig. 11-1. Types of asexual reproduction. (*A*) Binary fission in *Paramecium.* (*B*) Budding in *Hydra.* (*C*) Fragmentation in a flatworm, *Microstomum;* numbers indicate the sequence of fission planes that will divide the animal into 16 parts. (*After von Graff.*)

11-3. Sexual reproduction. Most animals and plants increase by a process in which new individuals develop from sex cells from the parents. This is *sexual reproduction.* Typically two sex cells of different kind (male and female) join to produce a new individual. Protozoans have some reproductive processes resembling the sexual phenomena of higher animals. In the *conjugation* of ciliates (*Paramecium,* etc.) two individuals of apparently like kind fuse together, exchange micronuclear materials, and then separate to continue binary fission. Among sporozoans (*Plasmodium,* etc.) two kinds of individuals (macrogametes and microgametes) are produced at certain stages; these fuse permanently in pairs to continue the life cycle. In the colonial flagellate *Volvox,* the same or different colonies produce two kinds of free individuals that combine in pairs, one of each, and produce new colonies (Chap. 16).

In multicellular animals, *sex* is the total of all structural and functional characteristics that distinguish *male* (♂) and *female* (♀). Both produce free *sex cells,* or *germ cells.* Those of males are minute and known as sperm, or *spermatozoa* (Gr. *sperma,* seed + *zoon,* animal); the female releases somewhat larger *eggs,* or *ova* (sing. *ovum*). Besides the necessary differences in reproductive organs, individuals of the two sexes may differ in external or internal form, in physiology, in behavior, and, among the higher animals, even in psychological characteristics.

The germ cells are produced in organs known as *gonads,* the sperm in *testes* (sing. *testis*), or spermaries, and the ova in *ovaries.* These are the *primary sex organs.* Most animals have ducts lined with glands and other parts associated with the gonads to form a *reproductive system* that aids in the reproductive process (Fig. 11-2). Any or all of these parts are single, paired, or multiple in different animals (Chaps. 18 to 29).

If both male and female systems are in one individual, as in flatworms, barnacles, and earthworms, the animal is termed *monoecious*

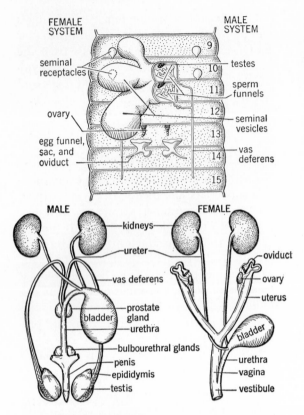

Fig. 11-2. Reproductive systems. *Above.* Earthworm (monoecious), both systems in one individual. *Below.* Cat (dioecious), male and female systems in separate individuals.

they travel through small ducts, or *vasa efferentia,* to a larger duct, or *vas deferens.* The lower end of the latter often is enlarged as a *seminal vesicle.* The vas deferens either leads directly to the exterior or through a copulatory organ, the *penis,* in species which mate for transfer of sperm directly from male to female. *Accessory glands* providing secretions to activate the sperm or for other purposes are sometimes present along the sperm duct. In mammals these are the prostate and bulbourethral glands.

The *female* reproductive system produces the ova as individual cells in the *ovary.* In some animals each ovum during its growth is surrounded by follicle cells, as in the frog. Each ovum in a mammal develops in a special *Graafian follicle* that enlarges as the egg matures and finally ruptures to release it (Fig.

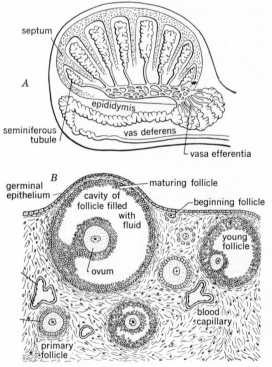

Fig. 11-3. The gonads of mammals. (*A*) Section of a testis. (*B*) Small section of an ovary, much enlarged, with several Graafian follicles.

(Gr. *monos,* one + *oecium,* house). In various other invertebrates and practically all vertebrates each individual is either male or female; the sexes are *separate,* and such animals are *dioecious* (Gr. *di,* two + *oecium*). The term *hermaphrodite* is applied to monoecious species and also to occasional abnormal individuals of dioecious species that contain both male and female systems.

11-4. Reproductive systems. There is variety in the details of the reproductive systems of different animals, but all have a basic similarity in pattern, even between the two sexes. In the *male* reproductive system the spermatozoa are produced in a series of compartments or tubules of the *testis* (Fig. 11-3). Thence

11-3*B*). The fluid of these follicles contains hormones important in reproduction (Chap. 9). The ovaries of mammals and some other animals are solid, those in a frog are sac-like, and those of insects comprise several tubular ovarioles. The ovum usually acquires its yolk while still in the ovary. Mature eggs are released from the ovary and pass down the conducting tube, or *oviduct,* being moved by the action of muscles in its walls or by cilia lining its interior. *Glands* in the wall of the oviduct may surround the egg with various materials such as the albumen (egg white) and shell in reptiles, birds, and other animals (Fig. 11-4). The lower end of the duct may be enlarged as a temporary storage reservoir for eggs before they pass out of the body. This portion of the duct is expanded as the *uterus* in the mammals and other animals that retain the eggs for development inside the body. In species that copulate, the terminal part of the female tract is specialized as the *vagina* to receive the male's penis; some have also a *seminal receptacle* for storage of the sperm received.

11-5. Origin of sex cells. There is much interest in the ultimate origin of the sex cells because they give rise to new individuals and serve to transmit hereditary characteristics between successive generations. The doctrine of germinal continuity by August Weismann (German 1834–1914) held that the sex cells,

or *germ plasm,* comprised a substance apart from external influences and from the body, or *somatoplasm.* For each new generation the parent germ plasm produces both the body (soma) and the germ plasm of new individuals. The continuity of germ plasm is clear in some invertebrates (*Ascaris, Sagitta,* etc.) where one cell in the early cleavage of the egg can be traced as the ultimate origin of the future sex cells. In birds, mammals, and others, however, no such early recognition of future germinal material is possible. Indeed, all the early ova in young mammals degenerate, and others form later from germinal epithelium (modified peritoneum) on the ovaries. We now recognize a direct continuity in the chromosomes, whereby each cell of the new animal contains the hereditary mechanism established in the egg (zygote) as it starts to develop.

In some animals the gonads appear during embryonic development but do not enlarge until the individuals approach sexual maturity. In others they form at the latter stage. Early germ cells in the gonads multiply by mitosis like somatic cells (epithelium, muscle, etc.); every chromosome divides longitudinally into strictly equivalent halves so that each daughter cell receives an identical set of chromosomes. The nucleus in each contains a dual set of chromosomes, the *diploid num-*

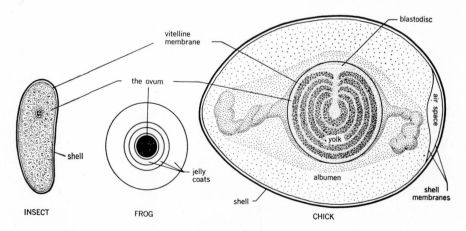

Fig. 11-4. Protective coverings of some animal eggs.

ber, $2n$ (except in some "haploid" bees, etc.). In every pair, one chromosome was derived from the male parent and the other from the female parent of the individual in question. The two members of each pair are termed **homologous chromosomes.** At the approach of sexual maturity the germ cells multiply rapidly; they are then known as **spermatogonia** in the male and as **oögonia** in the female. Before being able to participate in reproduction, however, their physical and physiological characteristics must change.

11-6. Maturation and meiosis. The process by which spermatogonia become spermatozoa and oögonia become ova is known as **gametogenesis** or **maturation,** and the resulting matured cells are called **gametes** (Figs. 11-5 to 11-8). The accompanying nuclear changes are termed **meiosis.** The gametes of male and female differ in form, size, and physiology, but the meiotic changes in their nuclei are comparable.

Meiosis consists of two nuclear divisions that follow without an interval, the *first* and *second meiotic* (maturation) *divisions.* These differ from mitosis in two important features: (1) The final number of chromosomes in a gamete is only half (the haploid number, n) of that present in a spermatogonium or oögonium (or somatic cell), and the set of chromosomes in a matured gamete includes but one member from each homologous pair that was present in the unmatured cells. (2) There is a random assortment in this reduction so that each gamete receives either *one or the other* member of each pair. Hence, when two gametes of opposite sex later join in fertilization, the chromosome number in the new individual will be that of the species ($2n$). The manner of division and segregation of the chromosomes during maturation, together with the random meeting of eggs and sperm in fertilization, affords a logical basis for many of the observed phenomena of inheritance on the premise that the chromosomes are the bearers of the determiners, or genes, for hereditary characters. The random sorting provides for variation in the combinations of characters that will appear in different individuals of the new generation (Chap. 12).

11-7. Spermatogenesis. As a male matures sexually, the spermatogonia in the testis multiply by mitosis until many are present; then maturation begins. Each spermatogonium increases in size, and is termed a **primary spermatocyte.** During the prophase of the first meiotic division, the diploid number of chromosomes ($2n$) appears in the nucleus, each chromosome being a single strand of particles (chromomeres). The 2 chromosomes of each homologous pair come to lie more or less parallel to one another, a phenomenon called **synapsis** (conjugation). Soon each chromosome divides longitudinally (or the one produces a second) to yield 2 **chromatids,** but the latter do not immediately separate. Every bundle then includes 4 components (chromatids) and is termed collectively a **tetrad** ($4n$). There is no further multiplication of chromosomes during maturation.

In each primary spermatocyte the chromosomes shorten and thicken; a spindle forms with the tetrads arranged at random on the equatorial plate. At the metaphase the paternal and maternal pairs of chromatids separate slightly; at the anaphase one pair goes to one pole of the spindle and the other pair to the opposite. From different tetrads the manner of segregation is by chance—free assortment. Some maternal and some paternal pairs of chromosomes go to one pole and those of opposite origin to the other pole. Each of the resulting 2 cells (with n chromosomes or $2n$ chromatids) is called a **secondary spermatocyte.**

Shortly a spindle forms in each secondary spermatocyte, and the chromosomes take an equatorial position, when the **second meiotic division** occurs. The 2 chromatids of each pair separate from one another as distinct chromosomes and go to opposite poles of the cell; the resulting 2 cells are called **spermatids.** A primary spermatocyte thus yields 4 spermatids, each containing n chromosomes, the haploid number. From each pair of homologous chromosomes in a primary spermatocyte, any one spermatid contains one representative, either paternal or maternal.

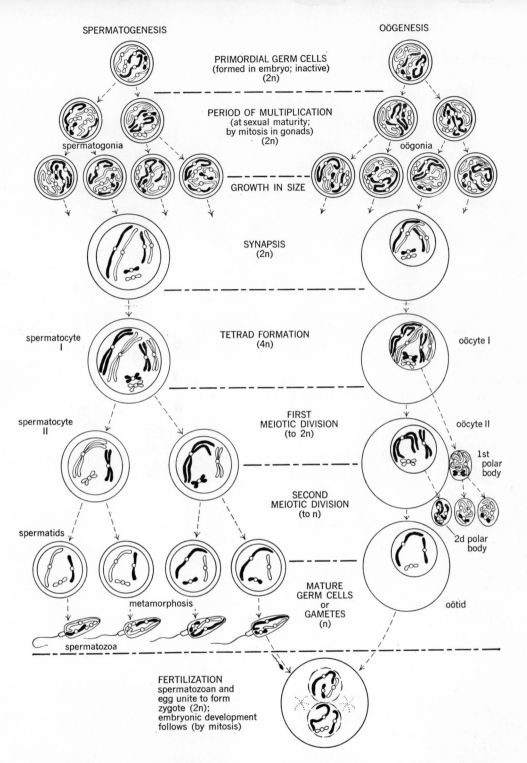

Fig. 11-5. Maturation of germ cells and fertilization; diagrammatic. The maturation process is similar in the two sexes as to nuclear divisions and chromosomes but differs as to the cytoplasm (*left,* male; *right,* female). The number of chromosomes is shown for each stage (2n, n, etc.). The species is assumed to have 6 chromosomes (diploid number); chromosomes derived from the previous generation are shown as white (maternal) and black (paternal), respectively. Compare Fig. 3-4 (mitosis) for details of phases in division.

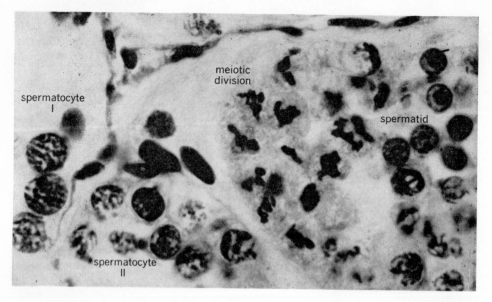

Fig. 11.6. Spermatogenesis in the testis of a salamander (*Aneides lugubris*). Stages are recognizable by the 4:2:1 ratio of volume in spermatocyte I, spermatocyte II, and spermatid.

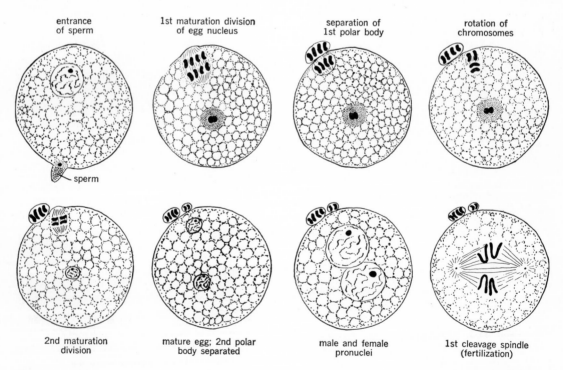

Fig. 11-7. Maturation of the ovum, sperm entrance, junction of pronuclei, and preparation for 1st cleavage in the roundworm, *Ascaris megalocephala.*

Following the second division, each spermatid undergoes a *metamorphosis.* Much of the cytoplasm is cast out, and the nucleus compacts to a small (densely staining) head. Behind the head is a midpiece containing one or two centrioles, and the posterior end of the cell becomes a slender cytoplasmic tail. This is the mature male gamete, or *spermatozoan.* Both maturation and metamorphosis are usually completed before the sperm escapes from the testis.

11-8. Oögenesis. The gonads of females produce fewer sex cells than those of males. In the ovary the oögonia become *primary oöcytes,* often enlarging with the addition of yolk. Synapsis, tetrad formation, and chromosome reduction occur as in the male; the division spindle forms near the cell margin. At the first meiotic division practically all the cytoplasm remains with one nucleus to form the *secondary oöcyte;* the other nucleus passes out on the surface of the cell as a microscopic *first polar body.* Likewise, in the second meiotic division, the cytoplasm with one nucleus forms the *oötid,* and the other nucleus is passed out as the *second polar body.* The chromosome content of an oötid results from chance assortment as with a spermatid. With slight change in nuclear position the oötid becomes a female gamete, or *ovum.* Thus each oögonium yields but one ovum; yet the nuclear divisions that produce the ovum and polar bodies are equivalent to those by which four spermatozoa are derived. In different species, meiosis either occurs in the ovary, or after the egg is set free, or requires that a sperm must penetrate the egg cytoplasm before it will be completed.

11-9. Gametes. The gametes of various animals differ in form and size, and those of the two sexes in any one species are quite unlike (Fig. 11-8). The ovum (any covering or shell being disregarded) is spherical or oval and nonmotile and may contain yolk to nourish the newly developing individual. Spermatozoa are small, motile, and able to swim in fluid. While usually thread-like, some are amoeboid and others of peculiar shapes. Their size is usually microscopic. Those of man are 52 to 62 μ long. The sperm cell is but a fraction of the egg in volume; with human gametes the ratio is about 1 to 195,000. Enough human ova to provide the present world population of 3 billion people could be put in a top hat and the sperm to fertilize them in a thimble!

11-10. Fertilization. The union of a mature spermatozoan and an ovum is known as *fertilization,* and the resulting cell is a *zygote.* The joining of two haploid (n) nuclei yields a zygote with the diploid number ($2n$) of the species. Fertilization involves the physical entry of the sperm and also physiological processes in both egg and sperm. A sperm cannot

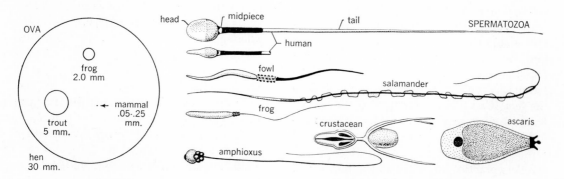

Fig. 11-8. The gametes of several animals. Size of ova in millimeters. Spermatozoa, greatly enlarged, but not to same scale. *(Mostly after Retzius.)*

effect the fertilization of an unmatured egg. Fertilization is an irreversible process and is usually species-specific; only in exceptional cases will "foreign" sperm fertilize an egg. Fertilization stimulates the egg to active cleavage and development and also provides for combining of hereditary characteristics from male and female parents. In different species, sperm penetrate the egg at various stages during maturation (from oögonium to oötid), but fusion of the egg and sperm nuclei occurs only after maturation in the egg is completed. Experimental evidence suggests that the outer (cortical) portion of the egg secretes a substance, *fertilizin*, to which the sperm react in effecting fertilization. On some eggs a *fertilization membrane* forms after entrance of one sperm and excludes others; the egg cytoplasm then separates slightly from its cell membrane.

A few monoecious or hermaphroditic animals may be self-fertilizing; but *cross-fertilization*, the combining of gametes from two different individuals, is the general rule. A monoecious animal commonly produces its eggs and sperm at different times; if formed simultaneously, they are usually self-sterile.

In *external fertilization* (1) the eggs and sperm are shed freely into open water (many invertebrates, some marine fishes); (2) the male and female are close together when eggs and sperm are extruded (lampreys, trout); or (3) there is simultaneous extrusion of eggs and sperm by clasped pairs (frogs and toads). In *internal fertilization* (4) the male places sperm packets (spermatophores) on the bottom of a pond or stream and these are taken into the seminal receptacle of the female (aquatic salamanders); or (5) by definite copulation sperm are transferred by the male into the female's vagina, later to fertilize eggs in her reproductive tract (nematodes, some mollusks, most of the arthropods, some fishes, all reptiles, birds, and mammals). Many water dwellers practice internal fertilization, and it is necessary for all terrestrial species because sperm can travel only in a fluid medium. In vertebrates having internal fertilization, the sperm travel up the oviduct where the eggs are usually fertilized. Artificial insemination is now a common practice with dairy cattle, seminal fluid from a bull being placed in the vagina of a cow to initiate pregnancy. About 7,700,000 cows are so inseminated yearly in the United States. The same practice, under medical supervision, has limited use in human beings when a husband is sterile.

11-11. Special types of sexual reproduction. Development of an egg without the entrance of a sperm is known as *parthenogenesis* (Gr. *parthenos*, virgin + *genesis*, origin). It occurs regularly in rotifers, aphids and thrips, some beetles, many ants, bees and wasps, and some crustaceans; males are unknown in some thrips and rotifers. Aphids have successive generations of parthenogenetic females during the spring and summer; then both sexes are produced by parthenogenesis. These mate in ordinary sexual reproduction, and the females lay fertilized eggs from which females hatch the next spring to continue parthenogenesis. The queen honeybee produces fertilized eggs (with sperm from her seminal receptacle) that develop into females, either workers or queens; but she also lays unfertilized eggs that yield haploid (n) males or drones (Figs. 23-14, 23-10).

Larvae of the gallfly (*Miastor*) produce eggs that develop parthenogenetically to yield other larvae. In liver flukes one larval stage, the sporocyst, produces unfertilized eggs that give rise to another known as the redia. Such parthenogenesis among larvae is termed *paedogenesis*. The larvae of some salamanders (Ambystomidae) may become sexually mature, mate, and produce fertile eggs, a phenomenon called *neoteny*.

Mature eggs of some sea urchins, frogs, and other animals that normally are fertilized may be induced to develop by *artificial parthenogenesis* as demonstrated by Jacques Loeb in 1900. The stimuli employed included shaking, heat, dilute organic acids, and hypertonic solutions (water with greater than normal concentrations of salts). By pricking thousands of frog eggs with needles, Loeb induced development in many eggs, obtained over 200 tadpoles, and reared nearly 100 frogs of both sexes through or beyond metamorphosis. The frogs were diploid as to chromosome number. One "fatherless" rabbit has resulted from artificial stimulation of an egg later implanted in the uterus of a female. The means for inducing artificial parthenogenesis are diverse, but all successful methods achieve the same result—activation of the egg. *Polyembryony* is the production of two or more individuals from one egg by separation of the cells in early stages of cleavage, as occurs in cases of identical twins in man and also in some armadillos and many parasitic wasps.

11-12. Reproduction in general. Most species have definite *reproductive seasons.* In temperate and cold regions these are usually in spring or summer when food is abundant and other conditions for survival of the offspring are favorable. Many invertebrates do not reproduce until the environmental temperature reaches a certain minimum. Other species are influenced by the kind of food available. With some birds and mammals the increasing length of daylight acts on the gonads through the pituitary gland to induce breeding.

Most animals are *oviparous;* the females release or lay eggs from which the young later hatch out. Many aquatic invertebrates, most insects, and all birds are of this sort. Other animals give birth to living young. Some of them are *ovoviviparous,* producing eggs with much yolk that develop within the oviducts ("uterus") of the female. Certain insects, sharks, and lizards, and the garter snakes and rattlesnakes are examples. The mammals and occasional other animals are *viviparous,* producing small eggs that are retained and nourished in the female's uterus.

The *number of eggs* produced by each female is inversely proportional to the average chance for survival of any one offspring to complete maturity. The number is largest where the hazards are greatest. Some parasites produce millions of eggs, the codfish up to 6,000,000, a brook trout up to 5,600, a quail averages 14, a robin 3 to 5, a deer or sheep 2 or 1, and the horse only 1. Some species produce several batches of eggs or broods of young in a single season or year. The *rate of development* until hatching is rather constant in birds and mammals, but with other animals it varies according to the environmental temperature or other conditions. The approximate time required is characteristic for each species, ranging from a few hours or days for some invertebrates to many months for the largest mammals.

Animals often have special *breeding habits* that make for greater success in reproduction. These include the courting performances of many vertebrates that ensure successful matings, the use of nests to provide protection for eggs, and the parental care of eggs and young. The eggs are carried on the body or in brood pouches by the females of some crustaceans, insects, and spiders and by either the male or female among certain fishes and amphibians. Birds sit on and incubate their eggs, and thus heat from the parent's body causes the eggs to develop at a uniform rate. In mammals the development of the young within the mother's uterus achieves a similar result. Young of some ants, bees, and wasps are provided with food in the nest, the termites and social bees feed and tend the young in their colonial nests, the nestlings of birds are fed with food gathered by the parents, and young mammals are nourished by milk secreted from the mammary glands of their mothers.

11-13. Sex ratio. The numerical relation between the sexes in a species is the *sex ratio.* Theoretically there should be equal numbers of male- and female-producing gametes; actually there is a differential in production of the two kinds of gametes or in mortality among embryos or later stages. The sex ratio is usually stated as numbers of males per 100 females. In mankind the primary ratio is high, but males experience greater mortality, both prenatal and postnatal. Some well-known ratios after birth are: mankind, 103 to 107:100; horse, 98.3; cattle, 107.3; dog, 118.5; house mouse, 100 to 118; chicken, 93.4 to 94.7. The ratio varies with race or breed, season, and other factors.

B. DEVELOPMENT

The starting point for the production of a new individual by sexual reproduction is the activated egg, or *zygote.* Repeated mitotic divisions result in many cells that differentiate to form the tissues and organs of the developing individual, or *embryo.* The science that deals with this subject is *embryology.* The following account outlines early development of the frog (Figs. 2-16, 11-10), with mention of some features of that in birds and mammals (Fig. 11-9).

11-14. Blastula. Soon after an egg is fertilized, the single-celled zygote becomes two cells, the two divide into four, and so on. This process of *cleavage* partitions the egg substance into an increasing number of smaller cells or *blastomeres,* each with an equal number of chromosomes. As cleavage continues, the cells become arranged in the form of a hollow ball, or *blastula,* within which a *blastocoel* (segmentation cavity) appears. Two major regions are evident, an upper *animal hemisphere* or pole of small, dark cells with little yolk and an opposite *vegetal hemisphere* below of larger, pale-colored cells rich in yolk

granules. Between them is a *germ ring* or *marginal zone* of medium-sized cells.

11-15. Gastrula. Cleavage is followed by the complex process of *gastrulation.* Cells of the vegetal and marginal regions gradually move inward and are overgrown by those of the animal hemisphere. A double-walled cup results, as might be produced by pushing in one side of a hollow rubber ball. This is termed a *gastrula.* The blastocoel is gradually obliterated, and the cavity resulting from gastrulation is the primitive gut, or *gastrocoel* (archenteron). The external opening of the gastrocoel is called the *blastopore.*

Gastrulation involves three related activities (Fig. 11-10E): (1) the yolk-laden endoderm cells of the vegetal hemisphere push or cup inward (invagination); (2) the germ ring, especially the dorsal lip of the blastopore, is inturned (involution); and (3) the ectoderm grows downward, eventually to cover the cells of the vegetal hemisphere (epiboly, or overgrowth).

When complete, the gastrula consists of (1) an outer layer of *ectoderm,* from cells of the animal hemisphere; (2) an inner layer of *endoderm* (entoderm), from cells of the vegetal hemisphere; and between these (3) a third layer of *mesoderm,* derived from the marginal zone. These are the *germ layers* from which various tissues and organs will form. The ectoderm will produce the external covering of the body, the nervous system, and the sense organs; the endoderm provides the lining of

Fig. 11-9. Sample stages of cleavage and gastrulation in eggs of chordates. (*A*) Amphioxus, cleavage holoblastic, little yolk; egg diameter 0.1 mm. *(After Hatschek.)* (*B*) Frog, modified holoblastic cleavage, much yolk; diameter 2 mm. *(Various sources.)* (*C*) Bird, meroblastic discoidal cleavage in small blastodisc on large yolk mass; diameter 30 mm. *(After Blount; and Patten, Early embryology of the chick, The Blakiston Co.)* (*D*) Mammal, cleavage holoblastic, practically no yolk; an outer and inner cell mass formed in blastula (6); gastrula formed by migration of endoderm cells from inner cell mass (7); egg surrounded during early cleavage by zona pellucida (from Graafian follicle of ovary), which later disappears. *(After Gregory; and Patten, Embryology of the pig, The Blakiston Co.)*

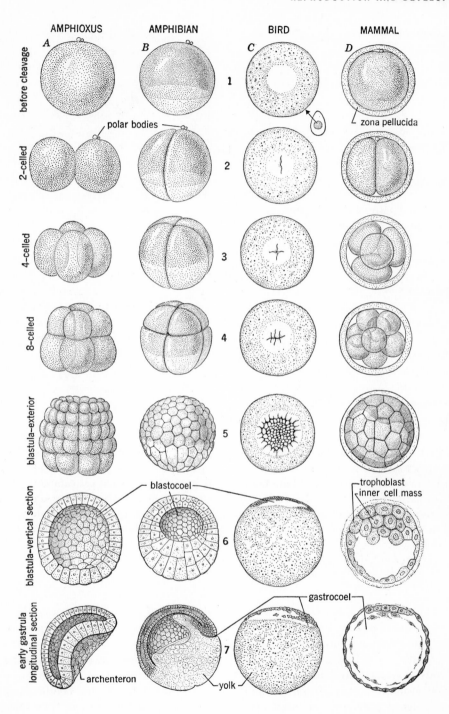

AMPHIOXUS   AMPHIBIAN   BIRD   MAMMAL

before cleavage

A   *B*   *C*   *D*   1

zona pellucida

polar bodies

2-celled   2

4-celled   3

8-celled   4

blastula—exterior   5

blastocoel   trophoblast
inner cell mass

blastula—vertical section   6

early gastrula longitudinal section   gastrocoel   7

archenteron   yolk

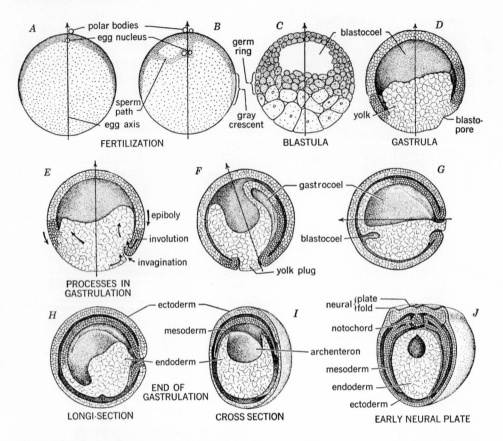

Fig. 11-10. Early embryology of the frog. Long arrow indicates egg axis. (*A*) Sperm at surface of egg. (*B*) Entrance path of sperm (in plane of paper) bisects gray crescent and determines plane of first cleavage. (*C*) Late blastula. (*D*) Blastopore formed, gastrulation begins. (*E*) Processes in gastrulation. (*F, G*) Gastrulation continues, rotation of egg on axis, anteroposterior and dorsoventral relations established. (*H, I*) Gastrula completed. (*J*) Beginning of organ systems. (*D–H*) Longi-sections; (*I, J*) Cross sections. (Compare Figs. 11-9, 11-11, 2-16.) (*A–C, E–G redrawn by permission from Curtis and Guthrie, Textbook of general zoology, John Wiley & Sons, Inc.; D, H–J, redrawn from Spemann, Embryonic development and induction, Yale University Press.*)

the digestive tract, its glands, and associated structures; and the mesoderm gives rise to the supportive tissues, muscles, lining of the body cavity, and many of the internal organs.

11-16. Body symmetry and axes. An *egg axis* may be visualized through the animal and vegetal poles. A *gray crescent* forms usually on a meridian 180 degrees from the point of sperm entrance and is bisected by the first cleavage plane. The latter then proves to be the future median plane of the embryo; hence

the path of sperm entrance establishes bilateral symmetry. The dorsal lip of the blastopore, where endoderm and marginal zone meet, grows over the cells of the vegetal hemisphere as gastrulation proceeds; when all the endoderm is inside, the original egg axis has rotated about 90 degrees. The former lower end of the axis is then at the completed blastopore, marking the posterior end of the future animal, so that the longitudinal body axis is indicated. The plate of mesoderm cells inturned at the upper lip of the blastopore indicates the dorsal region; and shortly after gastrulation the paired neural folds on the surface, forward from the blastopore, provide an external indication of the dorsal surface.

11-17. The embryo. After gastrulation the *differentiation* of the embryo begins. From the three germ layers there are outpocketings, inpocketings, thickenings, divisions, and other modifications that lead to the establishment of the organs and the organ systems (Fig. 11-11).

The nervous system starts dorsally as a pair of *neural folds.* The ectoderm between these sinks down, and the folds come together to form a *neural tube* (canal), which is enlarged at the anterior end to become the *brain.* On either side, between the neural tube and ectoderm, a line of cells forms as the *neural crests* to produce the dorsal or sensory roots of spinal nerves that grow into the cord. Motor roots later grow out ventrally from the cord. The early brain is of three primary vesicles, the *fore-, mid-,* and *hindbrain.* The forebrain produces the cerebral hemispheres and diencephalon, and from the hindbrain the cerebellum and medulla oblongata are derived. A rounded *optic vesicle* grows laterally on either side of the forebrain; as each meets the ectoderm on the side of the head region, the latter is stimulated to form a thickened *lens vesicle* that subsequently produces the lens of the eye. Meanwhile, the outer surface of each optic vesicle becomes concave by invagination and forms the *retina.*

The endoderm of the primitive gastrocoel becomes the inner lining of the *digestive tract.* Anteriorly, at the future pharynx, three outpocketings of the tract on either side meet three corresponding inpocketings from the side of the neck; these break through to form the *gill slits.* A single ventral outpocket, behind the pharynx, forms the *liver bud,* later to yield the liver and bile duct. An inpocketing of ectoderm (stomodeum) forms ventrally on the head region and a similar one (proctodeum) at the posterior end. In later embryonic life these break through to join the endoderm of the digestive tract, the stomodeum becoming the *mouth cavity* and the proctodeum becoming the anal canal, both lined by ectoderm. During larval life a ventral outpocket of the pharynx grows posteriorly, with two lobes, and gives rise to the *larynx, trachea,* and *lungs.*

During gastrulation mesoderm forms between the ectoderm and endoderm. Cells in its middorsal part become arranged as a solid rod, the *notochord,* between the nerve tube and primitive gut, to serve as a supporting body axis. Mesoderm at either side of the notochord grows down as a curved plate between the ectoderm and endoderm, and the two meet ventrally under the yolk mass. The thin lower part (hypomere) of each plate splits into two layers. The outer is applied to the ectoderm and becomes the *parietal peritoneum,* the inner surrounds the gut (and other organs later) to make the *visceral peritoneum* (and smooth muscle of the gut), and the space between the layers is the body cavity or *coelom.* The uppermost mesoderm (epimere) at either side of the nerve tube and notochord forms a lengthwise series of segmental blocks or *somites.* Each somite differentiates into three parts: a thin outer part (dermatome) becomes the *dermis* of the skin, a thick inner part (myotome) later gives rise to the *voluntary muscles,* and nearest the notochord a scattering of cells (sclerotome) grow about the nerve tube and noto-

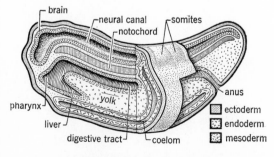

Fig. 11-11. Stereogram of early frog embryo cut away to show beginnings of organ systems.

chord to form the *vertebrae* (axial skeleton), first of cartilage but later replaced by bone. Between the ventral plates and the somites a third portion (mesomere) is the forerunner of the *excretory system* and parts of the reproductive system.

Further details of embryonic development are too many to follow here. After some days (depending on the species of frog and the water temperature) the embryo escapes from its gelatinous covering to hatch as a tadpole, or *larva.* Shortly it begins to feed and grow. Development continues for some months, and then a *metamorphosis* occurs by which the larva transforms into a frog (Fig. 2-16).

The orderly development from a single-celled zygote to a fully integrated and coordinated whole animal is a remarkable phenomenon of life. Growth occurs by increase in numbers of cells but size and form are determined by differential growth of body parts and all developmental processes depend on precise timing which is largely under hormonal control (par. 11-21).

11-18. Development of the bird and mammal. Eggs of birds, reptiles, and many fishes contain so much yolk that cleavage of the entire mass is impossible. The process begins in a small area of protoplasm, or *blastodisc,* at the animal pole. By superficial (meroblastic) cleavage a plate of cells is formed that corresponds to the spherical blastula of a frog (Fig. 11-9C). The subsequent development of the bird embryo has much in common with that of the frog, as to the way in which organs become established. Gill pouches and gill slits appear in the first few days but soon close. The endoderm and mesoderm on all sides spread around the yolk to form a *yolk sac* that is enclosed by the ventral body wall just before hatching. A calcareous *egg tooth* then forms on the tip of the beak, by which the embryonic bird cracks the shell and hatches out as a chick.

Eggs of all the higher or placental mammals are minute, practically yolkless, and retained within the female's body for development. The entire egg divides (Fig. 11-9D), and a yolk sac is formed. After the gastrula stage, the development of a mammalian embryo resembles that of the bird during its earlier stages; gill pouches and slits appear but soon close.

11-19. Embryonic membranes (Fig. 11-12). The embryos of reptiles, birds, and mammals have a series of *embryonic membranes* that protect against desiccation and shock and serve in respiration, excretion, and other necessary functions during embryonic life. These are the *amnion, chorion, yolk sac,* and *allantois;* each is composed of two layers of embryonic tissue. The amnion forms a closed sac about the embryo and is filled with a watery

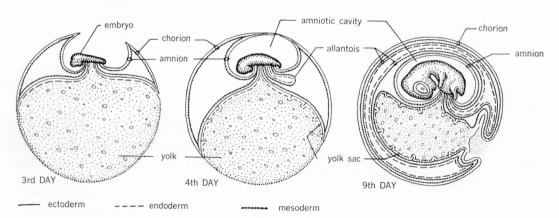

Fig. 11-12. Three stages in development of the embryonic membranes of the chick; diagrammatic longitudinal sections; shell, shell membranes, and albumen omitted (compare Figs. 11-4, 11-13).

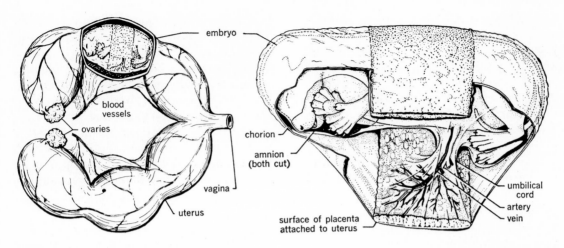

Fig. 11-13. *Left.* Entire reproductive tract of female cat; uterus cut open to show the position of one embryo. *Right.* Cat embryo with zonary placenta cut and part of embryonic membranes removed to show relations of umbilical cord, blood vessels, and membranes.

amniotic fluid to keep the embryo moist and protect it against shock or adhesion. The chorion surrounds the amnion. The yolk sac in reptiles and birds gradually incorporates the yolk into the digestive tract for nourishing the embryo. The allantois pushes out from the hind-gut to lie against the chorion and shell membranes. Blood vessels then grow out on its surface to serve as an embryonic respiratory and excretory organ. All these membranes are ruptured and discarded when the young hatch.

11-20. Placenta and umbilical cord. The minute mammalian egg passes down the oviduct to lie on the inner surface of the maternal uterus. An amnion soon forms and fills with fluid. The chorion and allantois grow out and make contact with the uterus, whereby embryonic blood vessels on the allantois are brought close to maternal blood vessels in the uterine wall. Processes, or *villi,* of the chorion become embedded in depressions of the uterine surface, and the resulting joint embryonic-maternal structure is called the *placenta* (Fig. 11-13). Nutrients and oxygen then pass from maternal blood vessels through several intervening cell layers to the blood of the embryo, and carbon dioxide and excretory wastes

move in the opposite direction; but there is no direct connection between maternal and embryonic circulations. The degree of intimacy between maternal and embryonic structures and the form of placenta vary in different mammals. The human placenta is complex; some lining tissues of the uterus disappear, and embryonic blood vessels on the chorionic villi are bathed in maternal blood (Fig. 29-4). A developing embryo that has acquired characteristic mammalian form is called a *fetus.* From the ventral surface of its abdomen a soft, flexible *umbilical cord* extends, conveying the two arteries and a vein that connect to embryonic capillaries in the placenta. When the fetus has completed its growth, *birth* (parturition) occurs. The maternal vagina dilates, and slow rhythmic contractions of the uterus gradually force the fetus to the exterior. The amnion is either ruptured in this process or is quickly torn by the mother, so that the newborn young may breathe air, and shortly the umbilical cord is severed. The embryonic part of the placenta either passes out with the fetus or descends later, as the "afterbirth," and is usually eaten by the parent in wild mammals.

11-21. Control of development. Hormones

(Chap. 9) regulate the sequence and timing of many events in development. They cause young adults to become sexually mature, stimulate the production of gametes, and induce sexual mating behavior. This is best understood in vertebrates, especially mammals, where hormones from the anterior pituitary and the reproductive organs have major roles.

Historically there are two contrasted theories to explain development. The *preformation theory* espoused by Harvey, Malpighi, and other early embryologists assumed that either egg or sperm contained a "germ," completely preformed but invisible, that expanded to visible size and form during development. The contrasted *theory of epigenesis* held that an egg lacks internal organization and that an outside force is responsible for development. Modern embryological research has shown that the egg cytoplasm has some preformed elements and that both external and internal forces act during development.

11-22. Organization. Eggs of various species differ in degree of organization before and after fertilization. In those of some jellyfishes the individual blastomeres may be separated, up to the 16-cell stage, when each will produce a complete but smaller embryo; eggs of amphioxus will do likewise in the 2-cell stage; and if the blastomeres of the 2-cell stage in a salamander are carefully separated, two complete embryos may result. In such "indeterminate cleavage" the undisturbed blastomeres combine to form a single embryo, but if parted each can produce a separate and complete individual. By contrast, separation of blastomeres or cell groups during cleavage in eggs of some mollusks (*Dentalium*) and tunicates (*Styela*) results in each producing only that part of the embryo which it would form in an undisturbed egg. This "determinate cleavage" indicates organization within the egg prior to cleavage.

One part may influence another, as is shown in eggs of amphioxus or of amphibians that are only partly separated in the 2-cell stage and yield ≻-shaped embryos with two anterior ends.

Evidence of subsequent organization in the egg and of the time or stage in which it occurs has been derived for amphibians by special (vital) staining and also by transplanting small areas of the embryo. An elaborate "presumptive organization" has been shown in the late blastula and early gastrula, and the several processes earlier described (par. 11-17) in gastrulation are confirmed. Between the 2-cell stage (when each blastomere may produce a separate embryo) and the end of gastrulation, materials for each of the principal regions of the early embryo have become differentiated (Fig. 11-14).

The dorsal lip of the blastopore is a region of strong influence in determining subsequent embryonic growth. If at the beginning of gastrulation a piece of presumptive epidermis is planted on the dorsal lip, it will be carried in and contribute to the production of muscle segments, gut wall, or other organs depending upon where it arrives; in any case, it contributes to either mesoderm or endoderm derivatives and not to ectoderm. Presumptive

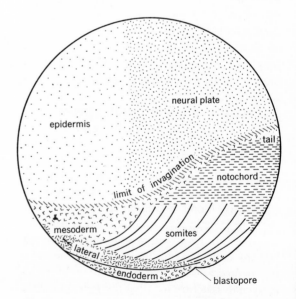

Fig. 11-14. Localization of formative areas on the egg of a salamander, *Triturus,* at the start of gastrulation. Epidermis and neural plate will derive from ectoderm; lateral plate, somites, and notochord from mesoderm. (*Modified from Vogt.*)

mesoderm transplanted into the ectoderm of a gastrula will become epidermis (ectoderm). Later, however, if part of the dorsal lip is transplanted to the ectoderm, it will induce the formation there of a secondary embryo on the host embryo (Fig. 11-15). The notochord and other dorsal-lip derivatives come from the transplant, but the nervous tissue arises from the local host ectoderm that otherwise would have become epidermis.

Evidence of time sequence in organization has been obtained by exchanging transplants of presumptive epidermis and neural plate (both ectodermal) between embryos of two salamanders having eggs of different color. Dark presumptive epidermis from *Triturus taeniatus* transplanted to the neural-plate region of the light-colored *T. cristatus* becomes neural plate if moved during the early gastrula stage but continues as dark epidermis, even in the brain, if transplanted in the late gastrula. In the early transplant the region determined the nature of the subsequent differentiation, whereas in the later one the material that was transplanted was already "determined" as to the kind of tissue it was to

produce. Determination of the fate of tissues in embryonic development was ascribed to "organizers" by Hans Spemann (German, 1869–1941). An example of the presence of organizers in later stages is to be seen in the development of the lens for an eye only in the presence of an optic vesicle. If the vesicle is removed, no lens develops; and if the vesicle is transplanted from the head to elsewhere in the body, a lens may develop wherever an optic vesicle touches ectoderm.

REVIEW

1. Is there modern evidence regarding spontaneous generation?
2. What are some types of asexual reproduction? Should parthenogenesis be included in this category, and why?
3. How do eggs and sperm differ in structure and function?
4. Define: gonad, ovary, monoecious, seminal receptacle, Graafian follicle, germ plasm, homologous chromosomes.
5. Distinguish between mitosis and meiosis. What is the purpose of each?
6. What are the stages in maturation of a male sex cell? How does maturation differ in a female cell?
7. What does fertilization accomplish as to development? As to chromosome number in the resulting new individual?
8. Why do many animals have a restricted "breeding season"?
9. What is accomplished by gastrulation? What are the structural features of a gastrula? How does this stage differ as between a frog and a bird?
10. From what germ layers are the following adult structures in a vertebrate derived: lining of stomach; cerebral hemispheres; lining of body cavity; mouth cavity?
11. What are embryonic membranes? In what vertebrates do they develop? What purposes do they serve?
12. How does a developing human being derive food and oxygen before birth? What structural features of mother and embryo are involved?
13. What is meant by "organization" in an egg before or after development begins?

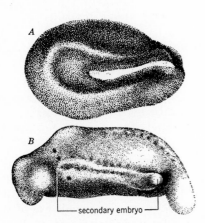

Fig. 11-15. Effect of an organizer. (*A*) Neural fold stage of a newt (*Triturus taeniatus*) with secondary neural plate—the white stripe—induced by transplanted organizer from another species (*T. cristatus*). (*B*) Side view of early embryo (*T. taeniatus*) with secondary neural tube and somites. (*After Spemann and Mangold*, 1924.)

12
Heredity and genetics

"Like tends to beget like," in animals and plants—the young of dogs are always puppies and those of cats always kittens, never puppies. Yet offspring usually differ among themselves and from their parents in varying degree. Two purebred collies will produce pups that grow to resemble their parents closely, whereas the chance mating of two mongrel dogs often yields a litter of varied types. The ancient Greeks knew that blue-eyed parents have blue-eyed children, that baldness and squint eyes follow in successive generations, and that certain eye defects run in particular families. This passage of characters from one generation to another is called *inheritance* or *heredity.*

Heredity is resemblance based upon descent, the occurrence in living organisms of qualities, either expressed or hidden, that are derived from their ancestors. It involves physical and physiological characteristics, instincts, and even psychological features in higher animals and man. Differences among individuals of a species are called *variations.* These are of two types: *somatic* or *environmentally-induced variations* due to differences in food, temperature, or other external factors; and *germinal variations* induced by differences in heredity that appear in certain offspring without reference to the environment. The science

of *genetics* seeks to account for the resemblances and differences due to heredity, their source, and their development.

Genetics aids agriculture by improving the form, yield, resistance to disease, and other features of domesticated animals and cultivated plants. Some knowledge of human heredity has been obtained and a part of this has practical applications. Genetics has helped the study of evolution, of embryology, and of other sciences. It has a cultural value in dispelling many faulty beliefs regarding inheritance.

Little of value was learned about heredity until the eighteenth century, when knowledge developed about sexuality in plants and plant hybridization. Kölreuter (German, 1733–1806) and others produced various fertile hybrids by artificial pollination and described the characters of both parent and hybrid plants. But they had no clear understanding of the hereditary process.

12-1. Mendel. The person who first made decisive experiments in heredity and who formulated the basic laws of genetics was Gregor Johann Mendel (1822–1884), a monk in the Augustinian monastery at Brünn, Austria (Fig. 1-8). He recognized heredity as of major importance for understanding organic evolution. He saw clearly that all earlier hybridizers had failed to discover any general laws of

Illustration at top of page: An important research material of genetics. Culture bottles with fruit flies (*Drosophila*).

inheritance because they had not traced individual characters through successive generations nor kept complete numerical records of their results. Mendel therefore planned careful experiments to overcome these difficulties. He chose the garden pea (*Pisum*) for study and spent two years in selecting races with distinctive and contrasted characters and in making certain that each original stock was pure. During the next six years he made many crosses, by artificial pollination, and carried each through three or more generations. Mendel kept count of all plants and seeds of each kind produced, analyzed the results, and from them deduced the two most important fundamental laws of heredity. His report (44 pages) of 1866 in an obscure periodical was brought to worldwide attention only in 1900 by three other investigators who independently had then reached similar conclusions.

Discovery of Mendel's findings gave great impetus to the study of heredity, and an enormous amount of careful work has since been done by many geneticists working with various plants and animals. Of especial value has been use of the fruit fly, or pomace fly, *Drosophila melanogaster*, by W. E. Castle, T. H. Morgan, and others. This small insect (Fig. 12-1) is reared easily in bottles provided with food, or "culture medium," for the larvae; a pair will produce 200 or more offspring, with successive generations every 10 to 14 days. Such abundant material made it possible to investigate problems requiring many individuals and generations and to apply mathematical analysis to the results.

12-2. Monohybrid cross. This is a cross in which the parents differ in one pair of alternative characters. When a true-breeding black guinea pig and a white individual are mated there is no blending of the characters (Fig. 12-3). The (hybrid) individuals of the next (F$_1$)[1] generation are not gray as one might ex-

[1] The parental generation is designated as P, the first generation of offspring as the F$_1$ (first filial), the second as the F$_2$, and so on.

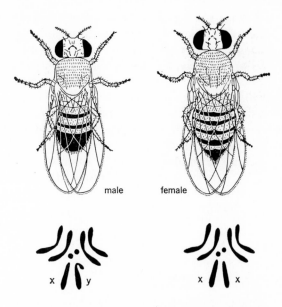

Fig. 12-1. The fruit fly, *Drosophila melanogaster*, used for studies in genetics. Much enlarged. Diploid sets of chromosomes shown, with sex chromosomes marked (XY, XX). Male fly smaller, with abdomen marked by 3 black bands, the last extending beneath the rounded posterior end. Female larger, abdomen swollen but pointed, with 5 black bands not joined ventrally.

pect from a mixture of black and white. Instead they are black, no matter which parent is black and which is white. These black hybrids, when crossed among themselves, yield in the following (F$_2$) generation a population of which, *on the average,* three-fourths are black, like the black grandparent, and one-fourth are white, like the white grandparent. The character of white coat disappears in the F$_1$ and reappears unchanged in the F$_2$. If the F$_2$ white animals are then crossed among themselves, only white individuals result (F$_3$), whereas among the black F$_2$ animals some (⅓) produce only blacks and the others (⅔) produce both blacks and whites, as in the F$_2$ generation. Thus, as Mendel said, when two contrasting characters are brought together in a cross, one is **dominant** (expressed or evident) in the next (F$_1$) generation, and the other is *recessive* (latent, or receding from view). In the following (F₂) generation these two characters are *segregated,* in an average 3 to 1 ratio. We may, therefore, state in modern terms *Mendel's first law: The factors for a pair of characters are segregated.* The factors responsible for a pair of alternative or contrasted characters, such as Mendel studied, are now termed *alleles* (allelomorphs).

Some examples of simple (monohybrid) characteristics in domestic animals are as follows (recessives in parentheses):

Horses: trotting (pacing)
Dogs: stumpy tail (normal tail)
Cats: tabby (black or blue); short-hair (long-hair or Angora)
Sheep: white fleece (black)

12-3. Mechanism of heredity. Mendel was the first to differentiate between the actual visible character and that "something" which caused its production. Obviously the character cannot be present in the germ cells that join in fertilization to produce a new individual, but something representing it and responsible for its production is there. This is now called the *gene* or *factor* for the character. A gene is the unit of inheritance that is transmitted in a gamete and controls the development of a character, by interaction with the other genes, the cytoplasm, and the environment.

Since the gametes are the only materials that pass onward from parents to form new individuals of the next generation, the mechanism of heredity must be sought in them. It will be recalled (Chap. 11) that (1) in meiosis each cell destined to become a gamete receives, by random sorting, either one or the other member of each pair of homologous chromosomes; (2) at fertilization there is a random meeting of an egg and a sperm; (3) the chromosomes of the egg nucleus and sperm nucleus join as a zygote; and (4) during embryonic growth and later, each cell in the new individual receives by mitosis an equal and like number of chromosomes derived from the zygote.

Since inheritance in sexual reproduction involves the transmission of characteristics from both of the parents by the gametes, the chromosomes are considered to be the means by which this occurs. Certain experiments have shown that (1) an egg deprived of its nucleus and then "fertilized" by a sperm produces an individual with only paternal characteristics; (2) mature eggs caused to develop by artificial parthenogenesis result in animals with only maternal characteristics; and (3) some cytoplasm may be removed from certain eggs and yet if the egg nucleus is fertilized by a sperm the resulting individual contains characteristics of both parents. Thus (with rare exceptions) hereditary transmission of characteristics is dependent upon the nucleus rather than the cytoplasm.

The modern *chromosome theory of heredity* assumes that genes are ultramicroscopic units contained in the chromosomes. Their physical and chemical nature is largely unknown. In the giant salivary gland chromosomes of *Drosophila* (Fig. 12-19), many crossbands can be seen, which possibly are the location (loci) of the genes. Some indirect evidence on the presence and arrangement of genes in chromosomes is discussed later in this chapter (see Linkage, par. 12-14).

12-4. Explanation of the Mendelian ratio. Hybrid individuals result from combining two gametes of different heredity, and a process of segregation must take place in the germ cells of such hybrids to account for the sorting out of genes to produce characters in the F₂ generation. Mendel realized this but knew nothing of the actual mechanism. The reduction divisions during maturation, and the random union of egg and sperm, both discovered since his time, explain this segregation.

If we represent the dominant gene for black (or pigmented) coat in guinea pigs by P and the recessive gene for white by p, then the genetic formulas for the parents (which contain the diploid number of chromosomes) are PP and pp, and for their respective (haploid) gametes are P and p. When the gametes of the parents join in fertilization, all the resulting offspring of the F_1 generation will be Pp and black. When the F_1 forms gametes, each sex will produce both P and p gametes. The possible combinations for the F_2 will be PP (black), Pp and pP (black), and pp (white), giving an average ratio of 3 blacks to 1 white individual. The events in this cross are outlined in Figs. 12-2 and 12-3.

Individual animals such as the "pure" parents, containing like genes for any one character (PP or pp), are termed **homozygous.** The F_1 hybrid, which appears black and yet contains a gene for white (Pp), is said to be **heterozygous;** it contains two kinds of genes of an allelomorphic pair. The entire genetic constitution of an individual, both expressed and latent, makes up its **genotype;** and its appearance, or the assemblage of characters that are expressed or evident, constitutes its **phenotype.** Both the parents and two of the F_2 (PP and pp) are homozygous, but the F_1 hybrid and two of the F_2 (Pp) are heterozygous; the F_1 hybrid is a black phenotype, and its genotype is Pp. In the F_2, the whites are homozygous recessives; of the blacks, ⅓ are homozygous dominants yielding only blacks, and ⅔ are heterozygous. The analysis may be restated

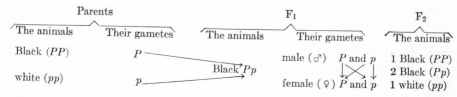

Fig. 12-2. Inheritance in a monohybrid cross.

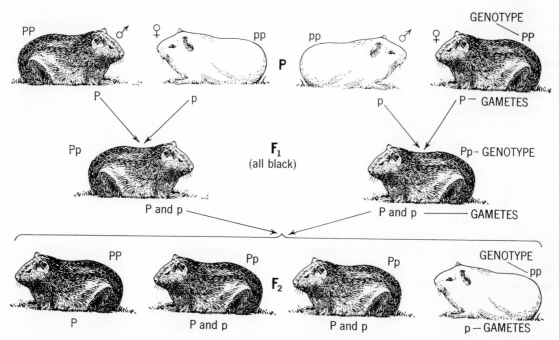

Fig. 12-3. Monohybrid cross. Inheritance of coat color in guinea pigs when pure-breeding black and white parents are mated.

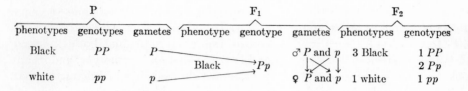

Fig. 12-4. Genetics of a monohybrid cross.

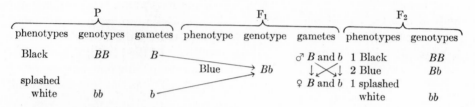

Fig. 12-5. Pattern of inheritance with incomplete dominance.

(Fig. 12-4) with phenotypes, genotypes, and gametes bracketed for the three generations.

Many other characters have been found to follow Mendel's first law.

12-5. Incomplete dominance. With some characters the F_1 hybrid is intermediate between the parents. Such incomplete dominance occurs in the Andalusian fowl, where the mating of a black and a splashed white produces "blue" offspring in the F_1, and the F_2 results are in the ratio: 1 black, 2 blue, 1 splashed white. The homozygous dominant is black, the heterozygous individuals are blue, and the homozygous recessive is splashed white (Fig. 12-5). Mendel's first law obviously applies here as well as in cases of complete dominance; but the heterozygous individuals are easily recognized.

12-6. Backcross. Offspring that show the dominant character in a cross are alike phenotypically but may be either heterozygous or homozygous for that character. To determine their genotype, the **test cross** or **backcross** is used, mating the dominant hybrid with a pure recessive individual. If, with guinea pigs, the black individual under test is homozygous (PP), all the offspring from a backcross with the recessive (pp) will be black (Pp); if, however, it is heterozygous (Pp), the offspring will be about equally black (Pp) and white (pp)

(Fig. 12-6). In practical genetics the backcross is a rapid means for "purifying" (rendering homozygous) desirable stocks.

12-7. Dihybrid cross. When parents differ in two pairs of characters, the F_1 offspring are termed **dihybrids;** in such crosses Mendel found that each pair of characters is inherited independently of the other. This may be illustrated (Fig. 12-7) in the case of the guinea pig where black or pigmented coat (P) is dominant to white (p) and rough or rosetted coat (R) is dominant to smooth (r). The mating of a black rough animal to a smooth white one is outlined in Fig. 12-8.

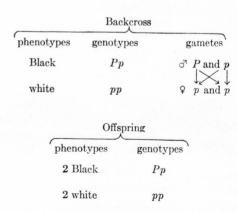

Fig. 12-6. Genetics of a backcross.

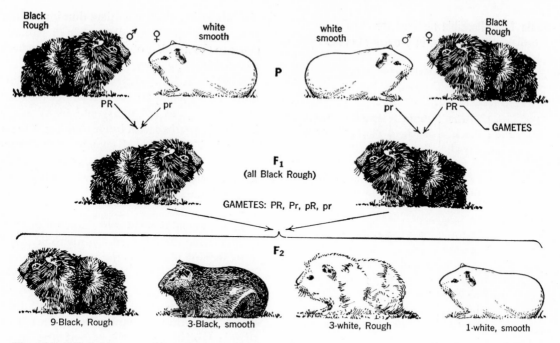

Fig. 12-7. Dihybrid cross, with guinea pigs differing in two independent pairs of Mendelian characters of the hair—color and arrangement.

Each sex forms four kinds of gametes, and the Punnett "Checkerboard" (Table 12-1) will show the 16 matings possible to produce the F_2 generation. The F_2 phenotypes include 9 black rough (any with *PR* genes) like the dominant parent and 1 white smooth (*pr*) like the recessive parent. Two new combinations have appeared, of which there are 3 black smooth (*Pr*) and 3 white rough (*pR*). The 9:3:3:1 ratio is characteristic of a dihybrid cross (Table 12-2).

There are $9 + 3 = 12$ black to $3 + 1 = 4$ white offspring and $9 + 3 = 12$ rough to $3 + 1 = 4$ smooth individuals. The ratio of 3 dominant to 1 recessive in each case follows Mendel's first law, as in a monohybrid cross. This shows the independence of each pair of characters, which is **Mendel's second law:** *When races differ from each other in two (or more) pairs of factors, the inheritance of one pair of factors is independent of that of the other(s).*

The four phenotypes involve nine different genotypes as shown in the analysis of the F_2 population; *PPRR, PPrr, ppRR,* and *pprr* are homozygous, and the other five are heterozygous. The appearance of new phenotypes and genotypes in dihybrid (and multihybrid) crosses is a practical means to obtain strains of animals or plants with combinations of characters different from those of the parents. In this cross, for example, there are two entirely new types of homozygous individuals in

	P	
phenotypes	genotypes	gametes
Black, Rough	*PPRR*	*PR*
white, smooth	*pprr*	*pr*

	F_1	
phenotype	genotype	gametes
Black, Rough	*PpRr*	*PR* *Pr* *pR* *pr*

Fig. 12-8. Matings in a dihybrid cross.

Table 12-1. Possible matings for the F_2 generation in a dihybrid cross

		Male gametes			
		PR	*Pr*	*pR*	*pr*
Female gametes	*PR*	*PPRR* Black Rough	*PPRr* Black Rough	*PpRR* Black Rough	*PpRr* Black Rough
	Pr	*PPRr* Black Rough	*PPrr* Black smooth	*PpRr* Black Rough	*Pprr* Black smooth
	pR	*PpRR* Black Rough	*PpRr* Black Rough	*ppRR* white Rough	*ppRr* white Rough
	pr	*PpRr* Black Rough	*Pprr* Black smooth	*ppRr* white Rough	*pprr* white smooth

Table 12-2. Analysis of the F_2 offspring from a dihybrid cross

Phenotypes			
9 Black Rough	3 Black smooth	3 white Rough	1 white smooth
Genotypes			
1-*PPRR* 2-*PPRr* 2-*PpRR* 4-*PpRr*	1-*PPrr* 2-*Pprr*	1-*ppRR* 2-*ppRr*	1-*pprr*

the F_2—black smooth (*PPrr*) and pure white rough (*ppRR*).

Increasing the numbers of independent factor pairs greatly enlarges the chance for new combinations.

In the monohybrid cross one pair of genes results in two combinations, black guinea pigs and white. In the dihybrid cross two pairs of genes produce four combinations, rough-black, smooth-black, rough-white, and

smooth-white. With complete dominance the relationship of the total number of pairs of genes to the number of phenotypes is 2^n, where n = number of gene pairs ($2^1 = 2$; $2^2 = 4$; $2^3 = 8$; etc.). The great variability seen in human beings may be due to the large number of chromosomes (23 pairs) and many genes involved, together with intermingling of races through time. Since each gamete carries structurally different chromosomes, each probably with one to many genes, there are millions of F_2 combinations possible in mankind (Fig. 3-9).

12-8. Special types of inheritance. The laws of Mendelian heredity apply only to bisexual animals and plants. In unisexual or asexual reproduction there is no joining of gametes from two parents but merely the splitting of the genetic material of a single cell. Variation occurs only through mutations and each of these establishes an independent line or, as referred to in bacteria and viruses, a strain. Vegetative reproduction in higher plants by clones and the various types of fission in protozoans are other examples. Also there are strains of some insects, rotifers, and other animals in which males are unknown and females reproduce without fertilization (parthenogenesis, par. 11-11).

Besides the simple types of Mendelian inheritance described, many others of more complex nature have been discovered that involve the interaction of two or more factors. For example, the form of comb differs in several breeds of domestic fowls, but each remains true within its breed (Fig. 12-9). The Wyandotte has a low regular **rose** comb with papillae, the Brahma a narrow, higher three-ridged **pea** comb, and the Leghorn and others an upright blade, or **single** comb. When fowls with rose (or pea) and single comb are crossed, the former is dominant, and the F_2 averages 3 rose (or pea) to 1 single. If rose is crossed with pea, however, the F_1 hybrid bears a **walnut** comb (resembling half a walnut meat) and the F_2 gives 9 walnut, 3 rose, 3 pea, and 1 single. The results differ from ordinary dihybrids

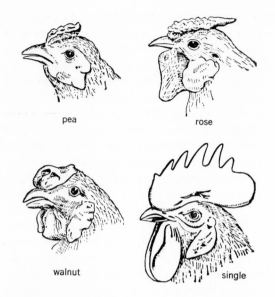

pea rose

walnut single

Fig. 12-9. Comb characters of male fowls. *(Adapted from Punnett, Mendelism, The Macmillan Co.)*

because the F_1 resembles neither parent, and two other types appear in the F_2. This is a case of interaction of ***supplementary factors*** in a cross involving two pairs of factors that affect one structure, the comb. If the dominant gene for rose is represented by R and its allele by r and that for pea by P and p, respectively, the

results may be explained as in Fig. 12-10. Single comb is thus a double recessive *(rrpp)*, rose comb contains either one or two R genes but only recessive p genes, pea comb has either one or two P genes but only recessive r genes, and walnut appears whenever at least one each of R and P are present.

12-9. Cumulative factors. In some cases either of two independent genes may alone produce a character but, when acting together, cause it to be accentuated; such ***cumulative genes*** are quantitative in expression. The pigmentation of Negro skin is an example, according to Davenport. A pure-blooded Negro has two pairs of genes for black pigmentation, BB and $B'B'$, whereas a pure-blooded white carries the paired bb and $b'b'$ for nonblack. Mating of such individuals results in mulatto offspring (F_1) with skin of intermediate color; two of the latter in turn will have children of different skin colors (Fig. 12-11). The figures in the checkerboard indicate the number of genes for black color in each individual; the offspring average, as to skin color, one full-colored Negro (4 B or B' genes), four dark mulattoes (3), six half-color mulattoes (2), four pale mulattoes (1), and one white-skinned (no dominant genes). The last might

P		F_1			F_2			
genotypes and phenotypes	gametes	genotype and phenotype	gametes ↓	→	RP	Rp	rP	rp
			RP		$RRPP$ walnut	$RRPp$ walnut	$RrPP$ walnut	$RrPp$ walnut
$RRpp$	Rp							
rose		$RrPp$	Rp		$RRPp$ walnut	$RRpp$ rose	$RrPp$ walnut	$Rrpp$ rose
		Walnut	rP		$RrPP$ walnut	$RrPp$ walnut	$rrPP$ pea	$rrPp$ pea
$rrPP$	rP							
pea			rp		$RrPp$ walnut	$Rrpp$ rose	$rrPp$ pea	$rrpp$ single

Fig. 12-10. Inheritance of comb characters in fowls.

have other Negro characteristics, however, as racial characteristics assort independently.

12-10. Lethal factors. Various species of plants and animals carry *lethal factors* which, when homozygous, stop development at some stage and the individual dies. Their presence is usually detected by an abnormal ratio in the offspring. A conspicuous case is the yellow race of the house mouse, *Mus musculus*. If a yellow mouse is mated to some nonyellow, half the young are yellow and half are nonyellow, a ratio to be expected from mating a heterozygous animal (yellow) with a homozygous recessive (any nonyellow such as agouti). If two yellows are mated together, the young average 2 yellow to 1 nonyellow, whereas the expected ratio among the young would be 1 pure yellow to 2 heterozygous yellow to 1 nonyellow—but the "homozygous yellow" dies as an embryo. Other lethals are known in *Drosophila,* cattle, sheep, hogs, and horses; and some human defects are thought to be due to such factors.

12-11. Multiple alleles. All the examples discussed previously involve pairs of alternative factors. In many other cases more than two alternative factors affect the same character; these are called *multiple alleles.* Thus, in the domestic rabbit among various color forms, there are the normal "wild" type, the complete albino with solidly white coat and pink eyes, and the "Himalayan" albino with pink eyes and a white coat except for black or dark brown on the ears, nose, and feet. The albino is a simple recessive to the wild type, and the Himalayan albino is likewise recessive to the wild type. When Himalayan and pure albino are crossed, however, all the F_1 offspring are Himalayan and the F_2 yields 3 Himalayan to 1 pure albino; there is no reversion to the wild type. Obviously, Himalayan and albino are alleles of one another, and both are alleles of the wild color. Other instances of multiple alleles are known for coat color in mice, guinea pigs, and rats. In *Drosophila* at least 14 alleles for eye color have been found, from white and ivory through buff and apricot to the wild-type red. Several series are known in plants, especially snapdragons and maize. No more than two alleles of a series can occur in any particular individual. Human blood groups involve multiple alleles (par. 6-8).

12-12. Sex and heredity. No factor mentioned previously has any relation to sex; either the male or the female may carry one factor and the other parent its alternative. The situation is different for some other characters, including that of sex itself. Somatic and early germ cells in male animals contain a pair

P		F_1		F_2			
genotypes and phenotypes	gametes	genotype and phenotype	gametes $\rightarrow$ $\downarrow$	BB'	Bb'	bB'	bb'
			BB'	4	3	3	2
$BBB'B'$ Negro	BB'	$BbB'b'$ Mulatto	Bb'	3	2	2	1
			bB'	3	2	2	1
$bbb'b'$ white	bb'		bb'	2	1	1	0

Fig. 12-11. Inheritance of skin color in mankind. Numerals in checkerboard indicate the number of genes for black color in each individual.

of homologous chromosomes in which one member is smaller than the other, and sometimes of different shape. These are the *sex chromosomes,* the larger being the **X chromosome** and the other the **Y chromosome;** in some species the latter is lacking. A pair of X chromosomes is present in females. Thus a male may be designated as XY (or XO) and a female as XX. All other pairs of strictly homologous chromosomes are termed *autosomes.*

Human cells, except gametes, contain 46 chromosomes—the 2 sex chromosomes, and 22 pairs of homologous autosomes (Fig. 12-12). During maturation the sex chromosomes segregate freely, like other chromosomes, so that an ovum contains 22 autosomes and an X chromosome, and a sperm has 22 autosomes and either an X or a Y chromosome.

If *A* is used to represent one haploid set of

Any Parent Generation			Offspring	
sex	genotypes	gametes	genotypes	sex
male	2A + XY	A + X A + Y	2A + XX	female
female	2A + XX	A + X	2A + XY	male

Fig. 12-13. Genetics of human sex.

autosomes, then the genetics of sex in human being can be diagrammed as in Fig. 12-13.

Thus sex is evidently determined by the kind of sperm that fertilizes an egg. As approximately equal numbers of the two sexes appear in the offspring of most animals, it is reasonable to assume that X and Y sperm are formed in equal numbers and that either kind has an equal chance of fertilizing an egg. The results are the same in species (many insects) that lack the Y chromosome, save that the female has an even number of chromosomes and the male one less. Among birds and moths the situation is reversed from that in other animals, there being two kinds of eggs and one of sperm; males are therefore XX, and females are XY.[1]

Prior to the discovery of sex chromosomes, there were many ingenious theories to explain sex. Various schemes have been tried to control the sex of offspring, especially in domesticated animals and mankind, but none is effective. In frogs and some invertebrates, alteration of environmental conditions affects the *sex ratio,* which is the proportion of males to females among offspring.

Some abnormalities of sex are known; occasional fruit flies, bees, and other insects are **gynandromorphs,** with some parts of the body showing male and the other female characteristics. **Intersexes** are intermediate between males and females and usually sterile. They

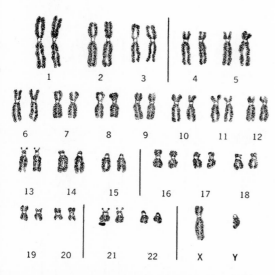

Fig. 12-12. The human chromosomes grouped according to size, position of centromere (white ring), and possession of satellites. Autosomes (1–22) and sex chromosomes (X, Y). Each chromosome appears distinctly double due to treatment with colchicine. (Male, diploid, metaphase, 2600×.) (*After Tjio and Puck, 1958, Proc. Natl. Acad. Sci.*)

---

[1] The Y chromosome evidently carries no genes for sex or other characters; yet, in species where it normally occurs, males without a Y chromosome are sterile.

have been seen in gypsy moths reared experimentally and also in pigs. *Sex reversal,* where an individual originally female has become a male or vice versa, is common in certain invertebrates (mollusks) and rare in vertebrates. Usually such abnormalities result from hormone imbalance rather than direct genetic influence.

12-13. Sex-linked inheritance. The X chromosome has been found to carry genes for *sex-linked* characters, the inheritance of which is therefore related to sex determination. In the fruit fly, *Drosophila,* where eye color is sex-linked (Fig. 12-14), the normal red eye color is dominant to white eye. If a homozygous red-eyed female and a white-eyed male are mated, all the F_1 flies are red-eyed; when the latter are intercrossed, the F_2 yields an average of 2 red-eyed females to 1 red-eyed male to 1 white-eyed male. If X_R represents the gene for red eye and X_r that for white eye, the results of this cross may be diagrammed as in Fig. 12-15. In the P generation each matured ovum carries an X chromosome with the gene for red eye, half the sperm carry an X chromosome with a gene for white eye, and the other sperm contain a Y chromosome with no gene for eye color. In the F_1 generation two kinds of eggs are produced, with the gene for either red eye or white eye, and of the sperm half have a gene (on the X chromosome) for red eye and half have no gene for eye color (Y chromosome). Four kinds of zygotes are thus possible. In the F_2, half the females are homozygous for red eye and half are heterozygous, and the males are equally red- and white-eyed.

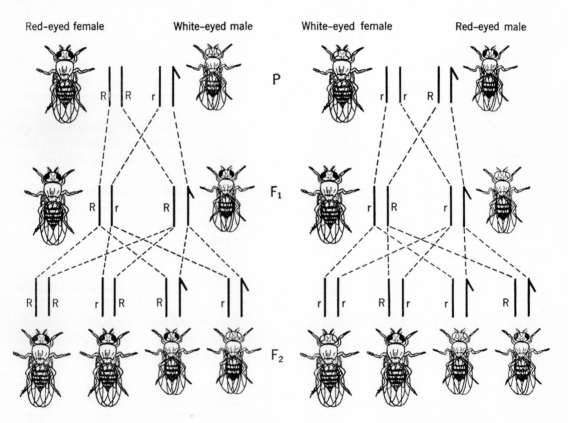

Fig. 12-14. Sex determination and sex-linked inheritance of eye color in *Drosophila*. The sex chromosomes are represented by vertical bars with symbols (R, r) for genes of eye color.

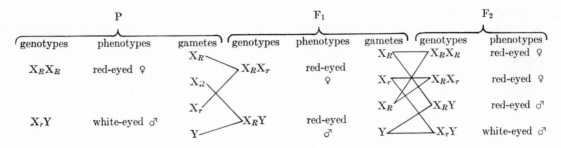

Fig. 12-15. Sex-linked inheritance of eye color in *Drosophila* with red-eyed female parent.

A somewhat different result is obtained in the opposite or ***reciprocal cross*** with a homozygous white-eyed female and red-eyed male. In the F_1 the males are white-eyed and the females red-eyed. In the F_2 there result approximately equal numbers of red-eyed females, white-eyed females, red-eyed males, and white-eyed males (Fig. 12-16).

About 150 sex-linked genes have been found in *Drosophila* (Fig. 12-17, chromosome I), and many sex-linked characters are known in other animals and in man; barred plumage in poultry and red-green color blindness in man (Table 12-3) are common examples.

12-14. Linkage. Independent assortment (Mendel's second law) was evident in the examples discussed earlier in this chapter; and in the preceding paragraphs some types of sex-linked inheritance were described. Many other characters of animals tend to be inherited together. The number of pairs of Mendelian factors present in any animal far exceeds the number of chromosome pairs, and so each chromosome must carry several or many genes. Characters that tend to be inherited together are said to be ***linked.*** Studies of the linkage relations in various animals and plants have shown that the genes occur in ***linkage groups,*** the members of each group being linked to one another in varying degree, while a pair in one linkage group assorts or combines independently with pairs in other linkage groups. When the linkage relations of many genes in a species are known, it is found that there are as many groups of linked genes as chromosome pairs. About 500 linked genes are known in *Drosophila melanogaster;* there are 4 linkage groups (3 large, 1 small), and there are 4 pairs of chromosomes (3 long, 1 short). *D. willistoni* has 3 linkage groups and 3 chromosome pairs, and *D. virilis* has 6 of each. Among plants, maize has 10 of each, and the garden pea has 7 of each. This evidence is highly important in showing that the genes are contained in the chromosomes.

12-15. Crossing over. If the genes for two

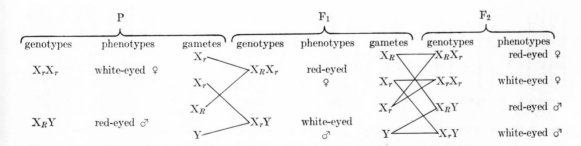

Fig. 12-16. Sex-linked inheritance of eye color in *Drosophila* with white-eyed female parent.

characters are in one chromosome and the latter remains intact through inheritance, their linkage will be complete, the two always occurring together; but such is not always the case (Fig. 12-17). The characters separate in a certain number of cases, the percentage of separations varying between different characters, although it is usually constant as between any two. Thus short ear and dilute coat color in mice are linked in over 99 per cent of individuals, but the percentage is variously lower with many other characteristics. When characters (genes) that were originally together become separated they are known as *crossovers.* During maturation the two chromosomes of a homologous pair are close together or intertwined at synapsis; ordinarily they separate with no interchange, but at times they exchange homologous parts with one another, and this is the physical basis of crossing over.

If the genes in a chromosome are in linear arrangement, then two far apart will have their linkage transposed by an exchange at any point between them, whereas if they are close together, the chance of crossing over is much less. Assuming that the frequency of crossing over indicates the relative distance between genes in a chromosome, T. H. Morgan and his coworkers constructed "chromosome maps" for known genes in each linkage group of *Drosophila.* In a mating involving any two linked characters 1 per cent of crossover is taken to represent 1 unit of distance between their respective genes.

Thus the three characters of yellow body, white eye, and ruby eye are all sex-linked and therefore pertain to chromosome I (X). In matings between yellow body and white eye, crossover occurs in 1.5 per cent of individuals, between white eye and ruby eye in 6.0 per cent, and between yellow body and ruby eye in 7.5 per cent; hence, the sequence is yellow-white-ruby, with 1.5 units of space between the genes for yellow and white and 6.0 units between white and ruby (1.5 + 6.0 = 7.5). Many crosses between various linked characters provide material for constructing chromosome maps (Fig. 12-18).

12-16. Giant chromosomes. The relatively huge chromosomes in the salivary glands of *Drosophila* and some other flies occur in permanent homologous pairs and when stained show many dark-colored transverse "bands," some wide and others narrow (Fig. 12-19). The bands give clues to the location of genes, as in cases of *deletion;* where a character has disappeared from a laboratory stock of *Drosophila,* part of one chromosome is missing at the position for the gene of that character in the chromosome map. Or part of a chromosome may become inverted, resulting in a

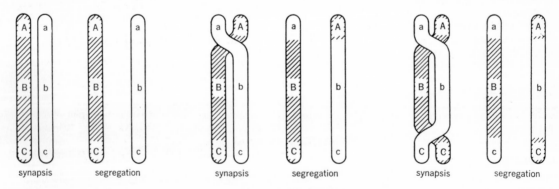

Fig. 12-17. Diagrams of crossing over, the exchange of genes between homologous chromosomes. *A, a; B, b; C, c,* represent pairs of allelomorphic genes in homologous chromosomes that pair during synapsis. *Left.* No change. *Middle.* One crossover. *Right.* Double crossover.

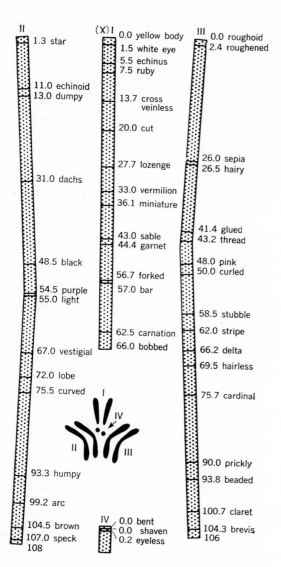

II	(X) I	III
1.3 star	0.0 yellow body	0.0 roughoid
	1.5 white eye	2.4 roughened
	5.5 echinus	
	7.5 ruby	
11.0 echinoid		
13.0 dumpy	13.7 cross veinless	
	20.0 cut	
	27.7 lozenge	26.0 sepia
		26.5 hairy
31.0 dachs	33.0 vermilion	
	36.1 miniature	
	43.0 sable	41.4 glued
	44.4 garnet	43.2 thread
48.5 black		48.0 pink
		50.0 curled
54.5 purple	56.7 forked	
55.0 light	57.0 bar	
		58.5 stubble
	62.5 carnation	62.0 stripe
67.0 vestigial	66.0 bobbed	66.2 delta
		69.5 hairless
72.0 lobe		
75.5 curved		75.7 cardinal
93.3 humpy		90.0 prickly
		93.8 beaded
99.2 arc		
		100.7 claret
104.5 brown	IV 0.0 bent	104.3 brevis
107.0 speck	0.0 shaven	106
108	0.2 eyeless	

Fig. 12-18. Chromosome maps for *Drosophila*. One chromosome of each pair is diagrammed with the relative positions for some of the many genes "mapped" by linkage studies. Numbers indicate relative distance of each from end of chromosome. Inset shows chromosomes of gonads.

local reversal in the sequence of bands, with consequent difficulty in pairing. This is important evidence associating the genes with the chromosomes.

12-17. Mutations. At times, new characters appear in the offspring of animals and plants

that upon test prove to be heritable; these are germinal variations, or *mutations,* caused by some change in the gene for the character concerned. A historic case was the sudden appearance in a true-breeding stock of red-eyed *Drosophila* of one white-eyed individual. When the latter was bred, this character proved to be heritable, and as it continued in succeeding generations the change was permanent. Over a thousand mutations have been observed in *Drosophila* (Fig. 12-20), and many in other animals and in plants. Most mutations in *Drosophila* and other animals are abnormalities, recessive defects, or lethals such as would not survive in nature. But distinctive mutations among domestic animals and plants have been preserved by selective breeding. Examples are the polled (hornless) Hereford cattle, the short-legged (Ancon) sheep, and the short-legged dachshund and the long-legged greyhound among dogs. The rate of mutation varies widely in different animals and for different genes; recent calculations indicate 1 mutation per 40,000 to 500,000 cell divisions. Most mutant genes are recessive, but some dominants have appeared. Fourteen or more mutations of one gene for eye color in *Drosophila* have been noted.

Only spontaneous natural mutations were

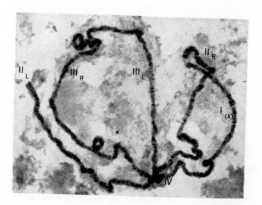

Fig. 12-19. Giant chromosomes from salivary glands of *Drosophila* (440×, photomicrograph). Dark cross-bands presumably are the location (loci) of genes. Each chromosome is diploid, the two parts not separated. Numbers as in Fig. 12-18.

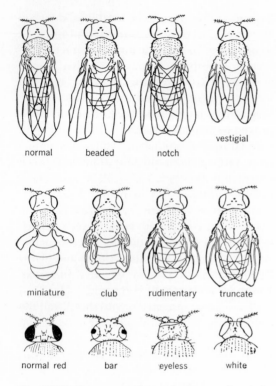

normal   beaded   notch

vestigial

miniature   club   rudimentary   truncate

normal red   bar   eyeless   white

Fig. 12-20. Some mutations of wings and eyes in *Drosophila* used in study of crossing over and linkage (compare Fig. 12-1). *(After Morgan and others.)*

found earlier, but certain chemicals and types of radiation have been found to induce mutations at increased rates. Mustard gas induces mutation, and colchicine causes duplication of chromosome sets (polyploidy) in plants. X-rays applied to *Drosophila,* maize, and barley may increase the mutation rate two hundred fold in some cases, and in proportion to the dosage. These mutations prove heritable, like natural mutations, but most of them are lethal.

Because of the wider use and therefore greater exposure of people to high-frequency radiations, induced mutations are of practical importance. X-ray technicians, workers in atomic-energy plants, and others are endangered because the effects of radiation are cumulative; continued exposure to small amounts over several years may be as serious for an individual as receiving an equivalent dosage (same number of "roentgens") in a few minutes. Mutations due to irradiation may not be evident for several generations because they usually are masked by dominant alleles and only are seen as homozygous recessives. The general level of radioactivity is increasing throughout the world with the "atomic age." The social and biological implications of this situation are scarcely perceived, but knowledge is sorely needed.

12-18. Theory of the gene. The evidence on characters, genes, chromosomes, and linkage was summarized by T. H. Morgan in his *Theory of the Gene* (Yale University Press) thus: (1) The characters of an individual are referable to paired genes in the germinal material, held together in a definite number of linkage groups; (2) at maturation each pair of genes separates (Mendel's first law), so that each gamete contains only one set; (3) the genes in different linkage groups assort independently (Mendel's second law); (4) orderly interchange or crossing over occurs at times between genes in corresponding (homologous) linkage groups; and (5) the frequency of crossing over furnishes evidence of the linear arrangement of genes in each linkage group and their relative position to one another.

The presence of a particular gene is recognized by some phenotypic characteristic that is produced in an organism. However, new techniques reveal several or many "genes" where only one was thought to exist. The question of "What is a gene?" thus becomes one of degree, or of deciding at what level to apply the term. The present tendency is to use the term gene for the point or small segment of a chromosome that is recognizable (between the two closest points of crossing over) as the site of a genetic change (mutation) or as an area that determines a single protein or polypeptide chain.

12-19. DNA and heredity. Although the precise structure and mode of action of genes are still unknown, much evidence indicates that the material involved in genetic control is DNA (par. 3-27).

Chemical studies show that the amount of DNA in diploid nuclei of a species is constant (6×10^{-9} mg. per nucleus in somatic cells; A. E. Mirsky); the haploid nuclei of eggs or sperm contain half this amount (and tetraploid nuclei twice as much). If chromosomes are treated with a specific enzyme that hydrolyzes DNA, an outline of the chromosome remains; but a proteolytic enzyme will subdivide the chromosomes. These results imply that the chromosome has a protein framework in which DNA is present.

Each gene is probably equivalent to a certain number and sequence of bases on the DNA strand. The sequence of bases in DNA is considered to serve as a code or storehouse of information, determining the sequence of amino acids in enzymes and other specific proteins of the cell. In this way the molecular structure of the gene is responsible for the physiological and morphological characteristics of the individual.

Not all genes or base sequences along the DNA chain act in the same way to determine, through RNA, the structure of proteins in a cell. Simple production of proteins (e.g., enzymes) cannot explain the change in level of production of certain enzymes during different stages in the metabolism or life cycle of an organism. Also, if all cells in an animal receive identical sets of genes, why do some become pancreas cells and secrete insulin while others become muscle cells able to contract? In other words, how are genes regulated in their action?

A theory of gene action, recently proposed by Jacob and Monod, seeks to answer this question. It assumes that only part of the DNA chain is used to code RNA which in turn codes a protein. Each such portion of the DNA chain may be called a gene and may be referred to as a structural gene since it produces a protein structure. The structural genes are held to lie next to portions of the DNA chain which do not produce RNA, but instead act to control the structural genes. These areas of the chain are termed *operator genes.* One operator gene is thought to control several structural genes in the manner of an on-off switch. When "on" the structural gene produces RNA which in turn acts to produce protein and hence various structures and metabolic pathways that function in the cell. When the structural gene is "off," no RNA, hence no protein, is produced. The combination of several structural genes and an operator gene is termed an *operon.*

Another group called *regulator genes* is thought to exist on the DNA strand. These are considered to produce substances which have the ability to combine with the end products of the structural genes (proteins) to form substances called *repressors.*

The repressor functions to turn off the operator gene and prevent further production of protein in the cell. Hence high production by the structural genes yields quantities of protein. This combines with the repressor substance to act on the operator and turn off production of more protein. When the protein level falls, the repressor has no protein with which to combine and inhibition of the operator gene is lifted. The operator gene again functions to initiate production of the structural genes until the protein level causes a shut-off once more.

12-20. Expression of the phenotype. Mendel chose sharply contrasting characters in his studies of garden peas and hence was able to reveal the fundamental laws of heredity. In recent years it has become clear that the simple 1 to 1 gene-character relationship is rare. More commonly and perhaps universally a single gene affects several characters and many genes may interact to influence each of the traits seen in plants and animals. This is called *pleiotropism.* Through gene interaction, it is the totality of genes or the *genome* that determines the phenotype. Also the biochemical reactions between the genes and the expression of the characters do not take place in a vacuum. They occur under constantly varying physiological conditions of the individual and in an external environment that is subject to change. Thus a person may have a genetic constitution that would result in white hands but due to a lack of niacin of the vitamin B complex in his diet the *expression* of hand color is altered by the addition of pigment. An example of environmentally induced change in expression of a character is the effect of temperature on hair color in the Himalayan rabbit. In an area of the back that was genetically determined as white, the hairs were pulled out; then the rabbit was moved to a cold room. The new hair that grew in was black. The question of whether heredity or environment plays a decisive role in development of an individual thus becomes meaningless. The two interact in every case to determine the individual phenotype.

12-21. Inbreeding and outcrossing. The mating of closely related individuals is called *inbreeding;* this may involve brother-sister matings or lesser degrees of relationship. Many races of domesticated animals and plants have been derived or improved by inbreeding, but practical breeders think that continued inbreeding leads to decline of vigor and the appearance of defects in offspring. Close marriages in human society, as between cousins, are usually banned for fear that defective children may result. Inbreeding tends to produce homozygous stocks. Since most genes for defects are recessive, it provides more opportunity for defective characters to appear. The results will depend on the genetic constitution of the stocks that are inbred. Guinea pigs carried through 23 generations of brother-sister matings by Sewall Wright and others ended with a stock reduced in size, fertility, and resistance to tuberculosis. Helen D. King, however, carried similar matings in white rats through 25 generations, using only the most vigorous individuals in each, and at the end the inbred animals compared favorably with crossbred controls. Similar experiments through more generations with *Drosophila* have ended with normal stocks.

Inbreeding with selection can produce satisfactory or improved stocks, combining desirable dominant characteristics in the homozygous condition.

Outcrossing, the mating of individuals not closely related, usually results in **hybrid vigor,** the offspring exceeding their parents in vigor and size. The mule is a familiar example, being larger and having more stamina than either of its parents, the mare and the ass. Outcrossing tends to produce heterozygous individuals in which any defective features are masked by dominant normal characters. Most human marriages are outcrosses, the human population is heterozygous, and defects are relatively rare. People in an isolated community are more likely to be inbred and hence show more defects than in the general population.

12-22. Artificial selection. Selective breeding and the perpetuation of mutations have produced breeds of domesticated animals differing markedly in physical, physiological, and psychological characteristics from the wild ancestors. The wild jungle fowl of India (*Gallus bankiva*) is small, and the hens lay only 12 to 24 eggs per year. Continued selection has produced from it many domestic breeds of poultry differing in size, coloration, and egg production. Bantams are only about 10 inches high and weigh about $1\frac{1}{2}$ pounds, whereas "meat fowls" such as the Cochins, Plymouth Rocks, and Rhode Island Reds are up to 16 inches tall and 6 to 8 pounds in weight. White Leghorn hens now average 120 eggs per year, and in some highly selected flocks each produces 200 or more.

Beef cattle, such as the Hereford, Shorthorn, and Aberdeen Angus breeds, are selected for shape (conformation) that yields desirable cuts of meat, whereas dairy breeds such as the Holstein-Friesian and Jersey have been developed for high milk production and high butterfat, respectively.

Dogs (derived from wolves and jackals of Eurasia) now include more than 100 breeds from tiny Pekingese to great wolfhounds and from short-legged dachshunds and bulldogs to long-legged greyhounds. The coat varies from white through many colors to black, and from nearly hairless in the Chihuahua to a dense, sleek coat in the collie and curly hair in the Irish water spaniel.

12-23. Twins. Since the sum total of characteristics in any one individual results from the action and interaction of many genes, the various offspring from one pair of parents will differ. When a female produces more than one young at a birth, each usually develops from a separate egg and the young are genetically different; but if the early blastomeres of one egg part and each gives rise to an individual, all the latter will have the same genetic make-up. The first condition produces *fraternal twins* (triplets, etc.) of the same or of different sex; they are no more alike than the other children in any one family. The second yields *identical twins,* always of the same sex, with like physical and physiological characteristics, and showing even the same mental traits and abilities.

12-24. Population genetics. Earlier in this chapter heredity was discussed in terms of mating selected pairs of homozygous parents having certain characteristics and determining the kinds of offspring expected in successive generations. Plant and animal geneticists seek to produce organisms with certain desired characteristics, such as larger size or greater resistance to disease. To do this, they make selected matings, first of parental stocks and later among the progeny in successive generations.

The situation is quite different in nature, where organisms live as populations in which individuals can mate freely with one another. A *population* is the total of living individuals of one species in an area. The races of mankind are natural populations, and human marriages are nonselective for most genetic characteristics.

Population genetics involves application of Mendelian principles to populations, especially as to gene frequencies and the propor-

tions of genotypes under various mating systems. Consider the case of a pair of autosomal alleles, D (dominant) and d (recessive), of equal occurrence. Matings between homozygous parents result as follows:

Parent genotype	DD	dd
Parent gametes	D	d
F_1 genotypes	Dd	Dd
F_1 gametes	D, d	D, d
F_2 genotypes	$DD + Dd + dD + dd$ or,	
	$\frac{1}{4}DD + \frac{1}{2}Dd + \frac{1}{4}dd$	

Thereafter random matings between the three genotypes of such a population will maintain the genotypes in the same proportions in succeeding generations.

This principle is embodied in the **Hardy-Weinberg Law,** which states that *in a given population with random mating and no selection between genotypes the relative frequency of genes* (alleles) *tends to remain constant from generation to generation.* The relationship of gene frequency to frequency of genotype follows the binomial expression $(p + q)^2$, the basic Hardy-Weinberg formula, where p is the frequency of a given gene, q that of its allele, and $p + q = 1$. Genotypic proportions are derived by expansion of the binomial.

It is assumed that (1) the population is so large that errors in sampling are unimportant; (2) there is no migration of individuals into or out of the population; (3) mutations do not occur or are so rare as to be negligible; (4) gametes carrying the two alleles are produced in equal numbers; (5) matings are random; and (6) all genotypes (dominant homozygous, heterozygous, or recessive) are equal in survival rate—that is, no artificial or natural selection occurs. Under this law, when the numbers of the two phenotypes for a pair of nonlinked alleles are known in a population sample, the genetic basis for their inheritance can be learned by simple calculations.

12-25. Human inheritance. The genetic characteristics of human beings pass from generation to generation like those of other animals and plants. Details are difficult to learn because of the long intervals between generations and the scarcity of records that specify the characteristics of many individuals. By tracing backward through family histories in which the peculiarities of many members are listed, the manner of inheritance for some physical features, physiological characteristics, and mental traits have been learned (Figs. 12-21, 12-22).

12-26. Eye color. The human iris is brown or blue, rarely pink. Pigment on the back of the iris produces blue eyes of various shades; if there is also pigment on the front, the color is hazel to dark brown. If pigment is lacking on both surfaces, the eyes appear pink (albino) because of the blood vessels in the iris. When both parents are blue-eyed, all their children have blue eyes; when one parent is heterozygous brown-eyed and the other blue-eyed, the children are partly brown-eyed, partly blue-eyed. Marriage of two brown-eyed persons usually results only in brown-eyed children; yet blue-eyed ones may appear. These facts indicate that eye color is a simple Mendelian character; brown is dominant to blue, and blue-eyed individuals are homozygous recessives for eye color.

12-27. Color blindness. The inability to distinguish red from green is a sex-linked recessive human character. Men with normal color vision neither have nor transmit the defect; "carrier" females enjoy normal vision but, being heterozygous for the character, may have color-blind children; color-blind males and females both transmit the defect (Table 12-3).

12-28. Mental characteristics. Some traits, both good and bad, are inherited like other characteristics, although the evidence about them may be difficult to interpret. Certain families have shown outstanding ability and leadership through successive generations, with many individuals distinguished in scholarship, the professions, the fine arts, business,

Table 12-3. Inheritance of color vision (red-green discrimination) in mankind

*The gene for this factor, being sex-linked, is carried on the X chromosome. Color blindness (**X**) is recessive to normal vision (X). The heterozygous "carrier" female has normal vision.*

Parents → ↓	Gametes ↓ →	Normal ♂ XY		Color-blind ♂ **X**Y	
		X	Y	**X**	Y
		Children			
Normal ♀ XX	X	XX ♀ normal	XY ♂ normal	**X**X ♀ carrier	XY ♂ normal
Carrier **X**X ♀	X	XX ♀ normal	XY ♂ normal	**X**X ♀ carrier	XY ♂ normal
	X	**X**X ♀ carrier	**X**Y ♂ color-blind	**XX** ♀ color-blind	**X**Y ♂ color-blind
Color-blind **XX** ♀	**X**	**X**X ♀ carrier	**X**Y ♂ color-blind	**XX** ♀ color-blind	**X**Y ♂ color-blind

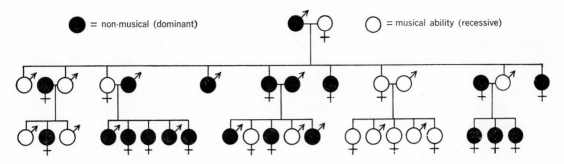

Fig. 12-21. Inheritance of musical ability. (*After Hurst,* 1908.)

statesmanship, and other fields of human endeavor (Fig. 12-21). Conversely, other family lines include many degenerate individuals. The "Jukes" family, studied by Dugdale and Estabrook, is one of bad pedigree that has been traced through several generations. From the marriage of a shiftless farmer's son and a prostitute a total of 2,094 descendants were traced; these included 299 paupers, 118 criminals, 378 prostitutes, and 86 brothel keepers. There was a general record of intemperance and illegitimate births, and half the total were feeble-minded.

Practically every organ in the human body may be subject to hereditary defects in structure or function, but mental defects such as feeble-mindedness and insanity are much more important. In the United States there are several million persons with an intelligence quotient of 70 or lower, from high-grade

morons to imbeciles and idiots. More than 300,000 cases are of hereditary origin, but only about 11 per cent of them are thought to be the progeny of feeble-minded parents (Fig. 12-22). The remainder derive from normal persons heterozygous for this character. The feeble-minded become juvenile delinquents, problem children, and cases for public charity and relief. They breed early and often and tend to increase their kind. Relatively few are in institutions, public or private. The end result is a rapidly mounting bill for their care and for dealing with the crimes they commit. Although 28 states have laws that permit insane and feeble-minded persons to be sterilized, only about 53,500 had been so dealt with up to 1952.

The human race has evolved through a long series of progressive changes to its present state (Chaps. 14, 29) and can be further modi-

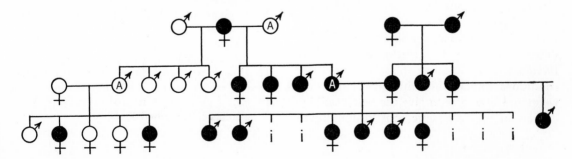

Fig. 12-22. Inheritance of feeble-mindedness. *Black,* feeble-minded; *white,* normal; ♂, male; ♀, female; *A,* alcoholic; *i,* died in infancy. In the two cases where both parents were feeble-minded note that all children were also feeble-minded. (*After Holmes, Human genetics and its social import.*)

fied for better or worse. In primitive peoples, many defective characters were weeded out by rigorous selective action of the environment. "Civilization" is mainly a control of man's environment, and it has increasingly tended to suspend such selection. Human races have crossed and recrossed so that mankind has become the most variable of all animals and has accumulated many hereditary defects. The frequent outcrossing in human populations and the common bans on marriage between closely related persons tend to make the human germ plasm heterozygous and to mask recessive defects. Since there is little selective mating to rid the human population of such defects, these continue unabated. Modern medicine helps the individual to survive but may actually be harming the race. In earlier centuries many defectives died before they became old enough to reproduce, whereas today such persons are repaired by medicine or surgery and survive to produce progeny that carry on their hereditary defects to the following generations.

12-29. Eugenics. Many organizations and persons are now interested in *eugenics* (Gr. *eugenes,* wellborn), a field of endeavor which seeks to improve the human race by applying the principles of genetics. If it were possible to control the matings between human beings, the race could be improved by eliminating certain serious defects and in many other ways, but this is not practical. Eugenists seek to determine the facts of human heredity, to educate the general public on the effects of good and bad matings, and to encourage legislation that will prevent matings between obviously defective persons. The further field of *euthenics* tries to improve the environmental conditions under which human beings develop and live so as to give the best possible expression to the genetic constitutions that

each one has. No measurable aid in human genetics will be possible until much fuller records on human inheritance are available and until means are learned to recognize heterozygous individuals who carry genes of serious defects and to limit the mating of such persons.

REVIEW

1. Who was Mendel, and why is he considered the "father of genetics"? What are Mendel's two laws?
2. Define: dihybrid cross, dominant, recessive, allele, gene, homozygous, genotype, phenotype, backcross, lethal factor, sex-linked inheritance, autosome.
3. Explain the Mendelian ratio in a monohybrid cross. Why are the numbers of phenotypes and genotypes actually obtained in the F_2 in any cross usually not exactly in the proportion expected?
4. Of what practical values are the backcross, the di- or multihybrid cross?
5. How do the results in a case of incomplete dominance differ from the usual monohybrid cross?
6. What are supplementary factors and cumulative genes?
7. In a mating of *Drosophila* for study of eye color does it make any difference whether the male or female parent is white-eyed? Why?
8. How does a crossing over affect the characters in subsequent progeny?
9. What is a mutation? How can mutations and inbreeding serve for improvement of a cultivated crop or domestic animal?
10. What are the essential points in the theory of the gene?
11. Contrast artificial selection with natural selection (see Chap. 14).
12. How do we know that blue iris in the human eye results from a single recessive gene?
13. Can a person with normal color vision have a color-blind mother? Father?

13
Animal ecology and distribution

Every living organism has a distinctive mode of life that depends upon its structure and physiology and also upon the kind of environment that it occupies. Physical and biological factors act to make a wide variety of environments on different parts of the earth. The conditions are rather constant in some tropical lands and seas, but over much of the earth the temperature, moisture relations, and sunlight change with the seasons. Collectively these influences are known as *climate*. The life cycle of each species is closely adjusted to the climatic conditions of its environment. No animal lives entirely to itself; on the contrary, each is part of an integrated living *community* that includes others of its kind, many other sorts of animals, and plants of few or many types. The scientific study of organisms under natural conditions is termed *ecology* (Gr. *oikos,* house), and their occurrence in space and time is called *distribution.*

Ecology

A. THE PHYSICAL ENVIRONMENT

Animals and plants are affected by various physical and chemical factors, the most important being (1) sunlight; (2) temperature; (3) water; and (4) gases and minerals. Each can be measured and its effects observed on animals, but all are interrelated and none acts independently. Sunlight provides the radiant energy used by plants in photosynthesis, but it also warms animal environments and raises the temperature of water, leading to evaporation (and eventually to precipitation of rain or snow). Temperature controls the speed of all chemical reactions, including the biochemical reactions in living organisms. Water is the solvent for soil minerals essential to plants, is a requirement in animal bodies, and is the medium in which many animals live.

13-1. Sunlight. All the energy used by organisms is derived from the sun (Fig. 13-1). Energy may be transformed from one type to another but is never created or destroyed (par. 3-14). Plants absorb the radiant energy in sunlight and, by the photosynthetic action of chlorophyll in their cells, produce carbohydrates from carbon dioxide and water; they also synthesize proteins and fats. The energy stored in these compounds is the ultimate source used by all animals. Energy relations underlie all physical and biotic processes on the earth and determine the activities of organisms.

13-2. Temperature. The degree of hotness or coldness of any object or body is called tem-

Illustration at top of page: Social life of the honeybee—several workers, a queen (long abdomen), and drone (upper left) on comb with open and closed brood cells.

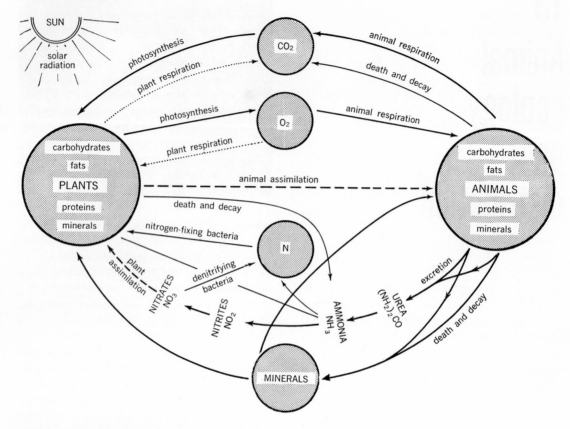

Fig. 13-1. The chemical cycles of carbon dioxide, oxygen, nitrogen, and minerals in nature. Arrows indicate the paths of movement of materials from the air (CO_2, O_2, N) and soil (minerals) to and from plants and animals.

perature and is measured on a scale, usually in degrees Fahrenheit or centigrade. Heat is a form of energy, and the amount in an animal or its environment is a factor of major importance.

The range of temperatures in the universe covers thousands of degrees, but most life on earth can exist only within a range from −20° to 60°C. or less. Heat tolerance is affected by moisture and really depends on the evaporating power of the air or the percentage of water vapor in relation to saturation at any given temperature. In the dry air on a desert, for example, a temperature of 32°C. (90°F.) is not uncomfortable to man, but the same temperature, coupled with high relative humidity, is difficult to tolerate in the tropics.

Many animals cannot tolerate the full extremes of temperature in their environments. To survive successfully within lesser limits, they have developed various adaptations. In regions of severe winter, the cold-blooded invertebrates, insects, amphibians, and reptiles remain in frost-free shelters below ground or within dead trees. Mammals and birds active in that season are insulated against loss of bodily heat by their fur or feathers. Freshwater inhabitants winter below the level of ice formation. During midsummer heat on deserts or semideserts, lizards are active mainly in early morning and toward evening, and most snakes then become nocturnal. In hot environments, evaporation of water from the skin (sweating) helps man, the horse, and some other mammals to maintain their body temperatures. Whales, seals, and other marine mammals have a layer of fat (blubber) under the skin that resists loss of body heat in the water.

13-3. Water. There is a constant interchange of water between the air, land, and sea and between living organisms and their environments. In addition, water profoundly influences the environments of organisms. The water cycle (Fig. 13-2) involves evaporation, cloud formation, precipitation, surface water run-off, and percolation through the soil. Water stores vast quantities of heat, and because its specific heat is so great (requiring 1 calorie to raise 1 gram of water 1°C. at 15°C.), any large mass is slow to warm up in the spring and slow to cool in the fall. Water is heaviest at 4°C. (39.2°F.). It expands as it cools below this point and changes to ice at 0°C. (32°F.). The force of this expansion is so great that rocks are split when water in crevices freezes; this is a process in soil formation. (The cracking of iron cylinders in an automobile when the jacket water freezes is a common ex-

ample of this power.) More important to organisms is the fact that ice floats, being lighter than water. But for this, ice would form at the bottom of lakes, and most large bodies of water would have permanent masses of ice in their depths. Instead, water sinks as it cools to 4°C., and warmer water rises, thus creating convection currents. These bring about a spring and autumn turnover in temperate lakes and protect organisms from temperature extremes, since those beneath the ice in deep lakes are never much below 4°C.

Land animals are affected by the moisture content of the air, or *relative humidity* (percentage of water vapor in relation to saturation at any given temperature). Some are suited to deserts of low humidity, others exist only where the atmosphere is practically saturated, and many live at intermediate humidities. For small animals the *microclimate* of the little places where they feed or find shelter is all-important, usually having a lower temperature and higher humidity than the general climate of the region in which they occur; in the Arctic a higher temperature is sought.

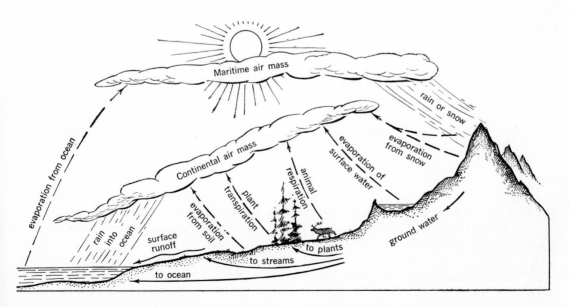

Fig. 13-2. The water cycle. Constant interchange of water between the air, land, and sea produces various daily and seasonal alterations in the environments of plants and animals.

In arid regions many small animals remain in seclusion by day, else they would soon die of desiccation. They venture out at night when temperatures are lower and the humidity greater, especially close to the ground. In areas having frequent summer rains, or where fields and gardens are irrigated, the humidity near the ground is such that small invertebrates are active during the daytime.

13-4. Chemical cycles in nature. The elements that go to form the bodies of plants and animals are all derived from the environment, and there is a constant interchange of these incident to the life and death of organisms (Fig. 13-1).

Carbon (C) is a constituent of all organic compounds in protoplasm (Chap. 3). From the carbon dioxide (CO_2) in air or water it is synthesized into the molecules of carbohydrates, and these, together with proteins and fats, make up the tissues of plants. The plants are eaten by certain animals, and after digestion and absorption in the latter (Chap. 5) the compounds of carbon become reorganized as animal protoplasm. In turn, these materials pass through other animals. Destructive metabolism in animals yields carbon dioxide as a respiratory waste that returns to the air or water.

Oxygen (O_2) is taken directly from the air or as dissolved in water (Fig. 7-2) to serve oxidative processes in animal bodies. It returns later to the environment either combined with carbon as carbon dioxide or with hydrogen as water. From the carbon dioxide used by plants the oxygen is released to the environment, but plants also use some oxygen in respiration. A "balanced aquarium" contains animals and plants in such quantities that their mutual needs and outputs of oxygen and carbon dioxide are in equilibrium.

Atmospheric *nitrogen* (N) can be used directly only by nitrogen-fixing bacteria in soil or in root nodules of some legumes, which combine it into nitrates (NO_3). Plants use nitrates to form vegetable proteins. These either return by decay to the soil or are eaten by animals and converted into animal proteins. In animal metabolism the latter are finally broken into nitrogenous wastes, mostly urea, $(NH_2)_2CO$, and then excreted. By action of other bacteria in soil or water such wastes are converted to ammonia and to nitrites; by further bacterial action either the nitrogen is returned to the air, or the nitrites are converted into nitrates.

Certain *minerals,* or inorganic chemical substances, are essential for both plants and animals (pars. 3-21, 5-12) in small but definite amounts that differ in various species. Plants obtain mineral constituents from the soil solution around their roots, and these return to the soil only by decay or burning of the plants. The supply for animals is taken partly from their food and partly from water, and in some cases directly from the soil. Minerals from animals return to the soil or water in excretions and feces and upon decay of their bodies (Fig. 13-3).

Phosphorus is an example of a "circulating" mineral needed in small amounts in protoplasm. Phosphates (—PO_4) are made available to plants through erosion from the great reservoirs of past ages in the rocks. Phosphorus normally is utilized by plants and animals and then returned to the soil through death and decay. Some is carried to the sea and a part is lost in the deep sediments but much of it is recaptured by fishes and marine birds. Man seeks the vast deposits of bird droppings (guano), such as occur on the coast of Peru and on Nauru Island in the South Pacific, for phosphate fertilizer to bring it back into the cycle.

B. THE BIOLOGICAL ENVIRONMENT AND ANIMAL INTERRELATIONS

Individual animals spend much of their time actively seeking food for energy and growth. They also need shelter for protection from adverse climate and enemies and they require breeding places.

13-5. Food. Both plants and animals com-

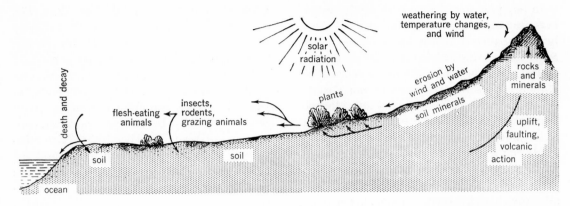

Fig. 13-3. The mineral cycle. Materials uplifted into mountains become disintegrated into soil minerals. By erosion and water or wind transport these move gradually toward the lowlands and the sea; meanwhile, some pass once or many times through plants and animals.

pete for the necessities of life in diverse ways. Each species has particular requirements, and every individual needs a certain amount of food of the right kinds. All animal food is derived ultimately from plants, which are the only real producers in any community. Plant-eating animals are the primary consumers. They, in turn, serve as food for other animals,

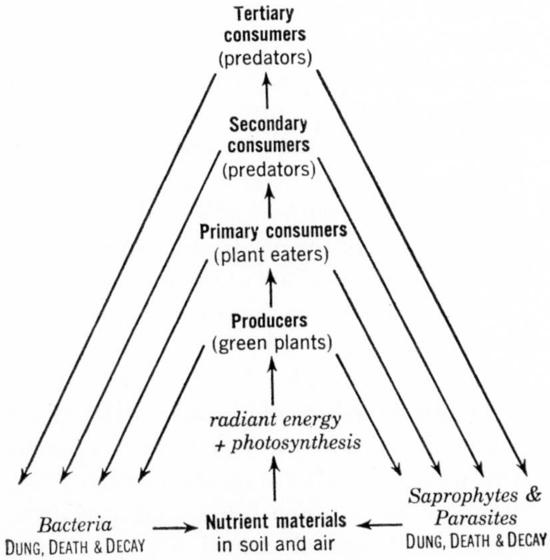

the secondary consumers, which are eaten by still others. The energy originally derived from the sun by plants thus passes in material form through a *food chain;* all food chains in a community constitute a *food cycle* or *food web* (Fig. 13-4). These relations are very complex, even in a small community, but may be illustrated by two simplified examples. In a pond the bacteria and algae synthesize materials from nutritive substances. Then, in sequence, small organisms are eaten by larger ones, thus:

Bacteria and algae → small protozoans → larger protozoans → rotifers, small crustaceans → aquatic insects → fishes

The large fishes, or any intermediate organisms, by death and decay, become food for bacteria, thus completing the circuit. Or the fishes may be taken by herons, mink, or men and end up elsewhere. On land a food chain may include the following:

Soil minerals, carbon dioxide, and water → plants → plant-eating insects, rodents, or grazing mammals → predaceous insects or small carnivores → larger carnivores

This ends with death and decay just as in an aquatic environment.

Fig. 13-4. The food cycle and pyramid of numbers. Going upward, the members of successive levels increase in size but decrease in total numbers.

In any predator chain the successive members are larger in size but fewer in total numbers. The reverse is true for parasite chains. Scavenger chains also are an exception, size and numbers bearing little or no relation to sequential position. Chains are not strictly linear but have many branches and alternative links. Any animal above the smallest takes food (prey) in relation to its size, neither so small that it cannot profitably gather enough nor too large for it to overcome successfully. Some food chains are long, but there are usually only about five successive stages. The huge whalebone whales, however, have a short food chain because they sieve enormous quantities of minute crustaceans from the sea.

Biomass is the total amount of living material in a given area or the total of all members of a species in an area.

A detailed account of energy transfer in a natural community is provided in a study by Howard T. Odum at Silver Springs, Florida. The huge artesian fresh-water spring has been stable for many years, discharging upwards of 300,000,000 gallons per day at about 23°C. Primary production is by submerged plants, mainly *Sagittaria loricata* and the encrusting layer of green algae. Dominant herbivores are turtles, mullet, sunfishes, other fishes, snails, some insects, etc. The smaller carnivores include sunfishes, catfishes, predaceous beetles, and small invertebrates. Top carnivores are large-mouthed black bass, gars, and alligators. "Decomposers" are bacteria and crayfishes. The turnover of biomass averages about eight times per year for a total primary production of 6.39 kg. per square meter (57,100 pounds per acre) of organic matter. The "pyramid," in grams per square meter of biomass, comprises producers, 809; herbivores, 37; carnivores, 11; top carnivores, 1.5; decomposers, 5. The net plant production is supplemented by bread fed to fishes by tourists (486 Kcal. per square meter per year). The local "system" loses some materials and organisms that are carried downstream.

13-6. Pyramid of numbers. The food web of any community has been characterized by Charles Elton as a pyramid of numbers (Fig. 13-4). Animals at the base are small and abundant, whereas those at the apex are few but large; of those between there is progressive increase in the size of individuals but a decrease in their numbers. In a deciduous woods, for example, aphids and other minute herbivorous insects may be enormously abundant, spiders and carnivorous beetles are fairly common, insectivorous birds are fewer, and the hawks and weasels preying on the birds are numerically sparse. The smallest kinds, because of their size, can reproduce rapidly, whereas larger members of the chain multiply more slowly. The largest predators at the apex are relatively so scarce that, in turn, they cannot serve profitably as prey for other species.

13-7. Shelter and breeding places (Fig. 13-8). Animals that live in large bodies of open water can avoid enemies only by superior ability in locomotion, but many species of the smaller waters and on land live in various types of *cover* and use retreats, or *shelters,* to avoid enemies and unfavorable environmental conditions. Small mammals, birds, lizards, and insects inhabit grassland, shrubbery, or trees; various marine fishes and invertebrates dwell amid seaweeds, rocks, or coral in shore waters, and some fresh-water fishes live among aquatic plants; and moles, pocket gophers, some snakes, various insects, earthworms, and other invertebrates are more or less continually within the soil. All these various animals find appropriate types of food, escape enemies, and avoid extremes of weather or other adverse influences in the several environments they inhabit.

Most animals also have special requirements for *breeding places* where the eggs or young are produced. For some the shelter serves, but others build special nests, as is done by many birds, some fishes, and various insects. Small animals breed wherever conditions are suitable. In many kinds of birds and some mammals, however, each pair establishes a *territory* to supply the food requirements of the parents and offspring for the breeding season; the territory is defended against invasion by others of the same species.

13-8. Competition. The members of a species all have the same requirements for the necessities of life (food, shelter, mates) and therefore compete with one another. In animals of solitary habit, the individuals live spaced apart so that each has better chance to satisfy its needs. The territories (par. 27-18) established by many kinds of birds and some mammals serve the same purpose. Excess individuals, denied their requirements, are eliminated. No two species, even if closely related and living together in the same biotic community (par. 13-14) have precisely identical needs, thus are not entirely competitive. The cormorant (*Phalacrocorax carbo*) and shag (*P. aristotelis*) are English sea birds of like form and habits living together in coastal waters. Cormorants, however, seek bottom-dwelling flatfishes and shrimps, whereas shags catch eels and herring in the upper waters. They nest in proximity on the same cliffs but choose different kinds of sites.

When animals of different kinds depend on one or more of the same necessities, they also compete with each other. Grasslands, for example, are the common forage area of grasshoppers and other plant-eating insects, rodents, rabbits, deer, and domestic livestock. There will be little or no competition for food in a season when more grass is present than all the grazers can consume. The same area, however, may display a life-and-death competition when severe drought results in a scant supply of grass. Species that have some latitude in choice of food may use other sources and thereby escape effects of decline in one kind of food.

An outside species sometimes is added to an existing community by migration or through introduction by man. If its requirements for some necessity are identical with those of a species already present, one of them may be reduced or eliminated. When starlings invade a new locality, they take over nest holes previously used by bluebirds or titmice—to the disadvantage of the latter. Many other biological "upsets" derive from competition of alien animals and plants. It is thought that competition was important in the geologic past when invaders replaced occupant species and the latter became extinct.

13-9. Predation. Every animal that consumes another animal is called a *predator* (or enemy) and the animal eaten is its *prey*. Any that consumes members of its own species is termed *cannibalistic,* and one that eats dead animals is a *scavenger*. Any food chain, after the first plant-eating animal, is a succession of predations. Predation differs from parasitism in that a predator destroys its prey outright, but a parasite usually continues to feed on its living host. As Elton says, predators live on capital and parasites on income.

13-10. Disease. Practically every animal species is subject to diseases produced by various types of organisms—viruses, rickettsias, bacteria, protozoans, parasitic worms, and arthropods. The disease organisms themselves must be considered as populations that in turn are affected by various factors in their respective environments; and they in turn influence the numbers and well-being of the animals on which they live. Disease is one of the agencies in regulation of animal numbers. Attention here will be confined to animals as parasites.

A *parasite* is an organism that lives on or in another species, the *host,* obtaining food and shelter at the latter's expense. The host can live without the parasite, but the latter normally cannot exist without its host. The parasitic animals include many PROTOZOA such as those causing malaria, amoebic dysentery, and other diseases; flukes, tapeworms, and other PLATYHELMINTHES; hookworms, root nematodes, and many other NEMATODA; all hairworms (NEMATOMORPHA) and spiny-headed worms (ACANTHOCEPHALA); various leeches (ANNELIDA); and many ARTHROPODA including fish lice, some barnacles and other CRUSTACEA, the mosquitoes, flies, fleas, and various other INSECTA, and the ticks and many mites (ARACHNIDA).

A species of parasite either inhabits one host species, or a group of similar hosts, or alternates between two or more host species; each kind of parasite is usually restricted to a certain site in its host. *Ectoparasites* such as leeches and lice live on the skin, and *endoparasites* dwell within the body, in the gut cavity (many worms) or other organs, in muscles (trichina) or other tissues, in the blood (some worms and protozoans), or even in blood cells (malarial parasites). Some parasitic insects and ticks in turn are intermediate hosts for parasitic protozoans or other organisms that they transmit to other hosts (Chaps. 16, 18, 22, 23).

Different parasites evidently arose separately in various phyla from free-living ancestors and have become variously specialized or degenerate for the parasitic mode of existence. Many have hooks or suckers for holding to their hosts; the gut is simplified (absent in tapeworms) because their fluid food is obtained directly by pumping or absorption from the host; and the reproductive organs are usually elaborated to produce enormous numbers of eggs or larvae to overcome successfully the hazards of reaching new hosts.

Some parasites have scant effect on their hosts, others injure the latter temporarily or permanently by the destruction of tissues or production of toxic secretions, and some kill their hosts. Harmful parasites are termed *pathogenic.* A host that recovers from the initial attack or damage often becomes a *carrier,* retaining some of the parasites which continue to pass out eggs or larvae that may infect other hosts. Parasitism is the mode of life for many species; for survival as a species the parasite should not unduly injure its host. Parasitism, along with some diseases, is one factor in the regulation of populations of host animals. Some of the most notable instances of such control occur among insects, where the matter is further complicated by secondary parasites, or *hyperparasites,* that parasitize the primary parasites.

13-11. Symbiosis. Parasitism and some other kinds of special interrelations between two organisms of different species are termed *symbiosis.* When one gains benefit by living with, on, or in another, without harm or benefit to the second, the case is called *commensalism.* The commensal "lives aboard his neighbor's vessel but does not eat his provisions." Some do get scraps from the host's "table." Examples are the remora that attaches by its dorsal sucker to some other fish for transport; the crabs that live regularly in the tubes of some echiurid and annelid worms; other crabs in the mantle cavities of sea mussels; the special barnacles that attach only to whales or sea turtles; and the hydroids that gain support and a wider forage range by fastening to shells of certain crabs.

A more intimate relation is that of *mutualism,* in which two species have acquired such close interdependence that life apart is impossible. A striking example is that of certain termites and flagellate protozoans. The termites eat wood but cannot digest cellulose; however, the flagellates in the termite gut can do so, and thus food is available for both. Termites experimentally rid of the flagellates soon die of starvation, and the protozoans cannot live a free existence. The green hydra (*Chlorohydra*) contains green algae (zoochlorellae), the one giving off carbon dioxide and the other oxygen as a by-product; sealed in a tube of water both live for some time by mutual aid. Similarly, yellow or brown algae (zooxanthellae) are present in various protozoans, sponges, coelenterates (corals, sea anemones), and flatworms. Some species of beetles, ants, and termites grow and tend "gardens" of peculiar types of fungi—that grow only under such care—and the fungi serve those insects as their sole food. Even man has a mutualistic relation with his crops of wheat and maize and some livestock that grow only with his aid. Something approaching mutualism, but often termed *slavery,* is the practice of ants that gather and tend aphids. The ants shelter and protect the aphids, and the latter produce secretions used as food by the ants. Both ants and aphids, however, can also live independently.

Cross-fertilization or *pollination* of plant blossoms by insects (occasionally by birds) is a mutual relation of wide occurrence and great importance because many plants are self-sterile. Pollen is transferred from flower stamen to an insect's body and to (another) flower pistil. Hive bees visit blossoms to obtain both nectar and pollen for their own needs (par. 23-15) and in so doing carry pollen between the flowers they visit. Many of man's staple food and forage crops depend on these flower-insect relationships.

13-12. Colonies and societies. All vertebrates, most arthropods, and many other invertebrates are *free-living* in that each individual gets about by its own efforts. By contrast, sponges, many hydroids, corals, bryozoans, tunicates, and others are *sessile*, being fixed to some substratum of rocks, plants, or shells of other animals. Among both categories, many species are *solitary* in that each individual is more or less independent, whereas others live in groups, or *colonies*. The many "individuals" of a colony among sponges, bryozoans, and tunicates are bound together structurally. In other cases the individuals in colonies of insects, schools of fishes, flocks of birds, and herds of hoofed mammals are structurally separate but integrated by behavior.

Solitary animals such as carnivores (mountain lions, mink, etc.), hawks, flycatchers, snakes, and predaceous insects forage best independently and pair up only for reproduction. Members of some other species assemble without reference to age or sex. In the winter flocks of robins, ducks, or starlings, many eyes and ears are of greater service when foraging or sleeping. Groups of bats, rattlesnakes, or lady beetles gather for hibernation with some advantage. Among active groups of mammals or birds there is often a "leader," and a gradation in dominance between individuals, as seen in the "pecking order" among fowls of one sex in a flock. Some sexual assemblages bring males and females together for mating, as with frogs, toads, gulls, and fur seals.

Societal organization occurs where many individuals of a species live together in an integrated manner so that each contributes in some specialized way to the welfare of all. The social habit has arisen independently in several orders of insects; it is highly developed among the termites, and in many bees, wasps, and ants. The transition from solitary to social life apparently is correlated with lengthening of adult life and increasing parental care. Solitary bees provision their nests, lay eggs, and depart, never to see their offspring. Social bees, on the other hand, feed their young regularly during development. Distinct *castes* have developed to perform such tasks as feeding, guarding the colony, etc. Worker and soldier castes differ in structure and physiology and cannot live independently. Success with them is measured in terms of the colony and not of the individual. Human society comprises integrated groups of like individuals that specialize in different trades or professions to the benefit of both the individual and the group as a whole.

13-13. Populations. All the animals of one species that occupy a given area comprise a *population.* Beyond the activities of its constituent members, a population has definite structure and organization. It grows and declines and has a certain composition as to ratio of the sexes and age groups that may change with circumstances. Population is stated in terms of density, numbers per unit of area. The rate of change—increase or decrease—is determined by the numbers of new individuals added (birth rate) vs. the losses from all causes (death rate). When additions exceed losses, the population increases, and vice versa. The course of a population with time can be expressed in a graph (Fig. 13-5).

Few people realize the huge populations of animals and plants that exist. Diatoms and protozoans may exceed 1,000,000 per liter of sea water. Censuses of the upper half inch of topsoil near Washington, D.C., revealed small organisms at the rate of 1,200,000 animals and 2,100,000 seeds or fruits per acre of forest soil;

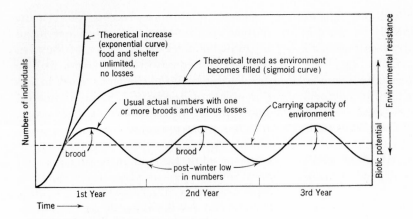

Fig. 13-5. Ideal curves of animal population growth.

the comparable figures for meadow soil were 13,600,000 animals and 33,800,000 plants. On croplands, grasshoppers sometimes number 20,000 to 200,000 per acre, and heavy infestations of eggs and larvae of the alfalfa weevil may total 8,000,000 to 22,000,000 per acre. The numbers of larger organisms are naturally much smaller—birds at 2 per acre over the United States, deer at 1 to 25 or 40 acres, and black bears at 1 per several square miles.

Some winter flocks of ducks have included more than 200,000 birds; the bison on the Great Plains originally numbered several millions; of these, about 3,000,000 were killed in 1872–1874 alone. In eastern North America, flocks of the now extinct passenger pigeon once darkened the skies for days during migration, and nearly 12,000,000 were killed and sold in one Michigan town in 40 days.

The potential rate of increase, or *biotic potential,* for all animals is very great, though slower in the larger forms. Any species would soon overrun the earth if it went unchecked, but *environmental resistance* in the form of competition, enemies, disease, and climatic limitations intervenes. The characteristic growth curve for a population when introduced into a new area (or a population of fruit

flies or flour beetles in a laboratory culture) is sigmoid or ∫-shaped (Fig. 13-5). Growth is slow at first because the few individuals do not readily meet for mating. After establishment, growth becomes very rapid, increasing in exponential fashion (like compound interest) until the population reaches the limit of its food supply, or until all suitable habitats are occupied, or until parasites and predators multiply to such an extent that the rate of increase levels off. Finally an *equilibrium* is reached, and the population fluctuates around this level, depending on variations in climatic and biotic factors. The equilibrium is also known as the *saturation level* or *carrying capacity* for a given locality, assuming that environmental conditions remain relatively constant; actually conditions change from season to season, year to year, and over periods of years. The "balance of nature," therefore, is a dynamic one, ever changing with shifts in the many environmental factors, some of which are also subject to cyclical changes.

Following the season for production of young in any species there is a surplus of individuals resulting in a *population pressure.* The reaction is a reduction in numbers by several means: dispersal to other areas and losses by predation, disease, or starvation. The effects are *density-dependent,* that is, related to the numbers per unit of area. All the factors of loss operate more severely when numbers are high; their effects lessen as numbers decline.

Severe unseasonable weather (hurricanes, droughts, floods, excessive heat or cold) is *density-independent* in its effect on decline in a species; the kill is in proportion to the number of animals present, but there is no special effect related to the density of numbers when the calamity occurs.

13-14. The biotic community. In 1887 Stephen A. Forbes wrote an essay on "The lake as a microcosm." He pictured the self-contained aquatic environment with all its fluctuating and interacting populations as a unit. This is now known as an *ecosystem,* and animals and plants comprise the *biotic community.* The community concept is difficult to delimit because habitats sometimes blend gradually into one another and, like the populations of which it is composed, the community is in dynamic equilibrium. Nevertheless, the biotic community, whether that of a fallen log, a lake, a meadow, or a forest, is more or less self-contained, with the plants and animals living together in an orderly manner. Like a human community it has certain structures and functions which are unique attributes of the group, over and above the individuals of which it is composed. Communities have producers, consumers, and decomposers, organized into food chains that together form a complex food web. They also are characterized by size and form, the individuals in a fallen log being small and often flattened, while those of a river are streamlined and often have adhesive organs. Within any biotic community one or a few species are *dominant* over the others, either in numbers or in physical characteristics or both. The dominant in a pine forest, for example, is

obviously the pine tree. It exerts a controlling influence over the community, creating the shade and the carpet of needles on which some of the associated plants and animals depend. The rarer species nevertheless are important because they lend stability to the community.

13-15. Ecological succession. Biotic communities are subject to change under the influence of seasonal and long-term climatic changes and also internal cumulative alterations of the environment. Thus there is a sequence or *succession* of communities in any given area. Typically a community passes through a pioneer stage and gradually matures; the final and relatively stable stage, called the *climax,* may persist for a long time. A classical example is the lake-pond-swamp-meadow succession. The biota is poor as to individuals and species in deep and relatively barren lakes; richer and different in species composition as the lake fills with organic sediment; still more distinctive in the pond or swamp stage; and finally, the swamp is overrun with rooted vegetation and becomes a meadow, when terrestrial communities are established (Fig. 13-6).

Analysis of pollen in cores from the bottom of a Connecticut pond (Deevey, 1952) showed that the succession from lake to pond required 11,000 years; the climate, as indicated by vegetational types, varied from cold (pine and spruce forests predominating) to warm (oak and other deciduous hardwoods). The various levels were dated by radiocarbon and the trees identified by distinctive pollen characteristics. The transition from deep, clear waters to a shallow pond was indicated by chitinous head capsules of a fresh-water midge larva (*Tanytarsus*) at lower levels and of a stagnant-water form (*Chironomus*) at the upper.

The principle of ecological succession is of practical importance in reforestation, range management, and other activities of mankind. Fire, for example, often denudes large areas

Fig. 13-6. Succession in plant cover and soil-making at edge of a large lake—providing new habitats for animals. Over a period of several centuries the shore line moves out into the original lake area, and new types of plants progressively occupy the new land. Over the years, replacement generations of animals keep to their respective habitats—fish and ducks to water and the killdeer (a shore bird) to the advancing beach. As new habitats develop, they also become occupied—earthworms and other invertebrates in the humus, arboreal squirrels in the trees, and so on. The rock on the original beach is a point of "reference." *(Adapted from R. and M. Buchsbaum, Basic ecology, by permission of Boxwood Press, Pittsburgh, Pa.)*

of climax forest. Attempts to restore the forest by planting dominant species of the climax stage usually result in failure (particularly in western North America) because of excessive sunlight, uncontrolled erosion, and competition from weeds, rodents, and shrubs favored in early stages of succession.

13-16. Ecology and conservation. Any change in the physical or biological character of an environment obviously affects different species in varying degree. To the natural forces that thus act ·upon the animal populations, the influences of man have been added in many places and with increasing vigor during recent centuries. Civilization is essentially an attempt by man to control the environment for his own advantage, υsually immediate; civilization involves applied ecology or ecological manipulation. Mankind has cut forests, drained swamps, irrigated arid lands, planted huge acreages of crops, and tried to kill off a wide variety of competitors and enemies from wolves and bison down to small insects and the many native (or introduced) plants classed as weeds. Agriculture, forestry, reclamation and irrigation, public health activities, and aid to game or fur species are all direct or indirect ecological manipulations. The perfecting of heavy bulldozers, gang plows, and power saws and of chemical poisons that can be distributed in quantity by airplane or from the ground to control insects or weeds has greatly multiplied man's ability to alter his surroundings. Much of this, however, is not constructive; accelerated erosion by wind and water after plowing up grass sod, stripping forests faster than they will regenerate, and various other effects are evident in many places. The disappearance of former large human civilizations that once flourished in the Near East and the decline in human "carrying capacity" of many other areas demonstrate that much human manipulation has been too hasty and ill-advised; it was largely exploitation with little regard for the future. A human civilization, like any plant or animal community, cannot long continue if its environment becomes damaged beyond recovery. Some current efforts at conservation of renewable (biological) natural resources are tending to correct certain evils of former environmental manipulations.

C. TYPES OF ANIMAL ENVIRONMENTS

That part of the earth containing living organisms is known as the *biosphere.* Within this relatively thin layer are many places, large and small, suitable for plants and animals. The term *habitat* is loosely used to indicate the place where an animal lives. The role or function that the organism plays in the community is called its *ecologic niche*—the habitat is the organism's "address," and the niche is its "profession." The most obvious major divisions of environments used by animals are the salt waters, fresh waters, and land, but even these grade into each other (Fig. 13-7).

13-17. Salt waters. Oceans, seas, and bays cover about 71 per cent of the earth, providing habitats that are extensive and stable. Their physical features include:

(1) *Temperatures* from 32°C. (89°F.) in the tropics to −2.2°C. (28°F.) in some polar regions, but rarely with an annual variation more than 5°C. (9°F.) at any one place; (2) dissolved *gases* varying with temperature and depth; (3) *salt content* averaging 3.5 per cent (NaCl, 2.35; $MgCl_2$, 0.5; Na_2SO_4, 0.4; $CaCl_2$, 0.11; KCl, 0.07; $NaHCO_3$, 0.02; and others); (4) average *depth* of oceans about 12,500 feet, but 35,640 feet (6.7 miles) in the greatest "deep"; (5) *pressure* increasing about 1 atmosphere for each 33 feet of depth so that animals of deep waters live under enormous pressures, but these are equalized throughout their bodies; and (6) *light* penetrating decreasingly down to 600 feet, a trace to 3,000 feet, with complete permanent darkness below.

Marine animals include representatives of all phyla and of all classes except the centipedes, millipedes, and amphibians. The ctenophores, brachiopods, chaetognaths, echino-

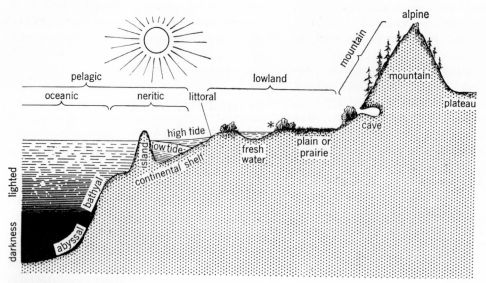

Fig. 13-7. An ideal section at the margin of a continent with indication of some common ecologic environments available to animals. The area labeled neritic is also called the continental shelf. The region marked with an asterisk (*) is enlarged in Fig. 13-8.

derms, and lower chordates are exclusively marine. Species and individuals are most abundant near the surface and decrease with depth, but some occur at the greatest depths. Dredgings by the English "Challenger" expedition gave the following results:

Depth, feet	Numbers of species
0–200	4,400
200–1,000	2,050
1,000–2,000	710
2,000–3,000	600
3,000–4,000	500
4,000–5,000	340
Below 5,000	235

The Danish "Galathea" expedition of 1952 dredged much more deeply, from about 8,200 feet down to 32,800 feet. The number of animal species decreased progressively from 60 to 6.

Marine animals are segregated ecologically as follows:

1. **Plankton.** Organisms that float and are moved passively by winds, waves, or currents; mostly of minute or microscopic size with surface large in relation to bulk, often with elongate body parts or ciliated; includes many protozoans and crustaceans, some mollusks, a few worms, and a host of larvae (sponges to tunicates) and microplants (diatoms, algae).

2. **Nekton.** Animals that swim freely by their own efforts; includes squids, fishes, sea snakes and turtles, sea birds, seals, whales, etc. Plankton and nekton animals of the open sea are termed *pelagic*. The pelagic region has two subdivisions: *Neritic,* overlying the continental shelf; and *Oceanic,* over the deeper waters.

3. **Benthos.** Strict bottom dwellers, segregated by depth and nature of the bottom:

a. LITTORAL or SHORE. Between the tide lines, alternately exposed to air and covered by water twice daily; strong wave action brings much food and oxygen; segregated according to nature of bottom (mud, sand, or rock) and zoned according to length of exposure between tides; population dense; protozoans to tunicates.

b. SUBLITTORAL. Below low tide line to depths of about 600 feet (100 fathoms) on the "continental shelf"; water well oxygenated, some wave action; many animals; protozoans to fishes.

c. BATHYAL. At depths of 600 to 12,000 feet; water quiet, progressively colder, little to no light; fewer animals, often with light-producing organs.

d. ABYSSAL. Below 12,000 feet; permanently cold, quiet water, complete darkness, oxygen scant; animals scarce, usually small and dark-colored, eyes large or none. The bottom of the deepest trenches is called the hadal zone.

In the benthos, some worms, echinoderms, mollusks, and crustaceans *crawl* over the surface; many worms and some bivalve mollusks are *embedded* or *burrow;* and many sponges, hydroids, anemones, corals, bryozoans, mollusks, barnacles, and tunicates are *sessile,* or *attached* to various objects. The littoral and neritic vary in width according to the slope of the coast; the width of the littoral also varies with the height of the tides— 12 inches at Galveston, Texas, but 18½ feet at Eastport, Maine.

13-18. Fresh waters. These differ from the sea in being scattered and isolated, of lesser volume and depth, and more variable as to temperature, content of gases and salts, light penetration, turbidity, movement, and plant growth. "Pure" waters contain mere traces of salts, but some saline and alkaline waters have large amounts. Carbonates (especially $CaCO_3$) are usually commoner than other salts. Some bodies of fresh water are nearly constant in volume, but those of arid regions often fluctuate from flood stages to small volume or dry up completely during a single season.

Fresh-water animals include many protozoans, a few sponges, coelenterates and bryozoans, many worms, rotifers and snails, various bivalve mollusks, crustaceans, larval and adult insects, and vertebrates from fishes to mammals. Many of the invertebrates produce eggs or other "resting" stages resistant to drying or freezing that may be blown about by winds or carried accidentally on the feet of waterfowl. They rarely have floating larvae, since these might be carried by streams to the sea and be lost. In any one place the kinds and numbers usually change markedly through the year.

1. **Running waters.** The cold mountain streams, brooks and creeks, and rivers of various sizes contain mobile animals that are segregated according to the rate of water movement, temperature, oxygen content, and character of the bottom. Thus trout live only in cool, well-oxygenated waters, whereas carp thrive in warm and even foul waters. Inhabitants of rapid waters often are flattened or have means for holding to the bottom.

2. **Standing waters.** These comprise lakes, ponds, swamps, marshes (Fig. 13-8), and bogs. Any of

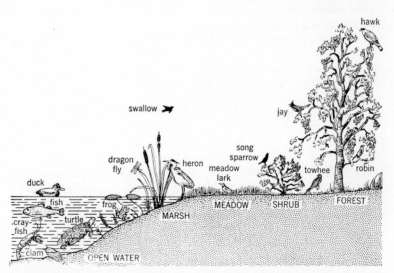

Fig. 13-8. Ecological distribution of some common animals of fresh water and land. In general, each keeps to a particular plant association or other subdivision of the environment.

them may be either permanent or temporary. They occur in all regions from polar and alpine areas to the tropics. Lakes in cold climates may be frozen for a long time in winter and those of temperate regions for shorter periods, but lakes of hot regions are always open. Large lakes afford more stable environments than flowing waters; they have littoral, benthic, and pelagic divisions and plankton. Water in large temperate lakes undergoes circulation because of temperature differences and wind action. In spring and fall this involves all depths; but in summer only the surface portion circulates over a definite plane, or **thermocline**, separating it from the cold and often poorly oxygenated water below, where there are but few animals.

13-19. Land. The interaction of many physical, climatic, and biological factors produces a wide variety of ecologic conditions on the continents and islands.

Lands differ in (1) the **chemical nature** and **physical texture** of the soil, sand, and rocks exposed on the surface; (2) the **topography**, which includes plains, rolling lands, hills, valleys, and mountains; and (3) the **altitude**, which varies from basins below sea level (Death Valley) to peaks exceeding 29,000 feet (Mount Everest). Some of the climatic variants are as follows: (1) **Air temperatures** vary at different places from far below freezing (where soil also freezes) to 60°C. (140°F.) on some deserts; in many localities the temperature fluctuates widely, by day or through a season, but there is only slight change in many tropical areas. (2) **Moisture** as rainfall amounts to 500 inches annually in a few tropical places but only mere traces on some deserts; the moisture content of air and soil varies from complete saturation to slight amounts according to place and time of year. (3) **Winds** and **sunlight** affect both the temperature and the moisture content of the air and ground. The physical and climatic conditions influence the plant cover that may grow on any land area, and the plants in turn affect the animal population, particularly where the latter depends directly upon plants for food and cover.

The principal terrestrial animals are mammals, birds, reptiles, insects, worms, and protozoans, with lesser numbers of amphibians, crustaceans, mollusks, etc. They are all mobile and live on the land surface, on plants, or at shallow depths in the ground. The subterranean habitat affords more uniform conditions than the surface. All animals that fly or "live" in the air return to the ground or to trees or rocks.

13-20. Climatic zones. It is a matter of common observation throughout the world that plants and animals are distributed according to more or less well-defined zones, depending in a general way on the climate. Tropical rain forests occur near the equator, and treeless tundra covers wide areas in the Arctic. Between these extremes are deciduous forests, coniferous forests, grasslands, etc. For any region of the world there is a sequence of **life zones** based mainly on temperature, as suggested by the correlation not only with latitudinal zones from the tropics to the polar regions but also with altitudinal zones from the bases to the tops of mountains (Fig. 13-9). Life zones are conspicuous on mountains in many parts of the world; in western North America distinct zones can be traversed within a few miles of travel or a few hundred feet of elevation.

Another ecological classification is by large and easily recognizable communities called **biomes**. The climax vegetation of a biome is of a uniform type or life form, though often of different species. Thus broad, thick leaves and heavy canopy are characteristic of the tropical rain-forest biome whether in Panama, New Guinea, or equatorial Africa; the grassland biome is similar in growth form though different in species composition on each of the continents; and the great deserts of the world support a type of vegetation (the desert biome) characterized by thorny plants having adaptations for conserving water.

Biomes in general are determined by climate. The freezing temperatures and short growing season of the Arctic are favorable to the growth of sphagnum and dwarf vegetation

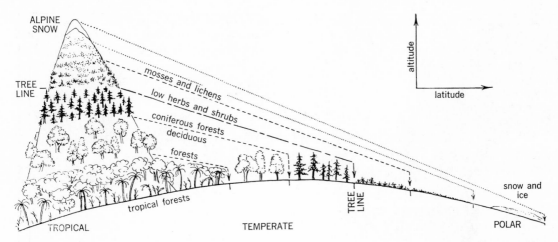

Fig. 13-9. Comparison of the latitudinal and altitudinal zones or associations of plants that provide the appropriate environments for various kinds of animals.

of the tundra, whereas the dry conditions of deserts, caused by adjacent mountain ranges that deplete winds of their moisture, are habitable only by desert-type vegetation and the associated animals. The biomes of North and Central America are as follows (Fig. 13-10).

1. **Tundra.** Treeless Arctic region; only the surface soil thaws out in the short summer; drainage poor, many ponds, marshes, and bogs; principal plants are bog (peat) mosses, lichens, sedges, grasses, and low herbs; mammals include musk ox, barren ground caribou, wolf, arctic fox, weasels, lemmings, arctic hare; conspicuous resident birds are snowy owl and ptarmigan (snow grouse); many migratory waterfowl and shore birds nest here in summer but go south in winter; no reptiles.

2. **Coniferous Forest** (boreal evergreen). South of tundra to northern United States, with extensions southward along mountain systems (Sierra-Cascade, Rocky, and Appalachian) to central America; winters bleak, summers cool, precipitation moderate; spruces, firs, pines, cedars; often includes shrubs and patches of grassland; mammals include moose and woodland caribou in the north and deer and elk toward the south, also the fur bearers—red fox, Canada lynx, marten, fisher, wolverine— with black bear and mountain lion, snowshoe

rabbit, and some small rodents; birds are various grouse, warblers, chickadees, jays, etc.; few reptiles and amphibians; trout, grayling, etc., in waters.

3. **Broad-leaved Deciduous Forest** (summer green). Especially from Mississippi Valley eastward; winters cold, summers warm and humid, with rain; oaks, maples, beeches, elms, walnuts, many shrubs and herbs; white-tailed deer, gray fox, wildcat, raccoon, fox, and flying squirrels; many warblers, vireos, and other small songbirds; many snakes and amphibians.

4. **Grassland** (prairies and Great Plains). Mississippi Valley westerly, Texas to Canada; winters of severe continental cold, summers hot, thundershowers. Great areas of hardy grasses (buffalo, bluestem, grama), trees locally along streams; bison, prong-horned antelope, wolf, coyote, badger, skunk, jack rabbit (= prairie hare), cottontails in thickets, ground squirrels; prairie chicken, burrowing owl, soaring hawks, meadowlarks; some snakes.

5. **Sagebrush.** Great Basin plateau between Rocky Mountains and Sierra-Cascade system. Dry, winters cold with limited rain or snow, summers hot. Sagebrush (*Artemisia tridentata*) and other bitter-flavored shrubs, bunch grasses. Prong-horned antelope, jack rabbit, ground squirrels, other burrowing rodents, coyote, badger, sage hen (largest American grouse), water birds in local ponds and marshes, many reptiles.

6. **Chaparral.** California hills and parts of moun-

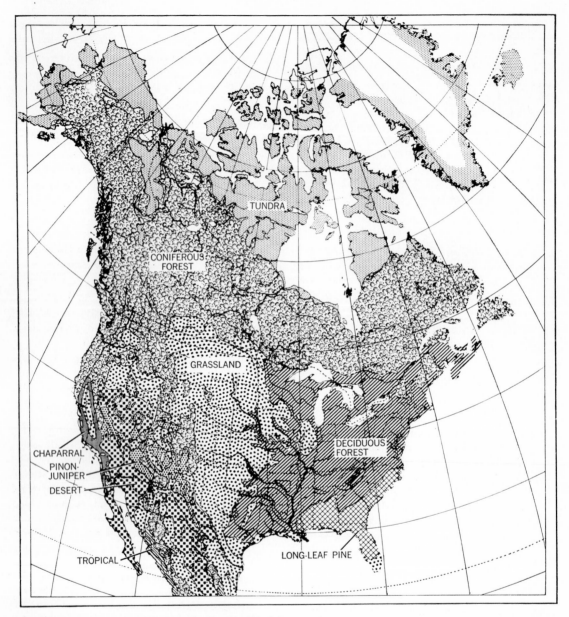

Fig. 13-10. Biomes of North America in simplified form.

tains. Rainy (snowy) winters, warm to hot dry summers. Chamise, manzanita, and other shrubs with thickened evergreen leaves. Mule deer, woodrat, chipmunks, brush rabbit, California thrasher, wrentit, lizards.

7. **Deserts.** Southeastern California to western Texas and southward. Soil rocky or sandy.

High summer temperatures, scant water at any time. Vegetation scattered; many herbs grow and flower soon after the occasional rains; cacti, yuccas. Smaller carnivorous mammals, many rodents active by night, few birds, many lizards, some snakes, few amphibians locally.

8. **Tropical Rain Forest.** Panama and parts of

Central America. Sustained moderate temperatures, abundant rainfall. Forest of evergreen broad-leaved trees, many vines, orchids, etc. Marmosas, opossums, sloths, anteaters, bats, monkeys, great variety of birds, reptiles, and amphibians.

13-21. Ecological changes due to mankind. Human activities have altered the ecologic distribution of many animals in various ways. The bison, mountain lion, and wolf have been reduced to the point of extinction over most of their original ranges. Trapping has reduced beavers and other valuable fur bearers. Excessive hunting has had a like effect on ducks, shore birds, wild turkeys, and other edible game birds. Clearing forest land to plant crops and build cities has destroyed the food and shelter of tree-using species, but the planting of trees and shrubs in parks and gardens has provided habitats for various animals that previously could not live on those sites. Draining swamps and lakes has destroyed the essential environment for muskrats, beavers, ducks, some fishes, and other species, whereas the irrigation of once dry open areas has enabled some aquatic and marsh-dwelling species to replace the rodents, reptiles, and other original denizens of those arid localities. The planting of agricultural crops over wide areas has afforded enhanced food supplies for various birds, rodents, and insects.

Distribution

No animal species occurs uniformly over the whole world, but each is restricted to a definite *range,* or area of *distribution.* The study of animal distribution and of the factors controlling it is known as *zoogeography.* Geographical distribution is concerned with spatial relations, barriers and avenues of dispersal, and historical origins, whereas ecological distribution is determined primarily by other factors previously described.

All the animals living in a particular area, large or small, are collectively termed the *fauna* (the equivalent term for plants is flora; the plants and animals together are referred to as the biota). The entire extent of land or water over which a species occurs is its *geographical range.*

The beaver, for example, has a geographical range that embraces much of North America and Europe; its ecological range comprises fresh-water lakes and streams bordered by aspens, poplars, or willows that may be cut to serve for food and for building dams; and its geological range includes, besides the present or Recent geologic time, also the Pleistocene and Pliocene epochs, when it had a wider geographical range. Some animals have a wide range, and other species are local in occurrence; some insects are known only from patches of plants covering but a few acres. Most animals have wider geographical and ecological ranges. The mallard duck inhabits fresh-water marshes through much of the Northern Hemisphere, the polar bear is restricted to Arctic shores and ice, and living elephants dwell in the forests of Africa, India, and nearby regions.

13-22. Factors regulating distribution. Since every species produces offspring in excess of the numbers that can survive within its normal range, this creates a *population pressure* by which individuals tend to expand the boundaries of their range. Other factors such as competition, enemies, disease, shortage of food, adverse seasonal weather, and decrease in available shelter act to reduce the population. The distribution of all animals, from protozoans to man, is consequently dynamic rather than static and always subject to change.

The external factors that limit distribution are termed *barriers.* These include (1) *physical barriers* such as land for aquatic species and mountain ranges, large rivers, and oceans for most terrestrial forms; (2) *climatic barriers* such as temperature (average, seasonal, or extreme), moisture (as rain, snow, air humidity, or soil moisture), amount of sunlight, and others; and (3) **biological barriers** such as absence of appropriate food or presence of effective competitors, enemies, or diseases. Many kinds of insects are limited to particular species of plants for their food, shelter, or breeding places, so that their distribution is controlled by factors that regulate these plants.

All plants and animals have limits of **tolerance** for each factor in the environment. In some cases, such as the tolerance to a poisonous substance in the soil or food, the range may be narrow, whereas tolerance to various wavelengths of light is commonly wide. In every case there is a minimum, an optimum, and a maximum; changes beyond the tolerance limits result in migration or death for the individuals or selection of the more tolerant (i.e., better adapted) individuals of a species. A species is limited in its distribution by the sum total of external influences, many of which are interdependent. Nevertheless, the range and equilibrium level of a population is ultimately subject to Liebig's **law of the minimum,** being limited by the essential factor present in least amount or by some critical stage or condition for which the species has a narrow range of adaptability. Oysters, for example, can live in various saline waters but breed only if the temperature exceeds a certain minimum.

12-23. Methods of dispersal. Free-living animals of some size become distributed by their own efforts. Birds, fishes, and others that migrate are quick to settle in any suitable new situation. Small aquatic animals and larvae and occasional large forms are carried about passively by water currents. Many small insects are wafted about in the air, mostly within a few hundred feet of the earth but some at higher levels, and thus may be deposited in new places. Migrating waterfowl carry eggs, seeds, and resistant spores of plants and animals to ponds or islands, sometimes over great distances. Rafts of trees, soil, and debris with animals on them may pass along large rivers and occasionally are seen far at sea; oceanic islands may have been populated by such means. Violent hurricanes sometimes transport small living animals. Some showers of organic matter in the United States have included earthworms deposited on a man's hat and on a buggy and many small fishes found after a heavy local rain in a previously dry cornfield in South Carolina. Parasites and commensal animals are transported by their hosts into new localities.

A species does not necessarily occur in all places suitable for it, but only in those to which it has access, and this depends on its own past history or that of its ancestors. Animal distribution of today is the joint result of existing barriers and of environmental conditions in the past. The continents have existed for long periods but have undergone many local alterations by elevation and erosion of mountain ranges, changes in the existence of lakes and streams, and the draining or flooding of lowlands. Some continents have been connected at times by **land bridges** and separated by seas at other periods in earth history. Warm climates extended to the polar regions in some periods, whereas glaciers blanketed much of the Northern Hemisphere several times during the Pleistocene epoch preceding the present. All such changes have altered the distribution of plants and animals. Older areas of land or water have been reduced or eliminated, and new ones have become available. Living organisms have been forced to move about, many species have been exterminated, and new species or groups have evolved to take advantage of new areas or environments.

Many North American animals are more closely related to species of eastern Asia than to those in South America. From this we infer that the shallow bottom of Bering Strait (300 feet deep) between Alaska and Siberia was exposed as a land bridge for terrestrial organisms in the late geological past (there are fossil remains of redwoods on islands there); the Isthmus of Panama is another bridge which has been interrupted at various times in the past, thus separating the Americas for considerable periods. Terrestrial species also need appropriate "ecologic bridges" of suitable environment through which to migrate. For example, the bison could not pass from North to South America because no open grasslands existed in the areas between.

D. GEOGRAPHICAL DISTRIBUTION

13-24. Zoogeographic realms (Fig. 13-11). These are the largest units in distribution and are defined by the land animals native to each.

The limits of each realm and its fauna reflect the past history of animal groups and also changes in the earth's surface that either permitted or prevented animal migrations. The Australian Realm has evidently been isolated longest and has many unique animals and plants. Its mammals include the egg-laying monotremes and many marsupials, the latter having "radiated" into a great variety of forms from huge jumping kangaroos to small burrowing marsupial moles. There is much evidence to indicate that the great Asiatic land mass was for long a center where various ani-

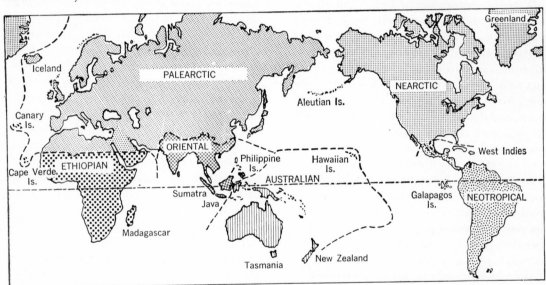

Fig. 13-11. The zoogeographic realms (separated by broken lines).

1. *Australian.* Australia, Tasmania, New Guinea, New Zealand, and oceanic islands of the Pacific. All monotremes, most marsupials (no placental mammals but bats and rodents), emu, cassowaries, brush turkeys, lyre birds, birds of paradise, most cockatoos, Australian lungfish. New Zealand has sphenodon and kiwi.
2. *Oriental.* Asia south of the Himalayas: India, Ceylon, Malay Peninsula, Sumatra, Borneo, Java, Celebes, and the Philippines. Tarsiers, macaques, gibbons, orang-utan, Indian elephant and rhinoceros, jungle fowl, peacock.
3. *Ethiopian.* Africa including the Sahara Desert, Madagascar, and adjacent islands. Gorilla, chimpanzee, African elephant, rhinoceros, and lion, hippopotamus, zebra, giraffe, many horned antelopes, ostrich, guinea fowl, secretary bird. Many lemurs in Madagascar.
4. *Neotropical.* South and Central America, Mexican lowlands, and West Indies. Llama, alpaca, peccaries, arboreal sloths, armadillos, anteater, guinea pig, etc., vampire bats, rheas, toucans, curassows and guans, most hummingbirds.
5. *Nearctic.* North America from the Mexican highlands to the Arctic islands and Greenland. Mountain goat, prong-horned antelope, caribou, muskrat.
6. *Palearctic.* Eurasia south to the Himalayas, Afghanistan, Persia, and Africa north of the Sahara. Hedgehog, wild boar, fallow and roe deer.

mal stocks originated and migrated to other regions. The great flightless birds are now in southern realms, the emu and cassowaries in the Australian, the ostrich in the Ethiopian, and the rheas in the Neotropical. Such *discontinuous distribution* occurs also with the tapirs in Malaysia and Central America, the limbless amphibians (caecilians) in the tropics of the New and Old Worlds, and others. The Palearctic and Nearctic realms are least separated, and their faunas have much in common so that they are often combined as the *Holarctic Realm.* This is characterized by the elk (red deer), moose, bison, beaver, marmots, most bears and sheep, mallard duck, golden eagle, trouts, and salmons. Few or no species or groups occur throughout any single realm, but some range in parts of two. The tiger occurs from India to northern China, the opossums from South America into the United States, and the mountain lion and rattlesnakes through both the Americas. Various subdivisions of each realm can be distinguished, each with a more or less distinct fauna.

13-25. Insular faunas. *Continental islands* stand in shallow waters close to the continents from which they were probably separated in the recent geologic past. The fauna of each resembles that of the nearby mainland, having identical species or closely related subspecies. It often includes various small mammals, reptiles, and amphibians probably resident in the area at the time of its separation from the continent, since they cannot travel through salt water. *Oceanic islands* arise by volcanic activity from great depths in the sea. The fauna lacks amphibians and mammals save for bats and occasional rodents, the latter possibly transported in native boats. Wide-ranging fishes, sea birds, and marine mammals visit their shores. The land birds and insects are peculiar and often include wingless forms, which are less likely to be swept away by storms. The Galápagos Islands under the equator off Ecuador have bats and some land birds related to mainland species. The principal land birds (Family Geospizidae) comprise

about 40 local forms, mostly finch-like but with some resembling warblers and woodpeckers. One of these employs a stick as a "tool" to probe for insects! The separate islands have various species of giant land tortoises, relatives of which occur on the mainland of South America and on certain islands in the Indian Ocean. The Hawaiian Islands, also oceanic, have one native bat and one rat probably brought by the Polynesians. The bird Family Drepanididae has "radiated" into various forms resembling finches, warblers, creepers, and other ecologic types. New Zealand is an island group with the features of an oceanic island. It lacked native mammals except for one unique bat, but had flightless birds, the now extinct moas and the living kiwi. Its most distinctive reptile (*Sphenodon*) is the sole living species of an otherwise extinct order, and its one "frog" likewise belongs to an ancient group.

13-26. Introduced animals. Many kinds of animals have been moved by man into regions where they were not native, some deliberately and others by accident. Many such *aliens* soon disappear, and some remain scarce, but others have become widespread and abundant. In each case the result depends on the suitability of the new environment, the availability of an unoccupied niche, the degree of competition with native species, and the extent to which the alien is affected by predators and diseases in its new home. Fleas, lice, tapeworms, and other parasites of man and domestic animals have been accidentally spread with their hosts to new lands; some have then shifted to native hosts, as the sheep tapeworm into American deer. The European corn borer, Japanese beetle, cotton boll weevil, codling moth, Argentine ant, and garden nematode are conspicuous alien pests now important on crops in the United States. The house mouse, Norway, black, and roof rats, house fly, and bedbug are aliens that are common domestic nuisances in most civilized regions. Attempts have been made to restrict the further spread of many such pests by quarantine laws.

Some deliberate but harmful introductions include the European gray rabbit in Australia and New Zealand, where it competes for sheep pasturage, the Indian mongoose taken to Jamaica and Hawaii to control rats but which destroyed native birds instead, and the "English sparrow" brought into the United States in hope of controlling the introduced gypsy and brown-tail moths but which merely has become a nuisance.

Some introductions by man have been useful, such as the ladybird beetles imported for the "biological control" of various scale insects harmful to fruit trees, the ring-necked pheasant established in many states as an additional game bird for hunting, the trout transplanted into various waters, and the striped bass, shad, and other fishes placed in lowland waters of the Pacific coast to supplement the few native food and game fishes originally there.

In general, the practice of transplanting alien animals and plants has benefited the human race. Nearly all domesticated animals (the turkey is an exception) have been imported from other places, and most of our crop plants are likewise aliens. The practice, however, is dangerous. Parasites and diseases often are more destructive in their new homes. Plants and animals harmless in their native lands may become pests when transplanted, like the prickly pear cactus and the European rabbit; introduced into Australia, both ran wild, covering millions of acres. The prickly pear was finally controlled by introducing the insect enemies which kept it in check in its native home on the American desert.

E. GEOLOGICAL DISTRIBUTION

13-27. Fossils. The animals living today are only part of a vast and continuing population that has inhabited the earth through millions of years (Figs. 13-12, 13-13, and end papers). Evidence of former animals and plants is provided by fossils. A *fossil* (literally something dug up) is a relic that is preserved by natural means in rocks or softer sediments that affords information as to the character of the original organism.

Dead animals are usually destroyed by scavengers or by decay; but if soon covered by silt beneath water, by wind-blown soil, or by volcanic dust, decomposition will be slow and the hard parts may persist. If the surrounding material later becomes rock and is neither crushed nor heated, the remains will survive for long periods. A fossil may be (1) an *unaltered hard part* such as a skeleton, a tooth, or a shell; (2) a *mold,* where hard parts once present are dissolved away by percolating waters to leave a cavity showing the original form; (3) a *petrifaction,* in which the original has been replaced particle by particle with other mineral substance to preserve all fine detail; or (4) a *cast* of mineral which fills a mold to show only exterior features. Even soft parts may leave impressions in fine sediments. Some fossil records of animal activities survive as tracks, burrows, tubes, and droppings. Fossil plants are common as impressions, or casts. Special types of fossils are the carcasses (with flesh, hair, etc.) of mammoths and woolly rhinoceros frozen in tundra soils of Siberia and Alaska; skin, hair, and dung of ground sloths in Nevada caves; skeletons of giant elk and other animals in peat bogs of Ireland and elsewhere; entire remains of insects and other small animals embedded in amber (fossil resin), as along the Baltic Sea; and skeletons of many species trapped in asphalt pits (former tar pools) of southern California.

Besides providing evidence of past life, fossils are used for identifying rock strata and for indicating a chronological or time sequence of such strata. They afford some information as to ancient environments and climates and as to the interrelations of bygone animals; and they furnish important data on the organic evolution of animals and plants down through time (Chap. 14). Many present-day species of animals occur also as fossils,

Fig. 13-12. Reconstruction of Middle Cambrian sea life (Burgess Shale, British Columbia, 540 million years old). (*A*) Grass-like alga. (*B*) Tubular sponge (*Vauxia*). (*C, D, E*) Pseudocrustaceans (*Sidneyia, Marrella, Hymenocaris*). (*F*) Sea cucumber (*Mackenzia*). (*G*) Polychaete (*Miskoia*). (*H*) Jellyfish (*Eldonia?*). (*I, J*) Trilobites. (*K*) Brachiopod (*Acrotreta*). (*Photo of group in Chicago Natural History Museum.*)

showing that they lived in earlier geologic epochs. Fossils show that in the past various groups such as dinosaurs came to great prominence and later perished completely. The fossil record is fragmentary at best. Remains are more complete and numerous in rocks of later geologic periods, whereas in the older formations they are scarcer and less perfect because the rocks have been disturbed and crushed by earth movements or changed by heat.

13-28. Geological time. Estimates of the age of fossils are derived mainly from study of radioactive minerals in fossil-bearing rocks.[1] The oldest recognizable rocks (Archeozoic) are considered to be about 2.6 billion years old, and the oldest rocks (Cambrian) with nu-

[1] Uranium upon radioactive decay yields primarily lead of atomic weight 206 (ordinary lead, atomic weight 207). Precise study shows that 1 per cent of uranium thus disintegrates in 66,000,000 years. Careful chemical analyses of the ratio of uranium to lead 206 in undisturbed rocks have provided an approximate time scale for the various strata of rocks containing fossils in the "geological column" and hence an estimate of the time when the animals there represented were living (Fig. 29-6; also end papers). The amount of decay of radioactive potassium to argon is another method for precise dating of rocks and is the basis for the currently accepted geological time scale (see end papers).

Time scales for more recent periods are the chronology established by studying the number and spacing of tree rings (covering about 1,000 years) and the percentage of disintegration of radioactive carbon, carbon 14 (about 10,000 years). Carbon 14 is produced in minute amounts by bombardment of CO_2 by cosmic rays in the atmosphere. Some of this carbon 14 enters into plant tissues and when analyzed, hundreds or thousands of years later, can be dated within fair limits of error. The limit for this method is about 40,000 years.

Fig. 13-13. Late Pleistocene life at Rancho La Brea tar pools, Los Angeles, Calif., 10,000 to 20,000 years ago. (*A*) Dire wolf (†*Aenocyon*). (*B*) Giant vulture (†*Teratornis*). (*C*) Saber-tooth cat (†*Smilodon*). (*D*) Horses (*Equus*). (*From painting by C. R. Knight in Chicago Natural History Museum.*)

merous fossils 600,000,000 years old. The time since the Archeozoic may be visualized by comparing it to the distance from New York to San Francisco (about 3,300 miles). One year is represented by 0.0804 inch (2.13 mm.), a human lifetime by 5.63 inches, the Christian era by 13.17 feet, and the time since early Pleistocene when man appeared by about 2.5 miles— but a short distance down the road of time (see Fig. 29-6).

REVIEW

1. What are the most important chemical substances in animal environments, and how does each affect animal populations?
2. What environmental factors serve to increase the population of a species? What factors act to reduce its numbers?
3. Distinguish between parasitism and predation.
4. What is the essential feature of symbiosis? Compare commensalism and mutalism.
5. Are there benefits from societal organization? Are there disadvantages?
6. How does an animal colony differ from a biotic community?
7. What is ecological succession? Give a simple example. Is succession of practical importance in human affairs?
8. What are some important physical features of salt waters? Of fresh waters? Of the land as an animal environment?
9. In what kind of biome do you live? How has it been altered by man?
10. How do barriers influence the geographic range of a species?
11. In what ways may animals spread from one place to another?
12. Why is the fauna of oceanic islands usually both meager and distinctive?
13. What is a fossil? How do fossils form? Of what value are they to our knowledge of geographic distribution, past and present?
14. What means are used to date animals (or plants) of the past?

14 Organic evolution

Mankind has long sought to learn how, when, and where life originated and the ways in which the many kinds of animals and plants have come into being. This chapter considers some scientific theories on these subjects and the evidence on which they are based.

We have no knowledge of life except on the earth. Of the billion or more "heavenly bodies" only Mars, 35,000,000 miles away in our planetary system, possibly could support life as we know it, having oxygen, carbon dioxide, water, and temperatures from 10 or 15°C. to freezing. White caps (snow?) show at the poles in the Martian winter, and some surface areas change seasonally from green or blue-gray to yellow or brown; also lines (canals?) in geometric pattern on light-colored areas have been reported. To some persons the color changes imply the presence of plant life, and the "canals" are considered evidence of intelligent beings; but difficulties in observation leave the subject of life on Mars one for debate.

14-1. Environments for life. The earth may have originated from condensation of extremely hot gaseous material (nebular hypothesis) or as a molten mass (planetesimal hypothesis), in either case having been derived from some other heavenly body. It cooled slowly, decreasing in volume, and in time acquired an atmosphere that retained water on the surface. The water filled depressions on the surface to form the oceans, which origi-

nally may have been very hot. The oldest exposed rocks indicate great volcanic activity on the then exposed lands. Life as we know it could not have existed until the waters and lands had cooled.

14-2. How life originated. There are several principal theories on the origin of life:

1. SPONTANEOUS GENERATION. Earlier it was believed that life originated repeatedly from nonliving materials by spontaneous generation; this idea was discredited by experiments in the seventeenth and nineteenth centuries (Chap. 11).

2. SPECIAL CREATION. Until the middle of the nineteenth century life was generally presumed to have been created by some supernatural power either once, or at successive intervals, or each species was presumed to have been created separately.

3. COSMOZOIC THEORY. Protoplasm in the form of resistant spores of simple living forms might have reached the earth accidentally from some other source in the universe. The extreme cold and dryness and the lethal radiations of interstellar space probably would not permit life as we know it to survive. And this theory provides no explanation as to the actual origin of life.

4. NATURALISTIC THEORY. At some time more than a billion years ago temperature

Illustration at top of page: A leaf insect (*Phyllium*) from Ceylon, showing protective resemblance to yellowing tree leaves—"veins" on forelegs and wings, frayed edges, and "discolored" fungus spots.

and moisture conditions became suitable for life. There was no free oxygen, but the atmosphere contained methane, ammonia, hydrogen, and water vapor. It is known from recent experiments that amino acids such as glycine and alanine are produced when the above mentioned gases are exposed to ultraviolet light or electrical discharges like lightning. Also the nucleic acid adenine has been produced in the laboratory by irradiation of a mixture of methane, ammonia, and water.

Aggregates of such organic molecules would have accumulated, probably in an ancient soupy sea, because there were then no bacteria to cause decomposition. In the long course of chemical evolution such aggregates competed (natural selection) for the limited store of raw materials and only the "fittest" survived. Some of these "proteins" were able to act as catalysts and eventually became autocatalytic—able to catalyze the synthesis of molecules like themselves. These probably derived their energy from fermentation of simple sugars like some present-day bacteria. Still later autotrophs developed that could use light-absorbing pigments such as chlorophyll to synthesize complex carbon molecules and give off free oxygen (photosynthesis). This resulted in the earth's present store of oxygen, all of which is estimated to pass through living organisms about every 2,000 years. Using solar energy, the one-celled green algae developed and became the food for the first animals, the one-celled protozoans. Once this stage was reached, cells could begin to form aggregations, first of like units and later differentiated to form tissues with division of labor, as seen in higher organisms.

This concept of the origin of life receives support by recent studies on *viruses* that live and multiply only within living cells. These causative agents of various diseases are so small (about 10 to 300 mμ) they can pass through filters that stop most bacteria. They are invisible in ordinary microscopes, but images of them can be projected on the electron microscope. Viruses behave like living organisms—they multiply by genetic descent and show evidence of change (mutation) in virulence. Yet several, including that of poliomyelitis, have been crystallized like inorganic substances (Fig. 1-3). The tobacco mosaic virus has been separated into two nonliving portions, a protein and a nucleic acid; when reunited, the combination again shows characteristics of life and causes infection in tobacco plants. As presently understood, however, viruses are not the ultimate link between living and nonliving matter since they can exist only in a special environment—within the cells of plants or animals—which is obviously not primitive. If a free-living virus existed, it would resemble in many ways an early stage in the development of life.

14-3. Where life originated. Since many simpler and lower animals are aquatic and marine and since the cells and body fluids of all animals contain salts (NaCl and others), it is inferred that life began in the oceans. The earliest animal remains are all in rocks of marine origin. Various organisms later invaded the fresh waters and then the land, and some secondarily became marine such as the early sharks and bony fishes, the plesiosaurs and other ancient reptiles, and the whales, seals, and sirenians among living mammals.

14-4. When life originated. One estimate places the age of the crust of the earth at 4,800,000,000 years. The oldest recognizable surface rocks (Archeozoic) are estimated to be 2.6 billion years old, and the first (Cambrian) that contain numerous animal remains were probably formed 600,000,000 years ago (Chap. 13). Since many groups of animals were then already differentiated, life may have begun fully 1,000,000,000 years ago. There is no conclusive evidence of any complete break in the record of life, so the conditions suitable for its existence must have prevailed somewhere on the earth throughout an enormous period of time.

14-5. Evolution. The data of astronomers indicate that the stars and the solar and other systems of the universe have undergone gradual change, or **cosmic evolution**. On the earth there is much evidence of gradual **geologic evolution** in the elevation and erosion of land masses, the transport of particles in water to form sediments, and the long-time changes in climates.

The animals now living and the many species of past times represented by fossils comprise a variety of forms, progressively more complex, from the one-celled protozoans to the higher invertebrates and vertebrates. Biologists interpret the history of animals (and plants) on the earth to have been a continuing process of **organic evolution** (L. *evolvere,* unroll), which has produced the existing species. According to the doctrine of organic evolution, existing organisms are the modified but lineal descendants of other species that lived in former geological times. This is "descent with modification," the process termed the "origin of species" by Charles Darwin. The processes of evolution are considered to be still in operation and therefore capable of experimental study. Existing knowledge as to the pattern of evolution is summarized in the natural classification (Fig. 15-1), which is a "genealogical tree" of the Animal Kingdom.

Evidence for organic evolution is derived from comparative morphology, physiology, and embryology, from the study of fossils (paleontology), from animals and plants under domestication, from experimentation, and from other fields of biology. Scientists and many laymen agree that there is abundant evidence for the *fact* of evolution, but there is difference of opinion as to the *processes,* or *methods,* by which evolution has taken place.

A. EVIDENCE OF EVOLUTION

14-6. Comparative morphology. All animals are alike in being composed of protoplasm organized as cells. If each species had been created separately, animals might have been infinitely varied in structure with no consistent pattern and no correlation between organs of like function. Instead, we find that the larger groups of animals, although variously unlike in appearance, have similar organ systems for digestion, excretion, and other necessary functions. The members of any one group show greater structural resemblance; thus the insects have one pair of antennae, six legs, and many other features in common. Finally, the members of a species comprise animals of similar structure throughout.

In examining animals for structural evidences of evolution it is necessary to distinguish characters that are of common origin (homology), and hence indicative of common ancestry in descent, from purely adaptive features that are of similar function (analogy) but of unlike origin. Thus, the skeletal elements in the wings of bats, birds, and pterodactyls (extinct flying reptiles) are homologous in that all are modifications of the common pattern of fore limb in land vertebrates. The wings of insects, however, are only analogous to those of vertebrates; although used for flight, they are derived, not from limbs, but presumably as extensions of the body wall (Fig. 14-1).

Studies in comparative morphology, embryology, and paleontology make it possible to trace the derivation of appendages of vertebrates from lateral folds on the bodies of lower chordates to the fins of sharks and bony fishes. The fins of some fossil fishes (CROSSOPTERYGII) contain skeletal elements that may be homologized with bones in the limbs of land vertebrates. Limbs of the latter show a wide range in adaptive modifications for special uses by changes in length or by fusion or reduction of parts (Fig. 14-2); yet all are homologous, being derived from the pentadactyl limb (Gr. *penta,* five + *dactyl,* finger).

Homologies are seen in every organ system of vertebrates, from lowest to highest and including man. The comparative account of organ systems in Chaps. 4 to 10 is some of the most striking evidence for evolution (see also Chaps. 2, 25 to 28). In all vertebrates (1) the nervous system includes an anterior brain with comparable divisions, paired cranial

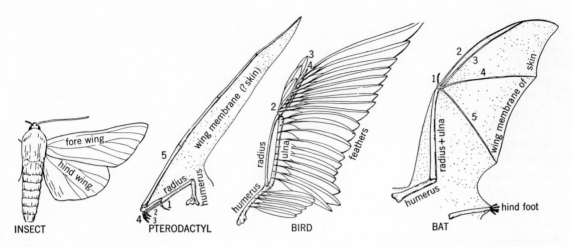

Fig. 14-1. *Analogy* between wings of insects (no internal skeleton) and of vertebrates (with skeleton)—of like function but different origins. *Homology* in the wing bones of vertebrates, all derived from the common pattern of fore limb in land vertebrates, but variously modified. Pterodactyl (extinct reptile) with elongate 5th finger; bird with 1st and 5th lacking, 3d and 4th partly fused; bat with 2d to 5th fingers elongate.

nerves, a single dorsal nerve cord, and paired spinal nerves to each body somite; (2) the brain case is followed by a jointed spinal column of separate vertebrae that support the body and enclose the nerve cord; (3) the digestive tract is ventral to the vertebrae and includes a liver and pancreas as the major digestive glands; (4) the ventrally placed heart connects to a closed system of vessels containing blood with both white and red corpuscles; and (5) the excretory and reproductive systems show many homologous fea-

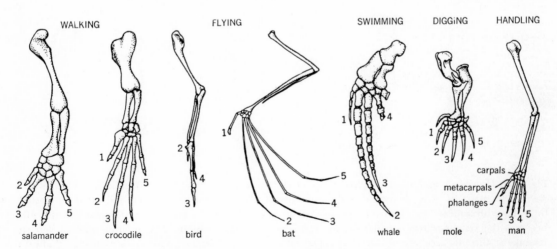

Fig. 14-2. Homology and adaptation in bones of the left fore limb in land vertebrates. The limbs are *homologous* in being composed of comparable bones (humerus, carpals, etc.), which in each kind of animal are *adapted* for special uses by differences in the length, shape, and bulk of the various bones; 1–5, digits or "fingers."

tures. In each system and organ there is agreement as to position in the body and general form and even in the microscopic structure of tissues. Consequently a frog, reptile, or mammal serves equally well for a basic study of vertebrate anatomy.

The organ systems, however, are not exactly alike but show progressive changes from fishes to mammals. In the brain the trend (Fig. 10-2) is toward enlargement of the cerebral hemispheres, which are centers of higher mental activities, and also of the cerebellum, or center of coordination. The heart is two-chambered in fishes, three-chambered in amphibians and most reptiles, and four-chambered in birds and mammals, eventually separating completely the venous and arterial blood (Fig. 14-3). In the excretory organs, drainage of

wastes is first from the coelom and later only from the blood (Fig. 8-3).

In like manner there are many homologies among invertebrates. All arthropods have segmented bodies with chitinous covering, a paired series of jointed appendages, a double ventral nerve cord, and many other features in common. A double ventral nerve cord is present also in annelid worms, primitive mollusks, and some other invertebrates.

14-7. Comparative physiology. Many basic similarities in physiological and biochemical properties parallel the morphologic features of organisms.

1. A classification based on the structure of oxy-hemoglobin crystals from vertebrate blood parallels the classification based on body struc-

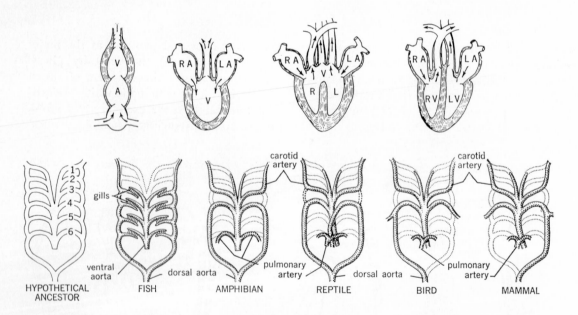

Fig. 14-3. Homology and embryonic sequence in the aortic arches and heart chambers of vertebrates. *Below.* Six pairs of arches develop in the embryos of all vertebrates, but parts indicated by dotted lines later disappear. In land vertebrates the 3d pair always forms the carotid arteries; the 4th becomes the systemic arches to the dorsal aorta, but only the right persists in birds and the left in mammals; the 6th arch always forms the pulmonary arteries. *Above.* The embryonic heart always begins with 1 auricle (*A*) and 1 ventricle (*V*); it remains thus in fishes. The auricle becomes divided (*RA, LA*) in amphibians; the ventricle becomes partly divided in reptiles and completely so (*RV, LV*) in birds and mammals. In embryos of higher forms the arches and chambers develop progressively through the succession of stages shown. Arrows indicate paths of blood flow.

ture. Crystals from each species are distinct, but all from a genus have some common characteristics. Furthermore, those of all birds have certain resemblances but differ from crystals obtained from blood of mammals or reptiles.

2. The precipitin tests are reactions of the blood serum. In such tests human serum is least distinct from that of anthropoid apes (gorilla, chimpanzee, etc.), more so from other primates (monkeys), and still more distinct from that of other mammals. Sera of mammals, in turn, are more sharply distinguished from those of other vertebrates.

3. Some hormones derived from endocrine glands show like reactions when injected into widely different animals. The thyroid gland in cattle controls their rate of metabolism; extracts of that gland may be fed to human beings deficient in their own thyroid secretion to speed up bodily metabolism. If beef or sheep thyroid is fed to frog tadpoles from which the thyroid gland has been removed, the tadpoles will grow normally and later metamorphose into frogs.

4. Many individual digestive enzymes present in different animals are essentially alike in physiological action. Trypsin, which acts upon proteins, occurs in many animals from protozoans to man; and amylase, which acts on starches, is present from sponges to mammals.

5. The various combinations of nucleotides that form nucleic acids all have a similar basis in the DNA and RNA molecules. This is strong evidence for the biochemical unity of all life.

14-8. Comparative embryology. Except for a few specialized types of reproduction, every multicellular animal originates as a zygote, or fertilized egg (Chap. 11). The egg of each species has the distinctive ability to produce an individual of that species, but there are many features of embryonic development common to members of any animal group. Fertilized eggs segment, have the blastula stage and a two-layered gastrula stage, then become variously differentiated. Many kinds of invertebrates have a trochophore larva. Eggs of vertebrates differ somewhat in mode of cleavage according to the amount of yolk present (Fig. 11-9), but the early embryos of

all are much alike; later, those of each class become recognizable, and still later family and species characters become evident (Fig. 14-4). The beginning embryo in a hen's egg has at first the vertebrate essentials of a notochord, dorsal nervous system, and gill pouches; later, it acquires bird features such as a beak and wings; and, much later, there appear the characteristics of a chick instead of a pigeon or duck.

A fish embryo develops paired gill slits, gills, aortic arches, and a two-chambered heart; these all persist in the adult to serve in aquatic respiration. Comparable structures appear in a frog embryo and are necessary during the fish-like life of the frog larva in water. When the larva transforms into an air-breathing frog, however, the gills and gill slits disappear, lungs become functional for respiration in air, the aortic arches change to serve the adult structure, and the heart is three-chambered for circulation of the blood to both the body and lungs. The amphibian begins with certain fish-like features necessary for an aquatic larva, and later these are altered for terrestrial life. Astonishingly, the early embryos of reptiles, birds, and mammals also develop a fish-like pattern of gill slits, aortic arches, and two-chambered heart (Fig. 14-5), although none of them has an aquatic larva and all respire only by lungs after birth. The embryonic gill slits soon close; the multiple aortic arches become the carotids and other arteries (Fig. 14-3); and the heart soon becomes three-chambered, later having four chambers in birds and mammals.

The presence of gill slits and multiple aortic arches in embryos of reptiles, birds, and mammals is not explained by a theory of special creation, but under a theory of evolution they are obviously ancestral relics. The fossil record indicates that aquatic, gill-breathing vertebrates preceded the air-breathing land forms. In point of time their sequence of appearance was fishes, amphibians, reptiles, birds, and mammals (see back end papers). The amphibians represent a transitional

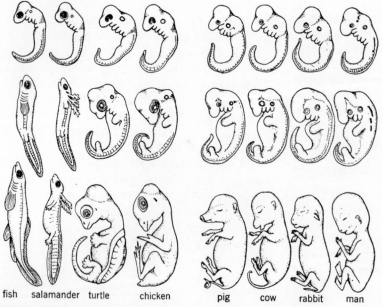

fish salamander turtle chicken pig cow rabbit man

Fig. 14-4. Series of vertebrate embryos in three successive and comparable stages of development. *Top.* All are much alike at the earliest stage. *Middle.* Differentiation is evident, but the four mammals (at right) are quite similar. *Bottom.* Later the distinctive characteristics of each become evident. (*After Haeckel,* 1891.)

phase, through which each frog still passes from aquatic respiration to air breathing (Fig. 2-16).

These and many other facts illustrate the "laws" of embryonic development stated by von Baer (German, 1792–1876): (1) General characters appear before special characters. (2) From the more general the less general and finally the special characters develop. (3) An animal during development departs progressively from the form of other animals. (4) The young stages of an animal are like the young (or embryonic) states of other animals lower in the scale, but not like the adults of those animals. The oft-quoted "theory of recapitulation," or "biogenetic law," of Haeckel (German, 1834–1919) states that an individual organism in its development (ontogeny) tends to recapitulate the stages passed through by its ancestors (phylogeny). Haeckel's theory has been both stoutly defended and vigorously criticized by different biologists. The "laws" of von Baer provide a more accurate statement.

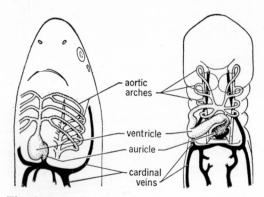

aortic arches

ventricle

auricle

cardinal veins

Fig. 14-5. Embryological evidence of evolution. *Left.* Adult shark. *Right.* Human embryo 3 mm. long, with 2-chambered heart, multiple aortic arches, and cardinal veins. Compare Fig. 14-3.

Many factors complicate the picture of embryonic development in its bearing on evolution. To the ancient (palingenetic) characters of embryos have been added other modern (cenogenetic) characters. Some of the latter appear early in development as with the embryonic membranes of reptiles, birds, and mammals. These are "new" features, not present in the lower vertebrates, but essential for protecting embryos of land vertebrates (Fig. 11-12). Another complication is the omission or telescoping of developmental features in relation to special environmental conditions, such as the absence of floating larvae in freshwater crustaceans and the omission of larval stages in some tree-dwelling frogs and most land salamanders.

14-9. Vestigial organs. Structures without use and of reduced size are termed vestigial organs. From the standpoint of special creation these are difficult to explain; from that of evolution they are obviously features in process of disappearing from living organisms that were functional and necessary for their ancestors. Various cave-dwelling fishes, crayfishes, and insects have the eyes reduced or absent, whereas their respective relatives that live out in the open possess eyes. Traces of the pelvic girdle and hind limbs occur in boas and pythons (Fig. 26-9) and in whales. Whalebone whales lack teeth as adults, but tooth buds occur in their embryos. "Scarce as hens' teeth" does not apply to bird embryos, which have transient tooth buds; and some fossil birds had teeth as adults. The flightless kiwi of New Zealand has degenerate wings with only rudimentary bones, and the great moas of that land lacked wings completely. Living horses have splint bones, which are vestiges of toes present in ancestral horses (Fig. 14-9).

Fully 90 vestigial features are present in the human body; conspicuous examples are shown in Fig. 14-6. The horse, rodents, and some other mammals have a large caecum or appendix as an accessory digestive chamber. In man the appendix is a slender vestige about $2\frac{1}{2}$ inches long serving no useful function and often the site of infection requiring surgical removal. The external ears of mammals are moved by special muscles; lacking need for

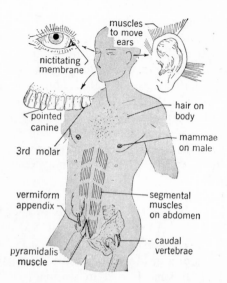

Fig. 14-6. Some vestigial structures in the human body. *(Partly after Kahn.)*

such movement in man, the muscles are usually reduced and nonfunctional. In the inner angle of the human eye is a whitish membrane representing the transparent nictitating membrane, or third eyelid, to be seen in the cat, bird, frog, and other land vertebrates. The human "wisdom teeth," or posterior molars, are smaller and more variable than the other molars and irregular as to time or manner of eruption; this suggests that they are becoming useless and may eventually disappear.

14-10. The fossil record. Important evidence of evolution comes from the study of *fossils.* The nature of fossils, means for estimating their age, and their distribution in time are discussed in Chap. 13 (see also end papers).

Leonardo da Vinci (Italian, 1452–1519) was the first to recognize that fossils were evidences of animal life in the past. The earliest important studies of fossils were made by the French comparative anatomist, Georges Cuvier (1769–1832). In 1800 he published an account of fossil elephants, relating them to living forms; later, in a classification of fishes, he employed both living and fossil species.

Cuvier, however, believed in special creation, and it was Darwin who first showed that fossils were evidence of the continuity and evolution of organisms. **Paleontology** (Gr. *palaios,* ancient), the study of fossils, is now an important science that links zoology and geology and provides many facts of evolution.

The geological record of past life is variously imperfect. It is like the remnants of a book that lacks all the beginning chapters, contains only scattered pages or parts of pages in the central part, and retains an increasing number of intact pages or parts of chapters toward the end. Records of past life result from a succession of accidental events. (1) The remains of a dead animal escape destruction and (2) become buried in sediment or ash (3) that survives undue heating, crushing, or folding such as would destroy the fossil. (4) The sediment or rock becomes elevated as a part of the land and (5) is not destructively eroded by water or wind. Finally (6) the fossil becomes exposed or is dug out and comes to the attention of a paleontologist. Some fossil remains are complete, but many are fragmentary, and all the known fossils represent only a fraction of the many plant and animal species that lived in the past. Some species or groups may never have become fossils because they were soft-bodied or because they lived where fossilization could not occur. Many fossils have been destroyed by alteration of the rocks or by erosion, and any now in rocks deep in the earth or under the sea are inaccessible (Fig. 14-7).

14-11. Invertebrates (see front end papers). Rocks formed prior to Cambrian time have since been so folded and distorted that they reveal few organic relics. Yet animals must then have been in existence for a long time, because the Cambrian rock strata, the oldest with many fossils, contain the remains of many invertebrates, including protozoans, sponges, jellyfishes, worms, brachiopods, echinoderms (sea cucumbers, crinoids), mollusks (gastropods, cephalopods), and arthropods (crustaceans, trilobites). The beginnings of most invertebrate phyla and of some classes cannot be traced, but the rise, continuance, and decline or extinction of others is well recorded. Trilobites (Fig. 14-8) were dominant when the record opens in the Cambrian; they increased in numbers and variety, then disappeared entirely in the Permian. Lamp shells (Brachiopoda) were abundant throughout the Paleozoic era (456 genera) and less numerous in the Mesozoic but persist today with about 70 genera and 225 species. The living *Lingula* is much as it was in the Ordovician, 400,000,000 years ago, and is perhaps the oldest living genus of animals. The great Phylum Arthropoda was represented by aquatic crustaceans, trilobites, and horseshoe crabs in the Cambrian period. Scorpions, the first air-breathing and land animals, appeared in the Silurian. The winged insects appeared suddenly in the Carboniferous, as several differentiated orders, and give no conclusive evidence as to which arthropod type they stem from.

14-12. Vertebrates (see back end papers). The origins of the vertebrates are obscured by imperfections in the geological record. Early stocks are thought to have been in fresh waters, from which no fossil-bearing strata have been found. The oldest vertebrate relics were evidently washed down to become embedded in marine deposits.

No vertebrate remains have been found in Cambrian rocks. Ordovician strata contain fragments possibly of ostracoderms, which were ancestral to cyclostomes, the lowest living vertebrates, without jaws or paired appendages. Silurian deposits have many ostracoderms and also spines and plates probably of placoderms, the earliest jawed vertebrates. By early Devonian time placoderms were abundant but ostracoderms less numerous. Further along in Devonian, however, both sharks and bony fishes appeared and then became abundant. Amphibians, with paired limbs, also are in the record of late Devonian. The reptiles undoubtedly began during the Carboniferous because by the end of that pe-

Fig. 14-7. A sample of the geological column: successive strata in north wall of Grand Canyon, Arizona; compare end papers. Eras and periods are marked (names in parentheses are of local rock formations). The fault line indicates a vertical shifting of strata among the oldest rocks. Two unconformities (*Un*) mark long gaps in the record; below each the rocks were deformed, elevated, and finally far eroded before the layer next above was deposited. The Mississippian represents the lower half of the Carboniferous Period. This site has no rocks of the Ordovician, Silurian, and Devonian periods or of the Mesozoic and Cenozoic eras. *(Photo by U.S. Geological Survey.)*

riod there were already several specialized types. Thenceforth, from the Permian to the Cretaceous, they were the dominant animals of land, sea, and fresh waters. Many became large in size, such as the brontosaurs, dinosaurs, and plesiosaurs. All the great reptiles disappeared at the end of the Cretaceous. Meanwhile, the first small reptile-like mammals began in the Triassic, and the first known birds appeared in the Jurassic. Early in the Tertiary (Paleocene) the mammals blossomed into a great variety, including some existing orders and others since vanished. The early

forms were replaced by more modern types, and the mammals reached a peak of diversity in the Miocene. Since then they have declined, a considerable number having become extinct at the end of the Pleistocene, just preceding the present or Recent period in which we live.

Thus, despite the fragmentary nature of the early record, ascending the geological column the vertebrate types appear in an orderly time sequence that corresponds to the increasing structural complexity of groups living today.

14-13. Horses. The Family EQUIDAE provides about the most complete record of evo-

Fig. 14-8. Representative fossils; covering matrix of rock removed. *Left.* Fossil bone bed from the Miocene of Nebraska, containing remains of rhinoceroses and other animals. *Right.* Accumulation of Devonian trilobites. *(Left, from American Museum of Natural History; right, from U.S. National Museum.)*

lution in an animal series (Fig. 14-9), leading to the existing horses, asses, and zebras of the Old World. Much of their ancestral development occurred in North America, but horses died out there late in the Pleistocene (or early in Recent time), for reasons unknown. The wild horses of the western states in the last five centuries all derived from stocks that were brought in and escaped from early explorers and settlers.

The principal changes in the horses through time include the following: (1) increase in size from that of a cat to some larger than existing horses; (2) enlargement and lengthening of the head anterior to the eyes; (3) increased length and mobility of the neck; (4) changes of the premolar and molar teeth from rooted types suited for browsing, with short crowns and surface cusps, to patterns suited for grazing, with practically no roots, tall crowns, and many enamel ridges, accompanied by deepening of the lower jaw; (5) elongation of the limbs for speedy running, but with loss of ro-

tational movement and fusion of bones in the foreleg to provide better hinge joints, together with support of the weight on the radius and tibia; and (6) reduction of the toes from five to one elongate toe (third) on each foot, which is covered by a hoof ("claw"); the lateral toes dwindle as "dew claws," and finally only small bones of the second and fourth toes persist as splints. By these changes the horse became a long-legged, swift-running mammal suited to live and feed on open grasslands, and having tall teeth with many enamel edges to grind harsh grassy vegetation through a relatively long life.

The real origin of horses is unknown. The record begins with †*Hyracotherium* (†*Eohippus*) in the lower Eocene of North America and Europe. It was a browsing forest dweller, about 11 inches tall, with short neck and head and a full set of 44 small short-crowned and rooted teeth that lacked cement. The front foot had four functional toes but the hind foot only three, the first and fifth toes being

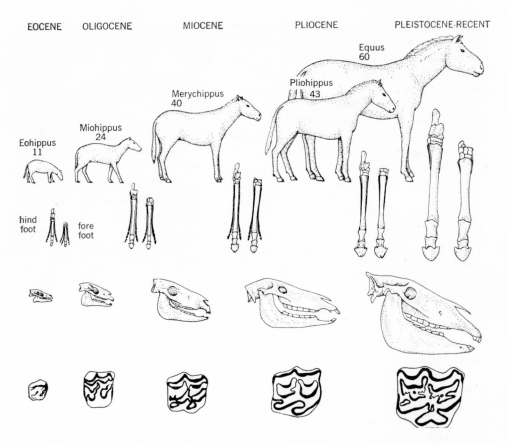

EOCENE   OLIGOCENE   MIOCENE   PLIOCENE   PLEISTOCENE-RECENT

Equus
60

Pliohippus
43

Merychippus
40

Miohippus
24

Eohippus
11

hind foot   fore foot

Fig. 14-9. Evolution of the horse. *Top row.* Progressive change in size and conformation from the little forest-dwelling "eohippus" (†*Hyracotherium*) of the Eocene epoch to the large, modern plains-inhabiting *Equus* (numbers are height at shoulder in inches). *Second row.* Bones of hind- and fore-feet, showing reduction in lateral toes (solid black), from *Eohippus* with 3 hind and 4 front toes to *Equus* with only the 3d toe functional on each foot, the 2d and 4th being represented by splints. *Third row.* Skulls showing changes in size and outline, and closing of postorbital process. *Bottom row.* Grinding surfaces of 2d upper molar, showing increasing complexity of enamel pattern (black). (*Top row adapted from R. S. Lull, Fossils, courtesy of the University Society, New York; others from W. D. Matthew, 1913, and R. A. Stirton, 1940.*)

represented by tiny splints. †*Mesohippus* of the Oligocene was the size of a sheep, with taller but rooted molars and three functional toes on each foot; the lateral toes were smaller, and only one splint (fifth) persisted on the forefoot. By Miocene time, several lines (†*Parahippus*, †*Merychippus*) had developed, including both browsing and grazing types. During Pliocene there were several distinct groups of horses (†*Pliohippus*, etc.) grazing

on the plains of North America. Some spread to Eurasia and †*Hippidium* to South America, the latter giving rise to some short-limbed genera that did not survive the Pleistocene. The lateral toes were reduced to dew claws that did not touch the ground. The cheek teeth were longer, with short roots, more folding of the enamel, and cement between the folds. Finally the earliest one-toed horses developed, during the Pliocene in North America, and later spread to all the continents except Australia. In Pleistocene, there were ten or more species of *Equus* of various sizes in North America, all of which disappeared in prehistoric time.

14-14. Human evolution. Many kinds of evidence indicate that man is a product of evolution. In both gross and microscopic *structure* the human body resembles closely that of the anthropoid apes, is like that of other primates, and has much in common with mammals generally (compare Figs. 4-4, 4-5, 5-3; Chap. 29). Homologies with other vertebrates are present in every organ system; some vestigial organs of man have already been mentioned (Fig. 14-6). Strictly human characteristics such as the upright posture, opposable thumbs, flattened vertical face, scant body hair, and greatly increased brain are differences in degree and not in kind from other mammals. Many relationships in *function* (physiology) parallel those of structure; in both man and anthropoids there are comparable blood groups, human blood can be distinguished by immunological tests from all others except anthropoids, and some mouth protozoans are common to man and other primates. The earlier *embryonic development* of man is essentially like that of other mammals (Fig. 14-4) and includes temporary gill slits and multiple aortic arches (Fig. 14-5). The *fossil record* of mankind includes a series of types (Fig. 29-7) that gradually approach the form of existing human races. Man's superior attainments over all other organisms are primarily matters of habits and behavior; these include social organization, modification of the environment to his own advantage, development of tools and of language, and the ability to transmit learning by teaching.

B. THEORIES OF EVOLUTION

Any effort to account for existing organisms and fossils must explain their origins, their likenesses and differences, their adaptations to various environments, and their distribution on the earth. Theories of special creation assume organisms to have been produced by a supernatural agency that provided for all such features. Theories of organic evolution postulate that since life began on the earth it has been continuous and that later organisms have been derived from earlier forms by the inheritance of variations, either large or small, and induced either by the environment or by processes within the animals.

Primitive human races have various myths to "explain" the origin of man and animals by the creative acts of supernatural powers. Until the last century most persons, including such scientists as Linnaeus, Cuvier, Agassiz, and Owen, believed that species had been created separately. Cuvier thought the disappearance of fossil species had resulted from a series of catastrophes, the last being the Biblical flood, and that after each of these the earth had been repopulated by new creations of higher types. Belief in catastrophes was dispelled by a Scottish geologist, Charles Lyell (1797–1875), who showed that the geological processes of sedimentation, uplift, and erosion are essentially continuous.

Some early Greek philosophers had vague notions of an evolutionary process, but Aristotle (384–322 B.C.), the first notable zoologist, thought that organisms were molded by a "perfecting principle," and his ideas prevailed for centuries (par. 1-10). Buffon (French, 1707–1788) was the first modern biologist to discard the concept of special creation. He believed that animals were plastic, that small variations produced by the environment were accumulated to make larger differences, and that each animal in the ascending series of types was transformed from some simpler ancestor. Erasmus Darwin (English, 1731–1802), grandfather of Charles Darwin, added the further idea that functional responses to external stimuli were inherited.

14-15. Lamarck and the inheritance of acquired characteristics. The first general theory of evolution was proposed by Jean Baptiste de Lamarck (French, 1744–1829), an anatomist and student of classification. His theory was outlined in 1801 and set forth fully in his *Philosophie zoologique* (1809). Lamarck recognized a fundamental continuity in the diverse kinds of animals and believed there had been progressive development in form and function. His theory in brief was as follows: The environment affects the shape and organization of animals; frequent continuous use develops and enlarges any organ, while by permanent disuse it weakens until it finally disappears; all acquisitions or losses wrought through influence of the environment and hence through *use and disuse* are preserved by reproduction.

The theory may be illustrated by two of his examples. Birds, he assumed correctly, were originally terrestrial. A land bird going to seek food in water would spread its toes to strike the water in moving about. The skin at the bases of the toes would be continually stretched, and muscular movements of the legs would promote an extra flow of blood to the feet. In consequence, the skin would become enlarged as webs between the toes, as seen in ducks, pelicans, and other water birds. Disuse Lamarck illustrated by the structure of a snake. In crawling through grass its body would be stretched repeatedly to pass through narrow spaces and the legs would not be used. Long legs would interfere with crawling, and four short legs could not move the body. Legs are characteristic of reptiles, and yet the snakes lost theirs. The eyes became lateral or dorsal the better to see when on the ground, and the tongue developed as a protrusible sensory organ to detect objects in front of the snake.

There is no reliable evidence for Lamarck's theory, and it has little support. The muscles of an athlete increase in strength and bulk with extensive use but recede if exercise is discontinued; children never inherit such acquired characteristics of a father. The docking of tails in horses, sheep, and bulldogs for many generations has not made these mutilations hereditary. Pavlov trained mice to come

for food at the sound of a bell and claimed that fewer and fewer trials were needed to teach mice of succeeding generations, but neither these nor other experiments designed to test the theory have produced convincing results. This conclusion is not surprising when it is recalled that a new organism develops from the germ cells of its parents, not from the somatic cells. Germ cells are set aside early in the growth of an individual and are subjected to little or no effect from the body cells or environment (Chap. 11).

14-16. Darwin and the theory of natural selection. Charles Darwin (1809–1882) was a methodical, painstaking English naturalist of broad vision. As a young man he served (1831–1835) as naturalist on the "Beagle," a vessel that explored South America, the Galápagos Islands, and other regions. From these studies he wrote excellent works on barnacles, mammalian fossils, geology, and coral reefs. The facts of animal distribution and the relations between living and fossil animals learned in his travels led him to consider the origin of species. He began taking notes on the subject in 1837 and the next year read Malthus's *Essay on Population,* wherein that author showed how populations increase in geometric ratio until checked by limiting factors. Darwin then recognized the struggle for existence within all populations and concluded that in such a struggle favorable variations would be preserved and unfavorable ones eliminated. In 1844 he wrote a summary of his theory but continued to gather data. Meanwhile Alfred Russel Wallace (1823–1913), an English naturalist, while studying the rich fauna and flora of the Malay Archipelago, independently and rapidly arrived at similar conclusions. In 1858 he sent an essay on the subject to his friend Darwin. Through the interest of Charles Lyell and the botanist Joseph Hooker, Wallace's essay and a brief of Darwin's conclusions were published together in the same year. In 1859 Darwin issued his theory in a book entitled *On the Origin of Species by Means of Natural Selection, or the*

Preservation of Favoured Races in the Struggle for Life.

This was the most important book of the nineteenth century. It contains (1) overwhelming evidence of the fact of evolution and (2) arguments for natural selection as the process. The doctrine of evolution was not original with Darwin, but his convincing presentation quickly won the support of scientists and of many laymen. Unscientific attacks on "Darwinism," as the theory was called, continued until after his death. Meanwhile a great scientific search began for additional facts bearing on the theory, and there was much speculation on natural selection.

The essence of Darwin's theory is as follows:

1. *Variations* of all grades are present among individuals and species in nature.
2. By the *geometric ratio of increase* the numbers of every species tend to become enormously large; yet the population of each remains approximately constant because many individuals are eliminated under various factors of climate, competition, etc.
3. This involves a *struggle for existence;* individuals having variations unsuited to the particular conditions in nature are eliminated, whereas those whose variations are favorable will continue to exist and reproduce.
4. A *process of natural selection* therefore is operative, which results in:
5. The *survival of the fittest,* or "the preservation of favored races."

14-17. Variation. Among animals that reproduce sexually no two individuals (save identical twins) are exactly alike. The individuals of every species vary in size, proportions, coloration, external and internal structure, physiology, and habits. Darwin recognized the widespread occurrence of variations; his theory assumes but does not explain their origins. In his day the laws of inheritance (Chap. 12) were unknown, and often he could not distinguish the heritable variations, which alone are important in evolution, from nonheritable variations produced by differences in food, temperature, or other environmental factors. Darwin saw that domesticated animals and plants are more variable in many ways than wild species. He knew that man has produced many domestic races by *artificial selection,* or breeding of individuals having heritable variations (characteristics) useful for human needs; also, that practical breeders have established and improved the many breeds of livestock and races of cultivated plants by gradually accumulating small but useful hereditary differences through many successive generations. He rightly believed that, in most cases, all the domestic breeds of a species had been derived from one wild ancestral species—all breeds of dogs from the European or Asiatic wolf or jackal, and all domestic poultry from the Indian jungle fowl. Many of these breeds now differ so greatly from one another in appearance that, if they occurred in the wild, any zoologist would classify them as distinct species and some as different genera! The domestic breeds of a species, however, all can mate with one another and produce fertile offspring. Having shown the wide diversity of domestic races produced from ancestral stocks by selection of small variations, Darwin assumed that small heritable variations in wild species were the materials of the evolutionary process in nature.

14-18 Geometric ratio of increase. All forms of life have the potentiality of rapid increase. The protozoan *Paramecium* (0.25 mm. long) can divide by fission about 600 times per year. If all survived and continued to divide, their total bulk after some months would exceed that of the earth. The fruit fly, *Drosophila,* completes its life cycle from egg to egg in 10 to 14 days, and each female may lay 200 or more eggs. In 40 to 50 days, if all survived and bred, they would number 200,000,-000; during one summer their numbers would become astronomical. Darwin assumed the elephant to breed at 30 years and live to 100 years, each female producing but 6 young; in 750 years about 19,000,000 would be alive.

The brown rat, English sparrow, and European corn borer in the United States and the European rabbit in Australia are examples of pests that have multiplied somewhat in keeping with their theoretical possibilities when introduced into new and favorable environments. Plagues of native insects and of meadow mice result at times when abundant food supplies are suddenly available and enable individuals to reproduce and mature rapidly.

14-19. Struggle for existence. Under ordinary conditions, however, animals never increase to such numbers as just indicated. The populations of most species tend to remain more or less stationary because of various checks (Chap. 13, Fig. 13-5). There are limitations in the food supply, shelter, and breeding places; individuals of a species compete with one another for these necessities and also with other species having similar requirements; an enlarged population of any species soon is levied upon by its predators and is a fertile field for parasites and diseases. The "struggle for existence" is not always a spectacular battle, as of a rabbit trying to escape from a fox, but is a continuing process in nature involving many factors, each of which eliminates some individuals. It acts at any stage in the life cycle of a species, from the egg, which may fail of fertilization, through embryonic development, larval stages, and adult life. Any individual animal is "successful" in the struggle for existence if it survives long enough to reproduce its kind.

14-20. Natural selection. Darwin assumed that in the struggle for existence individuals with slightly favorable variations enabling them to meet the conditions of life more successfully would survive in the struggle for existence and propagate their kind; this process Herbert Spencer termed the "survival of the fittest." Under this sort of *natural selection* those lacking such variations would perish or fail to breed so that the characters which they possessed would be eliminated from the population. In succeeding generations the process would continue and result in gradually adapting animals more perfectly to their environments. With a change in environmental conditions there would be a change in the sort of characters that would have survival value under natural selection. A species in a changing environment or one that had migrated to some new environment would be gradually altered to suit the new conditions. Animals failing to develop suitable new variations under any particular environmental conditions would soon be eliminated. In this manner, Darwin conceived the development of adaptations of whatever sort, the "origin of species" in changed or new environments, and also the disappearance of species in past geological time. Two portions of a species population having to meet slightly differing conditions would tend to diverge from one another and in time would be separated, first by small differences as subspecies and later, when isolated from each other, as species that could not interbreed. A continuation of such divergence would lead in time to the divergence of larger groups. In this manner, he conceived the great number of species and larger categories of the Animal Kingdom to have been established through the long duration of geological time.

Most biologists accept Darwin's theory as the best general explanation of evolution. They differ mainly in their later and better understanding of some of the essential biological processes involved, which were unknown in his day, but which have been learned by later research.

14-21. Origin of heritable variations. Darwin realized clearly that heritable variations occur in both wild and domesticated animals, but he had no knowledge as to how they are produced or of the exact manner in which they are inherited. (Mendel's precise laws, although published in 1866, were not generally known until 1900.) Starting about 1875, however, biologists began to study the processes in germ cells and their relation to reproduction; a little later careful attention was given to experimental breeding. Soon there was a wealth of new knowledge that afforded a clear understanding of the manner of origin of heritable variations and of the ways they are passed from generation to generation. These researches showed that the details of chromosome behavior and of genetics are all-important for understanding certain evolutionary processes. In summary, the most important points are as follows:

1. Chromosomes in cell nuclei carry in linear arrangement the ultramicroscopic genes that are responsible for development of characteristics in an individual.
2. Meiosis segregates members of homologous chromosome pairs and halves the total number for each gamete (see Chap. 11).
3. Fertilization, the random union of 2 gametes of unlike sex, brings together assortments of chromosomes (and therefore of genes) from 2 parents, resulting in production of individuals with different gene combinations (see Chaps. 11, 12).
4. Mutations (changes) occur in genes, and chromosome rearrangements take place; both result in altering the assortment of genes (hence characteristics) passed on to succeeding generations (Chap. 12).

Many mutations first detected in laboratory stocks of *Drosophila* now are known to occur in wild populations. Conversely, the "black" and "silver" mutations of the red fox, first known in nature, are now found in captive foxes on fur farms, where still other mutations have been discovered. From these and many other records it now seems likely that new mutations are constantly appearing in nature and that species populations are highly heterozygous. These conditions, then, provide a wide range of hereditary variations in wild species. Whether any particular variation will become a persistent characteristic in a species depends upon the size of the population, the degree of isolation or segregation of small groups of individuals, and other factors.

Different mutations may be beneficial, neutral, or harmful. The huge mass of experimental data (importantly from *Drosophila* and some plants) indicates that most of those found are harmful or neutral. Mutations useful to man are well known among domesticated animals and crop plants. In wild species mutations with superior adaptive value seem scarce, but this is to be expected, since any that appear are probably soon incorporated in the gene complex of the species to its advantage. Many harmful genes are damaging, however, only when homozygous (as those of lethal characters); in the heterozygous condition, paired with their normal alleles, the majority have no unfavorable effect. A characteristic that is harmful by itself or under one set of environmental conditions may be beneficial in combination with others or under different conditions. Indeed, some experimental data show that two characters, each harmful when alone, prove beneficial when combined.

14-22. Genic change and natural selection. Chromosome recombinations and mutations result in populations with altered assemblages of old characters and some new characters, thus increasing the total variability. As opposed to this, natural selection works in the direction of narrowing species variability by weeding out characters that are nonadaptive or of no value for survival. The total effect that the physical and biological environment imposes on individuals is the "screen" of natural selection—it passes or permits those better suited to survive and eliminates all others. Sexual reproduction provides for abundant multiplication of individuals (geometric ratio of increase), and the cellular phenomena in gene mutations, chromosome rearrangements, and fertilization add to the supply of variability; then these abundant resources are screened by natural selection.

14-23. Adaptations. All animals and plants are fitted for existence in the environments they inhabit. The degree of adaptation differs in various groups, some being narrowly or closely adapted and others being quite generalized. Adaptations commonly involve a combination of characteristics—structure, physiology, behavior, and mode of life. The honeybee (Chap. 23) shows many adaptations such as sucking mouth parts for obtaining nectar, the ability to subsist on sugars, the hairs and brushes used to gather pollen, the production and molding of wax into shelters for food and young, and the intricate pattern of habits of three castes in a social colony. Man is a generalized species, able to do many things in various ways and to live in diverse environments. The brown rat is generalized enough to live successfully in a wide variety of conditions as to climate, shelter, and food. The mole, by contrast, is narrowly adapted for life in the ground, with slender teeth to grasp worms, eyes covered and ears reduced, short fore limbs with huge palms bearing heavy claws to dig and "swim" through soil, and short reversible fur, which is not disarranged by moving forward or backward. Different mammals show adaptive modifications of teeth for various kinds of food (Fig. 28-8), and the bills of birds are adapted in relation to their food habits (Fig. 27-7). Other conspicuous examples are seen in the many parasites that can live in only a single host species and some, like the malarial parasite and liver fluke, that must alternate between two particular hosts to complete their life cycles (Chaps. 16, 18). *Adaptive radiation* is seen in the marsupial mammals in Australia that have "radiated" into diverse forms that run, jump, climb, burrow, or glide. *Adaptive convergence* often occurs when animals of different groups come to live in a common habitat. Large vertebrates of the ocean, from sharks to mammals (Fig. 14-10), all have streamlined bodies and paddle-like fins or limbs, which enable them to swim more effectively. Such adaptive characters are superimposed on the fundamental ones that make the shark a cartilaginous fish and the seal a mammal.

Many adaptive features are *protective* in various ways. Some *structural adaptations* that afford protection from enemies are the shells of armadillos, turtles, and various mollusks, the quills of porcupines, the stings of bees and wasps, and the venom of poisonous snakes. Still other adaptive characters tend to render many animals less easily detected by their enemies. In this category, *animal coloration* has excited much discussion among biologists. Many believe that it is highly adaptive in some species and helps them to evade enemies, whereas certain others discount its purposiveness and hold that animals are taken as prey in proportion to their respective numbers.

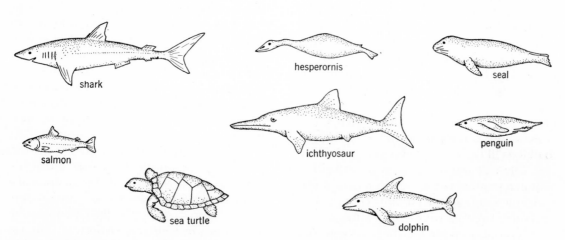

Fig. 14-10. Oceanic vertebrates—sharks to mammals—showing adaptive convergence for swimming, with streamlined bodies and paddle-like fins or limbs.

The coloration of black crows and white herons obviously bears no particular relation to their respective environments, but by **protective coloration** many species harmonize more or less with their surroundings. The hares, weasels, and ptarmigan of the far North molt into white coats when snow covers their surroundings. The ruffed grouse has a variegated pattern that blends with the leafy backgrounds of its woods habitat, and many oceanic invertebrates and fish larvae are transparent. Bark-inhabiting insects are commonly flecked with the colors of the backgrounds on which they usually occur. Many of these are cited as instances of camouflage, or **obliterative coloration,** whereby the outlines of the animal are obscured, save when it moves. **Warning coloration** is ascribed to some butterflies and other insects, considered to be distasteful to their enemies—they "advertise" their unpalatability. Bees and wasps with stout stings are often marked conspicuously with black and yellow.

There are many instances in which harmless or palatable species resemble other stinging or unpalatable species. Thus the viceroy butterfly is said to **mimic** the presumably unpalatable monarch butterfly (Fig. 14-11); and certain moths, beetles, and flies appear to have "copied" different species of wasps. Some long-horned beetles (CERAMBYCIDAE), for example, resemble wasps in form and color and also hover about flowers in wasp fashion. One African butterfly (*Papilio dardanus*) corresponds in color and form to three distasteful species of butterflies with which it occurs, three distinct types of females being produced in the progeny of a single pair of parents.

Some insects show **protective resemblance** to objects in their surroundings by both form and color. A certain geometrid caterpillar rests in a position that resembles a twig of the tree on which it lives; a butterfly (*Kallima*) of India when resting with folded wings resembles a dead leaf; and some walkingsticks (ORTHOPTERA) are like dead or green twigs and others like green leaves.

Fig. 14-11. Mimicry and protective resemblance. Viceroy butterfly, *Limenitis (Basilarchia) archippus* (above), which mimics the monarch butterfly, *Danaus plexippus* (below).

Recognition marks, or signals, are employed by some species of animals to aid in identification by others of their species and to warn the latter of danger. The white outer tail feathers of juncos, meadow larks, and other birds, the white rump patch on the American antelope, and the cottony-white tail of cottontail rabbits are all flashed into view when these animals are frightened.

Adaptations undoubtedly evolve over long periods of time, but there are some recent instances of rapid adjustment. For many years hydrocyanic acid gas proved successful in control of the red scale (Family COCCIDAE) on citrus trees in southern California; but by 1914 the standard fumigation dosage had become inadequate in one district, and later in adjacent localities. Investigation by Quayle and others showed that there were two races of the insect, one cyanide-resistant and the other not. At a certain concentration of the gas 45 per cent of the former but only 4 per cent of the latter survived. Crossing the two races showed them to differ in one sex-linked gene of "HCN resistance." Similarly, resistant stocks have appeared after years of spray control in other citrus pests and in larvae of the codling moth in apples. More recently among house fly populations sprayed with DDT, resistant stocks resulted after only a few generations. In these cases man has applied a new selective factor to the store of variability that included genes for both resistance and non-resistance.

Another rather quick adjustment was that of "industrial melanism" among moths in factory districts of England, Germany, and other European countries. With the increased outpouring of coal smoke that blackened local vegetation, melanic variants of several species of moths appeared and spread. Over several decades they became more frequent and largely replaced the original paler stocks. The dark form of the peppered moth (*Biston betularia*) formed only 1 per cent of the population near Manchester, England, in 1848 but had increased to 99 per cent by 1898. Now 80 per cent are dark in the eastern counties sooted by factory smoke, whereas only an occasional dark mutant is seen in unpolluted woodlands of southwestern England, the Scottish highlands, or Ireland. Field experiments by Kettlewell and Tinbergen showed that selected feeding by spotted flycatchers, nuthatches, robins, thrushes, and other birds is responsible for this striking change in the population. Of a mixture of specimens released in a clean forest in Dorset, the birds took six times as many dark and therefore conspicuous individuals as protectively colored pale moths. The opposite occurred in a blackened wood near Birmingham where three times as many light-colored individuals were taken as black forms.

14-24. Preadaptation. Within the store of variability of any species are many characters that are of no use in its immediate environment. Such characters may increase the potential adaptability of the species to new conditions. With a change to a colder climate, for example, a species with the potentiality to complete its life cycle during a shorter growing season will be able to survive or to invade areas beyond its original range. A species would be *preadapted* if able to survive under conditions to which it had not previously been exposed.

14-25. Orthogenesis. In some stocks of fossil and recent animals evolution seems to have proceeded along rather direct courses. Examples are the progressive reduction of digits and the enlargement of teeth in horses; the increase in tusk length and size and the reduction in number of molar teeth in elephants; and the successive elaboration of horns from small "nubbins" to great unwieldy growths on titanotheres (fossil mammals). The term *orthogenesis* (Gr. *orthos,* straight) has been applied to this phenomenon, implying that evolution has been directed by some internal but unknown factor. The linear elaboration of a feature beyond the limits of apparent usefulness has been explained, on a Darwinian basis, by assuming that characteristics seemingly unfavorable may actually have a survival value at some short but critical period in the life of the species.

14-26. Isolation and speciation. Darwin's title for his book *The Origin of Species* indicates the level at which evolution takes place. Changes (mutations, chromosome rearrangements, etc.) occur in individual animals and then by sexual reproduction are either preserved and spread through a population or are eliminated (natural selection). Thus the species is at the basis of the evolutionary process. A species is a natural interbreeding population that differs and is isolated from other populations. In asexual or parthenogenetic animals the question of interbreeding does not apply and any distinctive type or strain may be called a species. **Speciation** is the process by which new species are formed, and **isolation** is the essential step in their formation (par. 15-2). In contrast to adaptive changes in a continuous line (phyletic evolution), speciation is the splitting of an evolutionary line.

The number of individuals in many species is enormous—hundreds of thousands in common birds and mammals and millions or billions in widespread insects. The population of any one species, however, is not uniform in either distribution or characteristics. First, the individuals are not distributed evenly throughout the entire geographic range but are subdivided into smaller groups more or less isolated from one another. Each occupies a part of the range, and groups do not intermingle except along their boundaries because of limited powers of locomotion or various barriers. Second, the groups differ from one another qualitatively (size, color, etc.); these differences blend where representatives of different groups can interbreed (hybridize) along group boundaries. The term **race** or **subspecies** (Fig. 14-12) is applied to such local populations, and the total combined population is called a polytypic species. In some species the population is not broken into distinguishable groups but shows gradual continuous change of characteristics along a gradient—north to south, lowlands to highlands, or dry to moist climate. Such cases, known as **clines,** are exemplified by species of birds and mammals that are larger in cooler climates (Bergmann's Rule) or darker in warm, humid regions. Evidence from several fields—taxonomy, migration, experimental breeding, cytology, serology—shows that many a "species" in the ordinary sense is actually composed of numerous biological strains, stocks, or races.

Isolation, the segregation of stocks into smaller units, may be brought about in several ways: (1) **geographical,** by physical separation in distance; (2) **ecological,** in different types of environments, although in the same general region; (3) **seasonal,** where two populations breed at different times of year; (4)

physiological, where there is functional incompatibility in mating or in the production, fertilization, and survival of gametes; and (5) **behavioral,** where animals of two different groups will not mate with one another.

Species populations or subdivisions of a population separated by distance or other barriers are termed **allopatric** (Gr. *allos,* other + L. *patria,* country). Two or more different populations occupying the same area that maintain their distinctness are **sympatric** (Gr. *syn,* together).

In the study of population genetics (par. 12-24) the findings of Mendelian heredity are applied to population phenomena under the Hardy-Weinberg law. This law applies to large and freely interbreeding populations where there is genetic equilibrium and variability usually remains constant. Under such conditions evolution does not occur. It is the deviations from this norm, the mutations, selective mating, and survival of individuals with desirable traits that result in change. Changes are more rapid in small isolated populations such as occur in times of stress or when a few individuals reach a new habitat or remote island. In these populations variability is reduced rapidly or abruptly and the genotype tends to become homozygous. Purely by chance such populations come to differ from the original population in slight ways and become distinct stocks or races. This process is known as **genetic drift.**

The effects of isolation on speciation are well shown by "Darwin's finches," birds of the subfamily GEOSPIZINAE on the Galápagos Islands 600 miles off Ecuador. This group of oceanic islands, the largest 80 miles long, probably originated as volcanoes. The plant cover is diverse, thorn and cactus in lowlands where the ground is of jagged lava, but changing to moist forest in rich black soil on the mountain tops of 2,000 to 4,000 feet. Giant land tortoises and iguanas are the only large animals. Most distinctive of the few resident land birds are the finches, which have developed into 13 species. In turn, on separate islands, some

diaboli   utahense   melanosticum   mavortium   californiense   stebbinsi   nebulosum   tigrinum

Fig. 14-12. Geographic distribution of the subspecies of the tiger salamander (*Ambystoma tigrinum*; Mexican forms omitted). Each differs in pattern and occupies a distinct range as shown. Adjacent subspecies intergrade along their boundaries. Unshaded portions indicate areas of unsuitable habitat. The dorsal patterns of several subspecies are shown. (*Patterns mostly from Stebbins, 1951, Amphibians of western North America, University of California Press.*)

have diverged further into subspecies or less distinct populations. In the Darwinian view small differences so produced lead to "incipient species," and speciation is regarded as complete when two such forms later meet and remain distinct. Thus, on most of the islands there are three closely related species of ground finches (*Geospiza magnirostris, G. for-*

tis, and *G. fuliginosa*) that feed on seeds of relatively different hardness and that do not interbreed; presumably they evolved on different islands and later came together.

These finches illustrate another aspect of evolution—**adaptive radiation.** Ancestors of the Galápagos plants and animals must have been transported there by accidental means (par. 13-24). When the original finch stock arrived, there were probably few or no competitors or enemies. Under such circumstances the new arrivals would increase in numbers to the limit of the food supply and would become extremely variable. Competition then would develop for food; individuals capable of eating different types of food would be more likely to survive and reproduce their kind. Under this competitive pressure diversity results. Some of the types among the "finches" are (1) seed eaters (*Geospiza*) with stout, conical beak; (2) flower and nectar feeders (*Cactornis*) with long, tapered beak; (3) bud, leaf, and fruit eaters (*Platyspiza*) with beak suggestive of a parrot; (4) insect eaters (*Certhidea*) with slender bill and habits of a warbler; and (5) a woodpecker type (*Camarhynchus*) with stout, straight beak for digging in tree trunks. The related *Cactospiza pallida*, lacking the long tongue of a true woodpecker, uses a twig or cactus spine when probing.

These inconspicuous finches, on a group of remote tropical islands, have had an important part in evolutionary thought ever since the young Darwin (*Voyage of the Beagle*) wrote: "by far the most remarkable feature in the natural history of this archipelago . . . is, that the different islands to a considerable extent are inhabited by a different set of beings. . . . I never dreamed that islands about fifty or sixty miles apart, and most of them in sight of each other, formed of precisely the same rocks, placed under a quite similar climate, rising to a nearly equal height, would have been differently tenanted. . . . Hence, we seem to be brought somewhat near to that great fact—that mystery of mysteries—the first appearance of new beings on this earth."

———

The total picture that emerges from the study of evolution is an inspiring one—starting with the first bit of animal protoplasm, life has increased in diversity and perfection of adaptations through the ages, as revealed by the wide variety of both living and extinct forms. This suggests that potentialities for the future may equal or exceed those already achieved.

REVIEW

1. What are the essential features of several theories on the origin of life? Which seems most logical?
2. Define evolution as applied to animals and plants.
3. Distinguish between homology and analogy.
4. What evidence is there for homology in the organ systems of vertebrates?
5. In what ways do embryos give evidence of evolutionary relationships?
6. Do vestigial structures have any evolutionary significance?
7. What sorts of evolutionary evidence do fossils supply? What does the fossil record of vertebrates reveal?
8. What are the major changes in the horses from Eocene to Recent time?
9. Who proposed the first major theory of evolution? What were the essential features of the theory? Does it have support and acceptance today? Why?
10. What was Charles Darwin's biological background? How did he come to propose a theory of evolution?
11. What are the essential features of Darwin's theory?
12. Define: variation, artificial selection, natural selection, struggle for existence.
13. How may mutations be involved in organic evolution?
14. How do adaptive structures (including coloration) and habits benefit the animals that possess them?
15. Explain the term preadaptation.
16. What are the several kinds of isolation, and how are they involved in speciation?

Part two
The Animal Kingdom

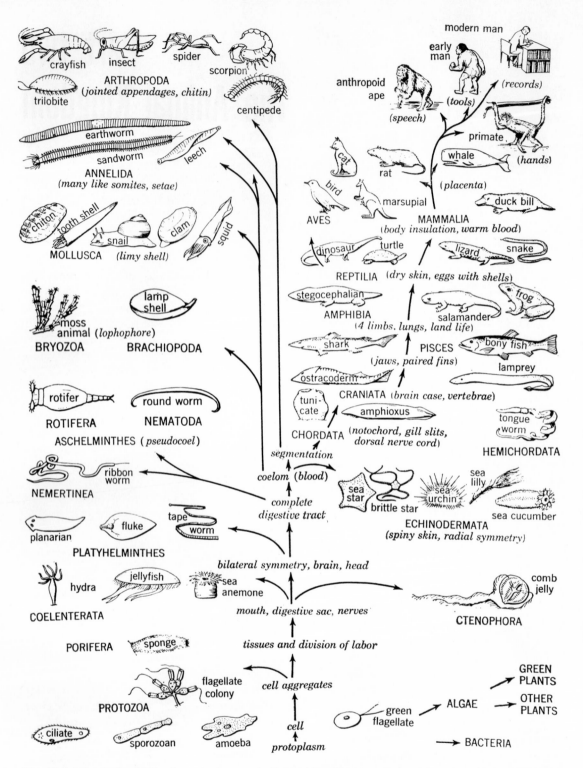

Fig. 15-1. The Animal Kingdom. A chart to indicate the probable relationships and relative position of the major groups (named in capital letters). All groups above a given characteristic (named in italics) possess that character. Figures not to same scale.

15
Classification of animals

The first enumeration of all known animals was made in 1758 and totaled 4,236 kinds. By 1911 an estimated 522,400 had been named, and the total now is over 1,000,000. New forms are still being named, and there may be several million kinds of living animals in the world today. For some animal groups in particular regions there are more exact figures. Thus North and Central America contain more than 3,600 forms of mammals and upward of 4,100 kinds of fishes in the salt and fresh waters. The birds north of Mexico number 1,420, the reptiles 438, and the amphibians 180. In a New York suburban garden, 75 by 200 feet, Lutz found 1,402 kinds of insects.

CLASSIFICATION

One major objective of zoology is to obtain a perspective of the entire Animal Kingdom; yet no one person can become acquainted with more than a fraction of the known animals. Hence some means is necessary to group animals for study; this is one of the purposes of the science of *classification*, also known as *taxonomy* or *systematic zoology*.

15-1. Methods and purposes. Various degrees of resemblance and difference are easily seen in any mixed assemblage of animals. Of the domestic animals on a farm, the cow and sheep both have horns and cloven hoofs but differ in size, shape, color, and body covering. A horse agrees with the cow and sheep in having long legs and teeth of the grinding type but lacks horns and has solid hoofs. A dog differs from all three in having nails and pads on its separate toes and having teeth of the stabbing and shearing types; it agrees in being covered with hair. The cat resembles the dog more closely than the hoofed animals. All these animals have hair and teeth, they produce living young, which they suckle, and they show many other features in common. As a group they all differ from the chickens and ducks, which are covered with feathers, lack teeth, and lay eggs—but these and all other birds have eyes, lungs, four limbs, and other characters like the four-footed animals named. So it is, by likenesses and differences, that animals may be divided into minor and major groups.

The inherent peculiarities or *characters* of animals are the basis of classification. These include structural features, size, proportions, coloration, and others. A character is usually more significant if constantly associated with others; thus every bird has, besides feathers, a beak, wings, clawed feet, a four-chambered heart, and warm blood.

A first purpose of classification is convenience, but the more important one is to show relationships. Animals may be classified in

Illustration at top of page: Materials for zoological classification—museum cases with bird and mammal skins, reptiles in alcohol, and dry skulls and mollusk shells.

various ways: as by grouping together all with shells, all of worm-like form, etc.; this was done by early zoologists. Increasing knowledge has shown that such arrangements bring together animals otherwise greatly different. The modern "natural system" of classification uses all available data as to structure, physiology, embryology, distribution, and other features; each group is distinguished by several to many characteristics. The natural classification is explained by the theory of evolution; it seeks to show relationships based on the inferred evolution of groups in the Animal Kingdom (Fig. 15-1).

For purposes of classification, characters that show **homology** or similarity of origin (and hence relationship) must be distinguished from those that exhibit **analogy** or similarity of use (but not necessarily of origin). The arms of man, forelegs of mammals and frogs, and wings of birds are homologous, being essentially similar as to structure of the bones, muscles, blood vessels, and nerves, although used for different purposes. By contrast, the wings of birds and butterflies are analogous, both serving for flight, but being unlike as to embryonic development and adult structure (Fig. 14-1).

15-2. Species. The basic unit or "building stone" in biological classification is the **species** (not specie; the plural is also species). A species is a group of individuals having many characteristics in common and differing from all other forms in one or more ways. The individuals of a species are all derived from a common ancestry, are related by "blood," and can breed with one another to produce fertile offspring that resemble the parents. As a general rule separate species do not interbreed, though hybrids between species do occur occasionally. Examples of common species are the house fly, yellow perch, bullfrog, and English sparrow. Often the total of individuals comprising a species can be subdivided into smaller groups known as **subspecies** that differ from one another in average rather than absolute characters. Each subspecies occupies

a separate range, and specimens from the boundaries of range of two adjacent subspecies are usually intermediate in their characteristics (Fig. 14-12).

15-3. Higher groups. Two or more species with certain characters in common form a **genus** (pl. *genera*). In turn genera having common characters constitute a **family,** the families are combined into **orders,** the orders into **classes,** and the classes into **phyla** (sing. *phylum*). All the phyla together comprise the **Animal Kingdom,** which is comparable with the Plant Kingdom. The scheme of classification is like a tree having many leaves (species), with one to many on a fine stem (genus), several stems on a larger twig (family), two or more of these on a little branch (order), a number of these on a larger branch (class), and the latter borne on the main framework (phyla), the whole forming a tree (kingdom). Intermediate categories (subfamilies, superclasses, subphyla, etc.) sometimes are needed to indicate properly the degree of relationship. There are cases where a group—genus or higher—contains only one representative because it is distinct from all others; such a group is termed monotypic.

15-4. General characteristics. The wide occurrence of some characters (Fig. 15-2) makes possible the recognition of groups larger than phyla (see classification outline farther on in this chapter). Animals of the Subkingdom PROTOZOA are of single cells or colonies of like cells, in contrast to those of the Subkingdom METAZOA which are many-celled (tissue animals). Within the METAZOA, the sponges (PORIFERA) form the Branch PARAZOA with no digestive cavity, in contrast to the Branch ENTEROZOA (all higher animals) with such a cavity. The digestive tract is absent in POGONOPHORA, incomplete (mouth only) in the COELENTERATA, CTENOPHORA, and PLATYHELMINTHES, but complete (both mouth and anus) in all others. The ENTEROZOA are further divided according to the number of germ layers laid down in the embryo: two, or **diploblastic** (COELENTERATA), vs. three, or

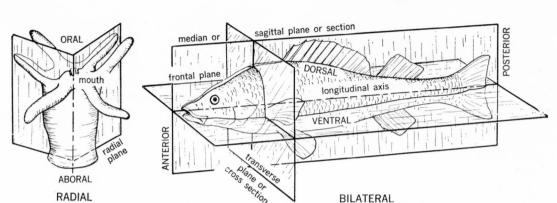

Fig. 15-2. Types of symmetry, and the axes, planes, and regions in animal bodies.

triploblastic (all others). The higher phyla (Bryozoa to Chordata) comprise the Eucoelomata, having a body cavity or **coelom** lined by peritoneum whence excretory and reproductive ducts lead to the exterior. In Mollusca and Arthropoda the coelom is far reduced, and the blood circulates in spaces between the internal organs called a **hemocoel.** Body spaces in the Entoprocta and Aschelminthes are unlined and termed

a **pseudocoel.** Other lower phyla lacking body spaces are termed the Acoelomata. Invertebrates include all animals that lack a backbone of vertebrae, in contrast to the vertebrates (Phylum Chordata: cyclostomes to mammals), which have a segmented vertebral column.

Besides the features just mentioned, some other characteristics are useful in classification (Fig. 15-3).

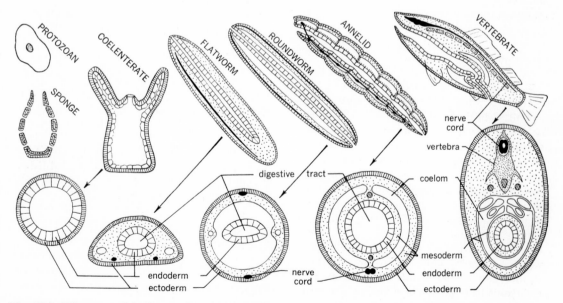

Fig. 15-3. Diagrams of body structure in various types of animals. *Above.* In median section. *Below.* In cross section, with indication of embryonic germ layers.

1. SYMMETRY. Many protozoans are *asymmetrical* because they are not divisible into equivalent parts; a few show *spherical symmetry.* The coelenterates, ctenophores, and echinoderms are *radially symmetrical* around a median axis through the mouth; planes through this axis will divide the animal into radial sectors (antimeres). Members of most other phyla are *bilaterally symmetrical;* a lengthwise vertical (sagittal) plane divides the animal into equal and opposite halves. In such animals the part that moves forward (and usually contains the mouth) is termed *anterior;* and the opposite end is *posterior;* the back or upper surface is termed *dorsal,* and the under surface (usually toward the ground) is termed *ventral* (L. *venter,* belly).

2. SEGMENTATION (Fig. 24-1A). In the annelids, arthropods, and chordates there is a linear repetition of body parts known as segmentation (metamerism); each repeated unit is a *somite* (metamere). In earthworms the successive somites are essentially alike, but they are unlike in different body regions of a crayfish or insect. Metamerism is conspicuous both externally and internally in annelids, is mostly external with arthropods, and mainly internal in man and other chordates (vertebrae, body muscles, some blood vessels, and nerves).

3. APPENDAGES. Protruding parts that serve in locomotion, feeding, and other ways are termed appendages; examples are the tentacles of sea anemones, minute setae of earthworms, antennae and legs of arthropods, and the fins, legs, and wings of vertebrates.

4. SKELETON. Most land dwellers and many aquatic animals have a skeleton for support or protection; it may be *internal* (frog, man, etc.) or *external* (coral, crab, insect) and may be of either inorganic or organic material.

5. SEX. An animal containing both *female* and *male* sex organs in one individual is termed *monoecious* (also hermaphroditic); members of most higher phyla are *dioecious,* each individual being either male or female.

6. EMBRYONIC DEVELOPMENT. In most phyla (flatworms, mollusks, annelids, arthropods, and smaller groups) the mouth derives from the embryonic blastopore. These forms are termed *protostomes* (Gr. *protos,* first + *stoma,* mouth). Cleavage is spiral and determinate (fate of embryonic cells fixed very early) and mesoderm arises from one blastomere. In the hemichordates, chaetognaths (?), echinoderms, and chordates—the *deuterostomes* (Gr. *deuter,* second), the mouth arises remote from the blastopore and the latter becomes the anus. Cleavage is indeterminate and radial, and mesoderm forms from the wall of the gastrocoel. Cleavage of the egg is complete or *holoblastic* in many invertebrates, amphioxus, amphibians, and mammals. In eggs with much yolk, cleavage is incomplete or *meroblastic,* confined to a limited part as in squids, insects, many fishes, reptiles, and birds.

7. LARVAE. The young stages known as *larvae* (par. 14-8) often provide important information on relationships not evident in adult animals. Many have features obviously adapted to particular environments such as cilia for swimming. Their basic structure, however, is usually characteristic for each phylum or class. Barnacles and tunicates, for example, were first properly classified by study of their larvae. Many aquatic invertebrates have a common type of larva—minute, transparent, and free-swimming. Often it is pear-shaped, the large end uppermost, and encircled by 2 lines of cilia that beat so as to suggest a rotating wheel, hence the name *trochophore* (Gr. *trochos,* wheel + *phoros,* bear). The upper end has a plate with a tuft of cilia and a sense organ. With various modifications this is the early larva of many marine flatworms, nemerteans, brachiopods, bryozoans, mollusks, and some annelids.

NOMENCLATURE

15-5. Common names. Each country has its common names for well-known animals. Thus a common sparrow of Europe now established throughout the United States is known in different countries as follows:

United States: English sparrow
England: House sparrow
Germany: Haussperling
Sweden: Hussparf
France: Moineau domestique
Italy: Passera oltramontana
Spain: Gorrión
Holland: Musch

Even in one country there are local names for a species; in the United States the mallard duck is known as greenhead, English duck, stock duck, and by many other names. Still other names are applied to the male (drake), female (duck, hen mallard), and young (ducklings). Thus confusion is likely between peoples of different nationalities or even within one country.

15-6. Scientific names. Early writers on natural history and zoology used long Latin "polynomials"—the mocking bird in 1731 was termed *Turdus minor cinereo-albus non maculatus* (thrush, small, grayish-white, without spots). When Linnaeus began naming and describing all known animals (plants and minerals) in his *Systema naturae,* he used Latin polynomials but later shortened these names and in the tenth edition (1758) used only two for each, a generic name and a specific name.

This **binomial nomenclature** has become universal in all countries for the scientific names of animals and plants. The names are in Latin or latinized words. The American mocking bird is named *Mimus polyglottos;* the English sparrow, *Passer domesticus;* the mallard, *Anas platyrhynchos.* To designate subspecies, trinomials are used: *Passer domesticus domesticus* for the subspecies of western Europe, *Passer domesticus niloticus* (*P. d. niloticus*) for the slightly different race of the Nile Valley. In technical works the name of the author or describer, sometimes abbreviated, is written after the scientific name, thus: *Passer domesticus* Linnaeus.

The International Code of Zoological Nomenclature is followed by most biologists to ensure uniform practice in the choice and use of scientific names.

Table 15-1 Some characteristics of the principal groups of animals

Cells	Germ layers	Symmetry	Digestive tract	Excretory organs	Coelom	Circulatory system	Respiratory organs	Segmentation	Phylum (Class)	Distinctive features (exceptions omitted)
1	..	v	..	..	..	..	..	..	**1** PROTOZOA	Microscopic: 1-celled or colonies of like cells
Cells many, arranged in layers or tissues (METAZOA)	2, diploblastic — Radial		0	0	0	0	0	0	**3** PORIFERA	Body perforated by pores and canals
				0	0	0	0	0	**4** COELENTERATA	Nematocysts; digestive tract sac-like
		Bi-radial	Incomplete	0	0	0	0	0	**5** CTENOPHORA	Comb plates for locomotion
	3, triploblastic — Bilateral			+	0	0	0	0	**6** PLATYHELMINTHES	Flat, soft; digestive tract branched or none
				+	0	+	0	0	**7** NEMERTINEA	Slender, soft, ciliated; soft proboscis
				+	ps	0	0	0	**9** Cl. ROTIFERA	Microscopic, cilia on oral disc
				+	ps	0	0	0	**9** Cl. NEMATODA	Cylindrical, tough cuticle; no cilia
			Complete (with anus)	0	+	0	0	0	**11** BRYOZOA	Grow as moss-like or encrusting colonies
				+	+	+	0	0	**13** BRACHIOPODA	Dorsal and ventral limy shell; a fleshy stalk
				+	+h	+	+	0	**14** MOLLUSCA	External limy shell of 1, 2, or 8 parts, or none; segmentation rare
				+	+	+	+0	+	**15** ANNELIDA	Slender, of many like segments; fine setae as appendages
				+	+h	+	+	+	**18** ARTHROPODA	Segmented, with jointed appendages; exoskeleton containing chitin
		Bilateral		+	+	0	0	0	**19** CHAETOGNATHA	Small; arrow-shaped, transparent; lateral fins
		Radial		0	+h	+	+	0	**20** ECHINODERMATA	Symmetry 5-part radial; tube feet; spiny endoskeleton
		Bilateral		+	+	+	+	+	**23** CHORDATA	Notochord, dorsal tubular nerve cord, gill slits; usually fins or limbs

+, present; 0, absent; *ps*, pseudocoel, not lined by peritoneum; *h*, coelom reduced, body spaces a hemocoel; *v*, symmetry various, or none.

SYNOPSIS OF THE ANIMAL KINGDOM

The following classification provides a general outline of the Animal Kingdom, and will serve for reference; it may be used for identifying many specimens to phylum and class. Alternative names for some groups are included in parentheses. Names of phyla are in boldface capitals and those of classes in italic capitals. General technical terms used here are defined in the glossary, and many special terms in the appropriate chapters of Part II. The geologic range in time and the approximate total numbers of living species (and subspecies) are indicated. Fossil groups are omitted. For each class the names of some conspicuous genera are given in italics, followed by common names when available.

Subkingdom A. Protozoa. UNICELLULAR ANIMALS.

Phylum 1. PROTOZOA. PROTOZOANS. Each individual one-celled, or in colonies of similar cells; no tissues; size usually microscopic. In salt and fresh waters, in soil, or parasitic in plants and animals. Precambrian to Recent; 30,000 species.................................(Chap. 16)

Subphylum A. SARCOMASTIGOPHORA. Pseudopodia or flagella as locomotor structures; nuclei of one kind; no spores.

Class 1. *SARCODINA* (Rhizopoda). Pseudopodia for locomotion and food capture; mostly free-living, in salt or fresh waters. *Amoeba,* free-living; *Entamoeba,* parasitic in mankind; *Globigerina,* foraminiferan; *Actinophrys,* sun animalcule or heliozoan; *Collosphaera,* radiolarian; *Badhamia,* mycetozoan; *Babesia,* piroplasmidian, in ticks, causing Texas cattle fever.

Class 2. *OPALINATA* (Protociliata). Many cilia-like organelles in oblique rows; no cytostome; all parasitic, mostly in intestines of frogs and toads. *Opalina.*

Class 3. *MASTIGOPHORA.* FLAGELLATES. One to many flagella for locomotion; free-living or parasitic. *Volvox; Euglena; Ceratium; Trypanosoma.*

Subphylum B. SPOROZOA. No cilia or flagella; nuclei of one kind; spores without polar filaments; all are internal parasites of other animals. *Monocystis,* in sperm balls of earthworm; *Eimeria,* the cause of coccidiosis in birds and mammals; *Plasmodium,* in mosquitoes and in birds, mammals, and man, causing malaria; *Sarcocystis,* in muscles, especially of mammals.

| *Amoeba* | *Euglena* | *Gregarina* | *Paramecium* | *Opalina* |
| SARCODINA | MASTIGOPHORA | SPOROZOA | CILIOPHORA | OPALINATA |

Fig. 15-4. Phylum PROTOZOA. Representatives of five classes.

Subphylum C. CNIDOSPORA. No cilia or flagella; spores with 1 or more polar filaments. Mostly parasites of fishes (Myxosporidea) or of other cold-blooded vertebrates and invertebrates (Microsporidea). *Myxidium,* cause of losses in fishes; *Nosema bombycis,* causes pebrine disease in silkworms.

Subphylum D. CILIOPHORA (Ciliata). CILIATES. Cilia present at some or all stages; nuclei of 2 kinds; mostly in fresh or salt waters. *Paramecium,* slipper animalcule; *Stentor,* trumpet-shaped; *Vorticella,* vase-like on stalk; *Diplodinium,* in stomach of cattle, etc.

Subkingdom B. Metazoa. MULTICELLULAR OR TISSUE ANIMALS. Body of many cells, usually, and arranged in layers or tissues.

Branch 1. MESOZOA. Digestive cells few, external, ciliated.

Phylum 2. MESOZOA. Worm-like; small; symmetry bilateral; body slender; an external layer of ciliated digestive cells around one or more reproductive cells; parasitic in cephalopods and other invertebrates; about 43 species. *Dicyema.*

Branch 2. PARAZOA. Digestive cells many, internal, flagellated; no digestive cavity.

Phylum 3. PORIFERA. SPONGES. Form vase-like, flat, globular, or branching; symmetry radial or none; color various; "body" surface with many pores connected to canals and chambers lined with flagellated collar cells (choanocytes) and one or more large exits (oscula); skeleton internal, of minute to microscopic spicules, or of irregular fibers, or none; sessile and marine; one family in fresh water. Precambrian to Recent; about 5,000 species . . . .(Chap. 17)

Class 1. *CALCAREA.* CALCAREOUS SPONGES. Spicules limy ($CaCO_3$), 1-, 3-, or 4-rayed; body surface bristly, osculum often fringed with spicules; color dull; mostly less than 6 inches long. *Leucosolenia, Scypha.*

Class 2. *HEXACTINELLIDA.* GLASS SPONGES. Form often cylindrical or funnel-shaped; spicules siliceous, 6-rayed, and in definite arrangement, separate or fused, sometimes resembling spun glass; no surface epithelium; collar cells only in finger-shaped chambers; marine, at depths of 300 feet to 3 miles. *Euplectella,* Venus' flower-basket.

Class 3. *DEMOSPONGIAE.* Some large and of brilliant color; skeleton of siliceous spicules, of spongin, of both, or none; canals complex. *Halisarca,* no skeleton; *Cliona,* bores into mollusks; *Spongilla,* gelatinous, in fresh waters; *Euspongia (Spongia),* bath sponge.

Branch 3. ENTEROZOA (EUMETAZOA). With digestive cavity or tract.

Division *A*. RADIATA. Symmetry radial or biradial.

Porifera   Hydrozoa   Scyphozoa   Anthozoa   Ctenophora

Fig. 15-5. Phyla PORIFERA, COELENTERATA (three classes), and CTENOPHORA.

Phylum 4. COELENTERATA (Cnidaria). COELENTERATES. Symmetry radial; the individual either a sessile cylindrical polyp, often in colonies, or a free-floating bell-like medusa with much gelatinous mesoglea; with stinging capsules (nematocysts); digestive cavity sac-like, sometimes branched; soft tentacles around mouth or margin of bell; nervous system diffuse; some with eyespots; no anus, head, or other organ systems; reproduction usually asexual in polyps and sexual in medusae; dioecious or monoecious; no sex ducts; all aquatic, chiefly marine, attached or floating. Lower Cambrian to Recent. 10,000 species . . . .(Chap. 17)

Class 1. *HYDROZOA.* HYDROIDS (and some medusae). Polyp generation well developed, colonial or solitary, usually budding off small free medusae having eyespots and statocysts. *Hydra,* in fresh waters, solitary, no medusa; *Tubularia, Obelia,* etc., all sessile, colonial; *Millepora,* stinging coral, nematocysts powerful; *Gonionemus,* medusa of some size; *Craspedacusta,* fresh-water jellyfish, 20 mm. in diameter; *Physalia,* Portuguese man-of-war, floating complex colony.

Class 2. *SCYPHOZOA.* JELLYFISHES. Mostly free-floating medusae of bell or umbrella form with strong 4-part symmetry and much mesoglea, gastric tentacles about mouth; a central "stomach" with pouches; bell margin with sense organs; dioecious, gonads in digestive cavity; polyp generation reduced or none; all marine. *Aurelia,* common coastal jellyfish; *Cyanea,* to 7 feet in diameter, Arctic waters and southward.

Class 3. *ANTHOZOA.* Sea Anemones, Corals, etc. All attached polyps (no medusae); a flat oral disc with hollow tentacles around mouth which leads into a gullet; digestive cavity divided by vertical septa on which are nematocysts and gonads; all marine, solitary or colonial. *Tubipora,* organ-pipe coral; *Alcyonium,* soft coral; *Gorgonia,* sea fan; *Pennatula,* sea pen, feather-like; *Metridium,* sea anemone; *Epizoanthus,* anemone living on hermit crab; *Acropora, Meandra,* etc., reef-building corals of tropical seas.

Phylum 5. **CTENOPHORA.** Comb Jellies. Symmetry biradial (radial + bilateral); body shape various; much mesoglea; usually with 8 rows of external comb plates for locomotion and 2 tentacles; digestive system with mouth, "pharynx," "stomach," and branched canals; no anus; no nemato- cysts; nervous system diffuse; an aboral sense organ; monoecious; reproductive cells form in digestive canals; a cydippid larva; no asexual stage; marine; solitary; 80 species. *Pleuro- brachia,* walnut-shaped, 18 mm. diameter; *Cestum,* Venus' girdle, ribbon-like, to 3 feet long; *Ctenoplana,* flat, creeping; *Beroë,* thimble-shaped, to 8 inches tall, no tentacles...(Chap. 19)

Division *B.* bilateria. **Symmetry bilateral (secondarily radial in** Echinodermata**); with organ systems and mostly with spaces between body wall and internal organs; digestive tract usually complete, with anus; mesoderm present.**

Section a. acoelomata. No body cavity; spaces in body filled with parenchyma.

Phylum 6. **PLATYHELMINTHES.** Flatworms. Symmetry bilateral; body soft, usually thin, leaf- or ribbon-like; digestive tract incomplete (no anus) and branched (or absent); muscle layers well developed; loose mesenchyme (parenchyma) fills spaces between organs; excretory system of many flame cells and ducts; nervous system with anterior ganglia or ring and 1 to 3 pairs of lengthwise nerve cords with transverse connections; usually monoecious; reproductive system of each sex with gonads, ducts, and accessory organs; fertilization internal, eggs microscopic, with shell, and containing yolk cells; development either direct or with one or more larval stages; free-living, commensal, or parasitic; more than 10,000 species.............(Chap. 18)

Class 1. *TURBELLARIA.* Free-living Flatworms. Epidermis ciliated, with many mucous glands; usually colored, some brilliant; usually a ventral mouth but no suckers; development usually direct; asexual reproduction in some. *Anaperus,* marine; *Microstomum; Euplanaria, Dugesia* (pigmented) and *Dendrocoelum* (milky white), both in fresh waters; *Bipalium,* terrestrial in moist places, *Leptoplana,* marine.

Class 2. *TREMATODA.* Flukes. Body covered with thick cuticle, usually unpigmented; mouth usually anterior, digestive tract with 2 main branches; suckers about mouth or on ventral sur- face; mostly monoecious; all parasitic. *Sphyranura, Polystoma,* on gills of fishes or amphibians; *Fasciola* and *Clonorchis,* liver flukes, and *Schistosoma,* blood fluke, all internal parasites with larvae in intermediate hosts.

Class 3. *CESTOIDEA.* Tapeworms. Body with thick cuticle; unpigmented; no digestive tract or sense organs in adult; a scolex with suckers (often also hooks) for attachment; body of few to

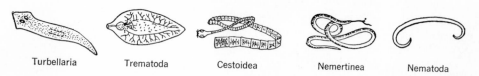

Turbellaria   Trematoda   Cestoidea   Nemertinea   Nematoda

Fig. 15-6. Phyla Platyhelminthes (three classes) and Nemertinea, and Class Nematoda.

many false segments (proglottids), each sexually complete; all internal parasites, usually with alternate hosts, adults in intestines of vertebrates. *Diphyllobothrium,* fish tapeworm of man; *Ligula,* larvae in freshwater fishes, adults in fish-eating birds; *Hymenolepis, Dipylidium, Taenia, Moniezia, Echinococcus,* in man and higher vertebrates.

Phylum 7. NEMERTINEA. RIBBON WORMS. Body slender, soft, very contractile, ciliated; no segmentation; often highly colored; a long pointed eversible proboscis in sheath; mouth anterior, digestive tract straight and complete, with anus; body spaces filled with mesenchyme (parenchyma); no coelom; 3 lengthwise blood vessels; 2 lateral branched excretory canals with flame cells; nervous system of anterior ganglia and 3 (2 to 4) lengthwise nerve trunks; sexes separate; gonads many; development direct or through larval stage; asexual reproduction by fragmentation; free-living, mostly marine, few in fresh water or terrestrial; 550 species. *Lineus, Cerebratulus, Geonemertes, Prostoma* . . . .(Chap. 19)

Section b. PSEUDOCOELOMATA. Spaces between body wall and internal organs not a coelom; anus present.

Phylum 8. ENTOPROCTA. Individuals minute, solitary or colonial, each on a stalk, with calyx bearing single circle of many ciliated tentacles; digestive tract U-shaped, both mouth and anus within circle of tentacles; body spaces a pseudocoel filled with parenchyma; monoecious or dioecious; attached to objects or animals in salt or fresh waters; 60 species. *Pedicellina, Urnatella.*

Phylum 9. ASCHELMINTHES. Size small or minute, body commonly slender; digestive tract complete, intestine usually straight, anus posterior; no anterior cilia (except rotifers).

Class 1. *ROTIFERA.* WHEEL ANIMALCULES. Body of trunk and tapering "tail" all covered by cuticle; anterior end with disc rimmed by cilia that move so as to produce a wheel-like appearance, and serve for locomotion and feeding; tail often jointed, and with "feet" having adhesive glands for attaching to objects; males minute; reproduction sexual and by parthenogenesis; mostly free-living and solitary; chiefly in fresh waters; 1,700 species. *Hydatina,* solitary; *Collotheca,* in tube
(Chap. 19)

Class 2. *GASTROTRICHA.* Microscopic, to 0.54 mm. long; mouth anterior, surrounded by bristles; dorsal surface spiny; ventral surface flat, with 2 lengthwise rows of cilia for locomotion; solitary, in fresh and salt waters; 200 species. *Chaetonotus.*

Class 3. *KINORHYNCHA* (Echinodera). To 1 mm. long, cylindrical; head of 2 rings encircled by spines; mouth with spiny retractile proboscis; body of 11 (or 12) rings covered by cuticle and bearing spines; digestive tract complete; sexes separate; marine; 30 species. *Echinodera.*

Class 4. *PRIAPULOIDEA.* Sausage-shaped; anterior end with swollen introvert bearing lengthwise rows of spines; body narrower, with transverse striations (not segmented); digestive tract straight, anus in posterior end amid gill lobes; pseudocoel large; adult lacks blood system, nephridia, and sense organs; sexes separate; marine; 5 species. *Priapulus* . . . .(Chap. 19)

Class 5. *NEMATODA.* ROUNDWORMS. Body round in cross section, slender, long, often tapered at ends, covered with tough cuticle; no segmentation; digestive tract complete, straight; lengthwise muscles only, producing flexing movements; excretory organs simple, 2, 1, or none; body spaces (pseudocoel) unlined; an anterior nerve ring and 6 lengthwise nerve cords; sexes separate, male smaller than female; gonads continuous with reproductive ducts; fertilization internal; development direct; no asexual reproduction; free-living in soil or water, or parasitic; 12,000 species. *Anguillula,* in vinegar; *Heterodera,* root nematode, in plants; *Ascaris, Oxyuris, Strongylus, Filaria,* in various birds and mammals; *Ancylostoma, Necator,* hookworms; *Trichinella,* trichina worm . . . .(Chap. 18)

Class 6. *NEMATOMORPHA* (Gordiacea). "HORSEHAIR WORMS." Body thread-like, not tapered, anterior end blunt; cuticle opaque, rough; longitudinal muscles only; digestive tract complete in young; body cavity either a complete pseudocoel or else filled with mesenchyme; nerve ring around esophagus and 1 ventral nerve cord; sexes separate; gonads 2, with ducts;

larvae parasitic in insects, adults free-living in water; about 15 species in North America. *Gordius* ....(Chap. 19)

Phylum 10. ACANTHOCEPHALA. Spiny-headed Worms. Body long and flat, rough in life, cylindrical and smoother when preserved; cuticle thin; anterior end with blunt retractile proboscis having rows of curved spines; no digestive tract; sexes separate; parasitic, larvae in arthropods, adults in vertebrates; 300 species. *Echinorhynchus*...................................(Chap. 19)

| Nematomorpha | Acanthocephala | Rotifera | Bryozoa | Brachiopoda |

Fig. 15-7. Miscellaneous phyla and groups.

Section c. EUCOELOMATA. With true coelom, usually lined with layer of cells.

Phylum 11. BRYOZOA (Ectoprocta). Moss Animals. Colonies branched and plant-like, or as low encrustations on rocks or shells, or as gelatinous masses; individuals many, minute, each in separate housing (zooecium); ciliated tentacles on lophophore (usually retractile) around mouth; digestive tract complete, U-shaped; coelom well developed and lined with peritoneum; nerve ganglion between mouth and anus; monoecious; gonads arise from peritoneum and eggs develop in brood pouch (ooecium) of peritoneum; larva a trochophore; colonies formed by asexual budding (by statoblasts in fresh-water species); mostly marine and sessile. Lower Ordovician to Recent; 4,000 species. *Membranipora, Alcyonidium, Bugula,* all marine; *Plumatella, Cristatella,* in fresh waters...(Chap. 19)

Phylum 12. PHORONIDEA. Phoronids. Body worm-like, cylindrical, unsegmented; anterior end with 2 spiral lobes (lophophore) bearing ciliated tentacles; digestive tract U-shaped; coelom lined, of 6 compartments; contractile blood vessels present; 2 nephridia; nerve ring below tentacles; monoecious; marine; larva free-swimming; adult lives in a self-secreted membranous tube in mud or sand; 15 species. *Phoronis.*

Phylum 13. BRACHIOPODA. Lamp Shells. External limy shell of 2 unlike valves, dorsal and ventral, lined by thin mantle; a fleshy stalk (peduncle) for attachment to rocks; mouth preceded by 2 fleshy spiral lobes (lophophore) supported on a shelly loop and bearing ciliated tentacles; digestive tract with or without anus; stomach with digestive gland; coelom well developed, lined; a small heart; nephridia 2 or 4; sexes separate, gonads paired; larva ciliated; no asexual reproduction; all marine. Cambrian to Recent; 260 living and many fossil species. *Lingula, Terebratulina, Magellania*...(Chap. 19)

Phylum 14. MOLLUSCA. Mollusks. Symmetry bilateral (viscera and shell coiled in some); segmentation rare; body soft, covered by a thin mantle that usually secretes a shell of 1, 2, or 8 parts; usually an anterior head and ventral foot for locomotion; digestive tract complete; a dorsal heart and blood vessels; respiration usually by gills; coelom usually reduced; nephridia 1, 2, 4, or more; nervous system typically of 3 pairs of ganglia, connectives, and nerves; many with sensory organs (smell, sight); sexes usually separate; gonads 1 or 2; usually oviparous; development direct or with larval stage; mostly in salt and fresh waters, some snails on land. Ordovician to Recent; 40,000 fossil, 45,000 living species....................................(Chap. 20)

Class 1. *MONOPLACOPHORA.* Body and foot oval; shell single; 5 or 6 pairs of gills; marine; Lower Cambrian to Devonian; 2 Recent species. *Neopilina.*

Class 2. *AMPHINEURA.* Chitons, etc. Body elongate, often elliptical, shell of 8 plates (or 1 or none); head reduced; foot large, flat; no tentacles; gills 5 to 80 pairs in groove between foot and

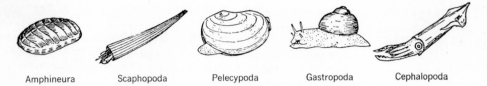

Amphineura   Scaphopoda   Pelecypoda   Gastropoda   Cephalopoda

Fig. 15-8. Phylum MOLLUSCA. Five of the classes.

fleshy girdle; sexes separate; 1 gonad; marine. *Chiton, Cryptochiton,* on rocks at ocean margin; *Chaetoderma,* small, worm-like, on ocean bottom.

Class 3. *SCAPHOPODA.* TOOTH SHELLS OR TUSK SHELLS. Shell and mantle slenderly tubular, slightly tapered and curved, open at both ends; foot conical; delicate "tentacles" about mouth; no gills; sexes separate; 1 gonad; marine, burrows in sand or mud, in shallow water and down to 15,000 feet. *Dentalium.*

Class 4. *GASTROPODA.* SNAILS, SLUGS, LIMPETS, AND WHELKS. Visceral mass usually asymmetrical in spirally coiled shell, either right-handed or left-handed (shell in some conical, reduced, or none); head distinct, with 1 or 2 pairs of tentacles and 1 pair of eyes or none; foot large, flat; original left auricle, gill, and kidney usually lacking; 1 gonad, usually with special ducts; mostly oviparous; marine, fresh-water or terrestrial. MARINE: *Acmaea, Patella,* limpets, shell flatly conical; *Haliotis,* abalone, shell ear-shaped, aperture large; *Strombus,* giant Florida conch, shell to 250 mm. long; *Urosalpinx,* oyster drill; *Tethys,* sea hare, to 300 mm. long, shell small and internal; *Clione,* pteropod, pelagic, sides of foot expanded as fins; *Doris, Aeolis,* nudibranchs or sea slugs, no shell. FRESH-WATER: *Viviparus, Lymnaea, Physa.* TERRESTRIAL: *Polygyra, Zonites, Helix,* land snails; *Limax, Ariolimax,* slugs, small shell within mantle.

Class 5. *PELECYPODA* (Lamellibranchiata). BIVALVE MOLLUSKS. Shell of 2 lateral valves, usually symmetrical, with dorsal hinge and ligament, closed by muscles; no head, jaws, or radula; mantle of right and left lobes, its margin usually forming posterior siphons to control water flow into mantle cavity; mouth with soft palps; foot often hatchet-shaped, extended between mantle edges when moving; gills plate-like; sexes usually separate; a larval stage; mostly marine, some in fresh water. *Ostrea,* edible oyster, and *Mytilus,* sea mussel, both attached; *Pecten,* scallop, marine, swims by clapping shells together; *Lampsilis, Unio,* fresh-water clams or mussels; *Mactra* (shell to 150 mm. long), *Venus, Ensis, Mya,* marine clams; *Pholas,* burrows in marine clay or rock; *Teredo,* shipworm, slender body, small shells, burrows in wood in salt waters.

Class 6. *CEPHALOPODA.* NAUTILI, SQUIDS, AND OCTOPUSES. Shell external, internal, or none; head large, eyes conspicuous and complex; mouth with horny jaws and radula, surrounded by 8 or 10 arms (or many tentacles); a siphon formed of mantle margins for locomotion; nerve ganglia grouped in head as "brain"; sexes separate; no larva; all marine. *Nautilus,* pearly nautilus, with external coiled shell; *Sepia,* cuttlefish, and *Loligo,* squid, 10 arms; *Octopus,* octopus or devilfish, 8 arms.

Phylum 15. **ANNELIDA.** SEGMENTED WORMS. Body soft, long, usually of many like segments bearing fine chitinous setae for locomotion; cuticle thin; both circular and longitudinal muscles well developed; digestive tract complete, usually tubular; coelom usually large, lined with peritoneum; blood-vascular system closed; paired nephridia; 1 pair of dorsal ganglia (brain) in anterior end and solid ventral (double) nerve cord extending length of body with a ganglion and pairs of nerves in each body segment; sensory cells and organs for touch, taste, and light; monoecious (earthworms, leeches) and development direct, or sexes separate and with larval stages; some multiply by asexual budding; marine, fresh waters, on land, or in soil; more than 8,700 species...(Chap. 21)

Class 1. *POLYCHAETA.* SAND WORMS, TUBE WORMS, ETC. Segmentation conspicuous externally

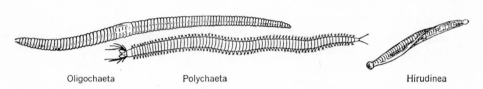

Oligochaeta   Polychaeta   Hirudinea

Fig. 15-9. Phylum ANNELIDA. The three classes.

and internally; somites many, with paired lateral lobes (parapodia) bearing numerous setae; a head region, with tentacles; no clitellum; tube dwellers usually with anterior gills; sexes usually separate; no permanent gonads; fertilization commonly external; a larval stage; predominantly marine. *Neanthes,* clam-worm; *Polygordius; Chaetopterus, Arenicola, Spirorbis, Serpula,* living in self-made tubes.

Class 2. *OLIGOCHAETA.* EARTHWORMS, ETC. Segmentation conspicuous externally and internally; no head or parapodia; setae few per somite; few with gills; clitellum secretes cocoon for eggs; monoecious; no larva; chiefly in fresh water and soil. *Chaetogaster,* commensal on fresh-water sponges and snails; *Tubifex,* in tubes in mud; *Enchytraeus,* in soil and on sea beaches; *Eisenia,* in manure piles; *Allolobophora, Lumbricus,* in soil.

Class 3. *HIRUDINEA.* LEECHES. Body pigmented, flattish; a large posterior sucker and often a smaller one at anterior end; no tentacles, parapodia, or setae; somites 34, inconspicuous, divided externally; clitellum slight; coelom filled by connective tissues and muscles; monoecious; eggs usually in cocoons; no larva; in fresh or salt waters or on land. *Placobdella,* on fresh-water turtles; *Hirudo,* medicinal leech; *Macrobdella,* to 300 mm. long, in fresh waters, attacks man, cattle, frogs, etc.; *Haemadipsa,* tropical land leech, southeastern Asia.

Phylum 16. SIPUNCULOIDEA. "PEANUT WORMS." Body slenderly gourd-shaped, highly contractile; anterior end (introvert) slender and retractile, with short hollow tentacles around mouth; no segmentation or setae; digestive tract slender, spiraled, anus dorsal at base of introvert; coelom large, undivided, ciliated, containing blood with corpuscles; anterior dorsal nerve ganglion and ventral nerve cord; sexes separate; marine; 250 species. *Sipunculus, Phascolosoma.*

Phylum 17. ECHIUROIDEA. Body sausage-like; anterior end with trough-shaped elastic proboscis (non-retractile) leading to mouth; intestine spiraled, anus at posterior end, joined by 2 anal pouches; circulatory system of dorsal and ventral vessels; 1 to 3 pairs of nephridia anteriorly; one pair of large ventral setae below mouth; adults unsegmented, larvae with 15 vestigial somites; monoecious; marine; 60 species. *Echiurus, Urechis.*

Phylum 18. ARTHROPODA. JOINT-FOOTED ANIMALS. Body typically of head, thorax, and abdomen, each formed of like or unlike segments (somites) variously separate or fused, and each somite typically with 1 pair of jointed appendages; exoskeleton with chitin covers all parts, molted entire at intervals; digestive tract complete, straight; coelom reduced, body spaces a hemocoel; heart dorsal, circulatory system open (lacunar); respiration by gills, tracheae, or lung books; brain dorsal, nerve cord ventral and double, with ganglia in each somite or concentrated anteriorly; sexes usually separate, gonads paired, fertilization internal; commonly with larval stages and metamorphosis; terrestrial or aquatic; free-living, commensal, or parasitic. Cambrian to Recent; more than 900,000 species..(Chap. 22)

Subphylum A. ONYCHOPHORA. Elongate; no head, but anterior end with paired short "antennae" and oral papillae; body somewhat cylindrical, unsegmented; 15 to 43 pairs of stumpy, unjointed legs; terrestrial. *Peripatus.*..(Chap. 22)

Subphylum B. †TRILOBITA. TRILOBITES. Body divided by 2 lengthwise furrows into 3 lobes; head distinct; abdomen of 2 to 29 somites and a fused caudal plate; all somites except last with biramous appendages; marine. Cambrian to Permian. †*Triarthrus*..............(Chap. 22)

Subphylum C. *CHELICERATA.* No antennae; body of cephalothorax, with 6 pairs of appendages (chelicerae, pedipalpi, and 4 pairs of legs), and abdomen; chiefly terrestrial.

Crustacea   Insecta   Arachnida   Chilopoda   Diplopoda

Fig. 15-10. Phylum ARTHROPODA. Representatives of the five principal classes and subclasses.

Class 1. *MEROSTOMATA.* Cephalothorax broadly joined to abdomen on which are 5 or 6 pairs of appendages; with compound lateral eyes; aquatic. *Limulus,* king crab; †*Eurypterus,* eurypterid (Chap. 22)

Class 2. *PYCNOGONIDA* (Pantopoda). SEA SPIDERS. Mostly small to minute; body short, thin; mouth suctorial, on long proboscis; marine. *Pycnogonum*......................(Chap. 22)

Class 3. *ARACHNIDA.* SPIDERS, SCORPIONS, MITES, TICKS, ETC. Abdomen lacks locomotor appendages; eyes all simple; no gills; terrestrial. *Epeira,* spider; *Sarcoptes,* itch mite; *Ornithodorus,* tick ....(Chap. 22)

Subphylum D. MANDIBULATA (Antennata). Body of 2 parts (head and trunk) or 3 parts (head, thorax with walking legs, and abdomen); 1 or 2 pairs of antennae; 1 pair of jaws (mandibles), 1 or more pairs of maxillae, and 3 or more pairs of walking legs.

Class 1. *CRUSTACEA.* LOBSTERS, CRABS, WATER FLEAS, BARNACLES, ETC. Two pairs of antennae, 1 pair of jaws, and 2 pairs of maxillae; some appendages biramous; respire mainly by gills; mostly aquatic. *Daphnia,* water flea; *Balanus,* barnacle; *Astacus, Cambarus,* crayfishes.....(Chap. 22)

Class 2. *INSECTA* (Hexapoda). INSECTS. One pair of antennae; head, thorax, and abdomen distinct; thorax typically with 3 pairs of legs and 2 pairs of wings; mainly terrestrial. *Melanoplus,* grasshopper; *Musca,* fly; *Apis,* bee...(Chap. 23)

Class 3. *MYRIAPODA.* Body of 2 parts; head with 1 pair of antennae, 1 pair of mandibles, 1 or 2 pairs of maxillae; trunk with 1 or 2 pairs of legs per somite; terrestrial............(Chap. 22)

Subclass 1. CHILOPODA. CENTIPEDES. Body long, flattened, of 15 to 173 somites, each with a pair of legs; terrestrial. *Lithobius, Scolopendra.*

Subclass 2. DIPLOPODA. MILLIPEDES. Body long, cylindrical; thorax of 4 somites, with 1 pair of legs on each; abdomen of 20 to more than 100 double somites, each with 2 pairs of legs; terrestrial. *Julus.*

Subclass 3. SYMPHYLA. To 6 mm. long; no eyes; adult with 12 pairs of legs; sex opening midventral between 4th pair of legs; terrestrial. *Scutigerella,* garden centipede.

Subclass 4. PAUROPODA. Minute; no eyes; antennae 3-branched; body cylindrical, of 11 (12) somites and 9 (10) pairs of legs; sex opening midventral on 3d somite; terrestrial. *Pauropus.*

Subphylum E. PENTASTOMIDA (Linguatulida). Worm-like, soft, unsegmented, but abdomen ringed; 2 pairs of ventral hooks beside mouth; parasitic in vertebrates. *Linguatula.*

Subphylum F. TARDIGRADA. WATER BEARS OR BEAR ANIMALCULES. To 1 mm. long; body cylindrical, unsegmented; 4 pairs of stumpy unjointed legs with claws; in moss or fresh waters. *Echiniscus.*

Phylum 19. CHAETOGNATHA. ARROW WORMS. Slender, transparent; body of head, trunk, and tail; bristles on hooks about mouth; paired lateral fins on trunk and a terminal fin on tail; digestive tract complete; coelom of 3 paired cavities; monoecious; free-living; marine; 50 species. *Sagitta* (Chap. 19)

Phylum 20. ECHINODERMATA. ECHINODERMS. Symmetry radial, usually 5-parted, around axis through mouth; no segmentation; body covered by delicate epidermis over firm (endo) skeleton of movable or fixed limy plates (usually of definite pattern) and with external spines (skin leathery, plates microscopic in sea cucumbers); digestive tract usually complete; coelom large, ciliated; water vascular system with tube feet for locomotion; sexes separate, gonads large, with ducts; ova usually fertilized in sea, larvae microscopic, ciliated; all marine. Cambrian to Recent; 5,500 species..(Chap. 19)

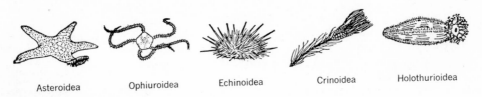

Asteroidea   Ophiuroidea   Echinoidea   Crinoidea   Holothurioidea

Fig. 15-11. Phylum ECHINODERMATA. The five living classes.

Class 1. *CRINOIDEA.* SEA LILIES, FEATHER STARS. Body flower-like, a box-like calyx of many plates and bearing slender branched arms; some species on aboral stalk; no spines or pedicellariae; tube feet suckerless. *Antedon, Metacrinus.*

Class 2. *ASTEROIDEA.* STARFISHES OR SEA STARS. Body commonly star-shaped or pentagonal; arms 5 to 50, more or less flexible, usually not sharply distinct from central disc; skeleton flexible, usually with short spines and pedicellariae; ambulacral grooves with 2 or 4 rows of tube feet; madreporite aboral; stomach large; mostly predaceous. *Asterias, Pisaster, Asterina,* common starfishes; *Solaster,* sun star, arms 7 to 14.

Class 3. *OPHIUROIDEA.* BRITTLE STARS. Disc small, rounded; arms 5, slender, jointed, flexible; tube feet in 2 rows, suckerless, sensory; no pedicellariae; stomach sac-like, no caeca or anus; madreporite oral; free-living, active. *Gorgonocephalus,* basket star, arms many-branched; *Ophiura,* brittle star.

Class 4. *ECHINOIDEA.* SEA URCHINS, SAND DOLLARS, ETC. Body hemispherical, disc-like, or egg-shaped; no arms; skeletal plates firmly sutured forming a shell (test) that bears many long movable spines and 3-jawed pedicellariae; tube feet with suckers; digestive tract long, slender, and coiled; mouth and anus either central or lateral; madreporite dorsal. *Arbacia, Strongylocentrotus,* sea urchins, hemispherical; *Echinarachnius, Dendraster,* sand dollars, flat; *Spatangus, Lovenia,* heart urchins.

Class 5. *HOLOTHURIOIDEA.* SEA CUCUMBERS. Body sausage- or worm-shaped, wall leathery to thin and translucent; no arms, spines, or pedicellariae; skeleton usually of scattered microscopic plates; tube feet usually present; mouth anterior, surrounded by retractile tentacles; digestive tract long, S-shaped, anus posterior; cloaca usually with respiratory tree. *Holothuria, Thyone, Leptosynapta.*

Phylum 21. POGONOPHORA. BEARD WORMS. Body string like, cylindrical (0.5–2.5 mm. diameter, 50–250 mm. long); in chitinous tube; body of 3 parts, the last with rings or adhesive papillae; no mouth, digestive tract, anus, or gill slits; 1 to many fringed tentacles on anterior end; circulatory system closed; 2 excretory coelomoducts; nervous system dorsal, embedded in epidermis; sexes separate; marine, mostly at great depths; 43 species. *Lamellisabella,* 3,500 meters, Okhotsk Sea, northwestern Pacific; *Siboglinum,* Indonesia.

Phylum 22. HEMICHORDATA. TONGUE WORMS, PTEROBRANCHS, ETC. Symmetry bilateral; unsegmented; body of 3 divisions; slender and worm-like, or vase-like in secreted tube; gill slits, many, 2, or none; digestive tract complete, straight or U-shaped; marine. *Balanoglossus, Saccoglossus, Cephalodiscus*..(Chap. 19)

Phylum 23. CHORDATA. CHORDATES. Having at some stage or throughout life: an axial rod-like notochord for support of body, a single dorsal hollow nerve cord, and paired gill slits between pharynx and exterior; segmentation usually evident; tail behind anus.

Group α. ACRANIA. No cranium, jaws, vertebrae, or paired appendages.

Subphylum A. TUNICATA (Urochordata). Tunicates. Larva minute, tadpole-like, with gill slits, and with both notochord and nerve cord in tail; adults tubular, globose, or irregular in form, covered with tunic or test (often transparent); gill slits many; notochord usually lost; nervous system reduced . . . . (Chap. 24)

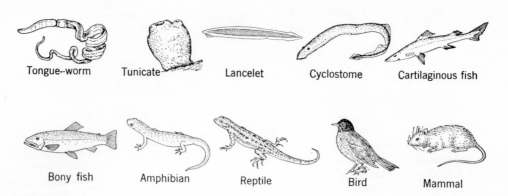

Fig. 15-12. Phylum Hemichordata and Phylum Chordata—two lower subphyla and classes of living vertebrates.

Class 1. *LARVACEA* (Appendicularia). Minute persistent larvae, separate, free-swimming, with notochord, "brain," nerve cord, and 2 gill slits. *Appendicularia.*

Class 2. *ASCIDIACEA.* Ascidians. Size and form various; solitary, colonial, or compound; usually sessile after metamorphosis when tail, nerve cord, and notochord are lost, and "brain" is reduced to a ganglion, but many gill slits persist; test well developed, permanent. *Ciona, Molgula,* simple ascidians; *Botryllus,* compound ascidian.

Class 3. *THALIACEA.* Chain Tunicates. Size various; adults free-living, without tail or notochord, test permanent, with circular muscle bands. *Salpa; Doliolum.*

Subphylum B. CEPHALOCHORDATA (Leptocardii). Lancelets. Small, slender, fish-like, distinctly segmented; notochord and nerve cord extending length of body, and many gill slits enclosed in an outer atrium, all permanent. *Branchiostoma,* amphioxus or lancelet . . . . (Chap. 24)

Group β. **CRANIATA.** Vertebrates. With cranium (skull), visceral arches, and "spinal column" of segmental vertebrae, all cartilaginous in lower forms but bony in higher ones; notochord extends from tail to base of cranium; anterior end of nerve cord with enlarged brain of specialized parts; head region with paired special sense organs (smell, sight, hearing); paired semicircular canals for equilibration; circulatory system closed, of arteries and veins, heart of 2 to 4 chambers, and with both white and red blood cells.

Subphylum C. AGNATHA. Jawless Vertebrates. No true jaws or paired appendages.

Class 1. *CYCLOSTOMATA* (Marsipobranchii). Lampreys and Hag Fishes. Body cylindrical, slender, with median fins only; skin smooth, no scales; mouth suctorial, with horny teeth; one median nasal opening; 2 pairs of semicircular canals; 6 to 14 pairs of bag-like gill pouches opening on sides of body; heart 2-chambered; aquatic. *Petromyzon, Entosphenus,* lampreys; *Myxine,* hag fish . . . . (Chap. 25)

Subphylum D. GNATHOSTOMATA. Jawed Vertebrates. One pair of visceral arches modified as biting jaws; 2 nasal capsules or tubes; 3 pairs of semicircular canals; usually with paired appendages (fins or limbs); sexes separate.

Superclass **a. *Pisces.*** Fishes. With median fins supported by fin rays; paired fins usually present; skin usually with scales containing limy material; nasal capsules not connected to mouth cavity; heart with 1 auricle; respiration by gills; aquatic............................(Chap. 25)

Class 1. *CHONDRICHTHYES*. CARTILAGINOUS FISHES. Skeleton of cartilage, notochord persistent; scales placoid, minute; mouth and 2 olfactory pits ventral on head; 5 to 7 pairs of gills, each gill in separate cleft; males with claspers; ova large, cleavage superficial. Carboniferous to Recent. *Mustelus, Squalus, Acanthias,* dogfish sharks; *Carcarias,* great white shark; *Raja,* rays; *Urobatis,* sting ray; *Manta,* devil fish; *Hydrolagus,* chimaera....................(Chap. 25)

Class 2. *OSTEICHTHYES*. BONY FISHES. Skeleton more or less bony; mouth usually terminal; skin usually covered with embedded dermal (bony) scales, of cycloid or ctenoid form; 4 pairs of gills in common cavity (not in separate clefts), covered on each side by a platelike operculum; air bladder usually present; no cloaca; ova small, cleavage superficial; in salt and fresh waters. Silurian to Recent; about 20,000 species. *Polypterus,* bichir; *Acipenser,* sturgeon; *Lepidosteus,* gar; *Clupea,* herring; *Salmo,* trout and Atlantic salmon; *Esox,* pike; *Catostomus,* sucker; *Ameiurus,* catfish; *Anguilla,* eel; *Gambusia,* top minnow; *Gaddus,* codfish; *Perca,* perch; *Hippoglossus,* halibut; *Mola,* ocean sunfish; *Neoceratodus, Lepidosiren,* lungfishes.......(Chap. 25)

Superclass b. **Tetrapoda**. FOUR-LEGGED "LAND" VERTEBRATES. Typically with 2 pairs of 5-toed limbs, variously modified, reduced, or absent in some; skeleton bony; nasal capsules (nostrils) connected to mouth cavity; some with external auditory canals; heart with 2 auricles and double circulation of blood.

Class 1. *AMPHIBIA*. AMPHIBIANS. Living forms covered by soft, moist, glandular skin; skull with 2 occipital condyles; heart 3-chambered; respiration by gills, lungs, or skin; eggs with gelatinous coverings, usually laid in water; larvae usually aquatic; adults aquatic or in moist places on land. Devonian to Recent; more than 1,900 living species. *Ichthyophis,* caecilian, limbless; *Necturus,* mud puppy; *Ambystoma, Triturus, Plethodon,* salamanders; *Bufo,* toad; *Rana,* frog (Chap.26)

Class 2. *REPTILIA*. REPTILES. Body covered with dry cornified skin, usually with scales or scutes; toes usually clawed; limbs and toes reduced or absent in some; skeleton bony, 1 occipital condyle; heart imperfectly 4-chambered; respiration by lungs; fertilization internal; eggs with much yolk, covered by shells; mostly oviparous; embryonic membranes present during development; young when hatched resemble adults; terrestrial, fresh waters, or marine, in tropics and warm temperate regions. Permian to Recent; more than 4,000 living species. *Chelydra, Chrysemys,* turtles; *Gopherus,* desert tortoise; *Sphenodon,* tuatara of New Zealand; *Anolis,* chameleon; *Sceloporus, Cnemidophorus,* lizards; *Heloderma,* Gila monster (poisonous); *Python, Charina,* boas; *Natrix, Thamnophis,* water and garter snakes; *Coluber,* racer; *Naja,* cobra: *Micrurus,* coral snake; *Crotalus,* rattlesnake; *Alligator,* alligator...........(Chap. 26)

Class 3. *AVES*. BIRDS. Body covered with feathers; fore limbs modified as wings for flight; heart completely 4-chambered; respire by lungs; "warm-blooded" (homoiothermous); eggs with much yolk and shell; oviparous; embryonic membranes during development; terrestrial and aquatic. Upper Jurassic to Recent; 25,000 species and subspecies. *Struthio,* ostrich; *Apteryx,* kiwi of New Zealand; *Aptenodytes,* penguin; *Ardea,* heron; *Anas,* duck; *Buteo,* hawk; *Bonasa,* grouse; *Larus,* gull; *Columba,* pigeon; *Dendrocopus,* woodpecker; *Passer,* sparrow.........(Chap. 27)

Class 4. *MAMMALIA*. MAMMALS. Body usually covered with hair; skin with various glands; teeth in sockets, usually differentiated in structure; limbs various, for walking, climbing, burrowing, swimming, or flying; toes usually with claws, nails, or hoofs; a thin muscular diaphragm between cavities of thorax and abdomen; male with penis; fertilization internal; females with ventral mammary glands secreting milk to nourish young; body temperature regulated. Triassic to Recent; 15,000 living species and subspecies. *Ornithorhynchus,* duck-billed platypus; *Didelphis,* opossum; *Macropus,* kangaroo; *Scapanus,* mole; *Myotis,* bat; *Pan,* chimpanzee; *Homo,* mankind (Chap. 29); *Rattus,* rat; *Physeter,* whale; *Elephas,* elephant; *Equus,* horse; *Cervus,* elk...(Chap. 28)

REVIEW

1. What is the purpose of scientific zoological classification? On what kinds of features of animals is it based?
2. Define the term species.
3. Arrange a table showing the groups in classification in descending rank from phylum to species.
4. What is meant by symmetry? By segmentation?
5. Why are scientific names necessary? Explain the meaning of binomial nomenclature.
6. From Table 15-1 write out some important characters for each of the phyla. Compare your results with the characteristics of these phyla in the Synopsis of the Animal Kingdom that follows the table.
7. Both the COELENTERATA and ECHINODERMATA have radial symmetry. List in parallel colums some characters for these two phyla showing that they are not closely related.
8. Make a comparison of the PLATYHELMINTHES and ANNELIDA to show why the first is placed lower in classification than the second.

16
One-celled animals

The Protozoa (Gr. *protos,* first + *zoön,* animal) are mostly one-celled animals of microscopic size. In the Animal Kingdom they comprise the lowest of the great groups, or phyla, in contrast to all the multicellular tissue animals, or Metazoa (Gr. *meta,* after). Structurally a protozoan is comparable to one cell of a metazoan, but functionally it is an entire organism that performs all the essential life processes. Some protozoans are simple in structure; others have "cell organs," or *organelles,* that are functionally analogous to the organ systems of multicellular animals. Fully 30,000 kinds of Protozoa are known, and in numbers of individuals they far exceed all other animals. Each species lives in some moist habitat—ocean waters or on the ocean bottom; fresh, brackish, or foul waters inland; soil or decaying organic matter. Many are free-living and free-swimming, others are sessile, and some form colonies. Still others live on or in certain plants and various animals, from protozoans to man. These interrelationships vary from casual occurrence to strict parasitism. Many protozoans serve as food for other minute animals. Some help to purify filter and sewage beds. Species that cause diseases such as amoebic dysentery, malaria, and African sleeping sickness are a scourge to mankind.

The Protozoa are divided, according to the structures they possess for locomotion (Fig. 16-1), into several groups: Sarcodina, or rhizopods, with pseudopodia; Opalinata, with oblique rows of cilia-like structures; Mastigophora, or flagellates, with one or more whip-like flagella; Sporozoa and Cnidospora, with no locomotor structures; and Ciliophora, or ciliates, with cilia throughout life.

16-1. Characteristics.
1. Small, usually 1-celled, some in colonies of few to many similar individuals; symmetry none, bilateral, radial, or spherical.
2. Cell form usually constant, oval, long, spherical, or otherwise, varied in some species and changing with environment or age in many.
3. Nucleus distinct, 1 or more; other structural parts as organelles; no organs or tissues.
4. Locomotion by flagella, pseudopodia, cilia, or movements of the cell itself.
5. Some species with protective housings, or tests; many species producing resistant cysts or spores to survive unfavorable conditions and for dispersal.
6. Mode of life free-living, commensal, symbiotic, or parasitic.
7. Nutrition various: (*a*) *holozoic,* subsisting on other organisms (bacteria, yeasts, algae, other protozoans, etc.); (*b*) *saprophytic,* subsisting on dissolved substances in the surroundings; (*c*) *holophytic,* or *autotrophic,* by photosynthesis as in plants. Some combine two methods.

Illustration at top of page: A marine foraminiferan (*Allogromia laticollaris*) with central one-chambered organic test sheathed by protoplasm and long, slender pseudopodia. (*Photo by Zack M. Arnold.*)

| Amoeba | Euglena | Gregarina | Paramecium | Opalina |
| SARCODINA | MASTIGOPHORA | SPOROZOA | CILIOPHORA | OPALINATA |

Fig. 16-1. Common representatives of the Phylum PROTOZOA.

8. Asexual reproduction by binary fission, multiple fission, or budding; some with sexual reproduction by fusion of gametes or by conjugation (in CILIOPHORA).

The PROTOZOA are descended from ancient unknown stocks of the earliest living organisms on the earth. The soft-bodied species have left no fossil record, but the extreme age of the phylum is proved by finding the hard remains of RADIOLARIA in Precambrian rocks. Some chlorophyll-bearing flagellates resemble the green algae in structure and physiology, suggesting a common origin for plants and animals. Most protozoans are so small that they are measured in microns (1 micron, $\mu =$ 0.001 mm.). Some are only 2 or 3 μ in length. A dozen *Babesia* may inhabit one red blood cell or several hundred *Leishmania* (flagellate) a single tissue cell. Most species are less than 250 μ long, but one ciliate (*Spirostomum*) grows to 3 mm. and a sporozoan (*Porospora gigantea*) to 16 mm.

AMOEBAS, ETC.

CLASS *SARCODINA*

The common amoeba, *Amoeba proteus,* is an example of a protozoan and of the Class SARCODINA (Gr. *sarcodes,* fleshy). Structurally it is about the simplest possible living animal —an independent cell with nucleus and cytoplasm but no permanent organelles. Yet this elemental organism can perform all the essential animal activities: it can move, capture, digest, and assimilate complex food, egest residues, respire, produce secretions and excretions, respond to changes (stimuli) of various kinds in both its internal and external environment, grow, and reproduce itself.

16-2. Structure. The amoeba (Figs. 16-2, 16-3) is a mass of clear, colorless, and jelly-like protoplasm, up to 600 μ long, of irregular shape, and undergoes frequent change of form. It consists of (1) a very thin, elastic external cell membrane, or *plasmalemma,* and beneath this (2) a narrow zone of clear, nongranular *ectoplasm* surrounding (3) the main body mass of granular *endoplasm.* The latter consists of (*a*) an outer stiffer *plasmagel* and (*b*) an inner *plasmasol* in which streaming movements are visible. Within the endoplasm are (4) a disc-like *nucleus,* not easily seen in the living animal; (5) a spherical, fluid-filled *contractile vacuole,* which at intervals moves to the surface, contracts, discharges its contents into the surrounding water, and then reforms; (6) one or more *food vacuoles* of various sizes, containing bits of food undergoing digestion; and (7) various other *vacuoles, crystals, oil globules,* and other *cell inclusions* ranging downward in size to or below the limit of microscopic visibility.

Briefly, the functions of these parts are as

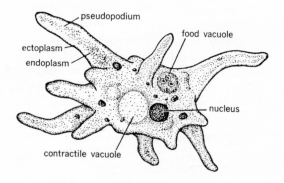

Fig. 16-2. Structure of *Amoeba* (Class SARCODINA).

follows: (1) The cell membrane retains protoplasm within the cell but permits the passage of water, oxygen, and carbon dioxide; (2) the ectoplasm lends form to the cell body; (3) the endoplasm contains the other structures and serves in locomotion; (4) the nucleus controls vital processes of the organism; (5) the contractile vacuole regulates water content; (6) the food vacuoles contain food in process of digestion; and (7) the other cell inclusions are reserve foods or other materials essential to metabolism. If the amoeba is cut in two, the cell membrane soon surrounds each piece and prevents loss of the protoplasm; the part without a nucleus can still move and ingest food but is unable to digest or assimilate the food and soon dies, whereas that with the nucleus will continue to grow and reproduce. An isolated nucleus, however, cannot survive. Thus it is that the nucleus and cytoplasm are interdependent.

16-3. Locomotion. The amoeba moves by forming and projecting temporary finger-like extensions, or *pseudopodia* (Gr. *pseudos,* false + *podos,* foot) at any place on its cell body. This sort of irregular flowing is termed *amoe-*

boid movement; it occurs in many protozoans and also in the amoebocytes of sponges and the white blood cells of vertebrates. Amoeboid movement is probably a basic characteristic of unspecialized protoplasm and like most fundamental processes is difficult to explain. It can be imitated in part by some mixtures of nonliving materials, where differences in surface tension account for certain kinds of movement. In the amoeba movement is possibly the result of changes within the colloidal protoplasm, from the fluid "sol" to the more solid "gel" condition, and vice versa. Three outstanding features of locomotion are (1) attaching to the substratum, possibly by a secretion; (2) transformation of plasmagel to plasmasol at the hinder end and the opposite process at the forward end of the animal; and (3) an increase in the elastic strength of the plasmagel as it passes backward. Attachment is best on rough surfaces but depends on the nature of the fluid about the animal and on the physiological condition of the amoeba.

16-4. Feeding. The amoeba eats other protozoans, algae, rotifers, and dead protoplasm. It may eat several paramecia or many small

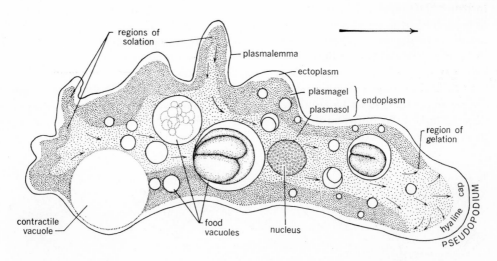

Fig. 16-3. Locomotion in *Amoeba.* The fluid inner plasmasol flows forward and is converted into plasmagel at the forward-moving pseudopod; the reverse process occurs in the opposite end and in pseudopodia that are being withdrawn. Large arrow indicates direction of movement of entire animal; small arrows that of endoplasm. (*After Mast,* 1926.)

flagellates daily and exhibits choice in selecting food. The amoeba is attracted by movements of the intended prey or by substances diffusing from it; unwanted or indigestible materials are usually avoided, as are very active organisms. Food may enter at any part of the cell surface by extending pseudopodia; these encircle the food (Fig. 16-4), which, with some water, is taken into the endoplasm as a *food vacuole.* The vacuoles are moved about by streaming of the endoplasm. A newly formed vacuole gives an acid reaction (to litmus or neutral red), probably because of a secretion that kills the prey quickly. Later the reaction becomes alkaline, and the action of enzymes secreted by the endoplasm is evident. Food particles lose their sharp outlines, swell, become more transparent, and then lessen in amount as the products of digestion are absorbed by the surrounding protoplasm. The materials that are absorbed serve for growth and reproduction and also provide the energy for locomotion. The vacuoles decrease in size as digestion proceeds, and any undigested residues are egested by being passed to the outside.

16-5. Respiration and excretion. The water in which the amoeba lives contains dissolved oxygen. This diffuses through the cell membrane, as in the internal respiration of cells in higher animals. Metabolism results in the production of waste products such as carbon dioxide and ammonia. For the well-being of the organism these must be eliminated; their disposal, mainly by diffusion through the cell membrane, is the process of excretion.

The contractile vacuole probably serves in part for excretion, but its principal function is to regulate the water content of the cell body. Water enters in food vacuoles, is a by-product of metabolism, and also probably passes into the cell by osmosis, since the protoplasm contains a higher concentration of salts than the surrounding water. An amoeba placed in water with a higher salt content than usual forms a smaller vacuole that discharges less often than before; and some marine amoebas have no vacuole. The contractile vacuole forms gradually by fusion of smaller vacuoles that start from fine droplets. When filled, it is surrounded by a temporary "condensation membrane" that vanishes as the vacuole discharges through the cell membrane into the surrounding water.

16-6. Reproduction. When the amoeba attains a certain size, it reproduces by *binary fission.* The cell body becomes spherical and covered by short pseudopodia, lengthens, and then constricts into two parts; meanwhile, the nucleus has divided by mitosis. Under ordinary laboratory conditions, the amoeba divides every few days, and mitosis requires about 33 minutes at 24°C.

16-7. Other Sarcodina. This class includes, besides various amoebas, some shell-forming protozoans. The shell or *test* may be secreted by the animal or formed of sand grains, etc. (Fig. 16-5).

The Genus *Amoeba* has many species of various sizes and shapes that live in fresh, brackish, and salt waters. Besides these free-living forms there are many commensal and

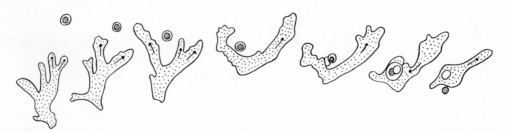

Fig. 16-4. *Amoeba.* Stages in taking of food and egestion of indigestible residue; total time 8 minutes. Arrows indicate movement of protoplasm in pseudopodia. (*After Schaeffer,* 1917.)

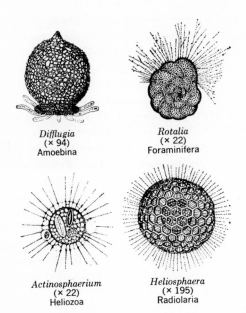

Difflugia
(× 94)
Amoebina

Rotalia
(× 22)
Foraminifera

Actinosphaerium
(× 22)
Heliozoa

Heliosphaera
(× 195)
Radiolaria

Fig. 16-5. Representatives of four orders in the Class Sarcodina. (*After Wolcott, Animal biology.*)

parasitic amoebas. Certain of them inhabit the gut of cockroaches and termites, while others (Genus *Entamoeba*) live chiefly in the digestive tract of land vertebrates. Parasitic amoebas usually form resistant cysts in which they pass from an infected host to a new one. *E. histolytica* (Fig. 16-6) is the cause of amoebic dysentery in man. Infected food or water carries the cysts into the digestive tract, where the amoebas are released, multiply, and often invade the intestinal wall. They may produce

abscesses in the intestinal mucosa and also in the liver, lungs, and other organs to which they pass by way of the blood stream. The feces become watery, and diarrhea results. The patient, if not treated, may recover somewhat and become a carrier, distributing cysts that contaminate drinking water and raw vegetables. In the United States an average of 10 per cent of people are infected, the percentage being lower in some regions than others and varying with economic status. Only a few suffer acutely from their infections.

The FORAMINIFERIDA are shell-producing protozoans that abound in the sea; their tests are 0.01 to 190 mm. in diameter, either secreted or made of sand or sponge spicules. They have lived in the oceans since Precambrian time, where their tests have accumulated to form rock strata. About 35 per cent of the ocean botton (48,000,000 square miles) now is of "ooze" from foraminiferan tests; the great pyramids of Egypt are carved of limestone formed from tests of an Early Tertiary type. The petroleum industry now studies fossil foraminiferans from drill cores in test wells to identify oil-bearing strata.

The spherical HELIOZOIA (sun animalcules) have many fine radiating pseudopodia; members of the RADIOLARIA have skeletons of silica or strontium sulfate. Their skeletons cover about 2,000,000 square miles of ocean floor as "radiolarian ooze," and fossil forms are found on land in many rock formations.

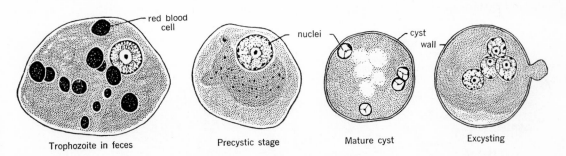

red blood cell

nuclei

cyst wall

Trophozoite in feces

Precystic stage

Mature cyst

Excysting

Fig. 16-6. *Entamoeba histolytica,* the parasitic amoeba of man that causes amoebic dysentery. Cysts are spread by fecal contamination of food and drinking water. (*Partly after Cleveland and Sanders, 1933.*)

Opalinids
Class OPALINATA

The OPALINATA (*Opalina,* etc.; Fig. 16-1) are mostly in the guts of frogs and toads. They have two to hundreds of nuclei of one type and no cytostome; in "sexual reproduction" their gametes fuse permanently. Like ciliates, they have many cilia in oblique rows on the cell surface.

Flagellates
Class MASTIGOPHORA

The presence of one or more long slender *flagella* (sing. *flagellum*) at some or all stages in the life cycle is characteristic of the MASTI-GOPHORA (Gr. *mastix,* whip + *phoros,* bearing). The flagella serve for locomotion and food capture and may be sense receptors. The cell body is usually of definite form, oval, long, or spherical, covered by a firm pellicle, and armored in some groups. Many species contain plastids with colored pigments; those with chlorophyll can synthesize food by the aid of sunlight and, as they seem akin to algae, are often classified as plants. Many flagellates are free-living and solitary, some are sessile, and some form colonies of a few to thousands of individuals. Various species abound in fresh and salt waters, where they constitute, with diatoms, a major part of the food supply for minute aquatic animals. Some inhabit the soil. Others are parasites of mankind and various animals, and some cause serious diseases. Reproduction usually is by longitudinal fission, but certain species undergo multiple fis-

sion, and there is sexual reproduction in one group. Free-living flagellates may encyst to avoid unfavorable conditions.

16-8. Structure. *Euglena* is a common, solitary, free-living flagellate that contains chlorophyll. The slender cell body is up to 0.1 mm. in length (Fig. 16-7), with a blunt *anterior end* that habitually travels forward; the opposite or *posterior end* is pointed. The body shape is maintained by a thin, flexible covering membrane, or *pellicle,* that is marked spirally by parallel striations or thickenings. Within this is a thin layer of clear *ectoplasm* around the main mass of granular, nonflowing *endoplasm.* The anterior end contains a funnel-like *cytostome,* or cell mouth, that leads into a short tubular cell gullet, or *cytopharynx.* A long *flagellum* extends out through the cytostome; it consists of a contractile axial filament surrounded by a delicate sheath and arises from a granule, the *blepharoplast,* within the anterior cytoplasm. Behind the cytopharynx is a permanent spherical *reservoir,* and nearby is a vacuole into which several minute *contractile vacuoles* empty. Fluid collected from the cytoplasm by the vacuoles passes into the reservoir and out the cytopharynx. Near the reservoir is a red *stigma,* or "eyespot," that is sensitive to light. The round *nucleus* is located near the center of the cell. Euglena is of green color owing to the *chloroplasts* (chromatophores) containing chlorophyll that often crowd its cytoplasm. Other cell inclusions are the *paramylum bodies,* which consist of a carbohydrate allied to starch.

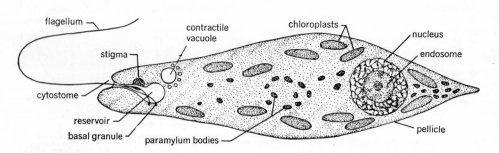

flagellum — contractile vacuole — chloroplasts — nucleus — endosome — stigma — cytostome — reservoir — basal granule — paramylum bodies — pellicle

Fig. 16-7. Structure of *Euglena,* a free-living flagellate (Class MASTIGOPHORA).

16-9. Movements. The flagellum beats back and forth to draw euglena through the water with a spiral rotation that enables the animal to follow a straight course (see *Paramecium*, par. 16-15). The animal may also crawl by spiral movements of the cell body. At times it performs worm-like "euglenoid movements" by local expansions and contractions that suggest the peristalsis in a vertebrate's intestine. Euglena reacts positively to light by swimming toward a source of favorable intensity, as a green plant turns to the light, but it performs an avoiding reaction to direct sunlight.

16-10. Nutrition. Some free-living flagellates capture small organisms, which are ingested through the cytopharynx and digested in food vacuoles in the cytoplasm, but such *holozoic nutrition* is rare or lacking in euglena. The latter utilizes *holophytic nutrition* whereby some food is synthesized within the body. This is done by photosynthesis, as in green plants, through the action of chlorophyll in the presence of light. Euglena commonly subsists by *saprophytic nutrition*, which is the absorption of nutrient materials dissolved in the water where it lives. In rich nutrient solutions, cultures of some euglenas will persist and multiply rapidly in weak light or darkness.

16-11. Reproduction. In active cultures, euglena reproduces frequently by longitudinal *binary fission* (Fig. 16-8). The nucleus divides in two by mitosis, then the anterior organelles —flagellum, blepharoplast, cytopharynx, reservoir, and stigma—are duplicated, and the organism splits in two lengthwise. Euglena also has inactive stages when it becomes nonmotile and secretes a surrounding cyst. It may also lose the flagellum, encyst, and then divide by longitudinal fission; repeated division may result in cysts containing 16 or 32 small daughter euglenas. Encystment is stimulated by lack of food or by the presence of chlorophyll (as in strongly illuminated cultures).

16-12. Other Mastigophora. Some flagellates are marine, forming an important part of the microscopic plankton, or "ocean mead-

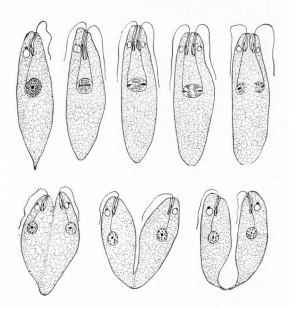

Fig. 16-8. *Euglena viridis.* Stages in longitudinal fission. (*Modified from Tannreuther, 1923.*)

ows," on which minute larvae of crustaceans and other animals feed. *Gonyaulax* on the California coast is eaten regularly by bivalves including sea mussels (*Mytilus*). It produces a substance, harmless to the mussels, but which causes "mussel poisoning" in man if these mollusks are eaten in summer, when they subsist largely on the protozoan. Upward of 400 cases of illness and 36 human deaths have been recorded on the Pacific Coast during recent years and some in Nova Scotia. When abundant (up to 40,000,000 per cubic meter of water) *Gonyaulax* causes "red water" in the sea by day and makes it luminescent at night. Fresh-water types include the colonial *Volvox* (Fig. 16-9) that grows as a hollow sphere (0.5 mm. in diameter), filled with watery jelly. Embedded in the gelatinous exterior wall are 8,000 to 17,000 minute (4 by 8 μ) individual cells, each with a nucleus, contractile vacuole, red stigma, green chloroplast, and two flagella. Protoplasmic threads connect adjacent cells and provide physiological continuity between them. The flagella beat collectively to roll the colony through the water.

Many flagellates are parasitic, living in the digestive tract or in the blood of animals and even in the latex cells of milkweeds. Blood parasites of the genus *Trypanosoma* (Fig. 16-9) cause human sleeping sickness in Africa and are transmitted by tsetse flies. *T. cruzi,* causing Chagas' disease in Central and South America, is carried by bugs (*Triatoma, Rhodnius*). Another blood parasite, *Leishmania,* causes kala azar and other diseases and is spread by direct contact or by blood-sucking flies (*Phlebotomus*).

Other flagellates (Order HYPERMASTIGIA) live in the gut of some termites. The termites eat wood but cannot digest the cellulose. The flagellates that thus receive "lodging and board" digest this material for themselves and their hosts, an outstanding example of mutualism (Chap. 13).

~~GREGARINES, COCCIDIA, HAEMOSPORIDIA, ETC.~~
~~SUBPHYLUM~~ *SPOROZOA* CLASS

The SPOROZOA (Gr. *spora,* seed + *zoön,* animal) are practically all parasites. The simple cell body is rounded or elongate, with one nucleus and no locomotor organelles or contractile vacuole. Some kinds move by change in shape of the cell body. Food is absorbed directly from the host (saprozoic nutrition), and respiration and excretion are by simple diffusion. Most sporozoans increase rapidly by multiple asexual fission, or **schizogony;** the cell becomes multinucleate by repeated mitoses, and then the cytoplasm divides. They also produce sexual **macro-** and **microgametes;** these join in pairs of opposite kind to form **zygotes.** The latter, in many species, form seed-like **oöcysts** by **sporogony,** and in this stage the organisms are spread from one host individual to another. A typical life cycle is thus:

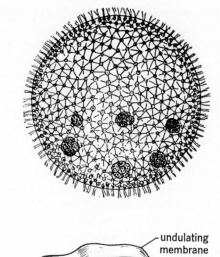

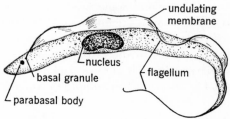

Fig. 16-9. Class MASTIGOPHORA. *Above. Volvox,* a free-living colonial flagellate, with 6 daughter colonies. (*After Hyman.*) *Below. Trypanosoma,* a blood parasite.

SPOROZOA are possibly the most widely occurring of animal parasites. Distinct species live in various animals from protozoans to mammals. Some stay within the host's cells and others in its body fluids or cavities. They inhabit variously the digestive tract, muscles, blood, kidneys, or other organs. Malaria in man, coccidiosis in fowls and rabbits, and certain fevers in cattle are examples of serious diseases caused by sporozoans.

The gregarines are parasites of the cells and tissue spaces of invertebrates. *Monocystis,* found in the seminal vesicles of the earth-

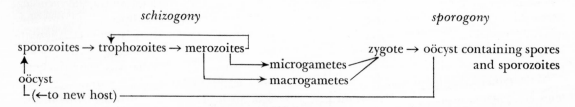

worm, is a common example. The coccidia live in epithelial cells of many vertebrates and a few invertebrates. Some inhabit the digestive tract and related organs. They cause the disease coccidiosis, which may be serious and even fatal in poultry, domestic mammals, and many wild species. *Eimeria stiedae* is a coccidian that often produces severe epidemics in domestic rabbits. The common practice of rearing rabbits in separate hutches, with feed in racks and frequent cleaning of the cages, is done to reduce transfer of this parasite from adults to young.

16-13. Malaria. The most familiar example of a sporozoan is *Plasmodium,* the cause of malaria (Fig. 16-10). This disease, a scourge

of man since ancient times, has caused an enormous amount of illness and innumerable deaths, especially in tropical and subtropical regions. The parasites are transmitted to man by females of certain species of mosquitoes of the Genus *Anopheles.* When the mosquito's mouth parts pierce the skin to obtain blood, the infective ***sporozoites*** pass from its salivary glands into the wound. They go into the reticulo-endothelial system lining sinusoids in the liver and multiply.

After several days each enters a red blood cell and becomes an amoeba-like ***trophozoite.*** It grows to be a ***schizont,*** which by multiple fission (schizogony) divides into 6 to 36 daughter ***merozoites*** according to the species. By

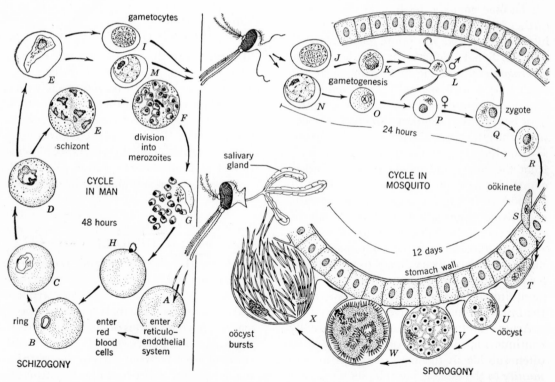

Fig. 16-10. Life cycle of *Plasmodium vivax* (Class Sporozoa), the tertian malarial parasite of man and anopheline mosquitoes. Sporozoites injected (*A*) during the biting of the mosquito enter cells on liver sinusoids and multiply asexually (schizogony); later the resulting merozoites enter red blood cells to repeat the cycle (*B–H*). Later gametocytes are formed (*I, M*); if drawn up by a biting mosquito, they transform into gametes in the insect's stomach (*J–L, N–P*). The zygotes (*Q–S*) encyst externally on the gut wall and form enlarged oöcysts (*U*) where, by asexual multiplication (sporogony), many sporozoites are produced to invade the salivary glands (*V–X*).

rupture of the corpuscle these escape into the blood plasma, to invade other red cells and repeat the cycle. After about 10 days the parasites are so numerous that the shock of their nearly simultaneous release produces a chill, followed by a violent fever in response to toxins from the liberated parasites. The chill-and-fever cycle thenceforth depends upon the species of parasite: every 48 hours in benign tertian malaria caused by *P. vivax;* and every 72 hours in quartan (fourth day) malaria caused by *P. malariae.* The cycle is lacking or irregular in aestivo-autumnal (malignant tertian) malaria caused by *P. falciparum. P. ovale,* with a 48-hour cycle, produces a mild infection ending in about 15 days.

After a period of schizogony, some merozoites become **gametocytes** but do not change further in the human host. If taken with blood into the gut of an appropriate female *Anopheles,* the female gametocyte soon becomes a **macrogamete,** and the male gametocyte divides into 6 to 8 sperm-like **microgametes.** Two gametes of opposite sex fuse as a **zygote.** This becomes a worm-like **oökinete** that penetrates the gut wall to lie under the membrane surrounding the gut. It then absorbs nutrients from the insect and enlarges as a rounded **oöcyst.** A single mosquito may contain 50 to 500 oöcysts. In 6 to 7 days the contents of each cyst divide (sporulation) into thousands of slender sporozoites. The cysts burst, the sporozoites migrate through the body spaces, and many enter the salivary glands to await transfer to a human host. The sexual cycle in the mosquito requires about 7 to 19 days, until the insect becomes infective.

Acute symptoms of malaria in man usually continue for some days or weeks and then often subside as the body develops an **immunity** to the disease, but relapses may occur at irregular intervals. In different persons the infection disappears in time, or lingers and causes damage to other organs, or results in death. Malarial patients are treated with chloroquine or other drugs. Healthy persons liv-

ing in malarial regions often take small doses of daraprim or chloroquine as a prophylactic. General reduction or control of malaria in a region requires (1) treating the human victims, (2) effectively screening dwellings to exclude mosquitoes, and (3) draining off or poisoning water to reduce mosquitoes by killing the larvae. DDT and other residual insecticides are highly effective in killing adult mosquitoes by leaving a toxic residue on walls and ceilings where mosquitoes rest. Mosquito fish (*Gambusia affinis*) are planted in waters to eat mosquito larvae and pupae. By applying control measures, public health workers have eradicated malaria over wide areas of the world where formerly it was endemic.

CNIDOSPORIDIANS
SUBPHYLUM *CNIDOSPORA*

In this group the spores have one or more polar filaments. The Myxosporidians typically have two polar capsules, each with a coiled filament. Most of them are parasitic in fishes. Microsporidians have one long tubular polar filament. They parasitize many invertebrates and cold-blooded vertebrates. *Nosema,* studied by Louis Pasteur, causes pebrine disease of silkworms and another in honeybees.

CILIATES, OR "INFUSORIA"
~~SUBPHYLUM~~ *CILIOPHORA* CLASS

Ciliates (L. *cilium,* eyelash) possess cilia throughout life, which serve for locomotion and food getting, and have two types of nuclei. Ciliates are the most specialized protozoans in having various organelles to perform particular vital processes. This results in a division of labor between parts of the organism, analogous to that between organ systems in a multicellular animal. Ciliates abound in fresh and salt waters. Many are free-living; some are commensal or parasitic in other animals; and a few grow in colonies. *Paramecium* (Fig. 16-11) is a ciliate common in fresh waters that

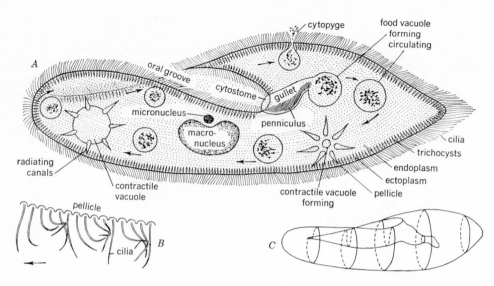

Fig. 16-11. Structure of *Paramecium caudatum,* a ciliate of fresh waters (Subphylum CILIOPHORA), 150–300 μ long. (*A*) The entire animal. Lines of dots indicate rows of cilia over the surface. Arrows show path of food vacuoles in endoplasm. (*B*) Enlarged sketch of a few cilia, showing how they beat in coordinated waves to drive the paramecium forward (to the left). (*C*) Outline of body form (cross sections) at different positions along its length.

contain some decaying vegetation. It multiplies rapidly in the laboratory in an "infusion" made by boiling a little hay or some wheat grains in water. The following account deals mainly with *P. caudatum.*

16-14. Structure. The slender cell body is blunt at the forward-moving or *anterior end,* widest behind the middle, and tapered at the *posterior end.* Over the exterior surface is a distinct elastic membrane, the *pellicle.* This is covered by fine *cilia* that are arranged in lengthwise rows and are of uniform length save for a posterior *caudal tuft* of longer cilia. Within the pellicle, the cell contents, as in amoeba, consist of a thin, clear external layer of dense *ectoplasm,* around the larger mass of more granular and fluid *endoplasm.* The ectoplasm contains many spindle-shaped *trichocysts,* alternating between the bases of the cilia, that may be discharged as long threads to serve perhaps in attachment or defense. From the anterior end a shallow furrow or

oral groove extends diagonally back about halfway along the lower or *oral surface* and has the cell mouth or *cytostome* at its posterior end. The cytostome opens into a short, tubular gullet or *cytopharynx,* ending in the endoplasm. In the gullet cilia are fused to form two lengthwise dense bands (the penniculus). On one side, just behind the cytopharynx, is the "cell anus" or *cytopyge,* which can be seen only when particles are discharging through it. In the endoplasm are *food vacuoles* of various sizes that contain material undergoing digestion; toward each end of the cell body is a large, clear *contractile vacuole.* The small, rounded *micronucleus* is partly surrounded by the larger *macronucleus.*

When specimens of *Paramecium* and similar ciliates are prepared by special methods (with nigrosin or silver salts) and studied by high magnification, the pellicle shows a hexagonal pattern of ridges surrounding cuplike depressions with a cilium projecting from

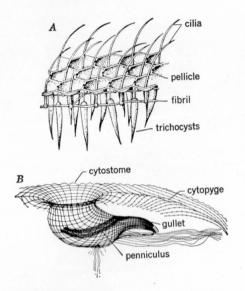

Fig. 16-12. *Paramecium multimicronucleatum.* (*A*) Structure of the pellicle and associated organelles. (*B*) The neuromotor system in part of the cell body. (*After Lund, 1935.*)

the center of each cup. Beneath the pellicle each cilium connects to a basal granule, and the granules are joined by longitudinal *fibrils.* Most ciliates have both transverse and longitudinal fibrils (Fig. 16-12*A*). The granules and fibrils comprise a *fibrillar system,* thought to coordinate ciliary action. Contractile fibrils (myonemes) occur in ciliates such as *Stentor* and *Vorticella,* but not in *Paramecium.*

16-15. Locomotion. The cilia beat backward to carry the paramecium forward in the water, and as their stroke is oblique, the animal rotates on its longitudinal axis; those in the oral groove beat more vigorously than the others, so that the anterior end swerves aborally. The body moves forward in a spiral course, counterclockwise as viewed from behind. Thus the asymmetrical animal may travel in a direct path. To swim backward, the ciliary beat is reversed, as is the path of rotation. If when swimming forward the paramecium meets some unfavorable chemical stimulus, it executes an *avoiding reaction* (Fig.

16-13)—the ciliary beat reverses, the animal moves backward a short distance, and then rotates in a conical path by swerving the anterior end aborally while pivoting on the posterior tip. While it is doing this, cilia in the oral groove bring "samples" from the water immediately ahead; when these no longer contain the undesirable stimulus, the animal moves forward again. The reaction is similar upon encountering a solid object: it reverses, rotates, and goes forward, repeating the process if necessary until a clear path is found.

16-16. Feeding and digestion. Paramecium feeds upon bacteria, small protozoans, algae, and yeasts. The constant beating of cilia in the oral groove sweeps a current of water containing food toward the cytostome, and movements of the penniculus gather the food at the posterior end of the cytopharynx in a watery vacuole. The vacuole becomes of a certain size, constricts off, and begins to circulate in the endoplasm as a *food vacuole;* another then begins to form in its place. Streaming movements (cyclosis) in the endoplasm carry the vacuoles in a definite route, first posteriorly, then forward and aborally, again posteriorly to near the oral groove. The contents of the vacuoles are acid at first and gradually become alkaline, as shown by use of congo red and other indicator dyes. As in amoeba, the food is digested by the action of enzymes secreted by the endoplasm. This process continues until the digested material is absorbed by the surrounding protoplasm and either stored or used for vital activity and growth. The vacuoles gradually become smaller, and any indigestible residues are egested at the cell anus.

16-17. Respiration and excretion. Respiration is by diffusion as with amoeba. The contractile vacuoles regulate the water content of the body and may serve in excretion. Liquid in the cytoplasm is gathered by 6 to 11 *radiating canals* that discharge into each vacuole. When a vacuole reaches a certain size, it dis-

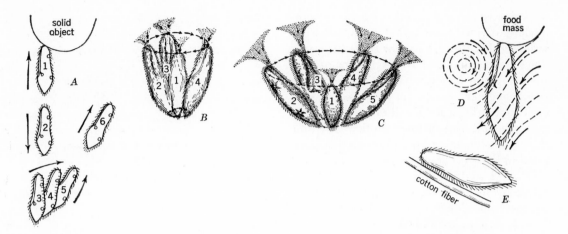

Fig. 16-13. Some reactions of *Paramecium* to contact. *Negative or avoiding reaction:* (*A*) Successive positions (1–6) in avoiding a solid object; rotation on the long axis not shown. (*B*) Weak reaction, anterior end swings in small circle. (*C*) Strong reaction, swings in large circle. *Positive reaction:* (*D*) At rest against a food mass; arrows indicate water currents produced by the cilia. (*E*) Resting on a cotton fiber; cilia in contact are motionless. (*After Jennings, Behavior of the lower organisms, Columbia University Press.*)

charges to the exterior. The vacuoles contract alternately, at intervals of 10 to 20 seconds.

16-18. Behavior. The responses of paramecium to various stimuli are learned by study of the avoiding reaction and of the grouping or scattering of individuals in a culture. The response is *positive* if the animal moves toward the stimulus and *negative* when it moves away. To an adverse stimulus the animal continues to give the avoiding reaction until it escapes. All adjustments are by *trial and error*. The response to *contact* varies; if the anterior end is touched lightly, a strong avoiding reaction occurs, but if touched elsewhere on the cell body there may be no response. A paramecium responds positively to contact with an object by coming to rest on it; this response is advantageous because food organisms are common about algae or plant stems. Paramecium seeks an optimum as to *temperature*, between 24° and 28°C. The response to *gravity* is usually negative; in a deep culture many individuals gather close under the surface film with their anterior ends uppermost. In a gentle *water current* the paramecia will mostly align with their anterior ends upstream. When subjected to direct *electric current,* the animals "head" toward the negative pole (cathode). To most chemicals the response is negative. If a drop of 0.5 per cent salt solution is introduced into a population, the animals respond with the avoiding reaction. To acids, however, the response is positive, even when the concentration is of sufficient strength to kill them.

The trichocysts of paramecium and some other ciliates have been thought to be organelles for defense against enemies, but even when discharged they seldom save the animal from its predator.

16-19. Reproduction. Paramecium reproduces by fission and at intervals undergoes two types of nuclear reorganization (conjugation and autogamy). In *binary fission* (Fig. 11-1) the micronucleus divides by mitosis into two micronuclei that move toward opposite ends of the cell, and the macronucleus divides transversely by amitosis; a second gullet forms, two new contractile vacuoles appear, and a transverse furrow divides the cytoplasm into two parts. The resulting two "daughter" paramecia are of equal size, each containing a set of cell organelles. They grow to full size before another division occurs. Fission takes about 2 hours to complete and may occur one to four times per day, yielding 2 to 16 individuals; all those that result by fission from one individual (uniparental reproduction) are known collectively as a *clone*. Upward of 600 "generations" per year may be produced. The rate of multiplication depends upon external conditions such as food, temperature, age of the culture, and population density; and also upon internal factors of heredity and physiology.

16-20. Conjugation. In paramecium and other ciliates there is, at intervals, a temporary union of individuals in pairs with mutual exchange of micronuclear materials; this is known as *conjugation.* The animals become "sticky," adhering to one another by their oral surfaces, and a protoplasmic bridge forms between them. The pairs continue to swim about during this process. A sequence of nuclear changes then occurs in each animal (Fig. 16-14).

The two individuals that join in conjugation are known to belong to different *mating types* (I, II); these are not "sexes," but members of one mating type will join only with one of opposite kind. The process of *autogamy* is a nuclear reorganization resembling conjugation but occurs within one individual.

16-21. Other ciliates. Examination of a drop of water from any quiet fresh-, brackish-, or salt-water source will usually reveal one or more species of ciliates and testify to the wide occurrence of these protozoans. Some of both solitary (*Vorticella, Stentor*) and colonial habit (*Zoothamnium*) are attached by stalks or other means. Besides many free-living species, some peculiar forms inhabit the caecum

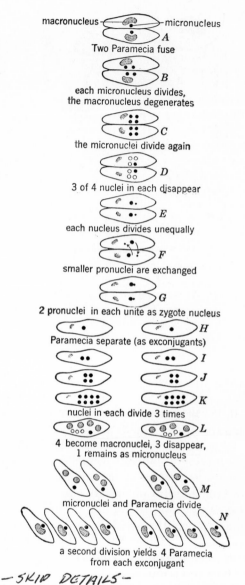

macronucleus ⟶ ⟵ micronucleus

A

Two Paramecia fuse

B

each micronucleus divides,
the macronucleus degenerates

C

the micronuclei divide again

D

3 of 4 nuclei in each disappear

E

each nucleus divides unequally

F

smaller pronuclei are exchanged

G

2 pronuclei in each unite as zygote nucleus

H

Paramecia separate (as exconjugants)

I

J

K

nuclei in each divide 3 times

L

4 become macronuclei, 3 disappear,
1 remains as micronucleus

M

micronuclei and Paramecia divide

N

a second division yields 4 Paramecia
from each exconjugant

— SKIP DETAILS —

Fig. 16-14. Diagram of conjugation in *Paramecium caudatum.*

and colon of horses and the rumen and reticulum of ruminants, numbering 500,000 to 1,000,000 per cubic milliliter of gut contents. A few ciliates are parasitic, such as *Balantidium coli* of the intestine in pigs, which also occurs rarely in man.

REVIEW

1. Why are the PROTOZOA placed first in animal classification? What are their principal characteristics?
2. Describe the structure of an amoeba. What purpose does each part serve?
3. What is amoeboid movement?
4. Lacking definite organs, how does an amoeba feed, respire, and excrete wastes?
5. How does a flagellate differ from an amoeba?
6. What are the types of nutrition among flagellates?
7. Explain "red water" of the ocean. What are some important diseases caused by flagellates?
8. How does a sporozoan differ from other types of protozoans?
9. Outline the life cycle of the malarial parasite, and indicate the places where it may be interfered with to reduce prevalence of the disease.
10. In what ways is paramecium a more complex animal than amoeba?
11. What is known of feeding and digestion in paramecium?
12. Compare the two principal ways by which paramecium reproduces.

17
Sponges
and
coelenterates

A. Sponges
Phylum PORIFERA

The sponges are lowly multicellular animals, unable to move, and often plant-like in form. Different species are variously thin flat crusts, vase-shaped, globular, branched, or irregular, and 1 mm. to 6 feet in diameter. Many are gray or drab, and others brilliantly red, yellow, blue, or black. All sponges live in water and attached to rocks, shells, or other solid objects; most species are marine, living from the low-tide line to depths of 3.5 miles, but one family is widespread in fresh waters. The name PORIFERA (L. *porus*, pore + *ferre*, to bear) refers to the porous body with many surface openings. The commercial bath "sponge" is the flexible skeleton of a marine species with all the once living protoplasm removed (Fig. 17-1).

17-1. Characteristics.

1. Symmetry radial or none; multicellular; 2 germ layers; cells imperfectly arranged as tissues, with mesenchyme between.
2. Body with many pores, canals, or chambers through which water flows; no appendages, movable parts, or organs.
3. Some or all internal surfaces lined with flagellated collar cells (choanocytes); digestion intracellular.
4. Usually an internal skeleton of fine, crystal-like rods (spicules), or of irregular organic fibers, or both.
5. Reproduction asexual (buds, or gemmules) and sexual (eggs and sperm); larvae ciliated and free-swimming.

Sponges resemble some colonial protozoans in having flagellated collar cells and intracellular digestion. They are unlike most multicellular animals (METAZOA) in lacking organs, in having their cells imperfectly arranged as tissues, and in the difficulty of recognizing limits to an "individual" in complex sponges. The sponges have been termed the PARAZOA (Gr. *para*, beside), implying that they are not in the direct line of evolution between unicellular and multicellular animals.

17-2. Simple sponge (Figs. 17-2, 17-3). *Leucosolenia*, a small, shallow-water marine sponge, consists of a group of slender vase-like tubes united at the base by irregular horizontal tubes. Each upright portion is a thin-walled sac, enclosing a central cavity, or *spongocoel*, and with one large opening, the *osculum*, at the top. The wall is made of (1) an outer *epidermis* of thin flat cells and (2) a continuous inner lining of flagellated collar cells, or *choanocytes*, loosely touching one another; between the two cell layers is (3) a gelatinous *mesenchyme*. The latter contains (4) free cells, or *amoebocytes* of several kinds, and (5) many

Illustration at top of page: Magnified portion of a limy coral, showing compartments with septa in which the members of the colony formerly lived.

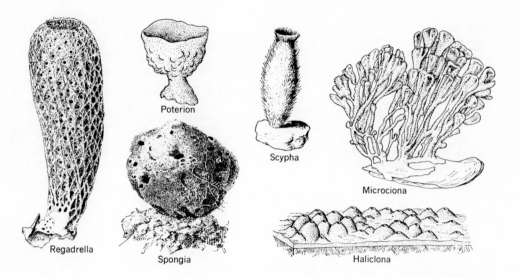

Fig. 17-1. Representative sponges. Class CALCAREA: *Scypha* (formerly called *Sycon*). Class HEXACTINELLIDA: *Regadrella*, glass sponge. Class DEMOSPONGIAE: *Poterion*, Neptune's goblet; *Spongia (Euspongia)*, bath sponge; *Microciona*; *Haliclona*, encrusting sponge. *(Regadrella and Scypha after Lankester, Treatise on zoology, A. & C. Black, Ltd.)*

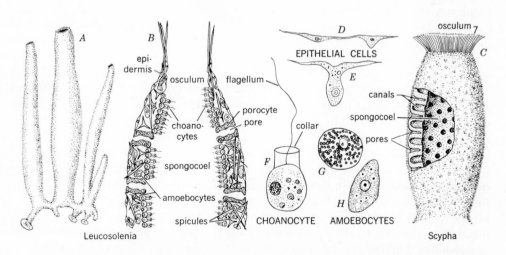

Fig. 17-2. Structure of simple sponges. (*A*) *Leucosolenia*, a small colony. (*B*) *Leucosolenia*, enlarged section at top of body. (*C*) *Scypha*, entire individual with part of body wall cut away (compare Fig. 17-3). (*D–H*) Cells of sponges. *(Adapted from Hyman, The invertebrates, McGraw-Hill Book Co.)*

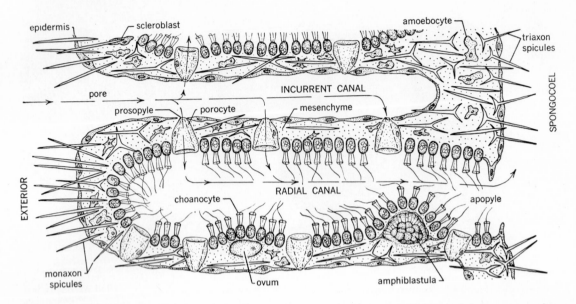

Fig. 17-3. Body wall of a *Scypha* sponge; diagrammatic section. Arrows indicate paths of water moving through the sponge. Compare Fig. 17-2C.

minute, crystal-like *spicules* of calcium carbonate; some spicules are slender rods and others three- or four-rayed. Piercing the wall are many microscopic openings, the *ostia*, from the external surface to the interior cavity; each pore is a canal through a tubular cell (porocyte) of the epidermis. Each collar cell has a rounded or oval cell body resting against the mesenchyme, and its inner free end has a transparent contractile collar around the base of a long whip-like *flagellum* (Fig. 17-2F).

The porocytes open and close, and the amoebocytes may move freely in the watery or colloidal mesenchyme. The flagella whip to and fro, bringing a continual flow of water into the many ostia, through the central cavity, and out the osculum. The water brings oxygen and food and removes wastes. The food is of microscopic animals and plants and bits of organic matter; these are caught and digested in the collar cells or passed to the amoebocytes. Lacking special sensory organs or nerve cells, stimuli probably travel slowly from cell to cell. The sponge cannot move and contracts but little.

17-3. Other sponges. In the slender sponge known as *Scypha* (formerly termed *Sycon* or *Grantia*), the thick body wall is folded, producing many short horizontal canals: (1) *incurrent canals* opening externally through small pores (ostia) but ending blindly within, and (2) *radial canals* closed at the outer ends but opening by minute pores (apopyles) into the central *spongocoel;* still smaller canals (prosopyles) connect the incurrent and radial canals. The exterior surface is covered by a thin *dermal epithelium,* the spongocoel is lined with thin *gastral epithelium,* and collar cells line the radial canals. The many canals greatly increase the surface area exposed to the water. Between the layers there is a jelly-like mesenchyme containing amoeboid cells. The supporting spicules are long and straight around the osculum, short and straight about the ostia, ⊥-shaped toward the spongocoel, and three-branched in the body wall. Straight spicules projecting from the body wall produce a bristly exterior surface.

Still other sponges have complex branched canals with collar cells only in spherical chambers (Fig. 17-4). Calcareous sponges (*Leucosolenia, Scypha,* etc.) have spicules of lime,

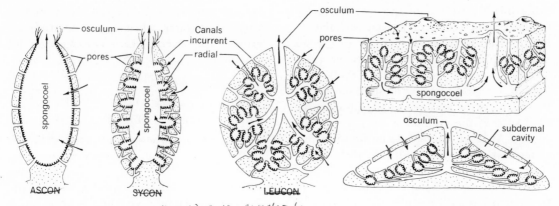

Fig. 17-4. Canal systems of sponges; diagrammatic sections. Epithelium, light lines; mesenchyme, stippled; areas with collar cells, heavy black; arrows indicate water currents. *Upper right*. Portion of an encrusting sponge. *Lower right*. Fresh-water sponge.

and the "glass" sponges of silica-like material. Many spicules are complex in structure, and those in some deep-water glass sponges fuse into a framework (Fig. 17-5). The bath sponges and others contain fine irregular and joined fibers of spongin, a sulfur-containing protein that is inert chemically. Spicules and fibers are secreted by special cells in the mesenchyme. The fresh-water sponges grow in lakes or streams as tufts or small masses on rocks, stones, and plants; some are yellow or brown, and others are green, containing fresh-water algae.

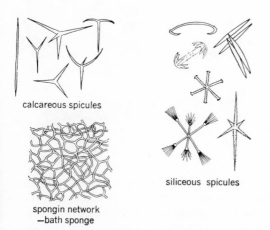

calcareous spicules

siliceous spicules

spongin network
—bath sponge

Fig. 17-5. Spicules and fibers of sponges. (*After Hyman.*)

17-4. Reproduction. Parts of a sponge lost by injury may be replaced by **regeneration.** Many kinds of sponges increase by **budding,** the buds either separating from the original sponge as the growth proceeds or remaining attached to increase the bulk or number of parts of the "colony." Fresh-water sponges and some others form internal buds, or **gemmules,** that serve to carry the species through cold, drought, or other adverse conditions. Gemmules are formed of groups of cells in the mesenchyme that are enriched by food and surrounded by a resistant cover. As the sponge dies, the minute gemmules drop out to survive until conditions again are suitable, when each starts growth as a new sponge.

In **sexual reproduction** some sponges produce both ova and sperm, whereas the sexes are separate in others. In either case the germ cells derive from cells (archeocytes) in the mesenchyme, where the ovum remains to be fertilized by sperm from another sponge. The developing egg becomes a larva, swimming by means of flagella for a few hours, then settles, attaches to some object, and grows into a young sponge.

17-5. Relations to other animals. Few animals eat or attack sponges, probably because of the spicules or of unpleasant secretions. But many arthropods, worms, mollusks, and some fishes inhabit cavities in sponges. Larvae of spongilla flies (Order NEUROPTERA) live in and feed on fresh-water sponges. In the sea some nudibranchs eat sponges. Some crabs attach bits of live sponge to their shells. One kind of sponge is common on snail shells used by hermit crabs and eventually absorbs the shell so that the crab soon lives within the sponge. Another kind grows on and burrows in mollusk shells, eventually destroying both shell and animal.

17-6. The sponge industry. Since ancient times man has used the fibrous skeleton of a bath sponge (*Spongia*) for washing and mopping. The waters of the Mediterranean and the Gulf of Mexico from Florida to the West Indies formerly yielded over two million pounds annually to divers and to dredges. The sponges are brought up, the living protoplasm is trodden down and allowed to decay, and then they are washed, cleaned, dried, and marketed. There is some culture of sponges to increase the supply; small pieces of living

sponge are fastened on clean rocky surfaces in shallow water, when by regeneration and growth for several years new sponges are produced.

B. COELENTERATES
Phylum COELENTERATA

The lowest animals with cells definitely forming tissues are the coelenterates (Gr. *koilos,* hollow + *enteron,* intestine). They include (Fig. 17-6) the hydroids of plant-like form (Class HYDROZOA) and the soft, nearly transparent jellyfishes that swim feebly (Class SCYPHOZOA), together with the sea anemones of flower-like appearance that abound on rocky shores and the corals with their limy skeletons that form reefs on tropical coasts (Class ANTHOZOA). The individuals are either separate or in colonies and of two kinds: (1) the **polyp** with a tubular body having one end closed and attached to some object and the other end with a central mouth surrounded

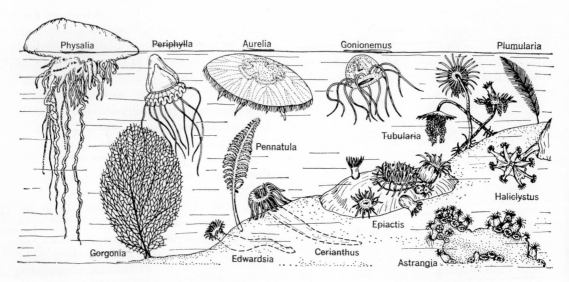

Fig. 17-6. Some marine coelenterates in characteristic habitats, all reduced but not to same scale. Class HYDROZOA, hydroids: *Tubularia, Plumularia, Gonionemus; Physalia,* Portuguese man-of-war. Class SCYPHOZOA, jellyfishes: *Haliclystus, Periphylla; Aurelia,* common jellyfish. Class ANTHOZOA, sea anemones, corals, etc.: *Gorgonia,* sea fan; *Pennatula,* sea pen; *Edwardsia, Epiactis,* sea anemones; *Astrangia,* stony coral; *Cerianthus,* burrowing anemone.

by soft tentacles; and (2) the free-swimming *medusa* with a gelatinous body of umbrella shape, margined with soft tentacles, and the mouth on a central projection of the concave surface. Both types are variously modified, and both appear in the life cycle of many species. All species are aquatic, and all but a few inhabit salt waters.

Individual hydroid polyps are usually microscopic, but colonies are a few millimeters to 2 meters long. Jellyfishes range from 12 mm. to over 2 meters in diameter, and anemones vary from rather small individuals to some a meter across the disc. Coral polyps are minute, but their collective skeletal masses may be miles in extent.

17-7. Characteristics.

1. Symmetry radial around an axis through the mouth; body of 2 layers of epithelium, with much or little gelatinous material (mesoglea) between: many microscopic stinging capsules (nematocysts) in one or both cell layers.
2. Skeleton absent in many, limy, or horny in some; muscle fibers in epithelium.
3. Digestive cavity sac-like (no anus); soft tentacles around mouth.
4. No blood, respiratory, or excretory organs; nervous system a network of nerve cells and fibers in body wall and tentacles; eyespots in some species.
5. Reproduction commonly by asexual budding in the attached polyp stage, alternating with sexual reproduction by eggs and sperm in the free medusa stage; some with simple gonads; no sex ducts.

HYDROIDS
CLASS *HYDROZOA*

17-8. Structure of hydra. The small solitary fresh-water polyp, *Hydra* (Fig. 17-7), is a slender cylinder (10 to 30 mm. long) with the lower end closed as a "foot" for attaching to objects. The opposite oral end bears 6 to 10 hollow **tentacles** around the small **mouth,** which leads to the **digestive cavity** or **gastro-vascular cavity** (enteron) within the body. The entire animal is very flexible; it may extend as a long, slender tube, bend, or contract to a short spherical form with the tentacles as mere knobs. The side of the body may develop lateral **buds** that asexually produce new individuals; at times it bears rounded **ovaries** or **testes** for sexual reproduction (Fig. 17-8).

The body wall is of but two cell layers: a thin external **epidermis** of low cuboidal cells and within a thicker **gastrodermis** serving mainly for digestion. Between the two layers is a thin, noncellular **mesoglea,** to which both layers attach, providing an elastic framework for the body and tentacles. Both layers contain cells of four major types, each being specialized in form and function to perform particular life processes; collectively they do all the things necessary in a living hydra.

1. The ⊥-shaped **epitheliomuscular cells** are closely spaced to form the body exterior; in the base of each is a contractile **fibril** attached lengthwise to the mesoglea; these fibrils act as longitudinal muscles that con-

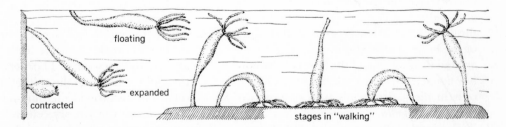

Fig. 17-7. Phylum COELENTERATA. Hydra, the fresh-water polyp; natural size to 30 mm. long. (*"Walking" after Wagner,* 1905.)

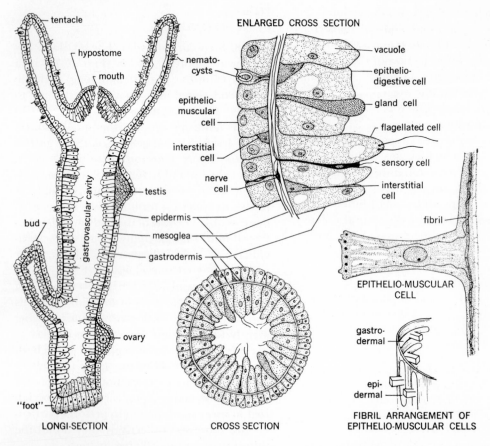

Fig. 17-8. Hydra. Structure as seen in microscopic sections. *(Epitheliomuscular cell after Hyman.)*

tract to shorten the body and tentacles. Similar *epitheliodigestive cells* form the principal lining of the gastro-vascular cavity and serve in the digestion of food. Their fibrils attach transversely inside the mesoglea and act as circular muscles to reduce the diameter and thereby extend the length of the body. There also are circular fibrils around the mouth and the bases of the hollow tentacles to close these openings. Many cells in the gastrodermis bear one or two whip-like *flagella.*

2. Tall *gland cells* cover the "foot" and secrete a sticky mucus by which hydra attaches to objects. Large gland cells occur about the mouth and others in the gastro-

dermis, the latter secreting enzymes for digestion of food.

3. Small rounded and undifferentiated *interstitial cells* between the bases of epidermal cells give rise to nematocysts, buds, sex cells, and other cells.

4. The *sensory cells* are slender and connect to the network of nerve cells that lies against the mesoglea. The nerve cells in turn join to fibrils in the epitheliomuscular cells. Thus is formed a *sensory-neuromotor mechanism:* the sensory cells *receive* stimuli, the nerve cells *conduct* the impulses, and the fibrils *react* to the latter. Except for the neuromotor organelles in some protozoans, this is the first and simplest neural

mechanism in animals providing for co-ordination in movements of the body and tentacles. There is no central ganglion or brain as in higher animals.

17-9. Nematocysts. The nematocyst is a minute capsule filled with fluid and containing a coiled *thread tube* that may be everted to aid in capture of prey or in locomotion. Each is in a modified interstitial cell, having on the exterior a trigger-like *cnidocil.* Some nematocysts occur singly, and others are grouped as a "battery" in one large epithelial cell. Nematocysts are commonest on the tentacles but occur elsewhere save on the basal disc and are of several types: the spherical *penetrant* with a long thread tube which can pierce small animals and inject a fluid to paralyze the prey; the pear-shaped *volvent* with a thread tube that coils on hairs or bristles of the prey; and two types of *glutinants* producing a sticky secretion. The cnidocil does not act as a trigger to mechanical stimuli, but nematocysts are discharged in the presence of substances diffusing from nearby small prey animals.

17-10. Natural history. Hydra lives attached to objects in the water but can twist and turn to capture prey. It can change location by looping movements (Fig. 17-7), by inverting and using the tentacles as legs, by gliding with the "foot," or by floating attached to a gas bubble secreted by the foot. When in need of food, the tentacles stretch about. Upon contact with a small crustacean, insect larva, or similar animal, nematocysts are discharged, and the coordinated movements of the tentacles then bring the prey into the mouth; once within the gastro-vascular cavity, the gland cells secrete digestive enzymes. Movements of the body wall and of the flagella serve to bring the digestive juices and food together. Some digestion is completed in the gastro-vascular cavity and this is *extracellular digestion* as in most multicellular animals; some food is taken into vacuoles in cells of the gastrodermis, where *intracellular digestion* takes place as in protozoans and sponges. Hydra thus combines the methods of animals lower and higher than itself. Indigestible residues pass out the mouth, which thus serves also as an anus.

Digested food is stored in the cells, being concentrated in places of active metabolism such as forming buds or gonads. The oxygen–carbon dioxide exchange of respiration and the excretion of wastes are performed by diffusion, mainly from the epidermis.

Hydra responds to environmental stimuli according to its physiological state, changing position and moving the tentacles when in search of food. Undisturbed specimens also contract the body and tentacles at intervals. If touched lightly, the part stimulated will turn away; but a stronger stimulus, such as disturbing the water, will result in sudden, complete contraction of all parts. Each species has an optimum light intensity, but the green hydra seeks more than other species. Hydras usually live in cool clear waters and avoid foul or warm waters. In some lakes they abound, even to depths of 180 feet, and occasionally infest fish nets, irritating the hands of fishermen by discharging nematocysts.

17-11. Reproduction. New individuals may arise by asexual *buds,* which form as an out-pocketing of the body wall containing epidermis, mesoglea, gastrodermis, and part of the gastro-vascular cavity. The bud lengthens, grows tentacles and a mouth, then constricts off at the base as a young hydra. Occasionally several form on one "parent" and may produce secondary buds, making a group that resembles a colonial hydroid. If a hydra is cut into two or more pieces, each can regenerate into a complete but smaller hydra. Parts of two hydras also can be grafted together.

Most species of hydras are dioecious, any one individual producing only male or female sex cells; a few species are monoecious, both sexes being in one animal. Gonad formation normally occurs in autumn, but at other seasons may be induced by lower water temperature. The gonads (ovaries producing eggs;

testes producing sperm) are the only sex organs; both arise from interstitial epidermal cells. A mature sperm from the testis of one hydra fertilizes an egg on another hydra. The growing blastula secretes a shell or cyst around itself and drops off into the water to continue development; later the young hydra emerges as a new individual (Fig. 17-9).

17-12. Colonial hydroids. Unlike hydra, most members of the Class HYDROZOA are marine, colonial, and fixed, resembling plants in form (Fig. 17-10). From the root-like base, branched stems arise, bearing hundreds of polyps of two kinds, *feeding* (hydranth) and *reproductive* (gonangium). Food captured by feeding polyps is digested and circulated through a common gastro-vascular cavity or enteron. From reproductive polyps small medusae resembling jellyfish are released into the water; they grow, then develop gonads producing eggs and sperm. The fertilized egg becomes a ciliated larva that in time settles to begin a new colony by asexual budding.

Hydra is an individual polyp that performs all life functions, including reproduction. In colonies like *Obelia* the feeding polyps perform all functions except reproduction; the gonangia are solely reproductive, forming the medusae for dispersal. Another hydroid (*Hydractinia,* on hermit crab shells) has separate

feeding, reproductive, and fighting polyps, the last being knob-like, without a mouth, and having many nematocysts. Finally the Portuguese man-of-war (*Physalia,* Fig. 17-6) has these three kinds of polyps plus a fourth which forms a large gas-filled float to support the colony. Such diversity in form and function of a basic type (the polyp) is termed *polymorphism.*

JELLYFISHES
CLASS *SCYPHOZOA*

17-13. Structure and natural history. In this class (Gr. *skyphos,* cup + *zoon,* animal) the medusa is an inch to several feet in diameter, consisting mostly of jelly-like mesoglea; the polyp is minute or lacking. The umbrella-shaped body of a jelly fish (Fig. 17-11) is fringed with *tentacles,* interrupted by 8 pairs of *lappets.* Around the *mouth* are 4 grooved *oral arms,* edged with nematocysts. Off the gastro-vascular cavity are 4 pouches containing the *gonads,* and a system of *digestive canals* branches through the body and to a marginal *ring canal.* Between each pair of lappets is a *sense organ* containing a light-sensitive *eyespot,* a hollow *statocyst* with limy granules serving for equilibrium, and 2 *sense pits* probably aiding in recognition of food.

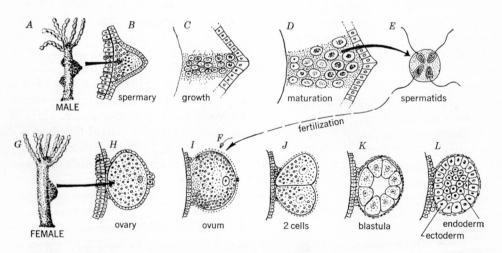

Fig. 17-9. Sexual reproduction of hydra. (*Adapted from Tannreuther,* 1908, 1909.)

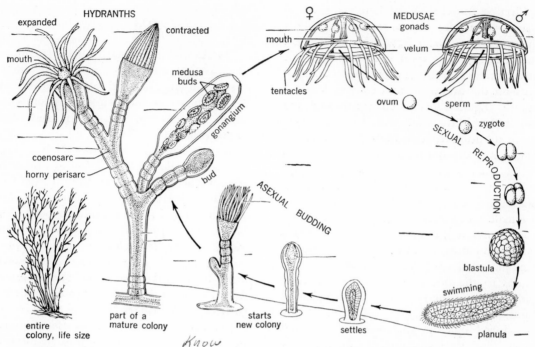

HYDRANTHS

expanded

contracted

mouth

medusa buds

coenosarc

horny perisarc

gonangium

bud

MEDUSAE

gonads

mouth

velum

tentacles

ovum

sperm

zygote

SEXUAL REPRODUCTION

ASEXUAL BUDDING

blastula

swimming

entire colony, life size

part of a mature colony

starts new colony

settles

planula

Know

Fig. 17-10. Structure and life cycle of a colonial marine hydroid, *Obelia* (Class HYDROZOA). The colony comprises polyps of two types, the feeding hydranths and reproductive gonangia, both formed by asexual budding on branched stems attached to the substratum by a root-like hydrorhiza. Free-swimming medusae of separate sexes bud off from the gonangia and later produce ova and sperm. The zygote develops into a ciliated swimming planula larva; this soon attaches and forms a new colony by budding. The three kinds of individuals illustrate polymorphism, and the alternation of asexual and sexual generations is termed "metagenesis." (*Modified from Wolcott, Animal biology, McGraw-Hill Book Co.*)

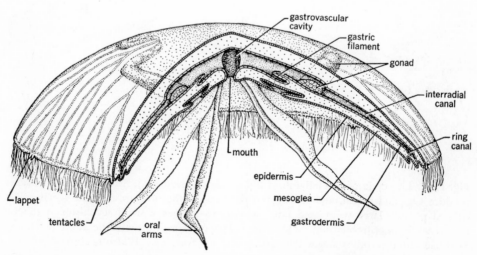

gastrovascular cavity

gastric filament

gonad

interradial canal

ring canal

mouth

epidermis

mesoglea

gastrodermis

lappet

tentacles

oral arms

Fig. 17-11. Structure of a jellyfish, *Aurelia* (Class SCYPHOZOA); one-fourth of the body cut away to show internal structure.

Circular muscles in the bell margin contract rhythmically to force water from within the concavity of the bell, whereby the animal swims feebly. The food is mainly of small invertebrates and fishes, captured by nematocysts on the oral arms and conveyed to the mouth. Digested food circulates through the canals. Respiration and excretion presumably are by diffusion from the body surface. A marginal *nerve net* coordinates contraction of the bell and movements of the oral arms.

The sexes are alike but separate (Fig. 17-12). Sperm from a male pass through the water to a female and fertilize eggs produced in her gonads (ovaries); the zygotes emerge to lodge on her oral arms, where each grows into a ciliated planula larva. The larva swims and later settles to the bottom to become a minute polyp (scyphistoma) that may produce lateral buds; by transverse fission it also yields a pile of 8-lobed ephyrae that become free and invert, and then each grows into an adult jellyfish.

SEA ANEMONES, CORALS, ETC. CLASS *ANTHOZOA*

The ANTHOZOA are marine polyps of flower-like form (Gr. *anthos*, flower + *zoon*, animal) of small to large size and rather firm texture. Besides the sea anemones and stony corals, the group includes the soft, horny, and black corals, colonial sea pens and sea pansies, and others; all lack a medusa stage. They abound in warm shallow waters, some are in polar seas, and some live to depths of 17,400 feet.

17-14. Structure. A common anemone (*Metridium*) has a short cylindrical body (Fig. 17-13). The upper flat *oral disc* has many short, hollow *tentacles* around a slit-like *mouth;* the *base* (pedal disc) serves for attachment to a solid object. The *gullet* (stomodeum) is a flat tube connecting the mouth and *gastro-vascular cavity* and having on one or both sides a ciliated furrow, or *siphonoglyph,* in which water flows to and from the interior. Internally, six pairs of complete *septa* or

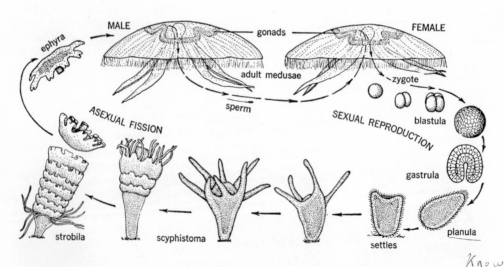

Fig. 17-12. Life cycle of the jellyfish, *Aurelia* (Class SCYPHOZOA). Adults of separate sexes produce eggs and sperm, and the zygotes develop on the oral arms of the female. The ciliated planula larva swims and later attaches to become a small scyphistoma; this by transverse fission (strobilation) yields several ephyrae which grow to be adult jellyfishes. Medusae reduced, other stages enlarged. *(After Agassiz; and Wolcott, Animal biology, McGraw-Hill Book Co.)*

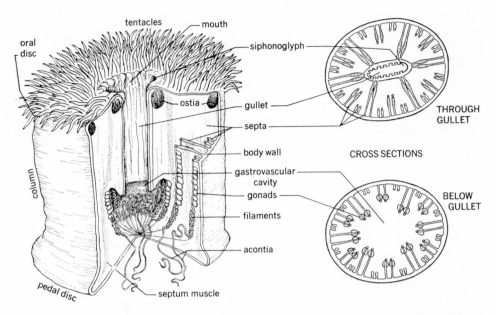

Fig. 17-13. Structure of a sea anemone, *Metridium* (Class ANTHOZOA). Part of the body has been cut away to show internal features. Cross sections through and below the gullet show the arrangement of the septa.

mesenteries divide the cavity into as many radial compartments, and other incomplete septa attach to the body wall but not the gullet. Openings (ostia) in the complete septa permit water to circulate between compartments. The free inner edge of each septum is a thickened *septal filament* continued below as a thread-like *acontium;* both parts bear gland cells and nematocysts. The acontia can be protruded through pores in the body wall or through the mouth. *Gonads* form along the septal margins.

Over the exterior surfaces is a tough epidermis, ciliated on the oral disc, tentacles, and gullet. The interior cavity is lined by gastrodermis. Both cell layers contain strong muscle fibers, arranged as in hydra, and there are longitudinal fibers in the septa. The mesoglea is of cellular connective tissue. There is a nerve net in the epidermis and nerve fibers occur in the septa.

17-15. Natural history. An anemone lives firmly attached to a rock or other solid object; many can creep slowly on the pedal disc.

When covered by water and undisturbed, the body and tentacles are well extended; but if irritated or if exposed by a receding tide, the body is closely contracted and the oral disc inturned. Cilia on the tentacles and disc beat to keep off debris. A constant current of water for respiratory use passes down the siphonoglyph, circulates in the gastro-vascular cavity and returns up the gullet.

The anemone eats mollusks, crustaceans, other invertebrates, and fishes. Such prey is paralyzed by nematocysts and carried by the tentacles to the mouth, but some objects are grasped directly by the mouth and gullet, both of which can gape widely. In the gastro-vascular cavity enzymes secreted from the filaments digest the food, which is absorbed by the gastrodermis. Undigested wastes are cast out of the mouth.

The sexes are separate. Eggs and sperm from the gonads emerge through the mouth, and fertilization occurs in the water. The zygote grows into a long ciliated gastrula; septa develop in the inner cavity, the blastopore becomes the mouth, and long, stiff cilia grow on the aboral end. The larva swims about and feeds on microorganisms; later it attaches aborally on the sea bottom and grows into a small anemone. Certain kinds of anemones reproduce asexually by fission or by fragmentation of the pedal disc.

17-16. Corals. Certain small, anemone-like polyps secrete limy cups which collectively form rigid masses able to withstand constant wave action along ocean shores. Generations of such polyps form coral reefs in tropical seas (latitudes 28°N. to 28°S.), where the water is 20°C. or warmer. These take various forms: (1) the *fringing reef,* up to a quarter mile from shore; (2) the *barrier reef,* separated by a lagoon of some width and depth from a shore; and (3) the *circular reef* or *atoll,* around a lagoon of water but not enclosing an island. The Great Barrier Reef along northeast Australia is 1,200 miles long and a few to 90 miles off shore. Warm parts of the Pacific Ocean have many atolls of various sizes.

Darwin inferred that coral atolls began as fringing reefs and that, as the island sank or was weathered away, there remained only the actively growing circular reef surrounding a lagoon. Recent borings on Bikini showed sand containing FORAMINIFERIDA of Oligocene age (about 30 million years ago) at a depth of 2,500 feet. Deeper borings to 4,630 feet on Eniwetok Atoll ended in hard volcanic rock, thus confirming Darwin's theory.

REVIEW

1. Sponges are fixed (sessile) and plant-like in form. Why are they classified as animals?
2. How do sponges differ from other multicellular animals (METAZOA)?
3. Distinguish between choanocyte and amoebocyte as to position and function.
4. What is the food of sponges, and how is it obtained? How and where is the food digested?
5. Describe the kinds of reproduction in sponges.
6. How and where are the following functions performed in a coelenterate: digestion, respiration, coordination of body movements, and excretion?
7. Name a coelenterate having both polyp and medusa stages. Outline its life cycle.
8. A swimmer in tropical waters is touched by the arms of a large jellyfish. There is sudden pain, and a rash develops. What structures of the jellyfish are responsible, and how do they function?
9. Define polymorphism, mesoglea, and radial symmetry; give an example of each.
10. How is a sea anemone able to capture and digest a fish?
11. What is coral? How is it formed? Where does it occur?

18
Flatworms and roundworms

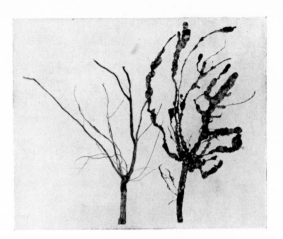

difficulties

A. FLATWORMS
Phylum PLATYHELMINTHES

Many kinds of animals with long bodies but no conspicuous appendages are called "worms" (Gr. *helminthes,* L. *vermes*). From the radial sponges and coelenterates they differ in form and in the presence of organ systems. The worm has an **anterior end** that habitually moves foremost "to meet the environment," and at the other end of the body is the **posterior end.** The animal travels or rests on a **ventral surface** which remains downward while the opposite or **dorsal surface** is uppermost. Both external and internal structural parts are arranged symmetrically to the right and left of a lengthwise body axis or plane; hence the animal is termed **bilaterally symmetrical.** All of these characteristics are common to the worms and to most other groups of animals higher in evolutionary development.

Lowest of the worms are members of the PLATYHELMINTHES (Gr. *platy,* flat), which have soft, thin bodies. This phylum includes three classes: the free-living flatworms (TURBELLARIA) of fresh or salt waters or of moist places on land; the flukes (TREMATODA), which are either external or internal parasites; and the tapeworms (CESTOIDEA), all parasitic and living as adults within the in-

testines of vertebrates. Flatworms vary in size from some turbellarians and flukes that are microscopically small to the broad tapeworm that may become 40 feet in length. Economically many flatworms are important because as parasites they affect the health of wild and domestic animals and of mankind.

18-1. Characteristics.

* 1. Symmetry bilateral; 3 germ layers; body usually flattened dorsoventrally; no true segmentation.

2. Epidermis soft and ciliated; or covered by cuticle and with external suckers or hooks or both for attachment to host.

* 3. Digestive system incomplete (a mouth but no anus) and usually much branched; none in tapeworms.

4. Muscle layers well developed; spaces between internal organs filled by loose cell masses (parenchyma); no body cavity.

5. No skeletal, circulatory, or respiratory systems; excretory system of many flame cells joined to excretory ducts.

* 6. Nervous system with a pair of anterior ganglia or a nerve ring and 1 to 3 pairs of lengthwise nerve cords with transverse connectives.

7. Sexes usually united (monoecious); fertilization internal; eggs microscopic; development either direct or with 1 or more larval stages; asexual reproduction in some forms.

Illustration at top of page: Roots of lima bean plants. *At left:* With galls of root nematode infection. *At right:* Of resistant stock, no infection—a benefit of applied research. (*Photo by R. M. Allard.*)

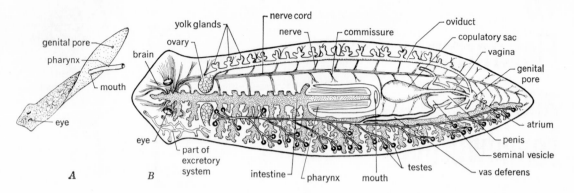

Fig. 18-1. Planaria, a free-living flatworm (Class Turbellaria). (*A*) External features. (*B*) General structure, somewhat diagrammatic. On the right (upper) side the testes, vas deferens, and parts of the digestive tract are omitted; on the left (lower) side the nerve cord, yolk glands, and oviduct are omitted; only a bit of the excretory system is shown on the left side anteriorly.

Free-living Flatworms
Class *TURBELLARIA*

The common small planarians (*Dugesia, Euplanaria,* etc.) inhabit cool, clear, permanent lakes and streams, where they avoid light by clinging to the under surfaces of stones or logs in the water.

18-2. Structure. The planarian (Fig. 18-1) has a thin, soft, flexible body, 5 to 25 mm. long, that may be extended, contracted, or turned in any direction. The exterior is covered by a single layer of *epidermis* that contains much pigment and many one-celled glands. Beneath the epidermis are layers of circular and lengthwise *muscle fibers* that contract to produce changes in body shape. Spaces between the fibers and internal organs are filled by a soft mass of cells, the *parenchyma,* and there is no body cavity. Dorsally on the anterior end ("head region") there are two dark *eyespots.* The entire ventral surface is covered by *cilia* that serve in locomotion. Midventrally the *mouth* opening is in an extensible muscular *pharynx* (proboscis), and the small *genital pore* is farther back.

Besides the mouth and pharynx, the *digestive system* includes a much branched but blind-ended intestine with one anterior and two posterior trunks that have many small lateral subdivisions. Planarians are carnivorous; small living or dead animals are sucked in by the pharynx. Digestion takes place in cells of the intestinal wall (intracellular) as in hydra, also in the intestinal cavity (extracellular). There being no circulatory or respiratory organs, the fluid in the parenchyma around interval organs serves to distribute the products of digestion and to carry oxygen diffusing in from the moist epidermis of the body exterior.

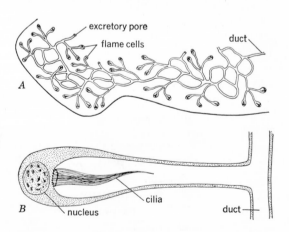

Fig. 18-2. Planaria. (*A*) Part of the excretory system. (*B*) One flame cell. Both enlarged. (*After Hyman.*)

The excretory system (Fig. 18-2) has many *flame cells,* with long waving cilia, that are located between body cells throughout the animal. Waste materials and excess water pass into the flame cells and are driven by the cilia into collecting ducts leading to *excretory pores* on the exterior surface. The *nervous system* is more advanced than that in coelenterates. Two anterior concentrations (ganglia) of nerve cells are joined as a "brain," whence nerve fibers connect to the head region and eyespots (Fig. 18-3; sensitive to light but forming no images). From the brain two longitudinal nerve trunks extend posteriorly, one in each side of the body; these have many cross-connectives and lateral branches.

An adult planarian contains both male and female *reproductive organs* (hence is monoecious). On each side the *male system* has many minute *testes* connected by small *vasa efferentia* to two larger *vasa deferentia* that extend along the body and enter a median sperm sac, or *seminal vesicle.* This sac joins the *penis* located within the genital atrium. The *female system* is somewhat similar; a rounded anterior *ovary* on each side connects to an *oviduct* along which are lateral *yolk glands.* The ducts enter a median *vagina* to which a sperm storage sac, or *seminal receptacle,* is attached, and the vagina opens into the genital atrium.

18-3. Natural history. At night planarians travel over fixed objects in the water but cannot swim freely. Commonly they glide along by action of the ventral cilia over a "mucous track" produced by epidermal glands; they also can contract or extend the body, turn, and crawl by muscular contractions. To mechanical or chemical stimuli, planarians show more organized responses than are seen in coelenterates. As the environment is tested by sensory cells or organs, coordination between the nervous and muscular systems produces locomotion in the desired direction—toward or away from an object (Fig. 18-4).

Recent studies reveal a form of learning and memory in these lowly creatures. If a planarian is exposed repeatedly to bright light, it will react only to the first few bursts. When exposed repeatedly to mild electric shocks, however, it continues to respond (contract). If these two experiments are combined (repeated bursts of light, then after a few seconds a shock), the planarian will later act as if "in anticipation" of the shock. This acquired reactivity is not centered in the brain because, when a trained worm is cut in half and each half is permitted to regenerate, both the "anterior" worm and the "tail" worm react to light. Further, if an untrained worm eats a trained one, the cannibal exhibits a signifi-

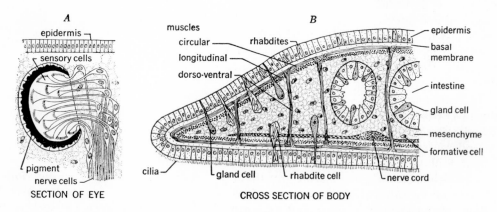

Fig. 18-3. Planaria. (*A*) Section through the eye. (*B*) Cross section of the body (excretory structures omitted).

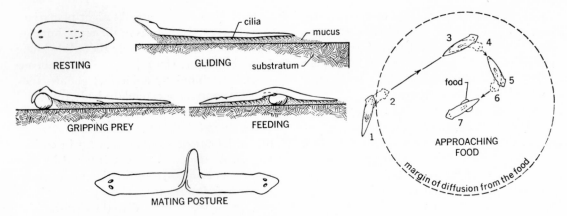

Fig. 18-4. Some activities of planarians. (*Mostly after Pearl, 1903.*)

cantly greater response to light. Thus memory is somehow stored throughout the body, presumably in dispersed parts of the nervous system, and can be transmitted through cells and tissues.

These animals have great powers of regeneration. Any body part destroyed by injury may be replaced, and if a planarian is cut into two or more pieces, each will later result in an entire individual. Some species multiply asexually by fission (Fig. 11-1). Flatworms also reproduce sexually. When two planarians mate, their posterior ventral surfaces come together and the penis of each enters the genital pore of the other for reciprocal transfer of sperm. Then they separate. Later, in each, the eggs are fertilized internally, each egg becomes surrounded by yolk cells, and several eggs are grouped together in a capsule. The capsule passes out of the worm and into the water. Development of the egg is direct, each yielding a young worm.

18-4. Other turbellarians. There are other fresh-water members of this group, mostly of slender form; and some live in moist places on land. Still others—leaf-like, oval, or of other shapes—inhabit rocks and marine growths at the seashore. Most turbellarians are free-living, but a few are parasites, and some are commensals that cling to the surface of other animals.

FLUKES
Class *TREMATODA*

All of this class of flatworms are parasitic. Two principal orders are recognized, based on differences in the life cycle. In the Order MONOGENEA each fluke inhabits only one host, and these flukes are mainly ectoparasites of fishes, amphibians, and reptiles; a single larval stage swims about to find the proper host or die, and from each egg only one adult is produced. Members of this order sometimes produce epidemics in fresh-water fishes. Those of the Order DIGENEA are all internal parasites specific to various organs. Two or more hosts are necessary to complete the life cycle, an invertebrate for the larval stages and a vertebrate for the adult.

18-5. Sheep liver fluke. *Fasciola hepatica* is a representative of the second type of fluke just mentioned. As an adult it is common in the bile duct of sheep, occasional in cattle, and rare in man. Moderate infestations cause sheep to be unthrifty, and heavy parasitism can cause death.

The body is leaf-shaped, up to 30 mm. long (Fig. 18-5), and covered by a resistant *cuticle.* Around the mouth is an *anterior sucker* and close behind it a *ventral sucker;* the *genital opening* is between the suckers. The *digestive system* has a mouth, muscular sucking pharynx, and a two-branched "intestine" with

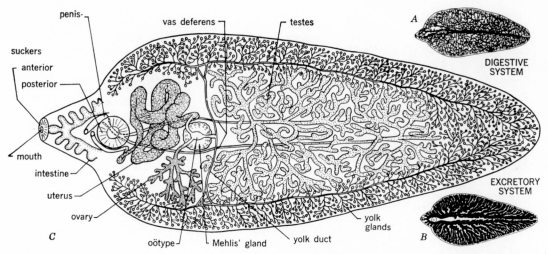

Fig. 18-5. Liver fluke of sheep, *Fasciola hepatica* (Class TREMATODA). (*A*) Digestive system. (*B*) Excretory system. Both natural size. (*C*) Reproductive system in ventral view and enlarged; digestive system shown only at anterior end. (*Modified from Sommer and Landois*, 1880.) *Note large amount of reproductive tissue. Not know individual structures*

many lateral subdivisions, but no anus; undigested food is egested through the mouth. Soft cellular *parenchyma* fills all spaces between the internal organs and the many complex *muscles,* there being no body cavity. The *excretory system* has many *flame cells* joined to one main canal that opens in a single posterior pore.

Complex male and female *reproductive systems* are present in each adult fluke. The *male system* has a pair of much-branched testes with ducts (vasa deferentia) leading to one sperm storage chamber (seminal vesicle) and an accessory gland and penis. The *female system* consists of an ovary with an oviduct connected to a central area (oötype) where two yolk ducts, a shell gland, and sperm-receiving sac (seminal receptacle) come together. Both male and female systems open through the one genital pore. The eggs are fertilized internally; then each receives yolk and a covering shell before moving down the coiled uterus and out the genital pore. In the sheep, eggs pass from the bile duct into the intestine and are voided with the host's feces.

The eggs require a moderate temperature and damp surroundings to complete their **complex development** (Fig. 18-6). From each a

microscopic, ciliated free-swimming *larva* (miracidium) hatches and in 8 hours must find a certain kind of fresh-water snail as an intermediate host; otherwise it dies. The entrance of many miracidia can kill a snail. Within the snail the larva undergoes two changes in form (sporocyst, redia) during which it may multiply asexually in numbers. A further change produces a disc-shaped larva (cercaria) with suckers and a tail; this burrows out of the snail's body and swims until it settles on a blade of grass. There it develops into the final larval form (metacercaria) which secretes a resistant cyst in which to live for months if not subjected to high temperatures or extreme dryness, or until ingested by the final host. If taken in with food, the cyst passes into the intestine and there breaks down by the action of digestive juices; the larva burrows from the intestine to the liver and bile duct, where it grows to become a mature fluke.

Many chances of failure beset the path of an animal with so complex a life cycle, and to compensate for these hazards each adult fluke may produce up to 500,000 eggs; in the snail a single miracidium may result in up to 300 cercaria larvae.

18-6. Other Trematoda. There are about

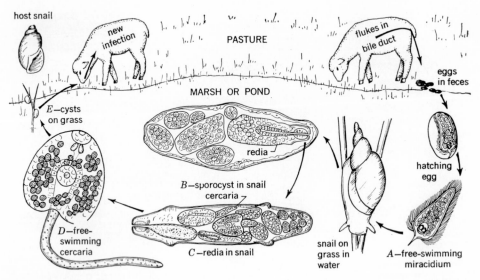

Fig. 18-6. Life history of the liver fluke of sheep, *Fasciola hepatica;* larval stages, about 85×; snail about natural size. (*Details from Thomas,* 1883.) *Know*

3,000 described species of digenetic flukes that parasitize vertebrates from fishes to mammals; but the complex life histories of only a few are known. Various kinds of flukes live in the intestine, liver, lung, or blood stream of human beings and are common parasites in the tropics and the Orient, where they cause much illness and many deaths.

Add Blood Flukes.

TAPEWORMS
CLASS *CESTOIDEA*

18-7. Structure and natural history. The cestodes (Gr. *cestus,* girdle + *oid,* like) are all internal parasites of vertebrates. They are mostly slender and long, with a flat, cuticle-covered body formed of a series of joined sections, *proglottids.* Most tapeworms are similar to the pork tapeworm of man, *Taenia solium,* which will serve as an example (Figs. 18-7, 18-8).

The anterior end has a small, knob-like "head," or *scolex,* with four *suckers* and a circlet of *hooks* by which it can attach to the intestinal wall of the host. The body (strobila) consists of several to 1,000 proglottids. Connecting head and body is a "neck" where new

proglottids form by transverse budding. When the oldest of these, at the posterior end of the body, become filled with fertilized eggs, they drop off and pass out of the host's body to the ground.

Each proglottid contains muscles, nerve cords connected with a nerve ring in the scolex, two excretory canals with flame cells, but no digestive organs. Food diffuses directly into the parasite's body, which is amid material being digested in the host's intestine. A complete male and female reproductive system is contained in each proglottid (Fig. 18-7). Self-fertilization within one proglottid, or in separate proglottids, or cross-fertilization with another tapeworm in the same host are all possible.

After the eggs are fertilized, provided with yolk, and enclosed in a resistant shell, the uterus, containing many eggs, enlarges to fill the whole proglottid, which is then "ripe" and separates from the rest of the worm (Fig. 18-8); the other male and female organs degenerate. The proglottid passes out with the host's feces to the ground, where the tissues disintegrate and the eggs are freed to be picked up with food by the intermediate host

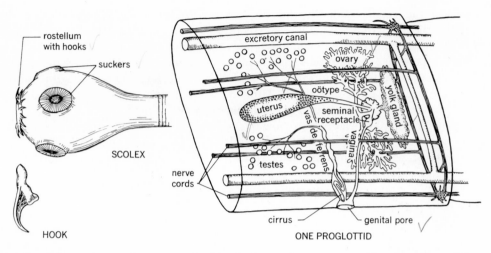

Fig. 18-7. Scolex and one proglottid of the pork tapeworm, *Taenia solium* (Class CESTOIDEA.) *Know*

(the pig in this example). The egg shell dissolves in the intestinal juices, and the first larval stage (oncosphere), formed while in the egg, travels through the blood or lymph vessels to encyst as a "bladder worm" in the pig's muscles. Incompletely cooked pork transmits the encysted larva to man, where the final adult form develops in the human intestine.

18-8. Other tapeworms. More than 1,500 species of tapeworms occur in various vertebrates from fishes to mammals. The adult stage of each is usually in a final host that preys upon some intermediate host, the flesh of which contains the infective stages. Common examples, with the intermediate and final hosts, are those of cattle and man; rabbit and dog or cat; dog louse or fleas and dog. The hydatid worm reverses the usual size

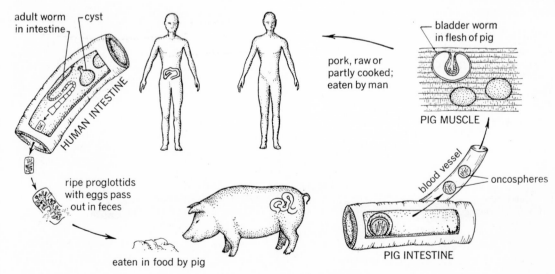

Fig. 18-8. Life cycle of the pork tapeworm, *Taenia solium*. (*Adapted in part from Buchsbaum, Animals without backbones, by permission of University of Chicago Press, copyright* 1938.) *Know*

sequence, the small adult in the dog or wolf and the dangerously large larval cysts in man and many domesticated mammals.

Some tapeworms are harmless; others may produce severe symptoms, but rarely is a tapeworm the primary cause of a death. Human infections are decreasing in civilized countries because of a wider knowledge as to how infections may be avoided, better detection and treatment of persons harboring tapeworms, and by inspection and refrigeration of meat to prevent contaminated cuts or carcasses from reaching the public.

B. Roundworms

Phylum ASCHELMINTHES
Class *NEMATODA*

The roundworms or nematodes (now placed as a class in Phylum Aschelminthes) are all much alike in general form, having slender cylindrical or tapered bodies (Gr. *nematos,* thread), resistant cuticle, a complete digestive tract, and no segmentation. Among multicellular animals they may be second only to insects in numbers. Many are free-living in soil or water, and others are parasites of some plants and various animals. Some kinds inhabit the roots of plants, and others live in the intestines, blood, or other organs of animals, particularly of vertebrates. Most nematodes are small or minute, but a few grow to a meter in length. Some parasitic species cause large losses in farm animals and certain crops, and others produce serious diseases in man.

18-9. Characteristics.

1. Symmetry bilateral; 3 germ layers; no true segmentation or appendages.
2. Body slender, cylindrical, with tough cuticle.
3. Digestive tract complete, permanent; mouth and anus at opposite ends of body.
4. Longitudinal muscle fibers only; body cavity unlined (a pseudocoel).
5. No circulatory or respiratory organs; excretory organs, 2, 1, or none.
6. Nerve ring around esophagus, 6 anterior nerves, and 6 (or more) posterior nerves or cords.
7. Sexes usually separate, male smaller than female; gonads continuous with sex ducts; fertilization internal; eggs microscopic, with chitinous shell; development direct, with several molts, no asexual reproduction.

The nematodes differ from flatworms in shape, absence of cilia and suckers, presence of a complete unbranched gut, and separate sexes. Their simple muscles permit only dorso-

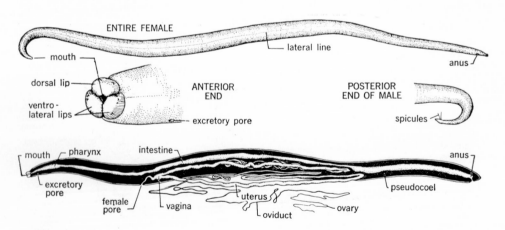

Fig. 18-9. Intestinal roundworm of the pig, *Ascaris megalocephala* (Class Nematoda). *Above.* External features. *Below.* Internal structure of a female.

ventral bending. The body cavity (pseudo-coel) lacks mesodermal lining, thus is unlike the true coelom of annelids or the paren-chyma-filled body of flatworms and nemer-teans; it resembles the cavity in rotifers. Di-gested food diffuses through the gut wall and through fluid in the pseudocoel; undigested wastes discharge through the anus.

18-10. Structure. The common intestinal roundworm of man and the pig (*Ascaris lum-bricoides*) is pink or yellow, the female being 8 to 16 inches long and the male 6 to 10 inches (Fig. 18-9). The slender, round **body** tapers toward either end and is covered with smooth, tough, and elastic **cuticle.** Along the body are four whitish **longitudinal lines,** one dorsal, one ventral, and two lateral. The **mouth** opens at the anterior end, between three rounded **lips** bearing fine papillae. The **anus** is a ventral transverse slit at the posterior end. The **male** worm has a sharply curved posterior end and two fine spicules project from the genital pore within the anus. The **female** worm is straighter; the genital pore (vulva) is midventral, at about one-third the distance from the anterior end.

The thin **body wall** (Fig. 18-10) consists of (1) the cuticle, noncellular and secreted by the epidermis; (2) the epidermis, a thin proto-plasmic layer containing nuclei but **no cell walls** (hence a syncytium); and (3) the muscle layer, divided into four lengthwise parts by the inward projections of the four longi-tudinal lines. Each **muscle cell** consists of a spindle-shaped fiber extending lengthwise be-neath the epidermis and a club-shaped medial process containing the nucleus. The lines and the muscle cells are the irregular outer bound-ary of the body spaces in which the other internal organs lie free.

The straight **digestive tract** consists of (1) the mouth; (2) a small buccal cavity; (3) a short, muscular sucking pharynx or esophagus that acts to draw in food; (4) a nonmuscular narrow intestine, composed of a single layer of tall cells (which absorb the digested food) covered externally by cuticle; and (5) a short rectum discharging through (6) the anus. No circulatory or respiratory organs are present. The inner part of each lateral line contains an **excretory canal;** both empty through a minute midventral pore just behind the mouth. A **nerve ring** around the esophagus connects to short anterior nerves and to six posterior **nerve cords** with various lateral branches and cross-connectives. The body sur-face bears minute papillae, probably sensory in function.

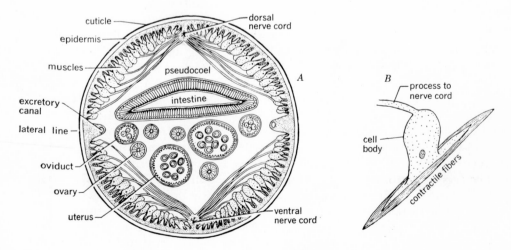

Fig. 18-10. Ascaris. (*A*) Cross section of a female. (*B*) One muscle cell. Both enlarged.

Each *reproductive organ* (gonad and sex duct) is a continuous slender tube, of gradually increasing diameter, closed at its inner end, looped back and forth in the body cavity, and attached only at the genital pore. The *male system* is single, successive parts being (1) the testis for sperm production; (2) the vas deferens for conduction; (3) the seminal vesicle for storing mature sperm; (4) the ejaculatory duct for ejecting sperm; and (5) a sac containing two penial spicules which are inserted in the female's vulva for attachment of the male and female during copulation. The *female system* is double and ≺-shaped, each branch is up to 125 cm. long and consists of (1) an ovary; (2) an oviduct; and (3) a uterus. The two uteri are joined to (4) a single short vagina opening at (5) the vulva.

18-11. Natural history. The adult ascaris is a parasite in the host's intestine and has problems of existence differing from those of a free-living animal. Obviously it is not easy to learn the physiological processes of an internal parasite in its normal habitat, but it seems that (1) locomotion and maintenance of position are chiefly by dorsoventral bendings of the body; (2) the cuticle protects the living worm against digestive juices of its host; (3) food is obtained from the semifluid materials in the host's intestine, being pumped in by the worm's muscular esophagus, and after digestion passes through its intestinal wall to be distributed by fluid in the body cavity to other tissues; (4) respiration depends on the breakdown of glycogen within the worm's body, since the intestinal contents of its host contain little free oxygen; and (5) the sensory papillae probably are receptors for chemical and tactile stimuli.

18-12. Reproduction. Male and female worms copulate within the host's intestine. The eggs are fertilized in the oviducts of the female, and each becomes covered by a tough chitinous shell (measuring 45 to 75 by 35 to 50 μ). A large female may contain 27,000,000 eggs at one time and lay 200,000 or more per day (Fig. 18-11). The eggs pass out of the

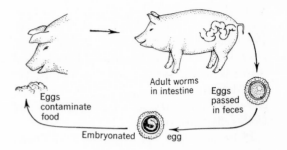

Fig. 18-11. Ascaris. Life cycle in the pig. (*Adapted from Koutz and Rebrassier, Ohio State University Press*, 1951.)

female worm, into the host's intestine, to leave with the feces. A period of development is needed before they become infective for another host. Under conditions of drought or cold they may be dormant for many months, but in a warm, moist, shady site they develop in 2 or 3 weeks. If such "embryonated" eggs (containing embryo worms) are swallowed by the proper host, while eating or drinking, they pass to the intestine, where the larvae (0.2 to 0.3 mm. long) hatch. The larvae burrow into veins or lymph vessels in the intestinal wall and travel through the heart to pulmonary capillaries of the lungs, meanwhile growing in size. In a few days they break into the air passages and move via the trachea, esophagus, and stomach to the intestine again, there growing to maturity.

No intermediate host is necessary. Young pigs usually acquire eggs from infected soil in pig yards or in dirt on the sow's udder when nursing. Adult pigs are rather immune to infection; any worms they contain probably were acquired when young. Human infection with *Ascaris* is not uncommon, and most persons in some rural places are infected. Worms found in man and pigs are identical structurally but differ physiologically in that infective eggs of the human *Ascaris* do not ordinarily produce mature worms in pigs, and vice versa. Passage of many larvae through the lungs may cause local inflammation and even a "pneumonia." Adult ascarids in the intestine may produce secretions toxic to the host, and the worms when numerous may obstruct the intestine. Worms sometimes migrate to the mouth or nose and may even penetrate the intestinal wall to invade other organs, causing serious illness or death of the host. Some animals and people become sensitized or allergic to the secretions of ascarids.

18-13. Other nematodes. Some parasitic worms have cutting teeth or hooks in the mouth for attaching and feeding, and those that live on plant roots have a sharp, hollow "spear" to puncture the cells and a muscular esophagus to withdraw cell "juices." The cuticle on many free-living species bears minute bristles, spines, or "scales" that aid in crawling through the soil. Some predatory nematodes have enlarged mouths with teeth.

The great host of free-living nematodes live variously in moist soil, in sand of ocean beaches, in fresh, stagnant, and salt waters, on the shores and bottoms of lakes and rivers, on the filter beds of waterworks, in hot springs, and in polar seas and ice. The upper 3 inches of an acre of alluvial soil may contain 3,000,000,000 nematodes. Some soil-inhabiting nematodes do severe damage to crop plants, others may be of neutral status, and some that prey on other nematodes probably are beneficial. Still others live in various parts of plants, including the roots, seeds, fruits, gums, leaf axils, bark crevices, and galls.

18-14. Relations to man. Many species parasitic in man, his domestic animals, and his cultivated plants are of great practical importance. Some do little or no damage, whereas others cause impaired efficiency, unthriftiness, and illness or death of the host. The effects depend upon the species, the numbers present, and other factors. Over 50 species are parasites of mankind. There are others in farm livestock and poultry, in all kinds of wild vertebrates, and in various invertebrates. Almost any vertebrate organ may be invaded by a nematode: the stomach, small or large intestine, lung, bladder, muscle, blood, etc. Each species usually is confined to one or a few related hosts, occasionally invades others, and usually occupies a particular organ. Most parasitic nematodes have a free-living egg or larval stage in soil or water. An occasional host contains enormous numbers, for example, a "pint" of stomach worms in man, or 40,000 worms in a 50-pound mammal. Infections with intestinal worms can be diagnosed by searching for the microscopic eggs in the feces, those of most species being of characteristic size, shape, and structure (Fig. 18-12). Treatment to eliminate nematodes requires use of some drug not too toxic to the host that will cause the worm to loosen and be carried out in the feces.

18-15. Root nematodes (Fig. 18-13). The common garden nematodes (*Heterodera radicicola* and *marioni*) have been found in over 1,000 varieties of plants; they infest fully 75 garden and field crops, fruit and shade trees, shrubs and weeds. Eggs of these worms are deposited in roots or soil, and the young upon hatching penetrate rootlets to feed on the tis-

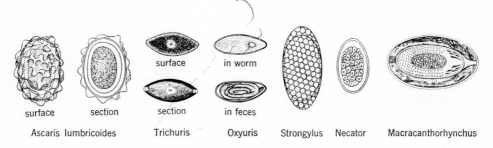

surface   section   surface   in worm
section   in feces

Ascaris lumbricoides   Trichuris   Oxyuris   Strongylus   Necator   Macracanthorhynchus

Fig. 18-12. Eggs of five nematodes and an acanthocephalan (*Macracanthorhynchus*); all much enlarged. (*After Ward, 1907.*)

Skip.

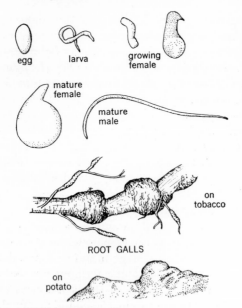

egg   larva   growing female

mature female

mature male

on tobacco

ROOT GALLS

on potato

Fig. 18-13. The root knot nematode (*Heterodera*). Egg, larva, and adults, all greatly enlarged. Root galls produced by the worms, about natural size. (*After Tyler, 1933.*)

sues. The roots react by forming small galls of scar tissue or "root knots" about the worms. The adult male is slender (1.2 to 1.5 mm.), but the female has a swollen body (0.8 by 0.5 mm.) producing 500 to 1,000 eggs. Fertilization may occur but is unnecessary. In soil the life cycle requires nearly 3 months at 58°F. but less than a month at 81°F.; hence several generations per year are possible in the warm southern and western states. The larvae within galls can withstand some drying and survive at 32°F. but die at lower temperatures. Root knot causes weakening or death of the plant, and soil infested with these worms often fails to yield profitable crops. The nematodes are carried into clean soils with plants, soil, manure, farm tools, or irrigation water from infested lands, and once established they are difficult to eradicate. Plant breeders have produced selected strains of some economic plants resistant to this nematode (see illustration at start of Chap. 18).

18-16. Hookworm. In many moist tropical and subtropical regions the hookworm is a

scourge of man. Among populations of low economic level that go barefooted and use no sanitary toilets from 50 to 95 per cent may be infected. Many persons in the southeastern states suffer from hookworm disease, as do workers in mines and tunnels. Both *Ancylostoma duodenale* and *Necator americanus* are common in man, the latter especially in the United States.

The adult worm (8 to 13 mm. long) has cutting teeth in its mouth (Fig. 18-14). It attaches inside of the small intestine, where blood, lymph, and bits of mucous membrane are sucked into the worm by action of its pumping pharynx. Feeding is facilitated by a secretion that prevents coagulation of the host's blood. A worm may pump more blood than it digests, and the wound it makes may bleed excessively, resulting in anemia.

Hookworms mate while in the host's intestine, and each female produces several thousand fertile eggs daily. These pass out with the feces and in warm, moist, shady places hatch in 24 to 48 hours; the larvae feed on excrement or other organic debris. When about 0.5 mm. long, they become infective to man, often burrowing through soft skin on the sides of the foot and causing "ground itch." The larvae travel in blood and lymph vessels, through the heart and to the lungs, from capillaries to air cavities, thence up the trachea into the esophagus and then down to the intestine. They soon mature and may live

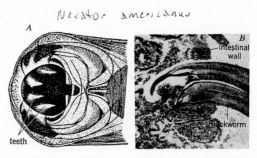

Fig. 18-14. Hookworms. (*A*) Mouth of *Ancylostoma duodenale* in anterior view, showing the teeth. (*B*) *Ancylostoma caninum* attached to intestinal wall in dog. Both enlarged. (*After Stiles; and Loess.*)

several months or years. Continued reinfection of the host maintains the worms in a person.

Children with a hundred or more hookworms are retarded physically and mentally, and persons of any age with many worms become anemic, have lessened energy, and are more susceptible to other diseases. Medical treatment will rid a person of these parasites. Wearing shoes and sanitary disposal of human feces will prevent infection. Other hookworms occur in domestic and wild animals.

18-17 Trichina worm. *Trichinella spiralis* occurs as a minute living larva encysted in the striated muscles of the pig, house rat, and man (Fig. 18-15), also in the cat, dog, and black bear. If an individual of any of these eats the flesh of another containing such larvae, the cysts are dissolved by the digestive juices and larvae are liberated in the intestine of the new host. In about two days they become sexually mature and mate; male worms are then about 1.5 mm. long and females 3 to 4 mm. The females burrow in the intestinal wall, live for some time, and each produces up to 1,500 larvae about 0.1 mm. long. These enter lymph spaces, are carried in the blood, and burrow into skeletal muscles. They grow to about 1.0 mm., then coil up, and become enclosed in cysts which later may be calcified. Such larvae mature only when the flesh containing them is eaten by another susceptible mammal but may live for years in man.

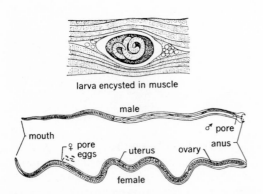

larva encysted in muscle

Fig. 18-15. The trichina worm, *Trichinella spiralis;* enlarged. Adults at bottom.

Mild infections cause no particular symptoms; about 16 per cent of people in the United States have some encysted trichinae. Heavy infections cause the disease trichinosis, which may be severe and can end in death. There is no specific treatment, and recovery is slow. Hogs and rats become infected by eating slaughterhouse scraps, garbage, or animal carcasses containing encysted larvae. Man receives infection by eating "measly" pork (occasionally bear meat) containing the microscopic cysts. Examination of pork in slaughterhouses for trichinae is economically impractical. The only protection is to *cook pork thoroughly,* by heating all parts to at least 137°F., pink color indicates inadequate cooking. Salami and headcheese may be dangerous unless thoroughly cooked. Refrigeration at −10°F. for 3 days will usually kill all larvae.

REVIEW

1. In what conspicuous ways does a flatworm differ from a coelenterate?
2. How does a planarian perform the functions of feeding, respiration, and excretion?
3. Compare the structural similarities and differences between a planarian and a fluke.
4. What would be the most logical places in the liver fluke's life history to attempt control measures?
5. How does a tapeworm differ from a planarian and a fluke as to manner of feeding? As to reproduction?
6. For the tapeworm as a species of animal what are the advantages and disadvantages of living alternately in two different kinds of host animals?
7. Name some conspicuous features separating roundworms from flatworms.
8. What is a "complete" digestive tract? Does it have advantages over an incomplete tract?
9. In what ways are the male and female reproductive systems of *Ascaris* alike, and how do they differ in structure and function?
10. What are some nematodes of economic importance? How does each influence the affairs of mankind?
11. How can one avoid trichinosis? How avoid hookworm disease?

19
Echinoderms and miscellaneous groups

A. Starfishes and Their Allies
Phylum ECHINODERMATA

The echinoderms (Gr. *echinos,* hedgehog + *derma,* skin) are common and conspicuous inhabitants of the seashore, easily recognized by external characters (Fig. 19-1). Most of the starfishes have 5 tapering arms, a few have up to 50, and some are of pentagonal shape. The brittle stars have 5 slender flexible and jointed arms on a small central disc. Sea urchins are hemispherical with a firm shell bearing long, movable spines, and the sand dollars are flat, hard discs. Sea lilies resemble flowers, having a cup-like disc bearing 5 slender branched arms. The sea cucumbers have soft, sausage-

Illustration at top of page: A multiarmed starfish (*Pycnopodia helianthoides*) from tidal pools on the California coast.

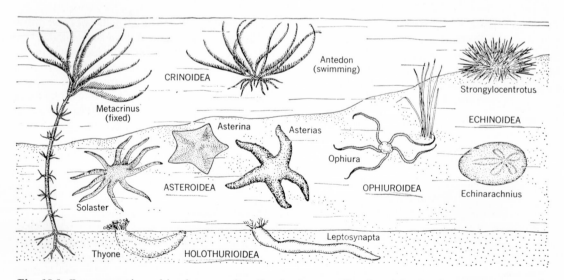

Fig. 19-1. Representative echinoderms as they live in the sea; all reduced in size, but not to same scale. Class CRINOIDEA: crinoids (*Metacrinus,* attached; *Antedon,* free-swimming). Class ASTEROIDEA: starfishes (*Asterias, Asterina*), sun star (*Solaster*). Class OPHIUROIDEA: brittle star (*Ophiura*). Class ECHINOIDEA: sea urchin (*Strongylocentrotus*), sand dollar (*Echinarachnius*). Class HOLOTHURIOIDEA: sea cucumbers (*Thyone, Leptosynapta*).

shaped bodies. Most members of the phylum are radially symmetrical. They are mostly free-living but slow-moving animals; some are abundant, but they do not form colonies. They all are marine, living from the tide lines to the greatest ocean depths—over 30,000 feet.

19-1. Characteristics.

1. Symmetry radial, usually 5-parted; no head or segmentation; many with tube feet serving for locomotion and food handling.
2. Body covered by soft epidermis over a firm (mesodermal) skeleton of movable or fixed limy plates and spines (skin leathery and plates microscopic in sea cucumbers).
3. Digestive tract simple (brittle stars lack an anus); body cavity (coelom) ciliated, usually large, filled with fluid containing free cells (amoebocytes); respiration by minute "gills" (papulae) projecting from body cavity, or by tube feet, or by a respiratory tree (sea cucumbers).
4. Sexes separate but alike externally; gonads large, sex ducts simple; eggs many, usually fertilized in the sea; larvae bilaterally symmetrical, minute, ciliated, usually free-swimming, with conspicuous metamorphosis.

Echinoderms once were linked with coelenterates as the RADIATA because of their symmetry, but they belong well up among the invertebrates. Indeed they have some chordate-like features such as (1) an internal mesodermal skeleton, not external as in other invertebrates; (2) mesoderm formed in the embryo from outpocketings of the primitive gut; (3) the anus formed from the embryonic blastopore; and (4) the mouth formed as an ectodermal inpocketing and not from the blastopore. The echinoderms may have regressed from a type that once was more advanced and active, since the larvae are bilaterally symmetrical and free-moving, whereas the adults are radial and sedentary. Radial symmetry and lack of a head enable a sedentary animal to receive stimuli equally well from all directions. As a group, the echinoderms are of ancient origin; their limy skeletons have left a long and detailed fossil record from Cambrian times onward.

The smallest of echinoderms is ½ inch in diameter. The largest starfish (*Pycnopodia*) spreads about 32 inches, the biggest sea urchin has a shell 12 inches in diameter, and the longest sea cucumber grows to 6 feet in length and 2 inches in diameter.

STARFISHES
CLASS *ASTEROIDEA*

19-2. Structure. The body of a common starfish (*Asterias*) comprises five tapering **arms** joined to a central **disc** (Fig. 19-2). The upper **aboral surface** has many short, hard, blunt **spines** attached to the internal skeleton and numerous fine, soft "**gills**" (dermal branchiae) projecting from the body cavity. Around the spines and elsewhere are many minute pincers, or **pedicellariae**, each with two jaws that snap shut when touched; they act to keep the body surface free of debris and may help to capture food. The minute **anus** is near the center of the aboral surface, and nearby is a rounded limy plate, the **madreporite**. Centered in the lower or **oral surface** is the **mouth**. From it, along each arm, is a conspicuous **ambulacral groove**, fringed by large spines, and containing many **tube feet** in four (or two) rows. The tip of each arm bears a short, soft **tentacle** and an **eyespot**.

The whole body is covered by soft ciliated **epidermis**. Beneath this is the **skeleton**, a framework of small limy plates (ossicles) of definite pattern and shape, bound by connective tissue and joined by muscle fibers. Inside the skeleton is the large **body cavity** (coelom) lined by ciliated epithelium and filled with circulating fluid containing free cells (amoebocytes). Extensions of the coelom into the "gills" bring the fluid close to the surrounding sea water, separated only by the thin coelomic lining and epidermis. Here respiratory exchange occurs, and the amoebocytes, carrying excretory wastes, can escape from the body.

The **water vascular system** (Fig. 19-3) is a

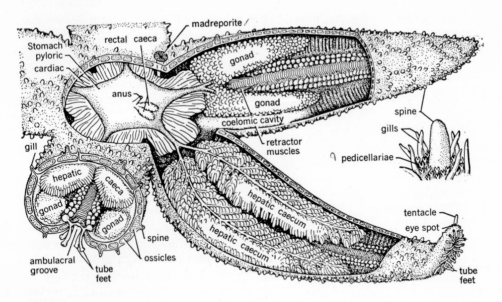

Fig. 19-2. Starfish. General structure. Three arms are cut off, one is seen in cross section at the left, the disc and aboral surface of two arms are removed, and the hepatic caeca removed from the upper right arm. Enlarged inset shows spine, gills, and pedicellariae.

series of rigid canals filled with sea water taken in through the **madreporite** and connecting to the tube feet. Each tube foot is a closed cylinder with muscular walls, having a sucker at the free outer end and a bulb (ampulla) at the inner end. When the bulb contracts, the contained fluid is forced into the tube foot, extending the latter as a slender flexible process

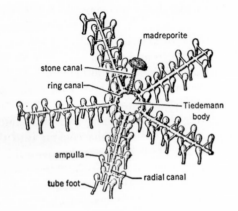

Fig. 19-3. Water vascular system of a starfish; diagrammatic. (*From Coe,* 1912.)

that can be moved about by muscles in its walls. Upon touching an object the muscles may contract, returning the water to the ampulla, so that the foot shortens. Withdrawal of the fluid lessens the pressure within the tip and causes it to adhere to the object because of the greater pressure of the sea water or atmosphere outside; the foot thus acts as a suction cup. Tube feet act separately or in a coordinated manner; they serve to hold the starfish to the rocks or bottom, for locomotion, and in the capture and handling of food.

The **digestive system** comprises (1) the mouth; (2) the stomach, of two parts: a large lower (cardiac) portion with thin, folded muscular walls, and a small (pyloric) section joined by ≺-shaped ducts from five pairs of digestive glands (hepatic caeca) in the arms; (3) a minute intestine; and (4) the anus. The circulatory and nervous systems are reduced and difficult to see. The sexes are separate. Each arm contains two **gonads** joined to a minute duct opening on the central disc.

19-3. Natural history. The starfish lives

attached to a clean, solid object. The stiff body can be fitted into a crevice among the rocks and can bend slowly when the animal moves. On any kind of surface the animal clings by its tube feet. To move, the arm pointing in a given direction is raised slightly, and the tube feet beneath are extended an inch or so; these grip the new surface and then contract to pull the body forward. The starfish may move in any direction, but once started it coordinates movements of the arms and tube feet. If inverted, the arms twist until some tube feet touch the substratum, then the entire body "folds over" until the oral surface again is downward.

The starfish eats mollusks, crustaceans, and other invertebrates, even catching some fishes by use of the tube feet and pedicellariae. When eating a clam, the starfish arches its body over the prey so that tube feet can grip the mollusk. Then the starfish everts its very thin stomach which is inserted between crevices in the shell margin, enzymes are secreted from the digestive glands, and the prey is digested. At some time in the digestive process the shell gapes, probably as a result of enzymatic weakening of muscles. Formerly the starfish was thought to exert a pull on the two shells of the mollusk until it opened and then the stomach was inserted. Recent work has shown that the pull is not of sufficient strength to do so. A captive month-old starfish ate more than 50 young clams in 6 days; yet a starfish may go long periods without food. On commercial oyster beds starfishes often eat many oysters, thus causing serious losses.

19-4. Reproduction. Great numbers of eggs and sperm are shed into the sea water, where fertilization occurs, and development is rapid (Fig. 19-4). In the *gastrula* stage, the blastopore becomes the anal end, the coelom buds off the primitive gut, and later the mouth forms as an inpocketing of ectoderm—all features that resemble embryonic development in chordates. The free-swimming ciliated *larva* acquires three pairs of lobes (bipinnaria stage) which later lengthen (brachiolaria

stage) when the larva is 2 to 3 mm. long. After 6 or 7 weeks the larva settles to the bottom and by a rather complex transformation becomes a small starfish. The female blood starfish (*Henricia*) produces a few large-yolked eggs that are held beneath her body, the larval stages are abbreviated, and the young emerge as minute adults. Starfishes readily regenerate arms when lost.

OTHER ECHINODERMS

19-5. Brittle stars (Class OPHIUROIDEA). These echinoderms have a small rounded central *disc* and five long *arms* that are slender, flexible, and fragile. Each arm comprises, many similar "segments" which are nearly solid, and provided with ball-and-socket joints and muscles. The small tube feet lack suckers. All digestive and reproductive organs are within the disc, and there is no anus. The basket stars have arms that are repeatedly branched.

Ophiurans hide by day under rocks or seaweed or lie buried in the sand or mud but become active at night. They move by rapid snake-like movements, holding to objects with one or more arms and pushing with others to jerk the body along. They also can swim by use of the arms, much as a person would do. They eat small crustaceans, mollusks, and other bottom dwellers, and in turn they serve as food for fishes. The sexes, usually separate, cast their eggs and sperm into the sea; the resulting (pluteus) larva has long arms. Later it metamorphoses, much as does a starfish. The arms of brittle stars break or can be cast off easily, and some species can even lose much of the disc, such parts being readily regenerated.

19-6. Sea urchins, sand dollars, and heart urchins (Class ECHINOIDEA). Members of this class have rounded bodies enclosed in a thin *shell*, or *test*, of firmly joined plates; they lack free arms but are thickly covered with movable *spines*. Sea urchins are hemispherical, heart urchins somewhat egg-shaped, and the

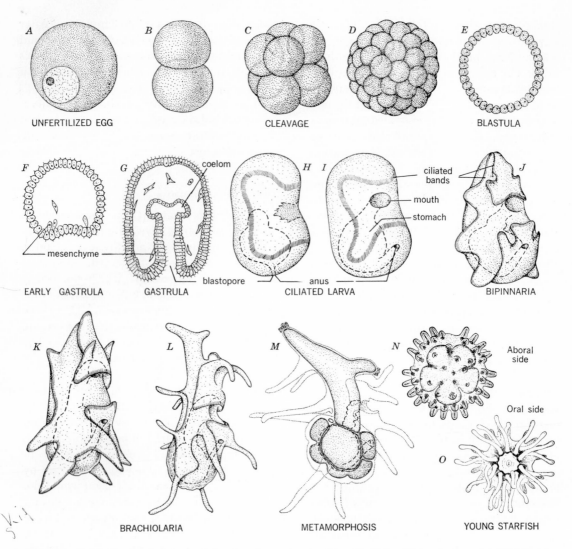

A UNFERTILIZED EGG

B *C* *D* CLEAVAGE

E BLASTULA

F EARLY GASTRULA

G GASTRULA

coelom

mesenchyme

blastopore

H *I* CILIATED LARVA

ciliated bands

mouth

stomach

anus

J BIPINNARIA

K *L* BRACHIOLARIA

M METAMORPHOSIS

N Aboral side

Oral side

O YOUNG STARFISH

Fig. 19-4. Development of a starfish, *Asterias vulgaris.* The blastula (*E*) and gastrula (*F, G*) are sectioned; the latter shows migration of mesenchyme cells and budding of coelomic cavities off the archenteron. The blastopore becomes the anus (*H*), and the stomodeum invaginates to form the mouth (*I*). The bilaterally symmetrical bipinnaria larva (*J*) produces three pairs of lateral lobes that lengthen in the brachiolaria larva (*K, L*), as do others on the ventral surface. The starfish forms on the lower right side of the brachiolaria (*M*), the upper parts of which are absorbed. (*Adapted from Field; Goto; and Brooks.*)

sand dollars are disc-like. Five pairs of the external plates are perforated for a series of slender *tube feet* that can extend out among the spines. Each spine has a cup-shaped base fitted over a rounded tubercle on the shell and can be moved by muscle fibers. Between the

spines there are three-jawed *pedicellariae* on long stalks.

The long *digestive tract* (Fig. 19-5) is coiled. From the mouth a slender esophagus joins the expanded stomach, which has sac-like pouches; the narrow intestine connects by the

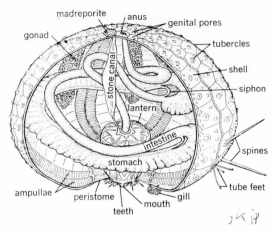

Fig. 19-5. Sea urchin. General structure. Most of the spines, pedicellariae, and tube feet omitted.

rectum to the anus opening on the aboral surface. A slender tubular **siphon,** lined by strong cilia, extends from the esophagus to the intestine; it may carry water directly to the latter and aid in washing out indigestible residues. There are 10 **gills** that protrude around the mouth, and the madreporite is aboral. Reproduction involves a pluteus larva. Echinoids have but little ability to regenerate lost parts. The urchins inhabit rocks or mud of the seashore, using the long spines and tube feet to move about, and some species excavate surface depressions in which they live. Sand dollars inhabit the sand, moving over it or through it by use of the short spines and tube feet. All echinoids feed mainly on seaweed, but they also eat dead animal matter and may take in sand or mud to extract the organic material therein. Fishes, starfishes, and marine carnivores are their chief enemies. Gonads of urchins are eaten by people in some regions.

19-7. Sea cucumbers (Class HOLOTHURIOIDEA). These soft-bodied animals have a leathery **skin** containing only minute limy **plates.** The sausage-shaped body has an anterior mouth encircled by 10 to 30 retractile **tentacles** that are comparable with the oral tube feet of other echinoderms (Fig. 19-6). Typically, there are 5 lengthwise series of **tube**

feet along the body, 2 dorsal series that are sensory and respiratory in function, and 3 ventral series used for locomotion. The body wall comprises cuticle, epidermis, a layer of circular muscles, and 5 double bands of strong lengthwise muscles. The action of the muscles over the fluid-filled body enables the animal to lengthen, contract, or make worm-like movements.

The slender, looped digestive tract is supported in the coelom by mesenteries. The anus is posterior, preceded by a muscular **cloaca** to which two branched, hollow **respiratory trees** usually are attached. Water, serving for respiration and excretion, is pumped in and out

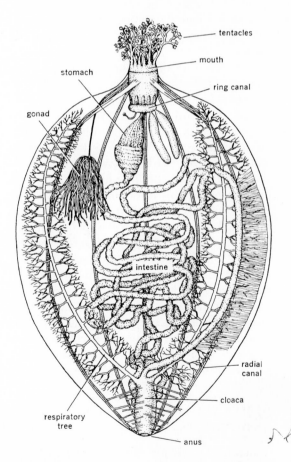

Fig. 19-6. Sea cucumber (*Thyone*). Internal structure; body wall cut lengthwise and laid open. (*After Coe,* 1912.)

of these tubes by action of the cloaca. The water vascular system includes a ring canal around the esophagus and canals joining the tube feet. The sexes are separate, and the brushy gonad connects to a single duct opening middorsally behind the tentacles.

Holothurians lie on the sea bottom or burrow in the mud or sand, leaving the ends of the body exposed; but they respond promptly if disturbed. The food is of organic matter in the mud or of small organisms captured by the tentacles. They travel by use of the tube feet and by muscular movements of the body. When irritated some types thrust out a series of sticky tubes (Cuvierian organs) from the cloaca to entangle an enemy. In the Orient certain sea cucumbers are gathered and dried as "trepang" or "bêche-de-mer," which is used for soup.

19-8. Sea lilies and feather stars (Class CRINOIDEA). These flower-like echinoderms have a central cup-shaped *calyx* of limy plates and 5 flexible *arms* forked to form 10 or more slender appendages with lateral projections. The calyx often is supported on a long jointed *stalk* with a root-like base attaching to the sea bottom (Fig. 19-7). Both mouth and anus are on the upper (oral) surface of the calyx. The minute organisms and detritus used as food are caught by tube feet on the upper surface of the arms and moved by ciliary action to the mouth. Some crinoids shed their eggs into the sea, and others retain them on the arms until the larvae hatch. The adults have great powers of regeneration. Many crinoids are attached briefly in the postlarval stage, but otherwise can swim by movements of the arms. The stalked species are gregarious, often forming colorful "gardens" in deep water.

B. MISCELLANEOUS PHYLA AND GROUPS

Besides the major phyla and classes described in other chapters, there are several additional groups of multicellular animals. Nearly all of them are aquatic, in salt or fresh

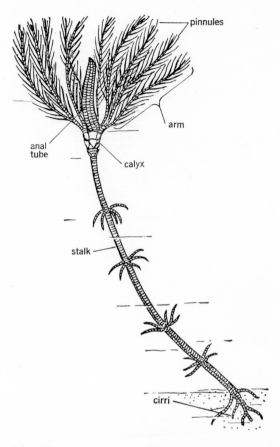

Fig. 19-7. A simple attached crinoid.

waters, some being common and others rare. Certain of these are described below. The remainder are listed here and summarized in the Synopsis of the Animal Kingdom (Chap. 15): MESOZOA, ENTOPROCTA, GASTROTRICHA, KINORHYNCHA, PHORONIDEA, SIPUNCULOIDEA, PRIAPULOIDEA, POGONOPHORA, and ECHIUROIDEA.[1] The position and relationships of many of these groups in classification are uncertain because they differ widely in structure and only a few are represented by fossils.

19-9. Ctenophores (Phylum CTENOPHORA; Fig. 19-8). This phylum comprises about 80 species of small marine animals with trans-

[1] Information on these groups is available in Storer and Usinger, "General Zoology," 4th edition (McGraw-Hill Book Company, 1965).

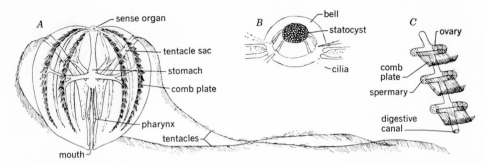

Fig. 19-8. Structure of a ctenophore. (*A*) *Pleurobrachia,* entire specimen. (*B*) Sense organ. *(Both after Hyman, The invertebrates, McGraw-Hill Book Co.)* (*C*) Reproductive cells in digestive canals under comb plates. *(From Bourne in Lankester, Treatise on zoology, A. & C. Black, Ltd.)*

parent gelatinous bodies and usually with eight rows of comb plates that serve weakly for locomotion. The "comb jellies" or "sea walnuts," as they are called, resemble coelenterates in having (1) biradial symmetry; (2) an oral-aboral body axis; (3) a gastro-vascular cavity with branches; and (4) gelatinous mesoglea. They differ in possessing (1) eight rows of comb plates; (2) mesenchymal or mesodermal muscles; (3) an aboral sensory region; (4) no nematocysts but with adhesive cells for capture of prey; and (5) no alternation of polyp and medusa stages.

A typical ctenophore has the mouth and sense organ at opposite ends, thus fixing the body axis. The eight equally spaced *comb plates* extend as meridians from pole to pole, each bearing a succession of small paddles or combs of fused cilia. The beating of these combs propels the animal with mouth end forward. Two flexible mucus-bearing *tentacles* protrude from the aboral end to entangle small animals which are conveyed to the mouth. Food is digested and distributed by a single system consisting of a pharynx, stomach, digestive glands, and excretory pores. Undigested waste passes out either the mouth or these pores. The food is of small mollusk and crustacean larvae, fish eggs, and small fishes.

The *sense organ* serves to orient the animal and coordinate the beating of the comb plates.

It contains four tufts of cilia that support a small rounded **statolith** of limy material.

Ctenophores are monoecious, and both eggs and sperm are produced by the endodermal lining in digestive canals beneath the comb plates. Mature sex cells pass out the mouth and are fertilized in the water, where development takes place, usually through a larval stage to the adult form.

19-10. Ribbon worms (Phylum NEMERTINEA; Fig. 19-9). These slender unsegmented animals have soft, flat bodies, usually a few inches in length, capable of great lengthening and contraction. Many are brightly colored with red, brown, green, or yellow, solidly, or banded and striped. Most of them live under stones, amid algae, or in burrows at the seashore, but some are in deep sea water and a few in fresh water. The food is of animals, living or dead.

Under the soft *integument* are circular and longitudinal *muscles.* The anterior end has a flexible *proboscis* that may be extended far out or completely withdrawn into a special chamber separate from the digestive tract. The proboscis may serve in offense and defense. The ciliated *digestive tract* extends throughout the body. There is a *circulatory system* with lengthwise blood vessels having cross-connectives, and the blood, either red or colorless, circulates as a result of bodily movements. The *excretory system* has branched

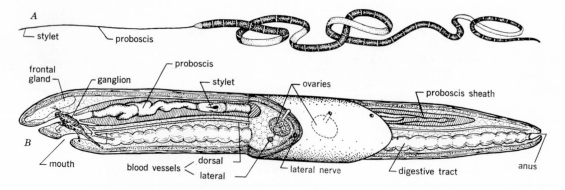

A
stylet
proboscis

frontal gland
ganglion
proboscis
stylet
ovaries
proboscis sheath

B
mouth
blood vessels { dorsal / lateral
lateral nerve
digestive tract
anus

Fig. 19-9. A ribbon worm (Phylum NEMERTINEA). (*A*) External form with proboscis extended. (*B*) Internal structure, diagrammatic. Left side removed except for part at middle of body; proboscis retracted into sheath.

lateral ducts and many flame cells, and the *nervous system* is linear, with ganglia above the mouth and a pair of lateral nerve trunks through the body. The sexes are usually separate, and the paired *gonads* open directly to the body surface. Adults *fragment* the body readily, and later each part regenerates to a complete worm.

19-11. Rotifers (Phylum ASCHELMINTHES, Class ROTIFERA). Lakes, streams, puddles, eaves troughs, and other fresh waters, large or small, usually contain many microscopic-sized multicellular animals known as rotifers or "wheel animalcules." Beating cilia on the

anterior end give a wheel-like effect that serves for locomotion. The cilia on this region and the chewing pharynx within the transparent body distinguish rotifers from all other minute aquatic animals.

A typical rotifer (Fig. 19-10) shows a *head region, trunk,* and slender, tail-like posterior *foot* with a *cement gland* which provides for temporary attachment to some object. The *body wall* is thin and covered by a transparent *cuticle.* The anterior *retractile disc* (corona) bears cilia that beat with a whirling motion, serving for locomotion and also to draw water with food and oxygen to the

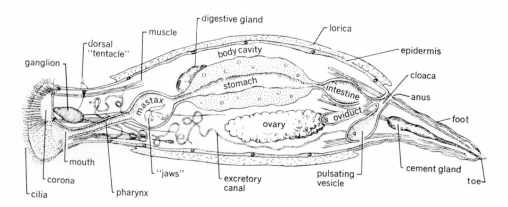

digestive gland
muscle
lorica
dorsal "tentacle"
body cavity
epidermis
ganglion
stomach
cloaca
mastax
intestine
anus
stomach
oviduct
ovary
foot
mouth
"jaws"
excretory canal
pulsating vesicle
cement gland
toe
corona
pharynx
cilia

Fig. 19-10. General structure of a female rotifer (Phylum ASCHELMINTHES, Class ROTIFERA). Much enlarged. (*After Delage and Herouard.*)

mouth. The complete *digestive tract* is mostly ciliated. The fluid-filled *body cavity* (not a coelom) contains a few *muscles*, two *nephridia*, a *pulsating vesicle*, a *nerve ganglion*, and a single *ovary* with *yolk gland* and *oviduct*. Males are known only in certain species; they are smaller than females and have one testis.

Rotifers are cosmopolitan, often abundant as to both species and individuals, and some are to be found only during limited parts of each year. Most species are free-living and solitary, commonest in waters with much aquatic vegetation. Others live attached, and a few are commensals or parasites. Rotifers feed variously on algae, or on juices of aquatic plants, or on other microorganisms. In turn, they serve as part of the food chain for other small fresh-water animals.

Females usually produce "summer" and "winter" eggs at different seasons (Fig. 19-11). The first are thin-shelled and develop by parthenogenesis; the second type yields male- and female-producing eggs, followed by a sexual generation.

19-12. "Horsehair worms" (Phylum ASCHELMINTHES, Class NEMATOMORPHA). Ponds of quiet water and drinking troughs often have very slender worms several inches long but only a millimeter or two in diameter (Fig. 19-12). According to an old belief, these are

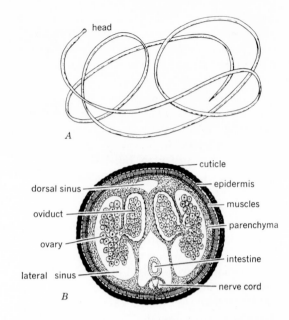

Fig. 19-12. The "horsehair worm," *Gordius* (Class NEMATOMORPHA). *A.* Entire worm. *B.* Cross section of female, enlarged. (*After Kükenthal.*)

horsehairs that have "come to life" in water. Actually they are members of a distinct group, sometimes associated with the NEMATODA but differing by having a lined body cavity filled with parenchyma, one nerve cord, and separate gonads and reproductive ducts. The body wall is relatively stout, the *digestive tract* is

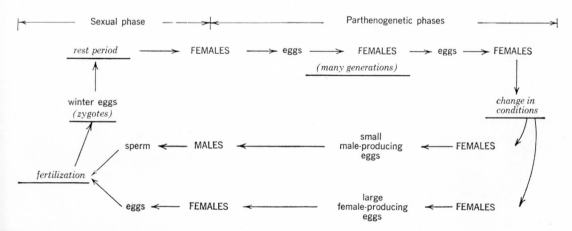

Fig. 19-11. Diagram of the life cycle of a rotifer, *Epiphanes* (*Hydatina*) *senta*.

complete in the young but closed at the ends or degenerate in adults, and there are no circulatory, respiratory, or excretory organs. A *nerve ring* around the esophagus connects to a single midventral *nerve cord*. The sexes are separate, each with two *gonads* with ducts to the cloaca. The female worms deposit long strings of minute eggs from which larvae emerge and bore into aquatic insects. Later larvae may transfer to beetles, crickets, or grasshoppers, and the adults emerge when such insects fall into water.

19-13. Spiny-headed worms (Phylum ACANTHOCEPHALA). These are parasites that live as larvae in arthropods and as adults in vertebrates. The anterior end bears a cylindrical *proboscis* armed with rows of recurved *spines* serving to attach to the gut of its host (Fig. 19-13); in many cases it is easily retracted into a *sheath*. The *body wall* comprises cuticle, epidermis, and circular and longitudinal muscles. The fluid-filled body cavity lacks a digestive tract in both larvae and adults; food is absorbed directly through the body wall. There are no circulatory or respiratory organs; two *nephridia* serve for excretion. There is an anterior *nerve ganglion*. The male has two *testes* discharging into the posterior bursa; the female has no permanent ovary; eggs are freed in the body cavity, fertilized, and covered by membranes, then discharged when embryos are in advanced development. Larvae of some acanthocephs are in crustaceans and the adults in aquatic vertebrates; others use insects and land vertebrates including pigs and man as hosts. Different species are 6 to 650 mm. (26 inches) long when adult.

19-14. Moss animals (Phylum BRYOZOA). Many of the bryozoans (Gr. *bryon,* moss + *zoon,* animal) are tufted or branched colonies, a few millimeters high, and are attached to objects in shallow sea water. Some resemble colonial hydroids and corals in appearance, but their internal structure is much more advanced. Their form suggested the names "moss animals" or "zoophytes" (plant-like animals). Some bryozoans are like mats, and others form thin crusts on rocks, shells, or kelp. All are aquatic, and most of them are marine, but one order is restricted to fresh waters. Bryozoans are known from Lower Ordovician time to the present. Their exoskeletons have aided in forming lime-bearing

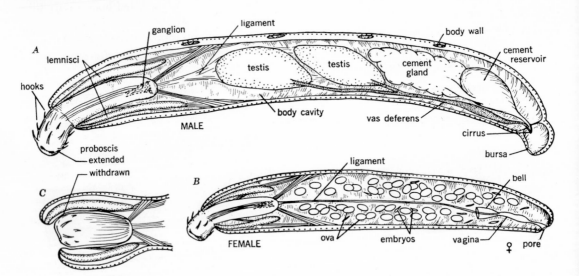

Fig. 19-13. Spiny-headed worm (Phylum ACANTHOCEPHALA). Enlarged and opened to show structure. (*A*) Male. (*B*) Female. (*C*) Anterior end with proboscis retracted. (*After Lynch,* 1936.)

rocks, and they are of economic importance in studying the cores from test wells for petroleum.

Bugula is a common bryozoan that grows as branched brown or purple tufts, 2 or 3 inches long, containing many individuals less than 1 mm. long (Fig. 19-14). Each **zooid** consists of a tubular chitinous housing, or **zooecium,** with the soft living parts, or **polypide,** inside. The anterior end bears a circle of ciliated **tentacles** that sweep in microscopic food organisms and also aid in respiration. The anterior end (introvert) may be entirely withdrawn, like the tip of a glove finger, by **retractor muscles.** The **avicularium,** another type of zooid, has jaws that keep minute animals from settling on the colony surface.

The U- or V-shaped **digestive tract** is complete, with a ciliated lining; the **mouth** is between the tentacles, and the **anus** opens close by. A special muscle (funiculus) draws the stomach aborally. There are no circulatory, respiratory, or excretory organs. The body cavity is a true **coelom,** lined by thin peritoneum and filled with fluid containing corpuscles. Some bryozoans have a **nerve ganglion** near the pharynx with fibers to the tentacles and elsewhere.

Bugula is monoecious; both ovaries and spermaries develop from the coelomic lining, the eggs in a portion of the coelom closed off as a brood pouch, or ooecium. Each egg becomes a ciliated trochophore larva which is liberated in the sea, soon to settle, apical end downward, and found a new colony by asexual budding. The fresh-water forms produce gelatinous housings bearing zooids on the surface, and they have a special mode of asexual reproduction to survive unfavorable conditions. Internal buds called **statoblasts** form in the funiculus and are enclosed in a chitinous shell. Upon the death and decay of the parent colony these are set free in the water either to float or to sink; they can survive freezing or drought and later produce new colonies.

19-15. Lamp shells (Phylum BRACHIOPODA). The brachiopods are like bivalve mollusks in having an external shell of two valves, but these are dorsal and ventral, rather than lateral as in the mollusks. Brachiopods have inhabited the sea bottom since Cambrian time. Their shells are widespread and abundant in rock strata of marine origin and are useful for correlating such deposits. All present-day brachiopods are marine, solitary, and usually attached to the bottom. Most of them are in

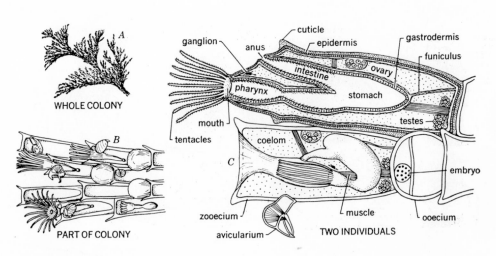

Fig. 19-14. Structure of a bryozoan, *Bugula* (Phylum BRYOZOA). (*A*) Whole colony, natural size. (*B*) Part of colony, enlarged. (*C*) Two individuals in longitudinal section, the upper expanded and the lower contracted.

shallow waters, but a few occur deeper, even down to 18,000 feet. Larvae of bryozoans and brachiopods are modified trochophores, and the lophophore in larval brachiopods resembles comparable structures in phoronids and bryozoans.

A typical brachiopod has the soft *body* between two stout, scoop-shaped limy *valves* (Fig. 19-15). The larger ventral valve has a posterior projecting *beak* perforated for passage of the fleshy stalk, or *peduncle*, by which the animal attaches permanently to the sea bottom. The *body wall* consists of an external epidermis, stout connective tissue, and a ciliated coelomic lining with two double folds extended anteriorly as the dorsal and ventral *mantle lobes*. A large W-shaped *lophophore* lies between the mantle lobes; it is fringed with long ciliated *tentacles* that circulate water in the mantle cavity for respiration and whip small food organisms into a groove leading to the mouth. The *digestive tract* comprises a short gullet, a stomach (with paired digestive glands), and a blind intestine. Three pairs of *muscles* close and open the valves, and two other pairs attaching to the peduncle and shell permit the animal to turn about. The

large fluid-filled *coelom* contains the internal organs, which are supported on mesenteries; branches of it extend into the mantle lobes and lophophore. A small contractile *"heart"* and blood vessels are present. At each side of the intestine is a large *nephridium* for excretion, with a fringed nephrostome opening from the coelom and a small exit into the mantle cavity. A *nerve ring* surrounds the gullet, with nerves to various organs, but special sense organs are absent. The sexes are separate; in each are two *gonads*, dorsal and ventral, respectively, and the nephridia serve as reproductive ducts, discharging eggs and sperm to the exterior. The fertilized egg grows into a free-swimming larva, which later attaches by a structure that becomes the peduncle.

19-16. Arrow Worms (Phylum CHAETOGNATHA). The little torpedo-shaped arrow worms, 20 to 70 mm. long, are often abundant as members of the ocean plankton. Many live no deeper than 100 feet and approach the surface at dusk and dawn when the light intensity is low. They feed actively on small crustaceans, larval fishes, and other small marine life, darting about like arrows. The chaetognaths are

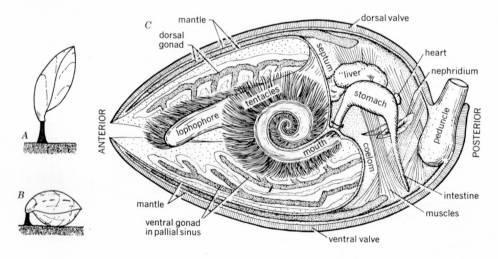

Fig. 19-15. A brachiopod or lamp shell (Phylum **BRACHIOPODA**). (*A, B*) Typical positions of living lamp shells in life. (*C*) *Magellania,* internal structure from left side; shells cut to midline, mantle and lophophore of left side removed. (*A, B, after Twenhofel and Shrock, Invertebrate paleontology, McGraw-Hill Book Co.*)

not segmented, they lack cilia on the epidermis and digestive tract, and the tail is postanal as in no other phylum except the chordates.

The arrow worm (*Sagitta,* Fig. 19-16) has a cylindrical body with **head, trunk,** and **tail** regions, two pairs of **lateral fins,** and a **caudal fin.** The **mouth** is a ventral slit on the head, followed by the muscular **pharynx,** slender, straight **intestine,** and **anus** at the end of the trunk. Each side of the mouth has a lobe with several sickle-shaped hooks, or **bristles,** of chitin that are worked by muscles to serve as jaws in the capture of food, which is swallowed entire. The **coelom** is of three pairs of cavities separated by median **mesenteries.** The **body wall** includes an epidermis of several cell layers, a thin layer of striated muscles, and the single-layered coelomic lining. Four lengthwise bands of **muscles,** two dorsolateral and two ventrolateral, provide for locomotion. The **nervous system** includes a pair of cerebral ganglia dorsal to the pharynx, connectives around the latter, and a ventral ganglion midway of the trunk, with nerves to various parts. Dorsally on the head are two **eyes,** and between them a longitudinal **olfactory organ,** all with nerves to the cerebral ganglia. On the body are small **tactile papillae.**

Chaetognaths are monoecious, and the sex cells are derived from the coelomic epithelium. In each trunk coelom is a solid **ovary,** with a slender **oviduct** opening laterally at the end of the trunk. Each caudal coelom contains a solid **testis** from which immature cells are released to mature as free sperm in the coelom, then collected by the ciliated funnel of a sperm duct opening laterally on the **tail.** Reproduction occurs through much of the year, and fertilization is internal. The young at hatching resembles an adult.

19-17. Tongue Worms (Phylum HEMICHORDATA). The hemichordates are small, soft-bodied animals, of sandy or muddy sea bottoms. They possess paired gill slits, a short structure formerly thought to be a notochord, and dorsal as well as ventral nervous tissue.

The acorn or tongue worms, *Saccoglossus,* etc. (Class ENTEROPNEUSTA) are slender and 25 to 2,500 mm. (1 to 100 inches) long. Most of them live in shallow water; but a few go deeper, even to 2,500 fathoms. They burrow shallowly by means of a soft proboscis. A sticky mucus secreted by glands in the skin causes formation of a tubular case of sand and other debris in which each animal lives. Some tongue worms have persistent and often unpleasant odors.

The body (Fig. 19-17) comprises a **proboscis,** a **collar,** and a long **trunk.** Behind the collar are numerous **gill slits** on either side. Ventral to these is a lateral ridge marking the presence of the gonads. Some species have paired transverse ridges, dorsally behind the gills, that indicate the digestive caeca. The **mouth** opens widely at the anterior ventral margin of the collar, behind the proboscis; a dilated **buccal cavity** follows and then the **pharynx,** with U-shaped openings high on either side that connect to the gill pouches. The straight **intestine,** with dorsal hepatic caeca ("liver sacs"), leads to the terminal **anus.**

The cavities in the proboscis and collar probably fill with water through dorsal pores; when these parts become turgid, the animal burrows through the sand or mud, aided by muscular movements of the trunk. A mixture

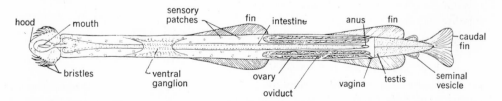

Fig. 19-16. The arrow worm, *Sagitta* (Phylum CHAETOGNATHA). Ventral view; natural size 20 to 70 mm.

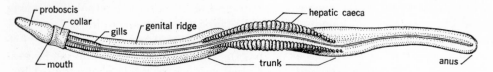

Fig. 19-17. The tongue worm, *Saccoglossus* (Phylum HEMICHORDATA), dorsal view. *(After Spengel.)*

of water and sand containing organic debris enters the mouth; the water passes through the gill slits for respiration, the organic material serves as food, and the sand passes out the anus.

The **circulatory system** includes a middorsal vessel in which colorless blood flows anteriorly (as in annelids) and a midventral vessel. They are joined to a dorsal "heart," and there are other branches near the gill slits. Contractions of the larger vessels probably cause the blood to circulate. A small, unpaired glomerulus, or proboscis gland, is thought to be the **excretory organ.**

The body wall comprises a thick, unicellular epidermis with many mucous cells, beneath which are muscle layers. There is also a small proboscis skeleton. The **nervous system** is of cells and fibers in the base of the epidermis. Concentrations of these provide a middorsal and a midventral nerve "cord" of small size, with a ring-like connective between the two in the collar. A thickened cord, hollow in some species, lies in the collar dorsal to the mouth cavity and has many nerve fibers in the epidermis of the proboscis. The **coelom** is represented by five cavities, one in the proboscis and a pair each in the collar and the trunk.

The sexes are separate, with multiple **gonads** in two dorsolateral rows from near the collar to the gastric caeca; each when mature releases its contents to the exterior through a separate pore, and fertilization is external. In some species the egg produces a small, ovoid tornaria larva, quite transparent, and with surface bands of cilia; at metamorphosis the proboscis and collar become evident. The American species develop directly without a larval stage. Tongue worms can regenerate the trunk region, proboscis, and collar.

Some minute colonial forms (*Cephalodiscus, Rhabdopleura,* Class PTEROBRANCHIA), of deep and shallow seas, resemble the tongue worms in internal structure but have only one pair of gill slits or none, and a crown of ciliated tentacles. *Cephalodiscus* secretes a "housing" that harbors many individuals, each with a U-shaped digestive tract. Pterobranchs reproduce both by budding and sexually. They are similar in appearance to bryozoans.

REVIEW

1. Why is the starfish called an "echinoderm"? What type of symmetry is shown by members of this phylum? Is this symmetry of advantage to echinoderms? Why?
2. What are tube feet, and how are they used?
3. How does a starfish respire? What keeps its "gills" clean?
4. What is a coelom? In what phyla of animals is a well-developed coelom present?
5. How does the larva of a starfish differ from the adult? Of what advantage to a sedentary animal is such a larval stage?
6. In what ways does a sea urchin differ from a starfish as to structure? As to kind of food utilized? Why cannot an urchin take the same sort of foods as a starfish?
7. Why are sea cucumbers classified with starfishes and sea urchins?
8. How do ribbon worms differ from flatworms?
9. Where and how does one search for rotifers? Of what value are they in the animal communities where they live?
10. How do horsehair worms become distributed over the country?
11. Why are "moss animals" not placed low in animal classification?
12. In what conspicuous ways do brachiopods differ from mollusks?

20
Mollusks

Animals of the Phylum MOLLUSCA (L. *mollis*, soft) have soft, unsegmented bodies, typically with an anterior head, ventral muscular foot, and dorsal visceral mass (Fig. 20-1). A thin fleshy layer or mantle more or less surrounds the body, and most mollusks have an external limy shell. The general form of body differs in the several classes. The chitons (Class AMPHINEURA, Order POLYPLACOPHORA) are elliptical, with 8 overlapping dorsal plates surrounded by a fleshy girdle, and they have a large flat foot. The tooth shells (Class SCAPHOPODA) have a slender and slightly tapered tubular shell open at both ends. Snails and slugs (Class GASTROPODA) usually have a long slender foot and a distinct head with tentacles and small eyes; the viscera of snails are enclosed in a single shell, usually of spiral shape, but the shell is either internal or absent in slugs. The oysters, clams, and other bivalves (Class PELECYPODA) are laterally compressed, with a small foot and no head; the body is most often enclosed between a pair of lateral shells hinged dorsally. The squids and octopuses (Class CEPHALOPODA) have a large head, two conspicuous lateral eyes, and slender muscular arms around the mouth; the shell is usually internal or lacking.

The "living fossil," *Neopilina* (Class MONOPLACOPHORA), has a single shell; it is distinctive among mollusks in having segmentally arranged coelomic cavities, nephridia, gills (5 pairs), and muscles.

Mollusks are widely distributed geographically and geologically; there are upward of 65,000 living and 35,000 fossil species; many are represented by enormous populations. Most mollusks are marine, living along the shores and in shallow waters, but some inhabit greater depths, and a few swim in the open ocean. Many snails and some bivalves

Illustration at top of page: A fleshy marine nudibranch (*Dendronotus*) with many-branched dorsal processes and tentacles extended while moving.

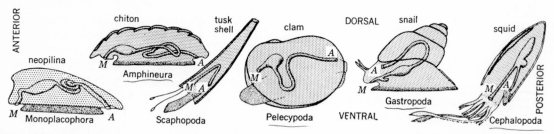

Fig. 20-1. Phylum MOLLUSCA. Relations in the six classes of the shell (heavy lines), foot (stippled), digestive tract (shaded), mouth (*M*), and anus (*A*).

inhabit fresh waters, but other snails and the slugs live on land. The majority of mollusks are free-living and can creep slowly; some attach to rocks, shells, or wood; others burrow, a few float, and the squids can swim freely.

In each class the size varies; extremes for the phylum are minute snails less than 1 mm. in diameter and a giant squid with a 20-foot body and 35-foot tentacles. This squid is the largest invertebrate known (Fig. 1-1).

20-1. Characteristics.

1. Symmetry bilateral, no segmentation (except in *Neopilina*); epithelium with cilia and many mucous glands.
2. Head region developed in gastropods and cephalopods, reduced in others; foot ventral and muscular; body enclosed in a dorsal mantle that secretes the shell (if present).
3. Digestive tract complete, mouth commonly with rasping organ (radula) of minute horny teeth (none in pelecypods); a large digestive gland ("liver"), and generally salivary glands.
4. Heart dorsal, usually in a pericardial sac, auricles 2 or 1, ventricle 1; an anterior aorta and often other blood vessels.
5. Respiration by gills (1 to many), by a lung in the mantle cavity, by the mantle, or by the epidermis.
6. Excretion by kidneys (nephridia), single, or 1 to 5 pairs; coelom usually reduced to cavities within the kidneys and gonads.
7. Nervous system typically with 3 pairs of ganglia (in head, foot, and viscera) and both lengthwise and cross-connectives; sense organs variously for touch, taste, and smell, for sight (eyespots, eyes), and for equilibrium (statocysts).
8. Sexes usually separate; gonads 2 or 1, with ducts; fertilization commonly external; mostly oviparous; development either direct or with larval stages; no asexual reproduction.

NEOPILINA

CLASS *MONOPLACOPHORA*

20-2. Structure and natural history. *Neopilina* has a single oval, cap-shaped *shell* up to 40 mm. long. The ventral surface bears a small head region, rounded flat ciliated foot, and *pallial groove* near the margin. The

anterior *mouth* has a wide flap (velum) at each side and branched tentacles behind; within is a food-rasping organ or *radula* with rows of teeth and a salivary gland. The *stomach* is joined by 2 liver lobes or digestive glands. A coiled intestine leads to the posterior anus. The segmented structures include 5 or 6 pairs of branched *gills* in the pallial groove, the same number of *nephridia,* 5 pairs of *retractor muscles* in the foot, and 5 pairs of *connectives* in the nervous system. The dorsal *heart* receives oxygenated blood from the gills and 2 ventricles connect from anterior blood sinuses. A *nerve ring* around the mouth joins 2 pairs of *nerve cords,* one pair each in the foot and the pallial fold, each with connectives. The 2 *gonads* near the intestine open through the 2 middle pairs of nephridia, the sexes being separate.

Neopilina is a little-known deep sea animal. Specimens dredged at depths of 11,000 feet or more had many radiolarians in the stomach, so the creature may be a detritus feeder. Fossil relatives of this little mollusk have long been known—they lived from the Lower Cambrian to the Devonian Period, 350 to 600 million years ago—and were distinctive in having paired muscle scars. The significance of the group became evident only when living specimens were dredged by the Danish "Galathea" Expedition in 1952. Others since have been dredged.

CHITONS

CLASS *AMPHINEURA*

20-3. Structure and natural history (Fig. 20-2). The chitons are marine, living mainly from the tide lines to moderate depths in coastal waters. The elliptical *body* is covered by 8 overlapping flat limy *plates,* rimmed by a thick, fleshy *girdle,* a part of the *mantle.* A large muscular *foot* serves the chiton for clinging and creeping on rocks. A shallow *pallial groove* between the mantle and foot contains 6 to 80 pairs of slender *gills.* The head region is reduced, lacking eyes and tentacles. The *mouth* contains a rasping organ, or *radula,*

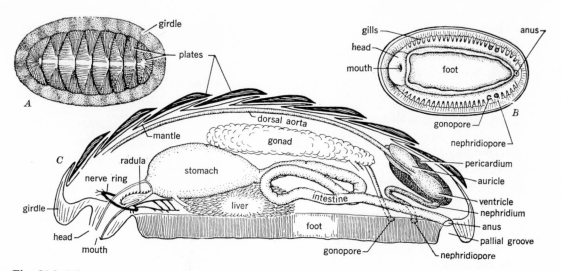

Fig. 20-2. The chiton (Class AMPHINEURA). (*A*) Dorsal view. (*B*) Ventral view. (*C*) Internal structure from the left side, with the shell, mantle, and foot shown in median section.

with many cross rows of fine **teeth** used to scrape the food, of seaweeds and microorganisms, from rocks. There is a short **pharynx,** a rounded **stomach** with connections from the "liver," and a long, coiled **intestine** ending at the **anus** posteriorly in the pallial groove. The **heart** is posterior, of two auricles and one ventricle connecting to an anterior aorta. On either side, a slender **excretory organ** extends from the pericardial cavity to discharge in the pallial groove. There is a **nerve ring** about the mouth, joined to 4 lengthwise **nerve cords** which have many cross-connectives. Some chitons have small **eyespots** or **eyes** in the epidermis over the plates. The sexes are separate, each with a fused **gonad** and 2 **reproductive ducts** discharging laterally in the pallial groove. The eggs are numerous and fertilized externally; development yields a free-swimming larva (trochophore) and then a small chiton. Chitons are eaten by other marine animals and in the West Indies are "sea beef" to local peoples.

TOOTH OR TUSK SHELLS
CLASS *SCAPHOPODA*

20-4. Structure and natural history. The SCAPHOPODA live partly buried in mud or sand

of the sea bottom from shallow waters to depths of 15,000 feet. The shell is usually under 2½ inches long, tubular, slightly tapered, and open at both ends. The pointed foot serves in burrowing. Around the mouth are delicate ciliated "tentacles," with expanded sensory tips that gather the microplants and animals used for food. Strings of empty tooth shells formerly served Pacific coast Indians for money.

SNAILS, SLUGS, ETC.
CLASS *GASTROPODA*

The conspicuous anterior head and long foot of the GASTROPODA (Gr. *gaster,* belly + *podos,* foot) are bilaterally symmetrical, but the visceral mass commonly is coiled and enclosed in a spiral shell, both asymmetrical. Ancestral gastropods probably were bilateral throughout, but in living species the digestive tract, heart, gills, kidneys, and some nervous structures have become rotated, even to 180 degrees, and certain parts have disappeared. This class includes the snails, limpets, whelks, conchs, and others with unchambered shells of one piece (univalve) and the slugs that are usually without a shell.

20-5. Structure. A common gastropod such

as the European brown snail (*Helix aspersa,* Fig. 20-3) has a fleshy **head** bearing two pairs of retractile **tentacles,** one pair of **eyes,** and the **mouth.** Joined directly to the head is the long muscular **foot,** on top of which are the soft internal organs, coiled inside the spiral limy **shell.** On the right side, a **genital pore** opens beside the head; the small **anus** and larger **respiratory pore** are in the soft mantle margin at the edge of the shell. The thin membranous **mantle** secretes and lines the shell and surrounds the viscera within. All exposed soft parts, which are covered by a thin mucus-producing epithelium, can be drawn entirely into the shell by a muscle extending internally to the top or spire.

The **digestive system** comprises (1) the mouth; (2) a muscular pharynx with a horny jaw and a rasping organ (radula) having rows of minute chitinous teeth; (3) a slender esophagus; (4) the large thin-walled crop; (5) a rounded stomach; (6) a long doubly spiraled intestine; and (7) the anus. Salivary glands beside the crop connect by ducts to the pharynx, and a lobed "liver" high in the shell connects to the stomach. Instead of gills, the land snail has a **lung** formed by a net of blood vessels lining the outer wall of the **mantle cavity;** air enters and leaves the cavity by the respiratory pore. Blood from the body is aerated in the lung, then pumped by the **heart** through arteries to the head, foot, and viscera. A single **kidney** drains from the pericardial sac surrounding the heart and discharges into the mantle cavity. Paired **nerve ganglia** are grouped around the pharynx and connect to nerves serving the various organs. The tip of each posterior tentacle bears an **eye** and probably an olfactory organ; two organs of equilibrium, or **statocysts,** lie anteriorly in the foot, and the epidermis probably contains other sensory structures.

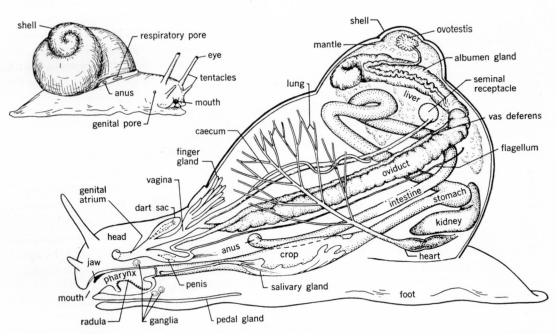

Fig. 20-3. Brown garden snail, *Helix aspersa* (Class GASTROPODA). (*A*) External features from the right side. (*B*) Internal structure from the left side. The lung is indicated by the branching blood vessels of the mantle cavity that connect to the heart.

Each snail has a combined male and female *reproductive system.* High in the shell is the *ovotestis,* producing both eggs and sperm. In the female system a duct from the ovotestis connects to the *albumen gland;* from the latter a large *oviduct* enters the *vagina,* which in turn leads to the common *genital atrium.* Connecting to the vagina is the duct of the *seminal receptacle* and also the *finger gland* and *dart sac.* In the male system sperm from the ovotestis pass through a *vas deferens* to the *penis,* located in a sac off the genital atrium.

20-6. Natural history. The snail is most active by night and in moist weather. By waves of contraction moving forward in the muscular foot, a snail glides slowly on a "slime track" secreted by a gland anterior in the foot. The food is of green vegetation that is moistened by the saliva, held by the jaw, and rasped to bits by the minute teeth of the radula. By day the snail withdraws its head and foot into the shell and hides in a crevice or some burrow; during dry weather a temporary covering (epiphragm) is secreted over the shell aperture so as to avoid desiccation.

Mating is preceded by a performance of "dart" exchange between two snails; then each inserts its penis into the vagina of the other individual for reciprocal transfer of sperm, following which the snails separate. Later batches of separate gelatinous-covered eggs are deposited by each in a damp place, and after many days minute snails hatch from these eggs.

20-7. Other gastropods. The many kinds of univalve mollusks vary in size, form, and habits (Fig. 20-4). More primitive types were marine; then evidently some migrated to fresh water and the land to become lung breathers. Today gastropods abound in salt and fresh waters and on land from the tropics to subpolar regions, even on deserts, and from 18,000 feet up in some mountains to 25,000 feet down in the sea.

Although mainly herbivorous, some are predatory, boring into and eating other mollusks, and a few are parasitic. Many snails are the necessary intermediate hosts for trematode flatworms (Chap. 18). Univalves are eaten by various vertebrates and invertebrates and by primitive peoples; one species is a delicacy among the French. Shells of various univalves

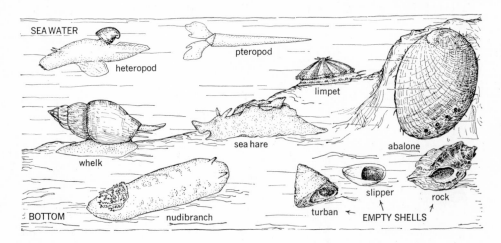

Fig. 20-4. Some marine gastropods in life, and some empty shells: *Fissurella,* limpet; *Haliotis,* abalone; *Crepidula,* slipper shell; *Tegula,* turban shell; *Carinaria,* heteropod; *Murex,* rock shell; *Buccinum,* edible whelk; *Aplysia,* sea hare; *Clione,* pteropod; *Doris,* nudibranch.

have been the "money" of native races, an example being the wampum of American Indians.

BIVALVES: CLAMS, MUSSELS, OYSTERS, ETC. CLASS *PELECYPODA*

Members of this class are bilaterally symmetrical, with the soft body compressed between two lateral shells that are hinged dorsally. "Bivalves" lack a head and have a wedge-shaped foot (Gr. *pelekys*, hatchet + *podos*, foot). These animals inhabit both salt and fresh waters; some creep, others burrow in sand or mud, and certain types attach to rocks. A fresh-water clam (Figs. 20-5, 20-6) will illustrate the anatomy of this class.

20-8. Structure. The somewhat oval *shells*, which protect the soft body, are marked by concentric growth lines centered around a swelling (the umbo) near the anterior dorsal edge. A dorsal *hinge ligament* holds the shells together dorsally and tends to make them separate ventrally. The interior surface of each valve has scars indicating points where the several muscles attach. These muscles act to close the valves and to extend or contract the foot.

The soft *body* consists of a plump median *visceral mass* containing various organs, and its anteroventral part forms the muscular *foot*. On each side there is a pair of thin, plate-like *gills*, and the body is surrounded by a lobe of the *mantle*. Each mantle lobe is a thin tissue adhering to the valve which it secreted; the free muscular margins of the mantle can be brought together to enclose the *mantle cavity* within. Posteriorly the mantle margins form two openings (Fig. 20-5B, C), a larger ventral *incurrent siphon* and a dorsal *excurrent siphon*.

The *digestive system* includes (1) a small mouth between two thin flaps (palps); (2) a short esophagus; (3) a rounded stomach which receives ducts from (4) a paired digestive gland or liver; (5) a slender coiled intestine; (6) a dorsal rectum surrounded by the heart; and (7) the anus opening into the excurrent siphon. A pouch near the stomach often contains a transparent rod (crystalline style) producing a starch-splitting enzyme useful in digesting plankton.

The *circulatory system* consists of a dorsal *heart* of 2 auricles and a muscular ventricle, enclosed in a sac (pericardial cavity). From the ventricle, blood is pumped through the anterior and posterior *aortas* to all parts of the animal, carrying nutrients and oxygen to

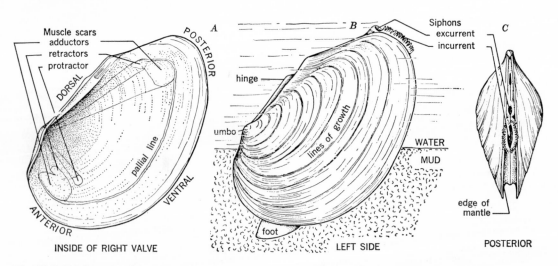

Fig. 20-5. Fresh-water clam, *Anodonta* (Class PELECYPODA). Shell and external features. Lines radiating from the umbo show the path of the muscle attachments as the shell grows in size.

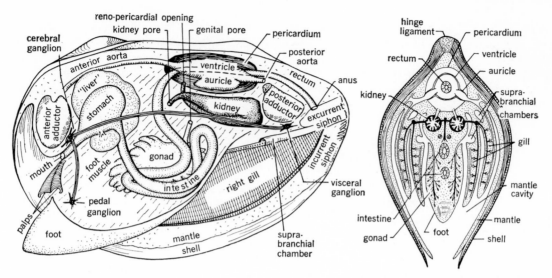

Fig. 20-6. Fresh-water clam, *Anodonta*. (*A*) Internal structure as seen with shell, mantle, and gills of the left side removed. (*B*) Cross section through the heart region. Both diagrammatic. (*B, after Stempell.*)

the tissues; in the kidneys organic wastes are extracted for excretion. Some of the blood returns in veins and some enters tissue spaces, then diffuses back to the heart; hence this is an "open" blood system.

The *gills* (Fig. 20-7) are the chief respiratory organs, aided by the mantle. Water is drawn into the incurrent siphon, passed through *pores* (ostia) in the gills, and the oxygen–carbon dioxide exchange occurs there. From the ostia, water tubes lead dorsally to a chamber connecting with the excurrent siphon.

Each *kidney* is U-shaped and drains waste from the pericardial cavity to discharge into the suprabranchial chamber.

The *nervous system* includes three pairs of nerve ganglia connecting with nerves to various organs. The *sensory structures* include light receptors in the mantle margin, organs of equilibrium (statocysts) in the foot, tactile organs, and chemoreceptors for testing water entering the incurrent siphon. If the silt content is high, water intake is reduced.

The sexes are separate but alike externally, with 2 branched *gonads* in the visceral mass.

20-9. Natural history. The fresh-water clam

lives in sand and mud or wedged between rocks, with the valves slightly spread, mantle margins closed, and the siphons exposed (Fig. 20-5*B*). Water containing food and oxygen is drawn through the incurrent siphon into the mantle cavity, where organic particles and microorganisms are trapped in mucus on the gills and mantle; this food is carried forward to the mouth by ciliary action. The water then passes through the gills and out the excurrent siphon. This bivalve can travel slowly by extending the foot, expanding it as an anchor, and then drawing the body forward.

20-10. Reproduction. Most bivalves discharge their eggs and sperm into the water, where fertilization occurs and microscopic larvae result, later to acquire a shell and become a miniature of the species. In the fresh-water clams and mussels, however, the gills of females become specialized as brood sacs that receive the mature ova. Sperm from males enter with inflowing water to fertilize the eggs, and a minute larva (glochidium; Fig. 20-8) develops. Then these larvae pass out the excurrent siphon into the water, where they attach to the gills or epidermis of fresh-water fishes. Once attached, a capsule forms over

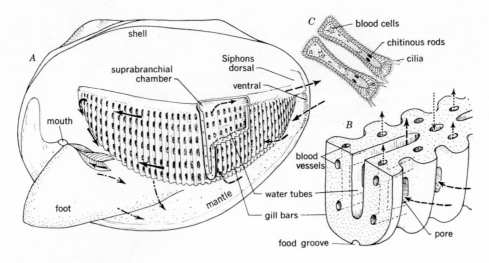

Fig. 20-7. Fresh-water clam. Diagrams of gill structure. (A) Outer left gill partly cut away to show internal structure. ←——, path of water; ←—, path of food particles caught in mucus and carried to mouth; ←·—·, path of rejected particles. (B) Portion of gill enlarged. ←·····, path of blood flow, down in afferent and up in efferent vessels. (C) Cross section of 2 gill bars much enlarged to show ciliated surfaces and blood cells.

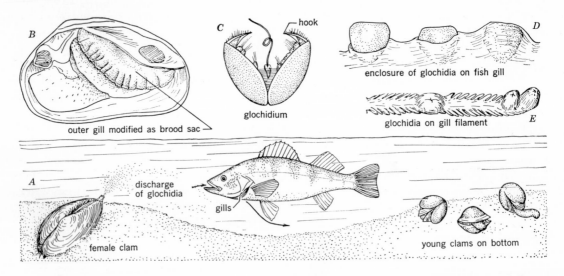

Fig. 20-8. Fresh-water clam. (A) Diagram of the life cycle. (B) The female's outer gill modified as a brood sac. (C) One glochidium. (D) Enclosure of glochidia by epithelium on gill of a fish. (E) Glochidia on a gill filament. (B–D, after Lefevre and Curtis, 1910.)

each young parasite, which then is nourished by the host's body fluids until it becomes a small clam and escapes to become free-living. Dispersal of these bivalves becomes possible by this peculiar larval existence on fishes. The hazards in reproduction are great for bivalves, and large numbers of eggs are produced—thousands in a fresh-water clam and 16 to 60 million in one oyster during a single season.

20-11. Other pelecypods. Most bivalves are marine and are commonest from the tide line into shallow waters, but some occur down to depths of 33,000 feet. The great majority live on the sea bottom or in burrows in mud or sand. A few burrow in clay or soft rock, oysters and others attach permanently to rocks or shells, and the slender shipworms or teredos tunnel into the wood of ships or wharves (Fig. 20-9). A few species are commensal or parasitic.

20-12. Relations to man. Bivalves have served mankind as food for untold centuries, and many coasts have "shell mounds" of the relics. One Indian mound on San Francisco Bay contained more than 1,000,000 cubic feet of discarded shells accumulated over an estimated 3,500 years. The United States annually harvests more than 136,000,000 pounds of oys-

ters, clams, scallops, and mussels valued at upward of $47,000,000. Good natural oyster beds in shallow waters are highly valued, and young (spat) are planted regularly to replace the adult oysters taken by tongs or dredges. Crushed oystershell is used in road building and in rations for poultry and other domestic animals. Various kinds of clams are dug by hand, and in many places there is a limit as to size, number, and season of take to conserve the stocks.

In many bivalves, if a small bit of material lodges between the mantle and shell, thin layers of shell lining (nacre) are secreted around the object to form a pearl. These may develop in fresh-water clams or in certain oysters, but the most valuable types occur in marine oysters of eastern Asia. The Japanese artificially introduce small particles under the mantle and then retain the bivalves in cages for several years until "culture" pearls are formed. "Pearl" buttons for clothing are cut from the shells of fresh-water clams.

The burrowing by teredos in wooden wharves or boats sometimes results in serious damage, which can be avoided only by covering the wood with special paints or metal, or by using concrete for piling.

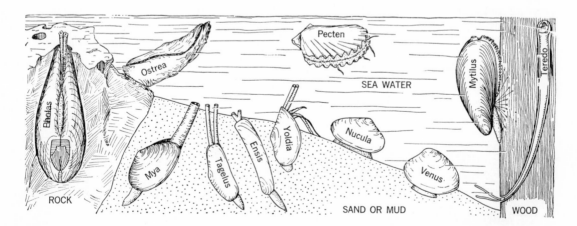

Fig. 20-9. Positions of some marine pelecypods in life; reduced but not to same scale. *Nucula; Yoldia; Ostrea,* edible oyster; *Mytilus,* sea mussel with byssus; *Pecten,* scallop; *Mya,* mud clam; *Venus,* quahog; *Tagelus,* jackknife clam; *Ensis,* razor clam; *Pholas,* rock borer; *Teredo,* pileworm or shipworm.

SQUIDS, OCTOPUSES, ETC.
CLASS *CEPHALOPODA*

The most highly developed mollusks are the CEPHALOPODA (Gr. *kephale,* head + *podos,* foot). A common example is the squid of coastal salt waters.

20-13. Structure and natural history (Fig. 20-10). The *body* is slenderly conical, enclosed by the muscular *mantle,* and bearing 2 triangular *fins* posteriorly. The *head* is large, having 2 conspicuous *eyes* and a central *mouth* surrounded by 10 slender flexible *arms* that bear suckers. A horny *"pen"* (the shell) stiffens the body, and cartilage-like material encloses the brain and supports the neck region. From the mantle cavity around the internal organs a tubular *siphon* opens below the neck. Water drawn into the mantle cavity can be forcibly ejected through the siphon for jet or rocket locomotion, the animal moving forward or backward, according to the direction of the siphon (Fig. 20-11). The fins serve for both steering and swimming.

The *digestive system* includes (1) the mouth; (2) a muscular pharynx with 2 horny, beak-like *jaws* and a rasping organ (radula) bearing rows of small teeth; (3) a long esophagus; (4) a muscular stomach and thin-walled caecum; and (5) a slender intestine ending at (6) the anus, which opens into the mantle cavity. Salivary glands connect to the pharynx;

a liver and a pancreas join by ducts to the stomach. The squid eats crustaceans, mollusks, and fishes, grasping them with its arms, biting with the jaws, and rasping the food with its teeth.

Connected to the intestine is an *ink sac* containing dark fluid which can be discharged through the siphon to produce an aquatic "smoke screen" aiding the squid to escape enemies. Inside the mantle cavity are two *gills* for respiration. Blood from the body tissues is carried by veins to the *branchial heart* and pumped through the gill capillaries; then it goes to two auricles and a ventricle of the *systemic heart* to be sent through arteries to all parts of the body. A pair of *kidneys* are the excretory organs. The *brain* is located above the pharynx; besides organs for equilibrium (statocysts), the squid has an *eye* unique among invertebrates in that it can form a real image.

The sexes are separate. The female produces heavily yolked eggs that are fertilized within the mantle cavity and then laid in long gelatinous capsules. There is no larva, the young emerging as miniature adults.

20-14. Other cephalopods. This class has swarmed the seas since Cambrian times; and fully 10,000 fossil species are known. The living cephalopods are all predaceous and mainly free-swimming (Fig. 20-11). Most familiar are the squids and octopuses. The

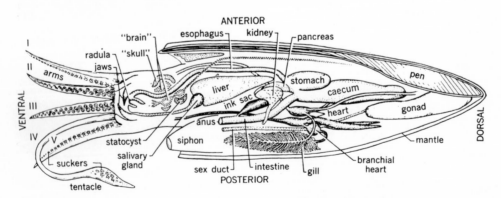

Fig. 20-10. The squid, *Loligo* (Class CEPHALOPODA). Internal structure as seen with body wall and arms removed on left side.

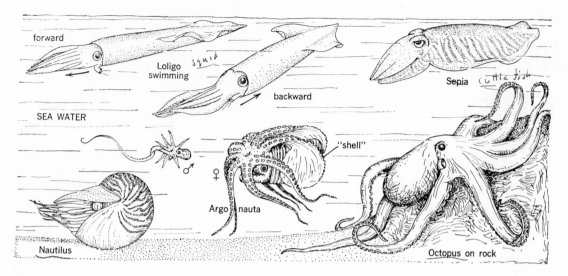

forward

Loligo swimming *squid*

backward

SEA WATER

Sepia *cuttle fish*

"shell"

Argo nauta

♂ ♀

Nautilus

Octopus on rock

Fig. 20-11. Representative cephalopods. *Loligo,* squid; *Sepia,* cuttlefish; *Nautilus,* pearly nautilus; *Argonauta,* paper nautilus; *Octopus,* octopus. Variously reduced.

larger species are more properly feared for their powerful jaws than their supposed ability to squeeze with their arms. Small squid often occur in huge schools; they are eaten by other marine animals and are used for both fish bait and food by mankind. The octopuses have a bulbous body, no shell, and eight long sucker-bearing arms. Usually they crawl on the bottom in tide pools, but they can swim by use of the siphon.

REVIEW

1. What are the common characteristics of the Phylum MOLLUSCA?
2. Tabulate the distinctive features of the 6 classes of mollusks as to shell, mouth parts, type of food used, manner of respiration and locomotion.
3. In a garden snail, what are the functions of the mantle, radula, foot, and statocyst?
4. How is reproduction in a land snail different from that in a fresh-water clam.
5. Describe the processes of feeding and of respiration in the fresh-water clam.
6. Of what particular value to the species is the glochidial stage in a fresh-water bivalve?
7. Which of the bivalve mollusks are of major economic value?
8. What structural features of a squid link it with other mollusks? Of what special advantage are the arms, siphon, and ink sac?

21 Segmented worms

In contrast to the worms previously discussed, those of the Phylum ANNELIDA (L. *annelus,* little ring) have bodies composed of many essentially similar segments or somites, usually evident both externally and internally. The earthworms (Class OLIGOCHAETA) live chiefly in damp soils, the marine worms (POLYCHAETA) in seashore areas, and the leeches (HIRUDINEA) in fresh waters or on moist ground.

Many annelids are free-living, others burrow or live in tubes, some are commensal on other aquatic animals, and a few are parasites of vertebrates. The common earthworms are mostly small, only a few inches long, but in Ecuador and Australia there are giant species growing to more than 7 feet long and 1 inch in diameter; by contrast the smallest species are under 1 mm. in length. The marine annelids vary from some of minute size up to a California species 5½ feet long. Different leeches range from 10 to 200 mm. in length, but most of them are small.

21-1. Characteristics.

1. Symmetry bilateral; body long and conspicuously segmented both internally and externally.
2. Appendages of minute chitinous rods or bristles (setae) on each segment (lacking in some forms); POLYCHAETA with tentacles on the head and setae on fleshy lateral lobes (parapodia).
3. Body covered by moist cuticle over a sensory glandular epithelium.
4. Body wall and digestive tract both with layers of circular and longitudinal muscles; body cavity (coelom) well developed (except leeches) and usually subdivided by septa.
5. Digestive tract complete, tubular, extending throughout the body.
6. Circulatory system closed, of longitudinal vessels, with branches to each segment; blood plasma with hemoglobin or other respiratory pigments.
7. Respiration by skin, or by gills in some tube dwellers.
8. Excretory system typically a pair of nephridia per body segment.
9. Nervous system of anterior dorsal brain (paired cerebral ganglia) connecting to midventral nerve cord extending the length of body, with ganglia and branches in each segment; touch, taste, and light perception cells present.
10. Sexes united and development direct; or sexes separate with larval stage; reproduction by budding in some species.

The annelids resemble the arthropods in having a segmented body covered by a cuticle secreted by the epidermis, in the pattern of the nervous system, and in the manner of mesoderm formation. They differ in having little or no specialization of body segments, simple

Illustration at top of page: A marine tube-dwelling annelid worm (sabellid), removed from its housing, with feathery tentacles (gills) on anterior end.

unjointed appendages, a large body cavity (coelom), a closed blood system, and no succession of larval stages.

EARTHWORMS, ETC.

CLASS *OLIGOCHAETA*

This group includes worms with few bristle-like setae per segment (L. *oligos,* few + *chaete,* spine). The common large earthworm of Europe and eastern North America (*Lumbricus terrestris*) is used for the following description.

21-2. External features. The cylindrical body (Fig. 21-1) may be up to 12 inches long and ⅜ inch in diameter and bluntly rounded at each end; the ventral surface is slightly flattened and paler in color. There is no distinct head. The entire body is conspicuously divided by transverse grooves into about 150 (115–200) ring-like *somites.* The **mouth** is in somite I (just behind the anterior lobe, or prostomium) and the **anus** in the last somite. Over somites XXXII to XXXVII there is a glandular swelling, the *clitellum,* that secretes a cocoon to contain eggs. On each somite except the first and last there are 4 pairs of minute bristles, or *setae;* each is secreted by a special cell, and each seta can be extended or retracted or moved in any direction by internal muscles. The setae serve as holdfasts when a worm is in its burrow or moving over the ground.

Besides the mouth and anus there are many small external openings on the body: (1) a **dorsal pore** connecting the body cavity and exterior in each groove between somites (from somite VIII or IX to the anal end); (2) one pair of excretory openings, or **nephridiopores,** lateroventrally on each somite (except I to III and the last); (3) two pairs of openings from the *seminal receptacles* laterally in grooves between somites IX to X and X to XI; (4) two openings from the **oviducts** ventrally on somite XIV; and (5) two openings from the **sperm ducts** on somite XV.

The body is covered by a thin **cuticle** secreted by the **epidermis** and moistened by mucus from the one-celled epidermal glands. Under the epidermis there is a thin layer of **circular muscles** and a thicker layer of **longitudinal muscles.** The opposing and varying contractions of these muscles over the fluid-filled body produces the many kinds of movements seen in the living worm. There is no skeleton.

21-3. Internal structure. The earthworm body is essentially of two concentric tubes (Figs. 21-2, 21-3), the outer **body wall** and straight **digestive tract** inside. The space between is the body cavity or **coelom,** which is divided into a series of ring-like compartments by thin transverse partitions, or **septa,** between the somites. The body cavity and all organs within it are lined with a thin smooth epithelium (peritoneum).

21-4. Digestive system. This consists of (1) the **mouth opening** and **mouth cavity** (somites I to III); (2) a short **pharynx** (somites IV to V) surrounded by a firm bulb of muscle fibers and glands; (3) the slender **esophagus** (somites VI to XIV); (4) a spherical thin-walled **crop** (proventriculus, somites XV, XVI); (5) the **gizzard** (somites XVII, XVIII)

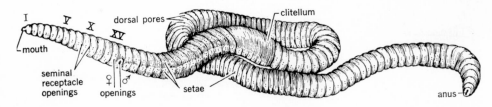

Fig. 21-1. The earthworm, *Lumbricus terrestris* (Class OLIGOCHAETA); external features. I–XV, somites.

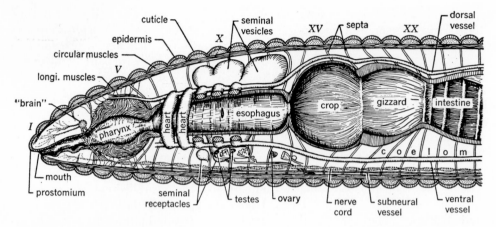

Fig. 21-2. Earthworm. Internal structure of anterior portion from the left side; body wall and digestive tract cut in median section. Two hearts, shown in place; nephridia omitted; reproductive organs of right side included. I–XX, somites.

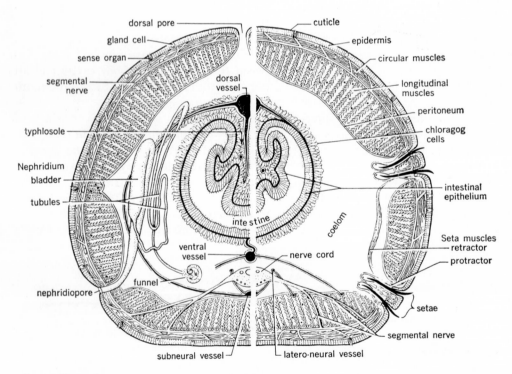

Fig. 21-3. Earthworm. Cross section. Left half shows an entire nephridium and a dorsal pore but omits setae; right half includes setae but no nephridium.

with heavy muscular wall and lined internally with cuticle; and (6) the long *intestine,* which continues to (7) the *anus.* The intestine is thin-walled and bulges laterally in each somite; from its dorsal side there is an infolded *typhlosole,* which, with the bulges, provides additional surface for the digestion and the absorption of food.

The food, chiefly leafy vegetation, is moistened by secretions of the pharynx and drawn into the mouth by muscular action. It is stored temporarily in the crop and then ground up in the muscular gizzard, where any sand present aids in the process. Enzymes secreted by the digestive epithelium serve to digest the food, which is then absorbed in the intestine; residues are passed out the anus. Small animals on the ground may be eaten, and any organic material in the earth is utilized by the worm while "eating" a new burrow.

21-5. Circulatory and respiratory systems. The *blood* consists of a fluid *plasma* containing a dissolved respiratory pigment (hemoglobin; responsible for the red color), and free, colorless *corpuscles* (amoebocytes). The blood circulates in a closed system of *blood vessels.* The principal longitudinal vessels are: (1) dorsal, above the digestive tract from the pharynx to the posterior end; (2) ventral, between the digestive tract and nerve cord; (3) a lateroneural on each side of the nerve cord; and (4) a subneural below the nerve cord. Each somite contains paired transverse vessels in the intestinal wall and body wall. Five pairs of hearts connect the dorsal and ventral vessels in somites VII to XI. Pulsations in the dorsal vessel and hearts are responsible for blood flow.

There is no organized respiratory system. The blood receives oxygen and gives up carbon dioxide in fine capillaries close under the moist cuticle of the body wall. Oxygen combines with the hemoglobin and is carried to various tissues. Blood flows forward in the dorsal vessel and backward in the ventral vessels.

21-6. Excretory system. Every somite (ex-cept I to III and the last) contains a pair of coiled tubular excretory organs or *nephridia* (Fig. 21-4). Each of these occupies parts of two successive somites. A ciliated funnel (nephrostome) lies in the anterior somite just before the septum, a duct penetrates the septum, and in the posterior somite the tube, coiled and well supplied with capillaries, ends in an enlarged bladder that discharges through an excretory pore (nephridiopore). Cilia in the funnel draw wastes from the coelom, and organic wastes from the blood capillaries diffuse into the nephridium to be passed out the excretory pore.

21-7. Nervous system (Fig. 21-5). Above the pharynx is the brain of two suprapharyngeal (cerebral) *ganglia,* which has lateral *connectives* around the pharynx joining the midventral *nerve cord;* the latter extends backward to the posterior end, having swollen *ganglia* and three pairs of lateral *nerves* in each somite. The cord and ganglia appear to be single but actually are paired structures. There are numerous nerves from the brain to the mouth region and anterior end of the body. The epidermis contains *sense organs,*

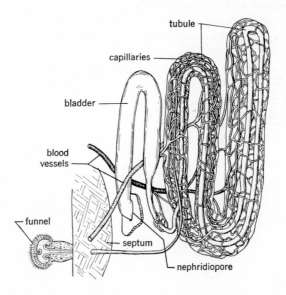

Fig. 21-4. Excretory organ of the earthworm, an entire nephridium, enlarged.

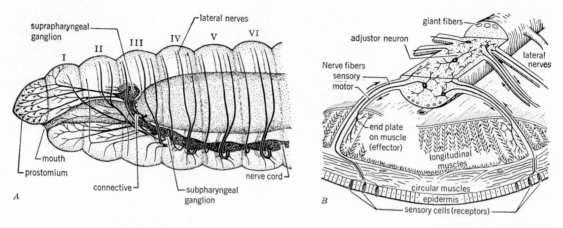

Fig. 21-5. Earthworm. Nervous system. (*A*) Ganglia and larger nerves of the anterior end. (*After Hess,* 1925.) (*B*) Stereogram of the ventral nerve cord and body wall to show a simple reflex arc. Sensory cells (receptors) in the epidermis connect to sensory fibers that pass in a lateral nerve to the nerve cord; the sensory axon joins through a synapse to a motor nerve that leads to the body muscles (effector). Arrows indicate the direction of nerve impulses.

each with a special sense cell projecting through the epidermis; and light perception cells are present.

21-8. Reproductive system. Each individual contains both male and female sex organs (Fig. 21-6). The *male system* includes (1) two pairs of small *testes,* and back of each (2) a *sperm funnel* connecting to (3) a short *vas efferens.* The two ducts on each side connect to (4) a larger *vas deferens* leading to (5) the *male pore* on somite XV. The testes and fun-

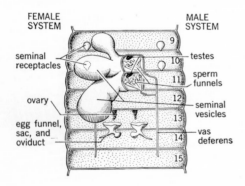

Fig. 21-6. Reproductive system of the earthworm, dorsal view (other organs omitted). Seminal vesicles cut away on right side.

nels are contained in (6) two pairs of large *seminal vesicles* in which sperm from the testes mature before being discharged during copulation. The paired *female system* consist of (1) two *ovaries* discharging mature ova into the body cavity, from which they are picked up by (2) *ciliated funnels* leading to (3) the *oviducts,* which open to the exterior on somite XIV. The female system also includes (4) two pairs of small spherical *seminal receptacles* (opening in somites IX and X), in which sperm received during copulation are stored until needed to fertilize eggs in cocoons.

21-9. Natural history. Earthworms occur over most of the world, being more numerous in good soils with much humus and abundant moisture. They inhabit burrows for protection from the weather and enemies and may penetrate 6 or 8 feet below the surface to avoid extremes of heat, cold, or drought. In heavy soil the worm excavates by literally eating its way; ingested earth is passed through the digestive tract and deposited at the surface in small mounds or "castings." In humus and soft topsoil the animal wedges its way between particles.

In moist soil of moderate temperature a

worm will lie near the upper end of a burrow by day, anterior end uppermost. At night it extends out to explore, forage, or mate, but the setae on posterior segments hold fast within the burrow so the worm may quickly withdraw if frightened. At times the worm entirely quits the burrow to travel on the surface. Flooding or a heavy rain may cause many to emerge.

Experiments show that earthworms react negatively to light and to dryness but positively to contact, especially on soil, and to moisture. They are sensitive to mechanical vibrations such as footsteps on the ground, but evidently do not "hear" mere sound vibrations in air. They remain hidden from daylight and at night withdraw quickly if a light is flashed on them. When turned up by a garden spade, they quickly seek the dark and moisture within the soil.

21-10. Reproduction. Earthworms reproduce through much of the year but most actively in warm, moist weather. Mating occurs at night and requires 2 to 3 hours. Two worms stretch out of their burrows to bring their ventral surfaces together, the anterior ends in opposite directions (Fig. 21-7). Special ventral setae of each penetrate the other to aid in holding them together; then each secretes a slime tube about itself. Sperm are exchanged, passing from somite XV of the one along ventral grooves on its body to enter the seminal receptacles of the other; thus there is reciprocal cross-fertilization. The worms then separate. Later the clitellum of each secretes a cocoon, which the eggs enter; then as the cocoon slips forward, sperm from the seminal receptacles enter to fertilize the eggs. The worm slips out of the cocoon, which closes to form a case that is deposited in damp earth. The young worms develop directly in several weeks.

21-11. Relations to man. Earthworms are used as bait for fishing, and there is much commercial culture for this market. On lawns and golf greens worm castings can be a nuisance, and control by poison has been used.

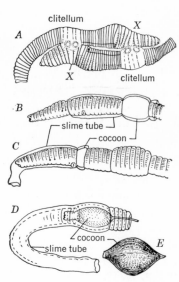

Fig. 21-7. Earthworm. Mating and cocoon. (*A*) Two earthworms in copulation (X = 10th somite). (*B*) Secretion of slime tube and cocoon. (*C*) Slime tube and cocoon slip forward. (*D*) Free tube containing cocoon. (*E*) Cocoon. (*A, after Grove*, 1925; *B–D, after Foot and Strobell*, 1902.)

Ancient medical writers mention irrational uses of earthworms in human medicine, and some of these are still followed in parts of Japan and China.

In nature the long-time effects of earthworms have certain practical values. In many soils thousands are present per acre, and their burrowing during most of the year turns over much surface soil. According to Charles Darwin, in favorable locations they may bring up 18 tons of soil per acre in a year, and a layer of cinders or gravel may be completely covered by the castings over a period of years. In extreme instances, the burrows may cause water seepage through irrigation ditches or increase soil erosion on sloping lands, but generally worm cultivation helps by turning over the top portion and allowing air and water to penetrate. Indeed, the depth of arable topsoil in less fertile areas may be gradually increased by the worms. Claims that adding cultures of earthworms to soil in gardens or orchards will give rapid increase in soil fertility are not true.

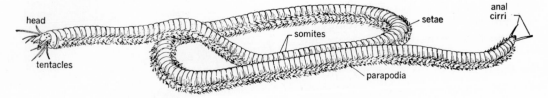

Fig. 21-8. Clamworm, *Neanthes virens* (Class POLYCHAETA). External features.

21-12. Other oligochaetes. This class includes upward of 2,400 species, which variously inhabit damp lake banks, fresh and foul waters, or the bottoms of deep lakes; a few live on the seashore or shallowly in salt water. Some are native in high mountains or Arctic snow fields. Many oligochaetes are food for birds, moles, fishes, and some invertebrates. Earthworms serve as intermediate hosts for a few parasites of domestic fowls and pigs.

MARINE WORMS
CLASS *POLYCHAETA*

The POLYCHAETA (Gr., many bristles) are common along seacoasts, where some are free-living and others inhabit tubes in sand or mud. The clamworm (*Neanthes, Nereis;* Fig. 21-8) is a common representative.

21-13. Structure and natural history. The long, slender, greenish *body,* of many similar *somites,* is rounded above and flattened ventrally. Unlike the earthworm, there is a dif-

ferentiated *head* with soft *tentacles,* two pairs of *eyes,* and the *mouth* (Fig. 21-9) with *jaws.* On either side of each somite there is a bilobed *parapodium,* bearing a bundle of *setae.*

The body is covered with firm *cuticle* over the *epidermis;* next within is a thin layer of *circular muscles,* then four bundles of *longitudinal muscles* (Fig. 21-10). The body cavity or *coelom* is lined with peritoneum and separated into somites by transverse *septa.* The *digestive tract* comprises the mouth, pharynx, esophagus, and stomach-intestine, there being no crop or gizzard. The pharyngeal region may be extended to form a proboscis. The food is of small animals.

The closed *circulatory system* includes single dorsal and ventral vessels with connectives and branches to all parts of the body, but no hearts. Blood plasma containing hemoglobin is pumped through the body by contractions of the dorsal vessel. *Respiration* takes place in capillaries of the parapodia and body wall, and *excretion* is by many pairs of nephridia.

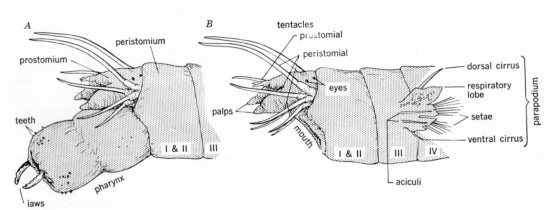

Fig. 21-9. Clamworm, *Neanthes.* Head region from the left side. (*A*) Pharynx extended. (*B*) Pharynx retracted.

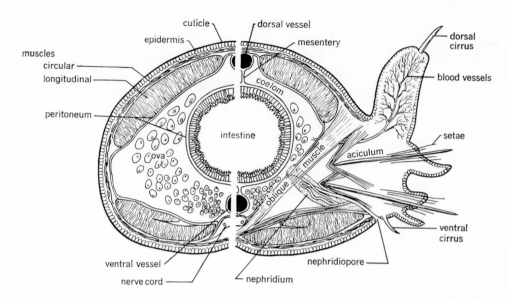

Fig. 21-10. Clamworm. Diagrammatic cross section. Left half with ova free in coelom; right half through parapodium.

The **nervous system** includes a "brain," nerves to the head and tentacles, connectives to the midventral nerve cord, and ganglia and nerves in each somite.

The sexes are separate, and **gonads** are present only during the breeding season. Eggs and sperm form on the peritoneum and when mature pass out through the nephridia or burst through the body wall. Fertilization occurs in the sea, and a minute ciliated larva is produced which later transforms into the young worm.

A few polychaetes inhabit fresh water, but most of them are marine, living from the tide lines down to more than 120 feet; a few go to greater depths. Various species crawl on the bottom, swim in the open sea, live amid rocks or plants, in temporary burrows, or inhabit permanent tubes. The free-ranging polychaetes are mainly carnivorous, some burrowing forms feed on bottom muck, and tube dwellers subsist largely on plankton.

Tube dwellers make various kinds of housing for themselves. Some plaster the walls with sand grains or bits of shell, held in place by mucus. Some secrete limy tubes attached to rocks. *Chaetopterus* makes a U-shaped parch-ment-like tube in muddy or sandy bottoms; the worm's body has specialized parapodia serving as fans to draw in water containing food and oxygen. The palolo worm (*Eunice*) has its burrows in coral reefs. At mating time both sexes emerge to swim at night, when the posterior somites of the body, in both males and females, laden with ripe sperm and eggs, are cast off and the gametes burst out.

LEECHES
CLASS *HIRUDINEA*

Leeches are familiar to most students because history tells of their medical use for bloodletting in the early days of the United States and in nineteenth-century Europe.

21-14. Structure. The **body** of a leech at rest is slender or oval and flattened dorsoventrally (Fig. 21-11). It comprises 34 **somites** (7 or 8 condensed in posterior sucker), but many more furrows mark the exterior. Anterior and posterior **suckers** are present, but there are no setae on the cuticle-covered body. An elaborate and powerful **muscular system** gives the animal great flexibility, permitting it to stretch, contract, and dilate.

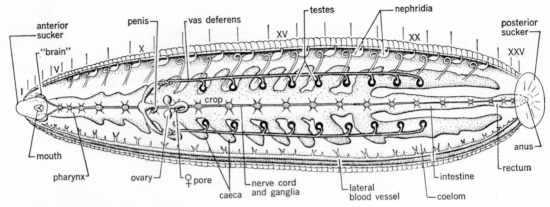

Fig. 21-11. The medicinal leech, *Hirudo medicinalis* (Class Hirudinea). Internal structure as seen in dissection from the ventral surface; I–XXV, somites.

The **digestive system** includes (1) the mouth surrounded by the anterior sucker; (2) a pharynx; (3) an esophagus; (4) a crop with paired lateral pouches (caeca); (5) a slender intestine; (6) a short rectum; and (7) the anus opening before the posterior sucker. The **circulatory system** is closed; blood circulates owing to pulsations in the vessels, and capillaries under the cuticle function as **respiratory organs. Excretion** is effected by paired nephridia, which are fewer than in the earthworm and of a peculiar type. The much reduced body cavity contains permanent gonads, a pair of **ovaries** and several of **testes**. Both sexes are represented in each individual, with a copulatory organ and also a vagina in the midventral genital pores. The leech has more sensory structures than other annelids.

21-15. Natural history. Leeches inhabit fresh waters or moist soil. Some are scavengers, and some are predators. The best known and most important are those that feed on blood of vertebrates, from fishes to man. These leeches fasten by their suckers and pierce the skin. A salivary enzyme prevents coagulation of the host's blood, of which the leech may ingest several times its own weight. This food is stored in the distensible crop and slowly digested over a period of several months.

Reproduction is by copulation and reciprocal fertilization or by a sperm packet deposited on the exterior body surface from one leech to another. Most species produce cocoons containing fertilized eggs, which are deposited either in water or in earth until the young develop; there is no larval stage.

Leeches are extremely abundant in some areas and a menace to vertebrate animals and man.

REVIEW

1. What "new" features in animal structure are first seen in annelid worms?
2. What conspicuous structural features are present in the clamworm but absent in the earthworm?
3. How does an earthworm feed, and what does it eat? What are some structural adaptations for using such food?
4. In what ways do the principal parts of the nervous system in an earthworm differ from those in a frog?
5. Are earthworms beneficial or harmful? Give reasons.
6. How is fertilization accomplished in earthworms?
7. Many marine worms construct tubes in which they live. What are some advantages of this mode of life?
8. How do leeches differ structurally from earthworms? What is a common food of leeches? What adaptations, structural and functional, do leeches have to use such food?

22
Joint-footed animals

The Phylum ARTHROPODA (Gr. *arthros,* jointed + *podos,* foot) contains fully 900,000 of the 1,000,000 or more known species of animals. It includes the crabs, shrimps, barnacles, and other crustaceans (Class CRUSTACEA), the insects (Class INSECTA; Chap. 23), the spiders, scorpions, ticks, etc. (Class ARACHNIDA), the centipedes (Class CHILOPODA), the millipedes (Class DIPLOPODA), and some less familiar and fossil forms.

The body is segmented externally in varying degree, and the appendages are jointed; both are variously specialized in form and function in different kinds of arthropods in keeping with their manner of life (Fig. 22-1, Table 22-1). All external surfaces are covered with an organic exoskeleton. The nervous system, eyes, and other sense organs are usually large, providing quick responses to stimuli. This is the only invertebrate phylum having many members able to live on land, away from moist surroundings; and the insects are the only invertebrates able to fly.

Arthropods of different kinds inhabit every

Illustration at top of page: Scorpion, an arthropod of ancient lineage, little changed since Silurian time.

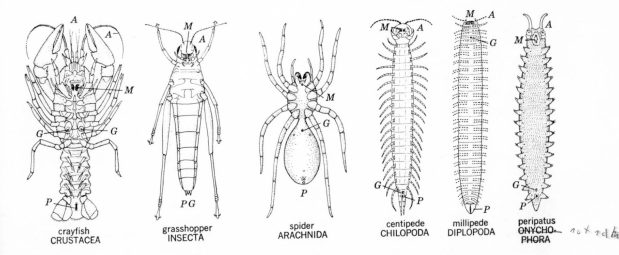

crayfish
CRUSTACEA

grasshopper
INSECTA

spider
ARACHNIDA

centipede
CHILOPODA

millipede
DIPLOPODA

peripatus
ONYCHOPHORA

Fig. 22-1. Phylum ARTHROPODA. Examples of six major groups in ventral view, showing body divisions, somites, appendages with their divisions, and the body openings. *A,* antennae; *M,* mouth; *P,* anus; *G,* genital opening(s).

Table 22-1. Phylum Arthropoda. General characteristics of the principal groups ₛkᵢₚ

		Crustacea Crustaceans	Insecta Insects	Arachnida Spiders, etc.	Chilopoda Centipedes	Diplopoda Millipedes	Onychophora *Peripatus*
Body divisions		Usually ceph-alothorax and abdo-men	Head, thorax, abdomen	Cephalo-thorax and abdomen	Head and long body	Head, short thorax, long abdomen	Head continu-ous with body
Paired appendages	Antennae	2 pairs	1 pair	None	1 pair	1 pair	1 pair
	Mouth parts	Mandibles Maxillae, 2 pairs Maxillipeds	Mandibles Maxillae, 1 pair Labium	Chelicerae Pedipalpi	Mandibles Maxillae, 2 pairs	Mandibles Maxillae, 1 pair	Jaws Oral papillae
	Legs	1 pair per so-mite, or less	3 pairs on thorax (+ wings)	4 pairs on cephalo-thorax	1 pair per so-mite	2 (or 1) pairs per somite	1 pair per so-mite
Respire by		Gills or body surface	Tracheae	Book lungs, or tracheae	Tracheae	Tracheae	Tracheae
Sex openings		2, hind part of thorax	1, end of abdomen	1, second somite of abdomen	1, end of abdomen	1, third somite near head	1, end of body
Develop-ment		Usually with larval stages	Usually with larval stages	Direct, except mites and ticks	Direct	Direct	Direct
Principal habitat		Salt or fresh water, few on land	Mainly terrestrial	Mainly terrestrial	All terrestrial	All terrestrial	All terrestrial

sort of environment and some species are enormously abundant. A few occur down to depths of 35,000 feet in the sea and others above 20,000 feet on mountains. Variously they occupy the air and land, the soil, and fresh, salt, or brackish waters. Some are parasites of plants, and others live on or in many animals. Many are gregarious; termites, bees, wasps, ants, and others have social organization with division of labor between several castes.

Crabs, lobsters, and shrimps serve as human food, smaller crustaceans are staple food of fishes, and insects and spiders are eaten by land vertebrates. Insects are man's chief competitors for crops, stored foods, clothes, and other property, although many kinds are beneficial. Certain insects, ticks, and mites carry

diseases to man, his domestic animals, and his crops.

Because of the limiting weight of the exoskeleton, no arthropod is of great size. A Japanese crab spreads to 12 feet with its slender legs, and an Atlantic lobster 24 inches long is recorded, but no living insect exceeds 11 inches. The smallest arthropods are under 1 mm. long.

22-1. Characteristics.

1. Symmetry bilateral; body of head, thorax, and abdomen (distinct or fused), usually segmented.
2. Appendages 1 pair (or none) per somite, each with few or many hinge joints[1] and opposed

[1] For brevity the divisions or segments of appendages are referred to as "joints"—3-jointed, etc.

muscles; commonly specialized, sometimes reduced, rarely lacking.

3. Exoskeleton containing chitin, often hardened, molted at intervals.
4. Muscles many and varied, of striated fibers, quick-acting.
5. Digestive tract complete, mouth parts with chewing jaws or else of sucking type; anus terminal.
6. Circulatory system open (lacunar); heart dorsal with arteries, no veins; coelom reduced.
7. Respiration various: by gills, tracheae (air ducts), book lungs, or body surface.
8. Excretion by coxal or green glands or by 2 to many Malpighian tubules on gut.
9. Nervous system of anterior brain (ganglia) connected to paired ventral nerve cords and ganglia with nerves in each body somite or ganglia concentrated anteriorly; sense organs for sight, touch, taste, and smell.
10. Sexes usually separate, often unlike; fertilization mostly internal; eggs with yolk; 1 or more larval (or nymphal) stages; parthenogenesis in some crustaceans and insects.

22-2. Cuticle and chitin. Arthropods are covered with an exoskeleton including a *cuticle,* with pores and fibers, secreted by the epidermis beneath. Best known of components in the cuticle is *chitin,* a complex organic substance insoluble in water, alkalies, dilute acids, or the digestive juices of many animals. The cuticle covers all exterior parts and lines the fore- and hind-gut, respiratory structures, and ducts of surface glands. In tracheal tubes and on gills it is very thin and permeable to gas exchange. On the body and appendages it may be soft and flexible (many larvae) or heavy and rigid (beetles, etc.) and may be further hardened with lime deposits (many crustaceans and millipedes). At joints it is flexible to permit movement. As a whole the exoskeleton protects internal organs, provides muscle attachments, and forms fulcra and levers of movable parts. It prevents loss of water and body fluids in terrestrial species. The exoskeleton is a rigid armor, and periodic molt is necessary for an arthropod to increase in size. In its life every individual has several molts; a new covering grows, the old one splits open,

the animal crawls out, expands slightly, then the new exoskeleton hardens.

A. CRUSTACEANS
CLASS *CRUSTACEA*

The CRUSTACEA (L. *crusta,* a hard shell) include the shrimps, crabs, lobsters, crayfishes, barnacles, and their kin. Most of the species are marine, but many live in fresh waters, and some, such as sow bugs, inhabit damp places on land. Most crustaceans are free-living and solitary; a few are gregarious and occur in vast schools, while others are commensals or parasites.

22-3. Characteristics.
1. Head of 5 fused somites with 2 pairs of antennae, 1 pair of mandibles, and 2 pairs of maxillae; thorax of 2 to 60 somites, distinct or variously fused; abdominal somites usually distinct, with telson at end; often with a shield (carapace) covering head and part of thorax; appendages variously modified.
2. Respiration usually by gills.
3. Excretion by 1 or 2 pairs of green glands; no Malpighian tubules.
4. Sexes usually separate; sex openings mostly paired; eggs often carried by female; parthenogenesis in a few groups.

The crayfishes (*Cambarus, Astacus;* Fig. 22-2) serve well as examples of the ARTHROPODA and CRUSTACEA. They are common in fresh-water streams and lakes, and some grow to 6 inches in length. The Atlantic lobster (*Homarus*) of salt waters is much larger but similar in structure.

22-4. External features. The crayfish body has two main parts, an anterior rigid *cephalothorax* (head + thorax) and the jointed *abdomen;* over the whole animal is an exoskeleton containing chitin, thin and soft at the joints to permit of movements but hard elsewhere. The whole body is composed of *somites* (head, 5; thorax, 8; abdomen, 6) each with a pair of ventral *appendages.* Somites of the cephalothorax are covered by a continuous shield or *carapace* over the dorsal and lateral surfaces with a transverse *cervical groove* marking off

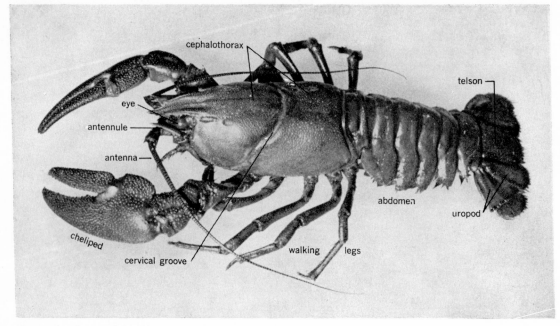

Fig. 22-2. The crayfish (Class CRUSTACEA). External features.

the head and thorax. The anterior end bears a median pointed *rostrum* with a stalked *compound eye* at each side. The *mouth* is ventral, surrounded by special mouth parts, and the *anus* opens ventrally in the broad median telson at the end of the abdomen. The *gills* are on either side of the thorax under the carapace. The *sex openings* are paired, those of the female at the base of the third walking legs and those of the male at the fifth pair.

22-5. Paired appendages (Figs. 22-2, 22-3). Ventrally on each somite is a pair of jointed appendages, with joints movable in several planes for dexterity. Each appendage con-

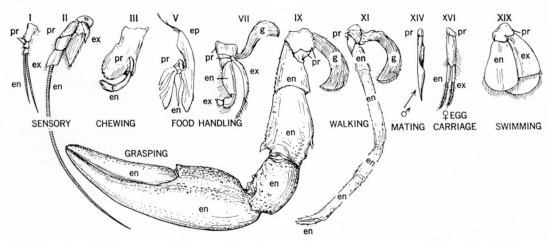

Fig. 22-3. Representative appendages of the crayfish (right side, ventroposterior view), showing structural differentiation to serve various functions, *pr,* protopodite; *en,* endopodite; *ex,* exopodite; *ep,* epipodite; *g,* gill.

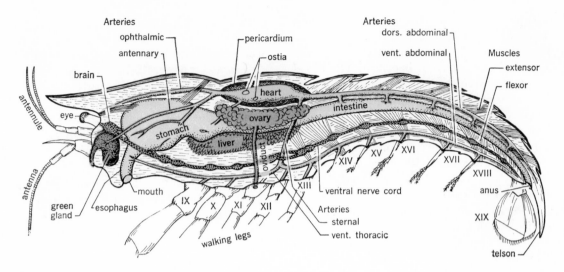

Fig. 22-4. The crayfish; internal structure of a female.

tains, inside the exoskeleton, opposed muscles to flex and extend the several parts.

The first and second appendages (short antennules and long antennae) are mobile sensory structures; the third to eighth (mandibles, maxillae, and maxillipeds) are the "mouth parts," used for cutting and handling food; the ninth is an enlarged "walking leg" with heavy pincer (chela) at the tip for offense and defense; the real walking legs, tenth to thirteenth, serve for locomotion, food handling, and body cleaning; the fourteenth to eighteenth are the abdominal swimmerets that aid in respiration and serve the female to carry eggs; numbers fourteen and fifteen in the male are for sperm transfer; the last pair, on somite nineteen, are the broad uropods, which, with the telson, serve for backward swimming. The appendages are variously modified from a basically two-branched type.

22-6. Digestive system (Fig. 22-4). This includes (1) the **mouth;** (2) a short **esophagus;** (3) a large two-chambered **stomach;** (4) a short **midgut** joining (5) the narrow tubular **intestine** running dorsally in the abdomen, and (6) the **anus.** Under the stomach are (7) two **digestive glands** ("liver") connecting to the midgut. Food is brought to the mouth by the second and third pair of walking legs and cut

or crushed to size by the mandibles. The stomach contains calcified **teeth** forming a **gastric mill** to grind the food; behind the mill is a hair-like **sieve** that allows only small particles to enter the hinder or pyloric part of the stomach. Enzymes from the liver digest the food, which is absorbed in the midgut; any undigested parts leave the anus as feces.

22-7. Circulatory system (Figs. 22-4, 22-5). The **heart** is middorsal in the thorax, suspended in a large sac (pericardial sinus) that

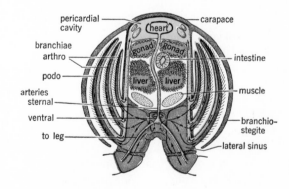

Fig. 22-5. The crayfish; cross section of body through the heart region; arrows indicate course of blood flow: blue, unoxygenated; red, oxygenated blood. The gills (branchiae) are sheltered by a covering (branchiostegite) on either side.

collects blood from open spaces in the body. Contractions of the heart pump blood to various parts of the body through *arteries* containing valves that prevent backflow. The blood escapes between the internal organs, then collects in sinuses connecting to the gills. There the oxygen–carbon dioxide exchange occurs, and then the blood flows back to the pericardial sinus from spaces among the tissues. Such an *open system,* without veins, is characteristic of arthropods in contrast to the closed systems of both annelids and vertebrates.

22-8. Respiratory system (Fig. 22-5). Along either side of the thorax, under the carapace and opening ventrally, are *gill chambers.* These contain layers of delicate, plume-like *gills* over which water carrying dissolved oxygen is kept circulating by action of the paired abdominal appendages. The blood plasma contains a bluish pigment, hemocyanin, that aids in oxygen transport, like the red hemoglobin of vertebrates.

22-9. Excretory system. Two large *green glands* in the head serve to remove organic wastes from the blood and body fluids. A duct from each opens at the ventral bases of the antennae. The cavities of the excretory glands and of the genital organs are all that remain of the body cavity (coelom) present in annelids and also in vertebrates.

22-10. Nervous system and sense organs (Fig. 22-4). The crayfish has a nervous system similar to that of the earthworm but larger. The *brain* (supraesophageal ganglia) dorsal in the head sends nerves to the anterior sense organs, and a pair of *connectives* around the esophagus lead to the double ventral *nerve cord.* The latter has *ganglia* in somites VIII to XIX that give off paired *nerves* to the appendages, internal organs, and muscles.

Arthropods, including crustaceans, have various sense organs that enable the animals to test the environment continually, to find food, shelter, or mates, and to avoid unfavorable conditions and enemies. In the crayfish, (1) most of the body has *tactile hairs* sensitive to touch; (2) the antennules, antennae, and mouth parts receive chemical stimuli (taste and smell) such as savory juices from a prospective meal; (3) the mechanism for balance is a *statocyst* under the base of each antennule that registers tilting of the body whereby the animal knows when and how to right itself; and (4) the *compound eyes* have a complex structure receiving images which are transmitted to the brain by the optic nerves (Fig. 22-6).

The *sinus gland* on the eyestalk in crustaceans produces a hormone that controls color adaptation in the epidermis and the compound eyes, regulates molt, affects calcium deposition in the exoskeleton, and is necessary for life. The hormone seems to be distributed by the blood stream.

22-11. Reproductive system. The sexes are separate. The *male* has two soft white *testes* fused beneath the heart. On each side a slender, coiled *vas deferens* extends ventrally to open at the base of the fifth walking leg. The *female* has a wider abdomen than the male. The two *ovaries* resemble the testes in form and location, and the eggs are discharged through an *oviduct* opening at the base of the third walking leg.

22-12. Natural history. The crayfish is a solitary bottom dweller that hides by day under stones or in crevices or burrows and keeps its body in contact with surrounding objects. The animal faces the entrance of its retreat, with the big pincers extended, the antennae waving about, and the abdominal appendages (swimmerets) performing respiratory movements. Other appendages are moved at times to receive stimuli or detect food. It grasps any food that passes within reach and will emerge to seize any that is nearby and then go back into its retreat. It resists attack by use of the strong chelae and tries to avoid being drawn out of its shelter; if the latter is opened or removed, the animal darts off to a new hiding place. The crayfish can walk forward, sideways, obliquely, or backward, using all of the four pairs of walking legs. By extending the abdomen, uropods, and telson and then

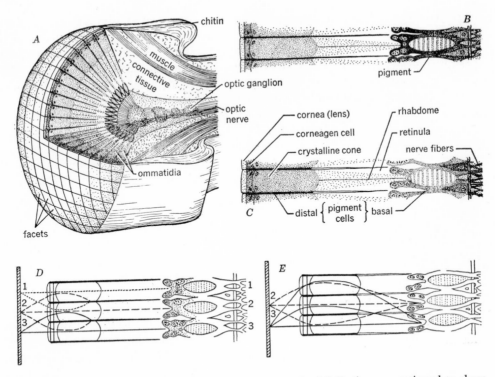

Fig. 22-6. Compound eye of the crayfish; diagrammatic. (*A*) Entire eye sectioned to show its general structure (facets are hexagonal in insects). (*B*) One ommatidium in the light, pigment extended. (*C*) Ommatidium in the dark, pigment contracted. (*D*) Apposition image formed of separate images on retinulae from points 1, 2, 3 on object. (*E*) Superposition image; each retinula receives both oblique and direct rays from more than one point. (*Adapted in part from Imms, Textbook of entomology, E. P. Dutton & Co., Inc.*)

suddenly flexing them under the body, the resistance offered these broad parts by the water enables the animal to "swim" or dart backward, and quick repetition of this action often enables it to escape danger. Crayfishes are most in evidence when feeding actively during the spring or early summer; in cold weather they retire to burrows or other safe retreats under water.

The food includes live insect larvae, worms, crustaceans, small snails, fishes, and tadpoles, besides some dead animal matter. Burrowing species feed extensively on stems and roots of plants. The enemies of crayfishes, besides mankind, include certain fishes, large salamanders, turtles, water snakes, birds, and some aquatic mammals.

22-13. Molt. Since increase in size is limited by the exoskeleton, young crayfishes molt several times a year and adults occasionally. Prior to molt some inorganic salts are reabsorbed from the exoskeleton, a new soft cuticle grows beneath, separate from the older, and the internal organs shrink slightly and soften. Then the old cuticle splits dorsally, and the animal slowly withdraws, leaving its former covering intact. While the new exoskeleton is soft, the animal increases in bulk, probably by taking in water; then the animal hides for several hours or days, avoiding enemies until its "armor" again affords protection.

22-14. Regeneration and autotomy. Crayfishes, crabs, and some other crustaceans can replace lost parts, chiefly appendages and eyes, by regeneration. This ability is greater in young individuals and less extensive than in the lower phyla. Upon loss or removal a new part becomes evident at the next molt and increases in size at successive molts until it may be fully restored. These crustaceans also have the power of self-amputation or autotomy of a cheliped or a walking leg. If broken or severely handled, the terminal five segments are cast off—sacrificed to the enemy. The fracture is at a definite breaking plane, and a cross partition inside the leg, plus quick clotting, limits the loss of blood; regeneration then follows in time.

22-15. Reproduction. In mating the male grasps and inverts a female, seizes her walking legs with his two chelae, and flexes his telson tightly over the end of her abdomen so that she is held motionless. He uses one of his fifth walking legs to press the tips of the two modified abdominal appendages (swimmerets) on his somite XIV onto the two sperm receptacles

between somites XII and XIII on her thorax. Sperm then pass in mucus along his swimmerets to lodge in her receptacles; then the animals separate. Later the female cleans her abdomen and abdominal appendages (swimmerets) and lies upside down with her abdomen sharply flexed: 200 to 400 eggs emerge from the oviducts and are fertilized by sperm from the seminal receptacles, then attach by a slimy secretion to her swimmerets. She later rights herself and backs into a shelter, where the eggs, hanging like berries, are aerated by movement of the swimmerets. In about five weeks miniature crayfish hatch (Fig. 22-7) and soon become independent. They molt six or more times during the first 2 months and live for several years.

22-16. Other crustaceans. The thousands of species of crustaceans show great variety in structure, coloration, habitat, and mode of life (Figs. 22-8, 22-9). Most of the larger kinds are predaceous, feeding on other smaller animals,

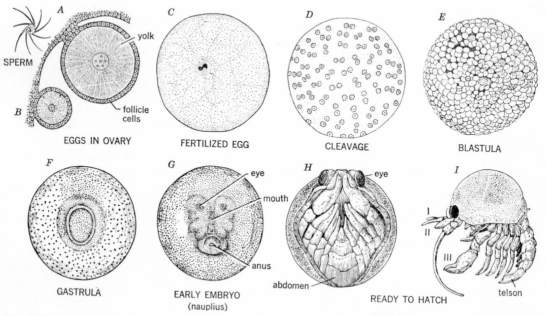

Fig. 22-7. Development of the crayfish; figures variously enlarged. (*B*) Eggs in ovary surrounded by follicle cells; when laid, they become attached to swimmerets on female. (*D, E*) Cleavage is superficial. (*F*) The shallow gastrula forms beneath the yolk. (*F–H*) Ventral views. (*I*) Young removed from egg just before hatching. (*A, B, from G. B. Howes, Atlas of zootomy, The Macmillan Co.; C–E, after Zehnder, 1934; F–I, after Huxley.*)

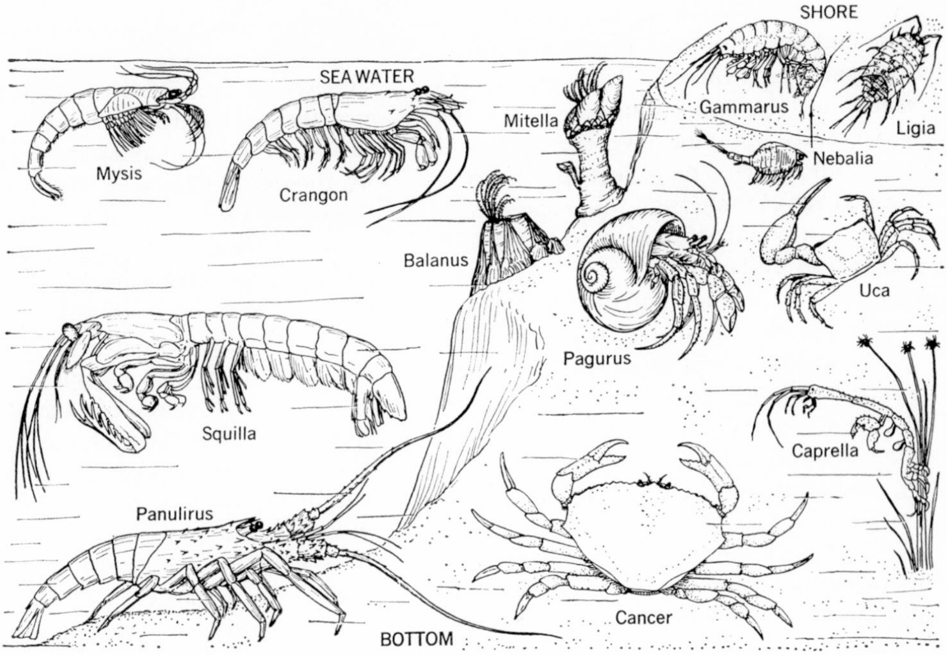

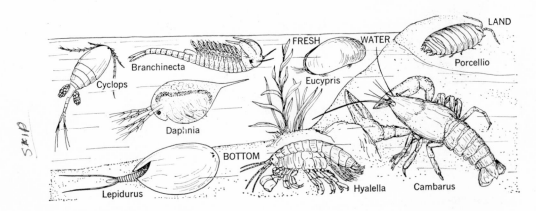

SKIP

Fig. 22-8. Some marine crustaceans in their respective habitats; mostly reduced, but not to same scale. *Mysis,* opossum shrimp; *Crangon,* shrimp; *Squilla,* stomatopod; *Panulirus,* spiny rock lobster; *Mitella,* goose barnacle; *Balanus,* acorn barnacle; *Gammarus,* sand hopper or amphipod; *Ligia,* isopod; *Nebalia; Pagurus,* hermit crab (in empty snail shell); *Uca,* fiddler crab; *Cancer,* edible crab, *Caprella,* "skeleton shrimp."

SKIP

Fig. 22-9. Some fresh-water crustaceans in their normal environments. *Cyclops,* copepod; *Branchinecta,* fairy shrimp; *Daphnia,* water flea; *Eucypris,* ostracod; *Porcellio,* sow bug (on land); *Lepidurus,* "tadpole" shrimp; *Hyalella,* amphipod; *Cambarus,* crayfish. Some enlarged (*Cyclops, Daphnia, Eucypris*), and others reduced, but not to same scale.

but the numerous small forms eat plant materials, and some bottom dwellers swallow debris from which their food is extracted. In reproduction the females usually carry the eggs externally, but some have internal brood pouches, and others reproduce parthenogenetically. Eggs of some fresh-water species are resistant to drought for 2 or more years and may be spread by the winds.

Some of the smaller aquatic crustaceans may be so abundant as to give distinctive color to bodies of water, and a single marine species may support whole schools of fishes or whales. There are seasonal fluctuations in species and numbers in both salt and fresh waters, some being commonest in spring, others in summer, and so on.

The young of certain species develop directly into miniature adults. Most marine forms, however, have several minute or small larval stages, often differing from one another and quite unlike the adults. The number of appendages is small in the younger stages and increases at successive molts. In sedentary species these larval stages are a means of dis-

persal since they are spread by water currents.

The barnacles (Fig. 22-10) are highly modified crustaceans in which the adult is monoecius, enclosed in a calcareous shell, and sessile. Most familiar are the goose and ship or rock barnacles that fasten to rocks and wood structures in shore waters; other species attach to crabs, sharks, sea turtles, and whales, and some are even parasitic. Eggs developed within the parent body hatch out as microscopic larvae that float or swim and feed; at successive molts they change form until they reach the adult stage. The larvae are the only means by which barnacles are dispersed because the adult becomes fixed to the substratum by secretions from a cement gland. The animal then literally "stands on its head" and kicks food toward its mouth by use of the thoracic appendages. So different is the anatomy of an adult barnacle from that of usual crustaceans that their relationships are understood clearly only by reference to the structure of the larvae.

A majority of crustaceans are free-living, but some are commensals, associated with

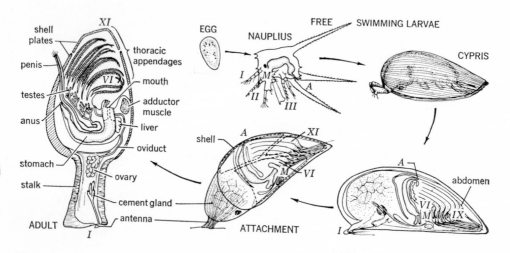

Fig. 22-10. The goose barnacle, *Lepas*. Adult with right side of mantle and shell removed. From the egg a free-swimming nauplius larva hatches that feeds and molts to become a cypris larva. The latter attaches by its antennules and cement gland, then transforms to the sessile adult stage. Egg and larvae much enlarged. *M*, mouth; *A*, anus; I, antennule; II, antenna; III, mandible; VI–XI, other appendages.

other animals in various relations, and still others are parasites. Some crabs dwell in tubes inhabited by annelid worms, and other small crabs live within the shells of oysters and mussels. The "fish lice" are crustaceans that have become ectoparasites of fishes, with their anterior appendages modified as suckers or hooks for attaching to their hosts; certain of these have mouth parts specialized to penetrate the host and suck blood. In some the larval form is parasitic and the adult free-living, and in others the reverse is true.

22-17. Relations to man. Flesh of certain crustaceans is much esteemed as human food. In 1964 commercial fisheries of the United States took 212 million pounds of shrimp, 270 million of crab, and 35 million of lobster, valued at a total of $115,925,000. Crayfish are eaten in some parts of North America, and all these plus other crustaceans are also eaten in many other lands. The blue crab (*Callinectes*) of the Atlantic coast is caught and held captive until it molts, then sold in the soft-shelled condition; it is eviscerated, cooked, and eaten entire—a great delicacy. The small crustaceans that abound in salt and fresh waters are important links in the food cycle for many fishes and other useful aquatic animals. Others (copepods) are the intermediate hosts for worm parasites of man and various vertebrates. Crayfishes in the Gulf states often damage fields of cotton and corn by eating the young plants, and occasionally their burrows injure levees. Sow bugs sometimes eat plants in gardens and greenhouses, and a wood-boring form damages wharves in salt waters.

B. TRILOBITES
SUBPHYLUM †*TRILOBITA*

The trilobites were primitive marine arthropods that abounded during Paleozoic times (Figs. 13-12, 14-8). The body was divided by two lengthwise furrows into three lobes. There was a distinct head, each somite had paired appendages bearing bristle-like setae, and development included a larval stage. Different species were 10 to 675 mm. in length. Many were bottom dwellers, but the larvae and some adults probably swam.

C. SPIDERS AND THEIR ALLIES
CLASS *ARACHNIDA*

The arachnids are a varied group including spiders, mites, ticks, scorpions, and others (Fig. 22-11). They are mostly free-living terrestrial animals of small size, and many of them are commonest in warm, dry regions. Some possess poison glands and claws (fangs) by which they stun or kill the insects and small animals used for food. Spiders and some others also have special glands to secrete silk for threads used to make their familiar webs, shelters, and egg cases.

Most members of this group are entirely harmless, but a few spiders and scorpions may cause illness or death to man. There is an age-old belief in southern Europe that the bite of a "tarantula" spider will be followed by melancholy and death unless cured by dancing, especially to the lively music of a "tarantella," whereby the poison will be eliminated by perspiration! Some mites injure plants, other mites and ticks parasitize man and animals, and still other ticks are intermediate hosts for protozoans and viruses that cause various diseases. The smallest mites are less than 0.5 mm. long, while the largest scorpion grows to 160 mm. long.

22-18. Characteristics.[1]
1. Body usually of distinct cephalothorax and abdomen; typically with 6 pairs of jointed appendages, all on cephalothorax, no antennae or mandibles.
2. Mouth parts and digestive tract mainly suited for sucking; some with poison glands.
3. Respiration by book lungs, tracheae, or book gills.
4. Excretion by paired Malpighian tubules or coxal glands, or both.

[1] Compare ARTHROPODA (par. 22-1 and Chap. 15), CRUSTACEA (par. 22-3), and INSECTA (par. 23-1).

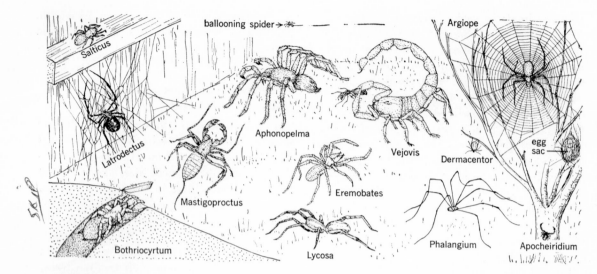

Fig. 22-11. Common members of Class ARACHNIDA in the habitats they occupy; not to scale. Spiders (Order ARANEAE): *Salticus,* jumping spider; *Latrodectus,* black widow spider; *Bothriocyrtum,* trap-door spider (in ground); *Dugesiella (Aphonopelma),* American "tarantula"; *Lycosa,* hunting or wolf spider; *Argiope,* orb-weaving spider with egg case. *Mastigoproctus,* whip scorpion; *Eremobates,* vinegarone (solpugid); *Vejovis,* scorpion; *Phalangium,* harvestman; *Apocheiridium,* false scorpion; *Dermacentor,* tick.

5. Nervous system with dorsal ganglia (brain) and ventral nerve cord having paired ganglia or else ganglia concentrated anteriorly; eyes usually simple and in pairs; sensory hairs on body.

6. Sexes mostly separate; sex openings single; fertilization usually internal; development usually external and direct, or one or more larval stages.

7. Chiefly terrestrial and solitary; either free-living and predaceous or parasitic.

22-19. The spiders (Order ARANEAE). More that 30,000 species of spiders are known that live in a wide array of habitats from the seashore to high mountains and from arid deserts to lush swamps and tropical forests.

22-20. External features (Fig. 22-12). The body consists of a distinct rounded and unsegmented *cephalothorax* and an *abdomen,* joined by a slender "waist." The cephalothorax commonly has eight *simple eyes* anteriorly and six pairs of *appendages* on the ventral side. The first pair (chelicerae) are spe-cialized as fangs connected by ducts to poison glands. The second pair is for chewing and squeezing food; in mature males the tips serve for sperm transfer. The next four pairs are walking legs, each of seven segments, ending either in claws or in clinging pads. All external parts are covered by cuticle-bearing bristles, some of which are sensory.

The external openings are (Fig. 22-1) (1) a minute *mouth* anteroventrally on the cephalothorax; all the others are ventral on the abdomen and include (2) the *genital aperture* anteriorly in the midline; (3) the slit-like entrance to paired *book lungs* at the side of the genital opening; then, in order posteriorly, (4) a *spiracle* connecting to short air ducts (trachea); (5) paired *spinnerets* for silk secretion; and (6) the terminal *anus.*

22-21. Internal structure. The *digestive tract* consists of (1) the mouth; (2) a slender esophagus; (3) the sucking stomach operated by muscles attached dorsally to the cephalothorax; (4) the main stomach with five pairs

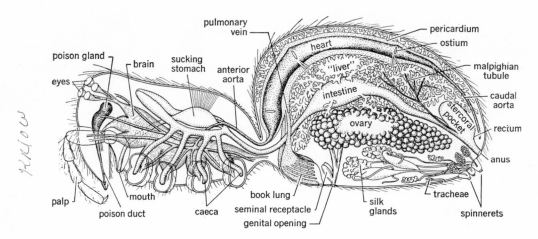

Fig. 22-12. Structure of a spider as seen with left side of body removed. *(Modified from Leuckart.)*

of pouches (caeca) also in the cephalothorax, (5) the intestine in the abdomen which receives ducts from (6) the much-branched digestive gland ("liver") and leads to (7) the rectum, where a large pocket enters just before (8) the anus.

The open *circulatory system* is similar to that of insects. The large tubular heart is dorsal in the abdomen, surrounded by a sac (pericardium) which collects oxygenated blood from the sinuses leading from the book lungs. Contraction of the heart forces blood through arteries to the stomach, legs, eyes, and poison glands. Oxygenation of the colorless blood occurs in the book lungs.

Spiders breathe air that enters external slits on the abdomen and circulates over leaf-like horizontal plates, the *book lungs,* peculiar to arachnids. Here the oxygen–carbon dioxide exchange occurs. If tracheae are present, they are like those of insects but limited to the abdomen. *Excretion* is by paired Malpighian tubules connecting to the intestine and by paired (coxal) glands in the cephalothorax, homologous to those of crustaceans.

The *nervous system* is concentrated. From the bilobed ganglion above the esophagus two thick connectives join a ventral ganglionic mass radiating nerves to all organs. The eyes

are simple, the sense of smell seems well developed, and there are many external sensory hairs.

The sexes are separate and often unlike. The male has two testes that join by coiled ducts (vasa efferentia) to one seminal vesicle leading to the genital opening. In the female the two ovaries connect by oviducts to a single vagina; two lateral seminal receptacles attach to the vagina.

22-22. Natural history. Spiders are free-living, solitary, and predaceous creatures that feed mainly on insects. They variously hunt their food, running it down or jumping on it, or trap their prey in webs; small insects are killed by the poison fangs, but larger catches may be bound with silk threads or fastened to the web before they are killed and "eaten" (sucked out). Individuals of most species live about one year but some large tarantulas have survived 20 years in captivity. Enemies include birds, lizards, and certain wasps; ichneumonid wasps oviposit in spider cocoons, and their larvae eat the spider eggs.

Spider silk is secreted through the spinnerets and hardens into a thread as it is spun into the air. It serves in various web formations, as a "dragline" to be paid out as hunting spiders travel, as a means of dispersal for spiderlings which climb high and spin long threads that are carried by the wind, and for snares, shelters, nests, and cocoons.

22-23. Reproduction. When a male matures, he deposits a droplet of sperm on a web and takes it up into the sac-like tip on the second pair of appendages. He then seeks a female, and they may go through a nuptial performance before he inserts these appendages into her genital opening to transfer the sperm. The female may kill and eat the male after mating, but this is not his invariable end. Later she lays eggs in a padded cocoon that is fastened on or near the web or attached to her abdomen until the spiderlings emerge. Females of some species carry the young for a few days after they hatch. Spiders increase in size and change in form, proportion, and color pattern with each molt. Before maturing a male molts about five times and a female seven or eight times.

22-24. Other arachnids (Fig. 22-1). The scorpions (Order Scorpionida; see chapter head) have large pincers on the second pair of appendages and a 12-segmented abdomen bearing a terminal sharp poison sting. They inhabit warm dry regions, hiding under stones or in shallow burrows by day and running actively at night to catch insects, spiders, and other scorpions used as food. Prey is grasped and torn apart, large animals first being paralyzed by the sting. Mating is preceded by a "courtship dance"; and the female produces living young, which ride for some days on her abdomen.

Whip scorpions (Order Pedipalpi) somewhat resemble scorpions but lack poison. They have large pincers, and the first pair of legs is specialized for touch sensation; some of them bear a slender abdominal "whip." They live in warm countries, are nocturnal, and prey on insects. The pseudoscorpions (Order Pseudoscorpionida) are like miniature scorpions, but without a sting. They live under stones, moss, or bark, and some are found in books or furniture; their food is of minute insects. The sun spiders (Order Solpugida) are of spider-like form, but without a "waist"; they also lack both silk and poison glands. Sun spiders inhabit warm, dry regions and have an undeserved reputation for being dangerous. The harvestmen or daddy longlegs (Order Phalangida) have compact ovoid bodies and extremely long legs by which they run readily. They lack poison but have "stink" glands for protection. They are common in temperate regions, and their food includes small insects.

The mites and ticks (Order Acarina) are small to microscopic in size, with the head, thorax, and abdomen closely fused and unsegmented. The body covering is membranous or leathery, sometimes with hard plates or shields. Mouth parts are borne on a slender anterior region, and the eight legs are laterally placed, often with bristles. The sexes are separate. From the egg a six-legged larva hatches out; it feeds and molts into an eight-legged nymph and later changes into the adult sexual form.

Mites (Fig. 22-13) abound as to species (20,000) and individuals in soil, stored foods, fresh and salt waters, and as parasites of both plants and animals. Ticks (Fig. 22-14) feed on vertebrate blood. Upon finding a host, the tick's mouth parts pierce the skin, and blood is sucked until the animal becomes gorged—"full as a tick"—and then drops off. In spring the female deposits her eggs under shelter on the ground, and hatching occurs a month or so later. The larvae, nymphs, and adults in turn climb on bushes to wait for appropriate hosts, to which they fasten; after feeding, they drop off to digest and to molt. Ticks can survive long periods without feeding, some for a year or more if they fail to find an appropriate host animal.

22-25. Relations to man. The bite of most spiders is harmless to man, and even a large "tarantula" does no more harm than a wasp. The genus *Latrodectus*, however, is dangerous; the black widow spider (*L. mactans;* Fig. 22-1) inhabits North and South America, the West Indies, and Hawaii. The adult female

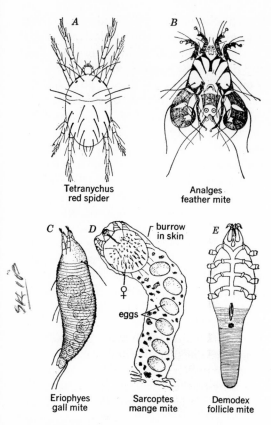

Tetranychus red spider

Analges feather mite

Eriophyes gall mite

Sarcoptes mange mite

Demodex follicle mite

burrow in skin

eggs

Fig. 22-13. Some representative mites; all enlarged, not to same scale. (*After Banks*, 1905.)

is shiny black and has a red hourglass mark ventrally on the abdomen. In the United States 5 per cent of the reported human poisonings by this spider have been fatal; most of these were in California, where the black widow causes more poisonings than rattlesnakes.

Some large tropical scorpions have powerful venom. In Mexico thousands of people are stung annually, causing hundreds of deaths, mostly in children. In recent years the danger has been decreased by bounties for destruction of scorpions and by treatment with a special scorpion antivenin when poisoned.

Many mites are economic pests; various species suck plant juices, blister leaves, or injure the buds and fruit of orchard trees; others damage roots and bulbs. The itch mite (*Sar-*

coptes) burrows in and irritates human skin; related forms cause mange on hogs, dogs, and other mammals; some produce "scab" in sheep and unthriftiness in fowls. Larval chiggers attack man, causing severe itching, and in the Orient they transmit the disease "scrub typhus."

Ticks afflict both domestic and wild animals, and a few attack man. If numerous, the host becomes anemic, bodily resistance is lowered, and death may even result. Certain species of ticks are intermediate hosts of serious diseases, notably Rocky Mountain spotted fever, affecting man, and Texas cattle fever, of great importance to the southern states livestock industry.

D. HORSESHOE CRABS AND EURYPTERIDS CLASS *MEROSTOMATA*

In Paleozoic seas there were ancient arachnoids, the eurypterids, some up to 9 feet in length. These animals and the living king or horseshoe crabs comprise a separate class of arthropods. The American horseshoe crab (*Limulus polyphemus*) inhabits shallow Atlantic coastal waters from Nova Scotia to Yucatan. The cephalothorax bears six pairs of appendages like other arachnoids and is covered by an arched carapace of horseshoe

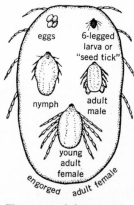

eggs

6-legged larva or "seed tick"

nymph

adult male

young adult female

engorged adult female

Fig. 22-14. Texas cattlefever tick (*Boöphilus annulatus*), 5×. Smaller stages inside outline of an engorged female.

shape. The hexagonal abdomen has spines dorsally, a slender bayonet-like telson behind, and six pairs of small thin appendages ventrally. Respiration is by book gills, and the sense organs include two lateral compound eyes and two median simple eyes.

These crabs burrow, swim, or walk on the bottom, are most active at night, and feed on small invertebrates. They mate in early summer, and groups of small, externally fertilized eggs are deposited shallowly in sand between the tide lines. The larvae at hatching resemble trilobites in having a segmented abdomen without appendages, but these features are lost at the first molt.

E. CENTIPEDES AND MILLIPEDES
C~~LASS~~ *~~MYRIAPODA~~*

The centipedes or CHILOPODA (Fig. 22-15) are long, slender, and flattened dorsoventrally with a body of 15 to 181 somites in different species. The head bears a pair of jointed antennae, mandibles, and two pairs of maxillae; the first body segment has a pair of jointed poison claws, and each other segment except the last two has one pair of jointed walking legs. The digestive tract is straight, with paired salivary glands anteriorly and a pair of Malpighian tubules for excretion posteriorly. The heart, surrounded by a pericardium, extends the length of the body and gives off lateral arteries in each somite. Respiration is by a set of tracheal tubes; the sexes are sepa-

rate, each with one dorsal gonad and a single ventral genital opening posteriorly.

Centipedes live mainly in warm countries, hiding by day and running about at night to prey on earthworms and insects; large species may capture small lizards or mice. Prey is killed quickly by the poison and chewed by the mandibles. Some species lay eggs, and others are viviparous. The young resemble the adults. Some tropical species are 6 to 8 inches long, and their bites are painful to man, but the smaller species are no hazard.

The "thousand-legged worms" or millipedes (Subclass DIPLOPODA; Fig. 22-15) have long, cylindrical bodies, and some species are brightly colored. The distinct head has two clumps of simple eyes and a pair each of short antennae, jaws, and maxillae. The thorax is of four single somites, all but the first with one pair of legs. The long abdomen has 9 to over 100 double somites, each with two pairs of jointed legs. The digestive and circulatory systems are somewhat as in centipedes, but respiration is by tracheae with a spiracle opening in front of each leg. The gonad is single, and the sex opening on the third somite.

Millipedes live in humid dark places, shunning the light, and travel slowly, with the body extended; they test the route of travel with the antennae. The many legs move in a series of waves from behind forward. Their food is of soft plant materials, but they will eat dead animal matter. A series of "stink" glands secreting objectionable fluids protects them from some enemies, and certain species roll up in a spiral when disturbed.

F. PERIPATUS
SUBPHYLUM *~~ONYCHOPHORA~~*

Members of this class (Gr. *onychus,* claw + *phorus,* bearing) comprise about 70 species of small "walking worms" (*Peripatus*) that live in dark, moist places in the Southern Hemisphere, Central America, Mexico, and the West Indies. A representative species is about 50 mm. long (Fig. 22-16). The anterior end has paired antennae and eyes, a mouth, and

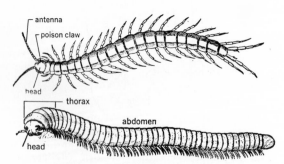

Fig. 22-15. *Above.* Centipede (Subclass CHILOPODA; *after Huxley*). *Below.* Common millipede (*Spirobolus,* Subclass DIPLOPODA, *from Haupt*).

jaws. The unsegmented cylindrical body is covered by thin, lightly chitinized skin which has many transverse rings and 14 to 44 pairs of short stumpy legs. There is an excretory opening beside each leg and one ventral genital pore anterior to the anus at the posterior end.

The body wall is of thin cuticle, epidermis, and complex muscle layers over an unsegmented cavity (hemocoel). The digestive tract is a straight tube with a long stomach-intestine; the open circulatory system consists of a single middorsal vessel; respiration is by simple tracheae; paired nephridia-like structures with funnels and ducts connecting to nephridiopores serve for excretion; and the nervous system is of paired cerebral ganglia and a pair of separate ventral nerve cords with no ganglia but many cross-connectives. The sexes are separate, with paired gonads but a single genital opening. Most species produce living young, part of the female oviduct being specialized as a uterus.

The ONYCHOPHORA are of special interest because they have both annelid and arthropod characteristics that suggest possible derivation of the ARTHROPODA from an ancient annelid-like ancestor.

G. OTHER ARTHROPODA

In addition to the arthropods already described in this chapter, there are several other groups of animals belonging to this phylum whose relationships and systematic position are not entirely clear. These are the sea spiders (PYCNOGONIDA), some worm-like parasitic forms (PENTASTOMIDA), the minute water bears (TARDIGRADA), the garden centipedes (SYMPHYLA), and the tiny pauropods (PAUROPODA). The characters of these groups are included in the synopsis of classification (Chap. 15).

REVIEW

1. Name the more important structural characteristics of the arthropods.
2. What are the principal groups (subphyla and classes) in this phylum?
3. Of what advantage is a body covering containing chitin?
4. How does a crayfish or lobster differ from a crab?
5. With various types of paired jointed appendages, what things can a crayfish do that are impossible for a snail or an earthworm?
6. Define hemocoel. How does it differ from the coelom of an earthworm?
7. Why are gills necessary to an animal such as the crayfish?
8. In what ways do the sense organs in a crayfish differ from those of annelids and mollusks?
9. Why is molt of the exoskeleton necessary? How is it accomplished?
10. Name some common kinds of crustaceans, and tell where each lives. List a few used as human food.
11. Why is a barnacle, with a limy external shell, classified as a crustacean? Why is it not a mollusk?
12. What are conspicuous structural features of spiders? What is their food, and how is it obtained and eaten? Of what value is spider silk? Where is it formed? Give some peculiarities of reproduction among spiders.
13. What is a mite? In what way is its structure unlike that of a spider? Of a crayfish? What characteristics make ticks persistent pests of animals? Are any dangerous to man?
14. How are centipedes and millipedes different, structurally, from other arthropods? How do they differ from one another?
15. What characteristics of *Peripatus* make it of special scientific interest to zoologists?

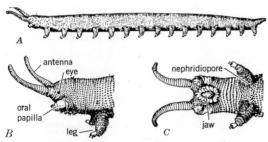

Fig. 22-16. *Peripatus* (Subphylum ONYCHOPHORA). (*A*) Entire animal, slightly enlarged. (*B, C*) Anterior end, lateral and ventral views. (*After Snodgrass,* 1938.)

23
Insects

Grasshoppers, flies, lice, butterflies, beetles, bees, and other members of the Class INSECTA (L., incised, into distinct parts) number fully 800,000 species. They comprise about three-fourths of the Animal Kingdom and far the largest part of the Phylum ARTHROPODA. They are the commonest of all land animals, the principal invertebrates living in dry environments, and the only ones able to fly. These habits are made possible by the chitinous body covering that protects the internal organs against injury and loss of moisture, by the extensions of this covering that form the wings, and by the system of tracheal tubes that enables insects to breathe air. Insects abound in all habitats except the sea; various kinds live in fresh and brackish waters, in soil, on plants of all kinds, and on or in many animals. They eat all sorts and parts of plants—roots, stems or leaves, sap or blossoms, seeds or fruits.

Many flower-visiting insects aid in pollination. Others use tissues, fluids, and excretions of animals, and scavenger insects eat dead animals and plants. Parasitic insects live in the eggs, larvae, or adults of other insects and on various animals and plants. Some insects transmit diseases to plants, animals, and man. Insects in turn are eaten by other insects, spiders, scorpions, and many vertebrates from fishes to mammals. Predaceous and parasitic species help to regulate the numbers of other insects. Because of the numbers and many biological relations of insects, they are of great economic significance; some are useful and many are harmful to man's interests. The science dealing with insects is known as **entomology** (Gr. *entomon,* insect).

23-1. Characteristics.[1]

1. Head, thorax, and abdomen distinct; head with 1 pair of antennae and with 3 pairs of mouth parts modified variously for chewing, sucking, or lapping; thorax (of 3 somites) with 3 pairs of jointed legs and usually 2 (1 or no) pairs of wings; abdomen of 11 or fewer somites with terminal parts modified as genitalia.
2. Digestive tract of fore-, mid-, and hind-gut; mouth with salivary glands.
3. Heart (dorsal vessel) slender, with an anterior aorta; no capillaries or veins; body spaces a hemocoel (coelom reduced).
4. Respiration by branched, cuticle-lined tracheae that carry oxygen from paired spiracles on sides of thorax and abdomen directly to the tissues; some aquatic forms with tracheal or blood gills.
5. Excretion by 2 to many fine Malpighian tubules attached to anterior end of hind-gut.
6. Nervous system of supra- and sub-esophageal ganglia connecting to double ventral nerve cord, with not more than 1 pair of ganglia per somite; sense organs include simple and compound eyes, chemoreceptors for smell on the antennae and for taste about the mouth, and

[1] Compare Phylum ARTHROPODA, Chap. 22.

Illustration at top of page: Cockroaches (*Blattella germanica*), an unpleasant alien pest. Female in center carrying egg case. (*Photo by R. L. Usinger.*)

various tactile hairs; some with means for sound production and reception; no statocysts.

7. Sexes separate; gonads of multiple tubules with 1 median duct posteriorly; fertilization internal; ova with much yolk and protecting shells; cleavage usually superficial; development with several molts and direct, or with several nymphal stages and gradual metamorphosis, or with several larval stages and a complete metamorphosis to adult form; parthenogenesis in aphids, thrips, gall wasps, etc.

Some insects are smaller than large protozoans, and others exceed the smallest of vertebrates in size. Certain beetles are but 0.25 mm. long, but most insects are 2 to 40 mm. long. The longest is an orthopteran, 260 mm. Two tropical moths have wingspreads of 280 and 240 mm.; some fossil insects exceeded 700 mm. (28 inches) in wingspread.

THE GRASSHOPPER

The grasshopper is generalized as to anatomy, has chewing mouth parts, undergoes a gradual or incomplete metamorphosis from the young or nymph stages to the adult, and lives independently for one season. Grasshoppers occur mainly in open lands, where they eat grasses and other leafy vegetation. The Carolina grasshopper (*Dissosteira carolina*), the American grasshopper (*Schistocerca americana*), and the eastern lubber grasshopper (*Romalea microptera*) are common examples.

23-2. External features. The body comprises a head of six fused somites, a thorax of three somites with legs and wings, and a long segmented abdomen ending with reproductive organs (Fig. 23-1). It is covered by an exoskeleton containing chitin, which is secreted by the epidermis beneath and molted periodically in the nymphs to permit of increase in size; adults do not molt. The exoskeleton is formed into hard plates, or *sclerites,* separated by *sutures* of soft chitin to permit movement of the body segments and appendages. Pigment in and under the chitin provides a variegated and protective coloration by which grasshoppers resemble the environments in which they live.

The *head* (Fig. 23-2) bears one pair of slender, jointed *antennae* with fine sensory bristles, two lateral *compound eyes* that are unstalked but constructed like those of the crayfish, and three *simple eyes* (ocelli). Much of the head is enclosed in a fused sclerite or *epicranium,* with a dorsal *vertex,* the lateral

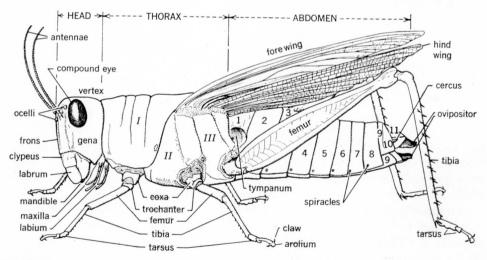

Fig. 23-1. External features of the grasshopper, a generalized insect. Female. I–III, somites of thorax; 1–11, somites of abdomen.

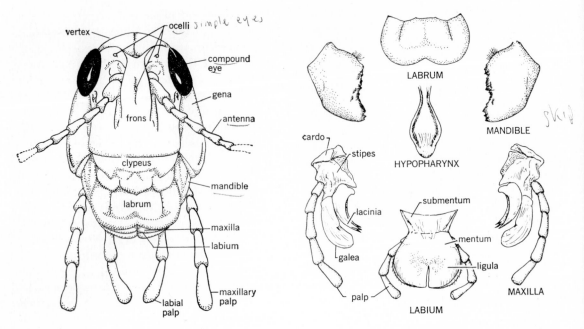

Fig. 23-2. The grasshopper. *Left.* Front view of the head. *Right.* Mouth parts in anterior view. Both enlarged.

cheeks or *genae* and the anterior *frons.* Below the latter is a broad plate, the *clypeus.* The mouth parts are of the chewing type, ventral on the head, and include (1) a broad upper lip or *labrum,* hinged to the clypeus; (2) a median tongue-like *hypopharynx* behind the mouth; (3) two heavy, blackish lateral jaws or *mandibles,* each with teeth along the inner margin for chewing food; (4) a pair of *maxillae* of several parts and with slender sensory palps at the sides; and (5) a broad median lower lip or *labium,* with two short palps.

The *thorax* consists of the large anterior *prothorax* with a dorsal saddle-like pronotum, the *mesothorax,* and the posterior *metathorax;* each bears a pair of jointed legs, and the meso- and meta-thorax each a pair of wings. The sclerites on each somite form a dorsal *tergum* of four fused plates, a *pleuron* of three plates on each side, and a single ventral *sternum.* Each *leg* is subdivided as follows: (1) the short *coxa,* articulating to the body; (2) a small *trochanter* fused to (3) the stout *femur;* (4) a slender spiny *tibia;* and (5) the *tarsus* of three parts, the proximal bearing

four pairs of *ventral pads* and the distal having a fleshy *arolium* between two *claws.* The arolia enable the grasshopper to hold on to smooth surfaces, and the claws to rough places. All the legs are used in walking and climbing. Each metathoracic leg has a large femur containing muscles and a long tibia that serve for leaping. The narrow *forewings* or *tegmina* are parchment-like. The *hind wings* are broad and membranous, with many veins, and fold under the forewings at rest. Each wing develops as a sac-like projection of the body covering and flattens to a thin double membrane that encloses tracheae, nerves, and blood vessels. The cuticle thickens along the sinuses to form strengthening nervures, or *veins* (Fig. 23-3). When of full size, the wings become hard and dry, but blood flow continues in some veins. The wing veins are of such constant pattern in species and higher groups of insects as to be useful in classification.

The slender cylindrical *abdomen* consists of 11 somites, the terminal ones being modified for copulation or egg laying. Along the

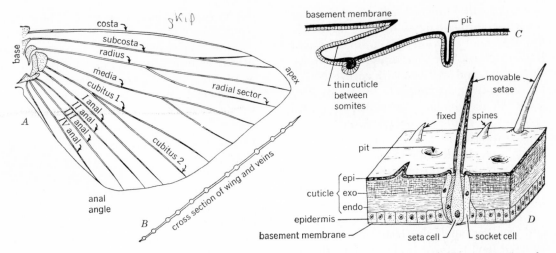

Fig. 23-3. The wings and body covering of insects; diagrammatic. (*A*) Generalized wing showing the principal veins. (*B*) Cross section of wing and veins. (*C*) Section of body covering at junction of two somites. (*D*) Structure of the body wall. (*A, B, after Metcalf and Flint; C, D, adapted from Snodgrass.*)

lower sides of the thorax and abdomen are 10 pairs of small *spiracles,* the openings of the respiratory system. The first abdominal segment has on either side a *tympanic membrane,* part of an organ of hearing. Both sexes have a small spine or *cercus* on either side behind the 10th somite. The end of the abdomen of a female has two paired lobes forming an *ovipositor;* a male has a ventral boat-shaped structure containing the *copulatory organ.*

23-3. Muscles. The head contains complex small muscles that move the antennae and mouth parts. In the thorax are large muscles that manipulate the wings and legs. Segmental muscles are conspicuous in the abdomen, where some perform respiratory movements and others control the reproductive structures.

23-4. Digestive system (Fig. 23-4). The mouth parts surround (1) the *mouth cavity*, from which (2) a slender *esophagus* extends to (3) the large, thin-walled *crop*. Below the

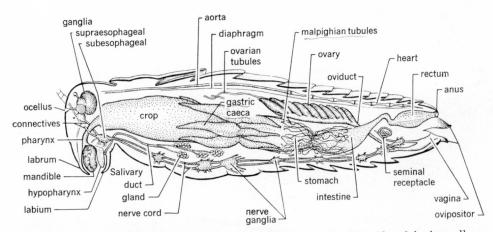

Fig. 23-4. The grasshopper. Internal structure as seen with left side of body wall removed; tracheae omitted. Compare Figs. 22-4, 22-12.

crop are small, branched *salivary glands* that discharge through ducts opening at the labium. Beyond the crop is (4) a small *gizzard,* lined by plates. The preceding parts comprise the fore-gut and are lined with cuticle. Next is (5) the midgut, or *stomach,* joined by (6) a series of six double, finger-shaped *gastric caeca.* The hind-gut, or (7) *intestine,* also lined with cuticle, consists of a tapered anterior part, slender middle portion, and enlarged *rectum* that opens at (8) the *anus.* Food is held by the forelegs, labrum, and labium, lubricated by the salivary secretion (containing enzymes), and chewed by the mandibles and maxillae; the palps bear organs of taste. Chewed food is stored in the crop, further reduced in the gizzard, and strained into the stomach. There it is digested by enzymes from the gastric caeca and absorbed. In the rectum, excess water is withdrawn from the undigested material, which is formed into slender fecal pellets and passed out the anus.

23-5. Circulatory system. The slender tubular *heart* is dorsal in the abdomen in a shallow *pericardial cavity* formed by a delicate transverse *diaphragm.* Blood enters the heart through pairs of minute lateral openings (ostia) and is pumped forward into a *dorsal aorta* to the head. There it emerges into the body spaces or *hemocoel* (not a coelom), between the internal organs, and moves slowly backward around these organs, finally to enter the pericardial sinus. Some blood circulates in

the appendages and wing veins. The system is open, or lacunar, as in other arthropods, without capillaries or veins. The clear blood plasma contains colorless blood cells that act as phagocytes to remove foreign organisms. The blood serves mainly to transport food and wastes, as there is a separate respiratory system. The *fat body,* a loose network of tissue between the organs, stores food reserves, especially in the young before metamorphosis.

23-6. Respiratory system (Figs. 23-5, 23-6). The paired *spiracles* connect to a system of elastic ectodermal air tubes, or *tracheae,* branching to all parts of the body. The finest branches, or *tracheoles,* carry oxygen to and remove carbon dioxide directly from the tissue cells. The tracheal wall consists of a single layer of thin cells that secretes a lining of chitin (cast off at molting), and the larger tubes are reinforced by a spiral thread to prevent their collapse. Longitudinal *air trunks* connect to the spiracles along either side. The grasshopper, unlike some insects, has several large, thin-walled *air sacs* in the thorax and abdomen, where alternate contraction and relaxation of the body wall serve to pump air in and out of the tracheal system. The finest tracheoles contain fluid in which oxygen dissolves before actually reaching the tissue cells; this fluid serves in internal respiration like the blood in vertebrates.

23-7. Excretory system. To the anterior end of the hind-gut are joined several thread-like

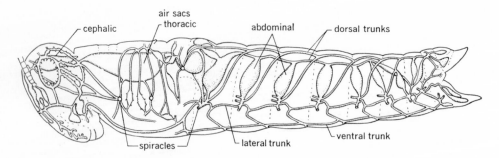

Fig. 23-5. The grasshopper. Respiratory system. Tracheal trunks, air sacs, and 10 spiracles of the left side. (*After Albrecht,* 1953.)

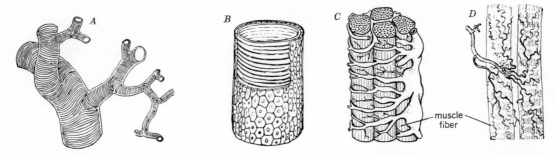

Fig. 23-6. The tracheae of insects. (*A*) Large trunks and branches. (*B*) Cellular wall of a tracheal tube and its internal spiral thread. (*C*) Terminal branches around muscle fibers. (*D*) Fine tracheoles distributed over muscle fibers. (*After Snodgrass.*)

Malpighian tubules that lie in the hemocoel and have their free ends closed. The tubule wall is a single layer of large cells that remove urea, urates, and salts from the blood to be discharged with the feces.

23-8. Nervous system (Figs. 23-4, 23-7). The brain, or *supraesophageal ganglion,* in the head comprises three pairs of fused ganglia with nerves to the eyes, antennae, and other head organs. It joins by two *connectives* around the esophagus to the *subesophageal ganglion,* also of three pairs. From the latter, the ventral *nerve cord* extends posteriorly. Each thoracic somite contains a paired *ganglion* with nerves to the legs, wings, and internal organs. There are only five pairs of abdominal ganglia; some originally separate have become fused. There is also a *sympathetic nervous system* with ganglia and nerves to the

brain, fore-gut, midgut, and heart, and from the last abdominal ganglion to the hind-gut and reproductive system.

23-9. Sense organs. The sensory receptors of the grasshopper are adapted for receiving stimuli from the air and land environment. They include (1) *tactile hairs* on various body parts, especially the antennae, mouth palps, abdominal cerci, and distal leg segments; (2) *olfactory organs* on the antennae; (3) *organs of taste* on the palps and other mouth parts; (4) the *ocelli,* which are sensitive to light and shade and may form crude images at close range; (5) the *compound eyes,* which function essentially like those of the crayfish; and (6) the *organ of hearing.* The latter is a stretched tympanic membrane set into movement by sound vibrations in the air; this affects a slender point under the membrane that connects

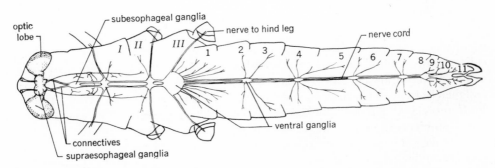

Fig. 23-7. The grasshopper. Nervous system in dorsal view; I–III, thoracic somites; 1–11, abdominal somites. (*After Riley,* 1878.)

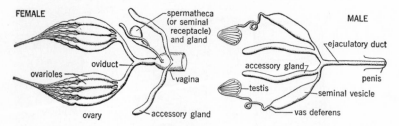

Fig. 23-8. Reproductive systems of insects; diagrammatic. *(After Snodgrass.)*

to sensory nerve fibers. The grasshopper produces sounds by rubbing the roughened hind tibia against a wing vein to set the latter into vibration.

23-10. Reproductive system (Fig. 23-8). The sexes are separate. In a *male,* each of the two *testes* is a series of slender tubules or follicles joined to a lengthwise *vas deferens.* The two vasa unite as a common median *ejaculatory duct,* which is joined by *accessory glands* and opens at the end of the large ventral male *copulatory organ.* In a *female,* each *ovary* is composed of several tapering egg tubes or *ovarioles,* in which the ova are produced, and is joined to an *oviduct.* The two oviducts unite as a median *vagina* that leads posteriorly and is joined by a small *seminal receptacle* (spermatheca), where sperm received at copulation are stored. The female tract opens near the ventral egg guide.

23-11. Natural history. In the warm days of early spring the young nymphs hatch from eggs laid in the ground the previous autumn. They resemble the adults but differ in proportions and have no wings or reproductive organs (Fig. 23-9). They eat tender vegetation and hide under plants or in crevices to avoid enemies and desiccation. After a few days the cuticle splits and is cast off; the molting nymph swallows air and increases in volume, and then its fresh cuticle hardens and darkens. Each individual has five (or six) nymphal stages, and its entire growth requires 30 to 50 or more days. The wings first appear as small pads, becoming larger at successive molts and unfolding to full size after the last molt into the adult stage.

Both nymphs and adults eat many kinds of vegetation, often migrating to new feeding grounds, and may damage farm and garden plantings. Feeding is most active in the mid-morning of sunny days with little wind. Adults of some species when crowded may perform long migrations.

Grasshoppers have many enemies. The eggs are eaten by some beetles, bee flies, moles, skunks, and mice, the nymphs by robber flies and digger wasps, and both nymphs and adults by large predatory insects and by frogs, reptiles, birds, and mammals. The eggs are parasitized by certain insects. Flesh flies (*Sarcophaga*) lay living maggots on adults, and tachinid flies deposit their eggs on grasshoppers in flight; the larvae of both burrow into their hosts and consume the fat tissues. Parasitized grasshoppers become logy and fail to reproduce, or die. The parasitic insects thus constitute a factor in grasshopper control. Both fungus and bacterial diseases also destroy numbers of grasshoppers. Man practices control by use of various toxic chemical sprays and poisoned baits on fields where grasshoppers are feeding.

23-12. Reproduction. After the adult stage is reached in summer, grasshoppers begin to mate. The male clings to the female's back, inserts his genitalia into her vagina, and transfers spermatozoa. After a further interval, egg laying begins. The eggs are 3 to 5 mm. long, about 20 are laid at a time, and one female may lay up to 10 lots. The adults die after breeding ends. In the ovary, each egg is enclosed by a delicate *vitelline membrane* and a brownish flexible shell, or *chorion,* that con-

Fig. 23-9. Development of the grasshopper. (*A*) Fertilized egg surrounded by chorion. (*B*) Cleavage, nuclei scattered. (*C*) Blastoderm cells surround yolk. (*D*) Germ band formed. (*E*) Early embryo, serosa, and amnion forming. (*F*) Later embryo with somites. (*G*) 8-day embryo. (*H*) 15-day embryo. (*I*) 20-day embryo, ready for diapause; 1, 2, 3, thoracic somites. (*J*) Embryo in diapause. (*K, L*) Blastokinesis, or rotation of the embryo. (*M*) Embryo before hatching. (*N–R*) The five nymphal stages with gradual increase in size and development of wing pads. (*S*) Adult with wings. (*A–F, generalized sagittal sections, after Johannsen and Butt; G, H, ventral views, after Slifer, 1932; K–M, lateral views after Burkholder, 1934; N–S, modified from Emerton in Riley, 1878.*)

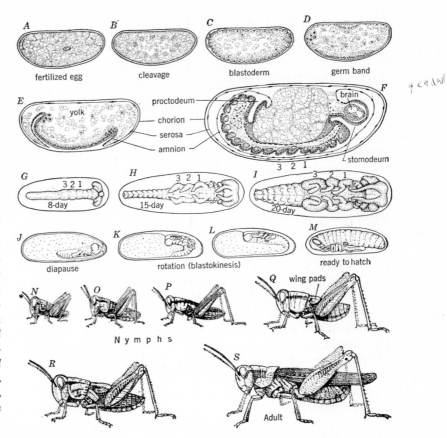

tains a minute pore, or ***micropyle,*** through which sperm enter during laying. The female uses her ovipositor to form a short tunnel in the ground where the eggs are placed, fastened together as an egg pod. Development begins at once and continues for about 3 weeks until the embryo is well formed. Then a rest, or ***diapause,*** ensues until spring, when growth is resumed and the young hatch and crawl to the ground surface. The diapause is a means to survive the adverse conditions of cold and lack of food in winter.

The fertilization nucleus within the egg yolk divides into scattered cleavage nuclei. These migrate to the periphery of the yolk, where each is surrounded by cytoplasm and a cell wall, and the cells form an epithelium (blastoderm) around the yolk. Those of a limited ventral area thicken as a ***germ band*** that will produce the ***embryo,*** and the lateral

and dorsal cells become the embryonic envelope, or ***serosa.*** At the ends and sides of the germ band, folds then form; their outer layers, inside the serosa, become the ***amnion,*** which encloses the embryo in an amniotic cavity. A lengthwise ventral furrow along the germ band folds up to form a layer (mesoderm + ?endoderm) above the germ band. The latter then divides by cross furrows, from before backward, into a linear series of somites that give rise to the head and its appendages, the thorax and its legs, and the segmented abdomen. The future fore-gut (stomodeum) forms as a pit at the anterior end and the hindgut (proctodeum) similarly at the posterior end. Later the midgut forms from endoderm cells, and the gut becomes a continuous tube. The tracheae develop as paired lateral invaginations of ectoderm. The nervous system arises as an infolding of ventral ectoderm into two lengthwise strands of cells that later produce the nerve cords, ganglia, and brain.

THE HONEYBEE

23-13. A social insect. The honeybee, *Apis mellifera* (Order HYMENOPTERA), resembles the grasshopper in general structure but is specialized in many features. It has both sucking and chewing mouth parts, undergoes complete metamorphosis from the worm-like larva through a pupal stage to the flying adult, feeds on nectar and pollen, and lives socially in a permanent *colony* comprising many individuals of three *castes* (Fig. 23-10). The *queen* lays the eggs; the males, or *drones,* serve only to fertilize new queens; and the thousands of sterile females, or *workers,* build and guard the hive, provide the food for all castes, attend the queen, and rear the young. Wild honeybees live in natural cavities of trees or rocks, but man has partly domesticated this species and houses it in *hives* of wood. Each colony lives amid vertical *combs* of wax that contain

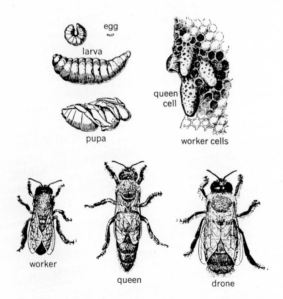

egg

larva

pupa

queen cell

worker cells

worker

queen

drone

Fig. 23-10. The honeybee, *Apis mellifera* (Order HYMENOPTERA); growth stages and three adult castes slightly enlarged; portion of comb reduced. (*After Phillips,* 1911.)

small lateral cells used to store honey or pollen and rear the young. Workers collect fluid *nectar* from flowers that is chemically altered and stored as the sirupy carbohydrate solution that we call *honey.* They take *pollen* to provide proteins for growth of the larvae, and also gather resins from plant buds which as *propolis* serve to cement and varnish crevices in the hive against wind and water. The worker bees use their *sting* to protect the colony and its honey against robbery by other animals, from bees to bears.

23-14. Structure and function. The body of a bee (Fig. 23-11) is densely covered by hairs with short lateral barbs where pollen grains lodge easily. Unbranched hairs occur on the compound eyes and legs. On each foreleg, the tibia is margined by an *eye brush* of stiff hairs for cleaning the compound eyes, and its distal end bears a flat, movable spine, or *fibula.* The latter closes over a bristle-lined notch on the proximal end of the tarsus to form an *antenna comb* through which the antenna is drawn to remove pollen or other foreign material. Long hairs on the large first segment of the tarsus form a cylindrical *pollen brush* to gather pollen from the fore parts of the body. On each middle leg, the flat tarsus has a similar brush to remove pollen from the forelegs and nearby body parts; and the inner distal end of the tibia bears a *spur* used to pick up wax. On the hind leg, the wide tibia is slightly concave externally and margined by incurving hairs to form a *pollen basket.* This has a comb of stiff hairs, the *pecten,* at its distal end and just below is a flat plate or *auricle,* on the proximal end of the tarsus. The outer surface of the tarsus has a *pollen brush* for cleaning the body posteriorly, and on its inner surface are about 10 rows of stiff, downward-pointing spines that form a *pollen comb.*

The thin delicate *wings* lie flat over the back at rest. In flight the two on each side are locked together by fine hooks bordering the hind wing that catch to a groove along the rear margin of the forewing (Fig. 23-11C). The wings may vibrate up to 400 times per second

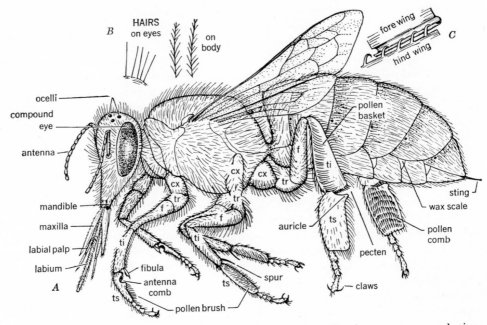

Fig. 23-11. The honeybee worker. (*A*) Mouth parts, pollen-collecting structures, and sting. (*B*) The hairs. (*C*) The wing-locking mechanism. Leg segments: *cx,* coxa; *tr,* trochanter; *f,* femur; *ti,* tibia; *ts,* tarsus. (*Adapted in part from Casteel,* 1912.)

with the tips moving in an ∞-shaped path. Workers are capable of long flights, even to 8 miles.

The smooth **mandibles** of workers serve to gather pollen and also to mold wax in making combs. The maxillae and labial palps form a tube around the slender **tongue,** or labium; by movements of the ligula and a pumping action of the pharynx, fluid nectar is drawn into the large crop, or **honey stomach.** Behind the latter are found triangular lips that form a **valve** (honey stopper) to prevent nectar or honey from entering the stomach except when wanted for food. The slender **intestine** is joined by about 100 **Malpighian tubules,** and the large rectum serves to accumulate feces for discharge through the anus after a bee leaves the hive.

The **sting** is a modified ovipositor and hence is present only in females: workers and queens. It comprises (1) a hollow dorsal **sheath** and (2) two **darts** grooved along their inner surfaces so they may slide along each other by the action of muscles at their inner bases, (3) at either side a sensory **sting palpus,** and (4) a large median **poison sac** supplied by two acid glands and a slender alkaline gland. The fluid is pumped into the wound made by the darts. A worker dies in about 2 days after using its sting, as all the poison apparatus and some adjacent parts pull off in the process. The queen's slender sting serves to combat rival queens and can be used more than once.

Each short **antenna** has many olfactory pits that provide a keen sense of smell, each compound eye has many ommatidia (Fig. 22-6), and the brain is large. Bees find their way and seek for food by both scent and sight. They can be trained to visit a food supply having a particular scent or associated with certain colors, except red, which they cannot distinguish from black. Glands on the abdomen produce a scent when bees are disturbed and may serve to "mark" new sources of food afield. Honeybees have a good sense of orientation, and each returns to its own hive. If a hive is moved, the absent workers return to the old site; but if confined within during the moving, they take account of the new location upon leaving and return to it.

23-15. Food. A worker bee, upon discovering a food supply in the field, fills her nectar stomach, returns to the hive, and either deposits the gathered nectar or feeds young bees. When the source is less than 100 yards away, she performs a "round dance," turning right and left in quick succession. If the source is more distant, she executes a different dance that informs other bees of its direction and distance. Beginning at a given spot, she makes a semicircular run, then a straight "wagging run" back to the point of origin, next a semicircle in the opposite direction, and again a run to the starting place. The total pattern is like a compressed ∞, repeated several times. Experiments by von Frisch and others (Fig. 23-12) show that the location of the food is indicated in relation to the position of the sun. If the supply is located in a place directly toward the sun, the axis (wagging run)

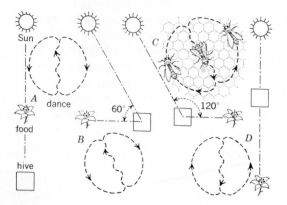

Fig. 23-12. Dance of worker bee on vertical comb in hive that indicates to other bees the position (angle) of the sun in relation to direction of food source from hive (*A*, 0°; *B*, 60°; *C*, 120°; *D*, 180°). Circles show path of dancer for each. *C* enlarged to show successive positions of the same dancer on comb and the wagging movements; other workers (not shown) crowd around the dancer. (*Adapted from von Frisch.*)

is vertically upward; if at an angle to the sun, the axis of the dance is at that angle. The frequency of runs decreases with greater distance of the food source from the hive (24 turns per minute for 500 meters, but only 8 turns for 5,000 meters). The length of the "straight runs" and the sounds produced during these runs are proportional to the distance to the food. The nature of the food supply is communicated by odor from the plant source on her body or in the nectar brought. Other bees keep their antennae touching the scout during her dance in the darkness of the hive.

When the bee visits a flower, (1) pollen taken by the mandibles is moistened with honey and (2) mixed with that gathered on the pollen brushes of the forelegs; (3) it is then taken by the pollen brushes on the middle legs, which in turn are (4) drawn between the pollen combs of the hind tarsi; (5) each of the latter is then scraped over the opposite leg to deposit pollen on the pecten or outer surface of the auricle, and (6) by flexing the tarsus on the tibia the pollen is pushed upward and packed into the pollen basket. The bee thus accumulates a bulging load of sticky pollen in both baskets, returns to the hive, and pushes her load into a cell, to be tamped down by the heads of young workers. Propolis is carried similarly but is removed by other workers.

Nectar held in the honey stomach is acted upon by salivary enzymes, cane sugar (sucrose) being inverted to dextrose and levulose. Upon returning to its hive, a worker regurgitates this fluid into a cell of the comb, where the young "house bees" work it over in their mouths, causing further chemical changes; they evaporate the excess water by fanning with their wings and then seal the cell with wax. Honey averages 17 per cent of water and 77.5 per cent of sugars, with small amounts of minerals, enzymes, and pollen; its color and flavor vary according to the nectar source.

23-16. Reproduction. The reproductive system is vestigial in workers but highly developed in queens. About 7 days after emerging, a young queen mates with a drone high in the air. The drone's copulatory organs then are torn away and remain in the queen's genital bursa until removed by workers after her return to the hive. The spermatozoa thus received into her spermatheca must serve for all the fertilized eggs she will ever lay. Her ovaries enlarge to fill the long abdomen, and in a day or two she begins to lay. She can control the process of fertilization. Unfertilized eggs produce drones, or males (genetically haploid, 16 chromosomes) and fertilized eggs yield females (diploid, 32 chromosomes). In the season of nectar flow, a queen lays up to 1,000 eggs per day, gluing each to the bottom of a cell. The tiny worm-like *larva* has no legs or eyes. For two days all larvae are fed on "royal jelly" produced by pharyngeal glands of young workers. Thereafter, drone and worker larvae receive mainly honey and pollen, but queen larvae continue chiefly on royal jelly, which causes them to develop differently and to become larger. Each larva has several molts and grows; then its cell is capped with wax, and the larva within spins a thin *cocoon*. There, as a *pupa*, it undergoes complete metamorphosis and finally cuts the cell cap with its mandibles to emerge as a young bee. The time of development for each caste is standardized because of the temperature regulation in the hive:

Queen: egg, 3; larva, $5\frac{1}{2}$; pupa, $7\frac{1}{2}$ = 16 days
Worker: egg, 3; larva, 6; pupa, 12   = 21 days
Drone: egg, 3; larva, $6\frac{1}{2}$; pupa, $14\frac{1}{2}$ = 24 days

To mankind, the honeybee is a symbol of industry and cooperation, gathering food in time of plenty against the needs of winter. When the warmth of spring brings early flowers, the workers gather nectar and pollen, the queen lays rapidly, and new workers soon swell the colony population. Overcrowding leads to *swarming,* in which the old queen and several thousand workers emerge as a dense swarm and fly off to a new site previously located by worker scouts. Prior to this, some queen larvae were started in the old colony. One of the queens emerges, usually stings the other queen larvae, is fertilized in a mating flight, and returns to serve the old hive in egg laying. A queen may live for three to five seasons and lay a million eggs. Drones are produced during active nectar flow; but thereafter, when brood production ceases, they are mostly driven out to starve and die. Many of the workers hatched in autumn survive until spring, but those born earlier in the year use up their energy more rapidly—like a battery —and live only 6 to 8 weeks.

23-17. The hive. Each comb (Fig. 23-10) in a hive is a vertical sheet of wax, fastened to the top (and sides) of a frame. The *worker cells,* where workers are reared and honey or pollen is stored, are about 5 mm. across, and the *drone cells,* 6 mm. across, serve to rear drones and for storage. Large, vertical, peanut-like *queen cells,* open below, are built along the lower comb margins for queen rearing. The wax is secreted as small flakes by glands in pockets under the abdomen on workers. Once formed, the combs are used for years, the cells being cleaned and polished for reuse.

Honeybees are about the only animals that achieve "air conditioning." In summer they fan their wings vigorously to ventilate the hive, to keep the temperature inside at about 33°C. for brood rearing, and to evaporate excess water from honey in open cells. In hot, dry weather they carry in water to humidify the colony and to dilute the honey if necessary. During winter, when the stored honey is used as food, they form a compact cluster and produce heat by active body and wing movements. Clusters form at 14°C. (57°F.) or below and can raise the hive temperature to 24° or 30°C., even when the outside air is at or below freezing.

Bee colonies are reduced by dearth of nectar or pollen and by exhaustion of honey stores in winter. Adult bees are eaten by toads, skunks, and bears, the latter having a proverbial liking for honey as well. Two serious "foul brood" diseases cause heavy losses in colonies if unchecked.

OTHER INSECTS

23-18. Form and function. The adults of insects, with few exceptions, are alike in having one pair each of antennae and compound eyes, a fused head, a thorax of three somites with six legs (hence called Hexapoda), and a distinct abdomen. Within these limits members of the various orders, families, and species show great diversity in details of structure and habits. Many of their features are adaptive modifications to particular modes of life.

The *coloration* is produced by pigments (chemical), or by surface structures (physical), or by a combination of these. Some pigments are deposited in the exoskeleton and others in the epidermis or deeper. The iridescent colors of some beetles, butterflies, and others are produced by differential interference of light falling upon microscopically fine surface ridges or parallel plates of cuticle. Many insects are *protectively colored* so that they resemble their immediate surroundings. Some that are considered to be bad-tasting are described as warningly colored, and some inoffensive species mimic the color or appearance of others that are bad-tasting or poisonous (Fig. 14-11).

The exterior *cuticle* is often waxy and not easily wetted. The *body* is adaptively streamlined in some aquatic bugs and beetles, is depressed in cockroaches and others that live in crevices, and is fusilage-shaped in the fast-flying dragonflies. The hairy covering on some nocturnal moths may insulate them against chilling, and the hairs on many flies and bees serve in the gathering of pollen.

The *antennae* are plumed in some gnats and moths and of varied shapes in beetles. All insects have *eyes* except some larvae that live concealed from the light, some adults that inhabit caves or nests of termites or ants, some biting lice, and the nonsexual castes of some ants and most termites. The *mouth parts* are of two main types, for either chewing or sucking, as in the grasshopper and bee, respectively. Many species with sucking mouth parts have means for piercing tissues, as in the mos-

quitoes and fleas that "bite" other animals and the aphids that puncture plants.

The *legs* are variously modified, for running in tiger beetles, jumping in fleas, swimming in water bugs and beetles, skating in water striders, burrowing in mole crickets, and spinning in embiids. The *wings* are commonly thin and membranous. The forewings are hardened as elytra in beetles; they are leathery in some ORTHOPTERA, and the forward half is thickened in HEMIPTERA. Flies (DIPTERA) and male coccids have the hind pair represented by minute, knobbed halteres (balancing organs), and the fore pair is reduced on male stylopids. The primitive insects (PROTURA, THYSANURA, etc.) and the lice, fleas, and some other parasitic forms lack wings; ants and termites are also wingless save for the sexual castes. The embryo in many insects has abdominal appendages, but there are rarely any on adults except for the cerci and copulatory organs. The *muscles* are numerous and complex; about 2,000 are present in a caterpillar. Many insects are disproportionately powerful as compared with larger animals; a honeybee, for example, can pull twenty times its own weight and can lift a load equal to four-fifths its weight in flight.

The *digestive system* shows various modifications in relation to food habits. The salivary glands of bloodsucking insects produce anticoagulants that keep the blood fluid during ingestion and digestion. *Respiration* is performed by a tracheal system in most insects, but through the thin body covering in COLLEMBOLA, some PROTURA, and some endoparasitic larvae. Adult aquatic insects that dive carry down a film of air on the exterior of their nonwettable bodies or beneath their wings to serve for respiration. Some aquatic larvae, such as those of mosquitoes, must extend their spiracles above the water to breathe, but the larvae of caddis-flies and others have thin *gills*—tracheal or blood—that take up oxygen dissolved in water. Some larvae that live in bottom muck deficient in oxygen probably satisfy their respiratory needs by oxygen obtained in the metabolism of food.

The *nervous system* is annelid-like in the lowest insects and in many larvae of higher forms, with paired ganglia in each body somite, but in the adults of some flies and others the posterior ganglia are concentrated forward in the body. Sound production is possible in many ORTHOPTERA, HEMIPTERA, cicadas, certain moths, some mosquitoes and flies, and some beetles and bees. The mechanism of production varies and in some may be merely incidental to their manner of flight. Light production is an ability of glow-worms, fireflies, and others; some flash in unison.

23-19. Distribution. Some insects such as the house fly are of exceedingly wide occurrence, over a continent or more, whereas other species are limited to a few acres. Insects occur from sea level to well above 20,000 feet on the highest mountains. Airplane surveys show that many insects inhabit the air, especially by day during the summer; they are mostly below 1,000 feet, but some have been taken up to 14,000 feet. By such means species are constantly being carried to new localities. Some beetles and others live on seabeaches between the tide lines, and a few water striders (*Halobates*) live on the ocean surface; but there are very few submerged marine insects.

23-20. Seasonal occurrence. Life on land exposes insects to greater extremes of environmental conditions than experienced by most inhabitants of the sea and fresh waters. They have to withstand seasonal changes in temperature and food supply. Many species are abundant in warm seasons and far reduced at other times. Some, such as yellow-jackets, overwinter as adults that hide away to hibernate in shelters where their bodily metabolism is far reduced. Others survive as pupae or larvae. In many species all individuals die at the close of the warm season and then are represented only by eggs that will develop and hatch the following spring.

23-21. Sensory perceptions and behavior. Insects respond to many stimuli that provoke sensations in man, including light, chemical stimuli (smell, taste), touch, and sound, but their perceptions differ in both kind and magnitude. They detect chemical stimuli far too delicate for the human nose or tongue, and some react to ultraviolet rays but not to red or infrared. These reactions are of aid in finding food and mates and shelter for themselves, their eggs, and their young.

The simplest kinds of response are *reflexes* (par. 10-16) such as the action of a bee's sting, which will operate reflexly if touched even when severed from the body. The invariable type of response by which an animal orients itself to or away from a stimulus is known as a *taxis*. A *Drosophila* is guided by its olfactory organs to overripe fruit that bears the yeast upon which the fly feeds by a *positive chemotaxis* to certain alcohols and organic acids in the fermenting fruit. Many insects find mates by a similar taxis to the delicate scents emitted by the opposite sex. The moth that flies directly to (and even into) a flame shows *positive phototaxis,* and the cockroach that runs for cover when suddenly exposed to a lamp a *negative phototaxis.* Aquatic larvae of caddisflies often show *positive rheotaxis* by aligning themselves head foremost in a current of water. The term *kinesis* is used to describe undirected locomotor reactions where the speed of movement or frequency of turning depend on the intensity of stimulation. The cockroach, besides avoiding light, seeks shelter in crevices where its body is in contact with the shelter—this is *thigmokinesis.* Taxes and kineses, and some other types of reactions, enable insects and many other animals to find and occupy the small habitat or microclimate in which each kind is most successful in carrying out its life cycle.

Other kinds of behavior in insects are based on *instincts,* which consist of series or chains of coordinated reflexes by the whole organism. The complex series of events by which a solitary wasp constructs a nest, deposits an egg, provisions it with paralyzed insects, and skillfully closes the cell is an example of chain instincts. Still other aspects of insect behavior are plastic, or modifiable, and involve experiences of an individual that are registered as organic memory. An example is the hive bee, which learns to associate color with a food supply.

23-22. Flight. Insects, birds, and bats are the only animals capable of true flight. The wings of insects (Figs. 23-3, 23-13) are unique structures in being derived as extensions of the body integument quite unlike the limb wings of the vertebrates (Fig. 14-1). The ability to fly enables insects to escape enemies, to find food and mates more readily, to lay their eggs in places not easily reached by other animals, to extend their feeding ranges, and to disperse and occupy new territory.

23-23. Water conservation. When the ancestors of insects left the water and moved to the land and air, they experienced changes analogous to those of amphibians and reptiles as compared with fishes. The sense organs became adapted to function in air, the chitinous body covering resisted the loss of body fluids by evaporation, and the tracheae provided a means for breathing air. All insects except those in humid environments must conserve body water because moisture may be lost in respiration and in evacuating food residues. Insects in dry situations extract water from food residues in the rectum and gain some metabolic water as a by-product of the oxidation of food.

23-24. Food. Fully half the known species of insects are **phytophagous,** feeding on plant tissues or juices. Grasshoppers eat a great variety of plants, the potato beetle uses only those of the Family SOLANACEAE, the larva of the monarch butterfly eats only milkweeds, and that of a common copper butterfly only a single species of sorrel. Most termites and certain beetles subsist on wood, but some of them and certain ants eat fungi exclusively; among such insects are some that produce their own food by planting, fertilizing, and tending "fungus gardens." The **saprophagous** insects include beetles, fly larvae, and others which eat dead animals, and the **carnivorous** species are those which capture and devour insects or other living animals.

23-25. Enemies. Insects are eaten by a wide variety of other insects and vertebrates and by some human races and tribes; they also are subject to many diseases that act to reduce their numbers.

23-26. Reproduction. Fertilization is always internal. Most species are **oviparous** and lay their eggs singly or in clusters, on or in the ground, on the plants or animals where their larvae feed, or in plant tissues. Those with aquatic larvae oviposit in or near water. The eggs of some hatch in a few hours, but others require many months. The aphids and some other insects are **viviparous,** producing living young. Eggs of tachinid flies deposited on other insects hatch almost immediately. The

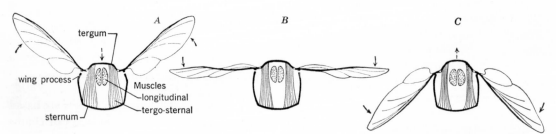

Fig. 23-13. Wing movements in the flight of an insect. (*A*) *Upstroke:* Contractions of the tergo-sternal muscles depress the tergum and carry the wing bases downward, each acting over a wing process as a fulcrum. Rotation of the wings is produced by still other muscles. (*C*) *Downstroke:* Contraction of the longitudinal (and other) muscles causes the tergum to bulge upward and forces the wing tips downward. (*After Snodgrass.*)

living young of tsetse and hippoboscid flies develop within the "uterus" of the female parent, where they are nourished by special secretions.

Parthenogenesis, or reproduction from eggs without fertilization, occurs in aphids, thrips, gall wasps, saw-flies, and others. The generations of aphids in spring and summer consist only of females that reproduce by parthenogenesis, but later both sexes are produced in the same manner (Fig. 23-14). These mate, and the fertilized females then lay eggs that remain quiescent over winter to produce females for the next spring. A special type of parthenogenesis (paedogenesis) occurs in the fly *Miastor* and a few other insects. Each larva produces 7 to 30 larvae, and these in turn yield others. Some later larvae pupate to become male and female flies. The chalcid wasps that parasitize eggs of butterflies and moths exhibit *polyembryony;* an egg begins development, then divides into 100 or more masses each of which grows to be a larva that transforms into a wasp.

The larvae of tachinid flies (DIPTERA) and of the ichneumonid, braconid, and chalcid wasps (HYMENOPTERA) are *parasites* of other insects, and the scelionids (HYMENOPTERA) are egg parasites. The parasites weaken or kill their hosts or destroy the eggs and thus serve to control the populations of the latter; but as the supply of host individuals declines, so must that of the parasites, which fluctuate in numbers with their hosts. This matter is further complicated by hyperparasitism, wherein parasites in turn are themselves parasitized by other species.

The cynipids or gall wasps (HYMENOPTERA) and the cecidomyids or gall flies (DIPTERA) are small insects that oviposit in plant tissues. Some substance then injected or resulting from growth of the larvae causes the plant to produce characteristic swellings, or *galls.* The latter are of distinctive form and location (stem or leaf) according to the host plant and the kind of insect involved. Galls are also produced by some aphids and psyllids (HOMOPTERA) and by certain gall mites (ACARINA).

The number of offspring varies in different insects, from the single larva hatched at a time

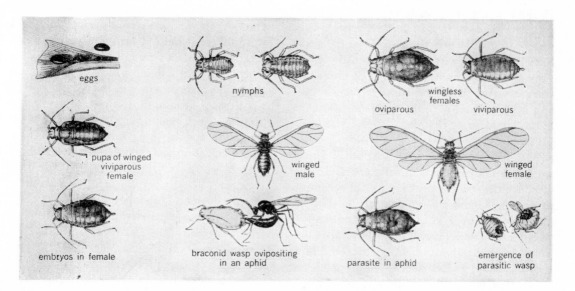

Fig. 23-14. Stages in the life cycle of the spring grain aphid (*Toxoptera graminum,* adult male 1.5 mm. long), an insect having both parthenogenetic and normal sexual development. Also showing parasitism of the aphid by a wasp. (*After U.S. Bur. Entomology Bull.* 110.)

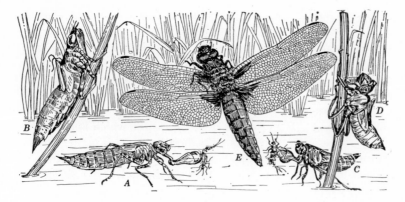

Fig. 23-15. Life stages of dragon-flies (Order ODONATA), insects with incomplete metamorphosis and aquatic developmental stages. *Aeschna:* (*A*) Nymph capturing prey, with labium extended. (*B*) Nymphal skin. *Libellula:* (*C*) Nymph. (*D*) Nymphal skin. (*E*) Adult at rest with wings extended. (*After Brehm.*)

by some viviparous flies to the million eggs, more or less, laid by a queen bee. The actual number from any one female is less important than the rate of increase, which is very rapid in some species with short life cycles. The pomace fly (*Drosophila*) lays up to 200 eggs per female, and the entire cycle requires only 10 days at about 80°F. The house fly may complete its cycle in 8 to 10 days during hot weather. Parthenogenesis in aphids and others likewise leads to extremely rapid multiplication under optimum conditions of temperature, moisture, and food supply. The successive generations of offspring from a single aphid could cover the earth in one season if all survived!

23-27. Growth and metamorphosis. Since an insect lives in an armor-like exoskeleton, it can change form or increase in size only after a molt, and none molts after attaining the adult stage. The increase in dimensions at successive molts is about 1.4 but varies according to the duration of each stage. The primitive Orders PROTURA to THYSANURA attain adult form and size by slightly graded changes and hence are called the AMETABOLA (Gr. *a,* not + *metabolos,* change). The HEMI-METABOLA (ODONATA to THYSANOPTERA) un-

dergo a gradual or incomplete metamorphosis (Fig. 23-15). The young hatch as small *nymphs,* somewhat resembling the adults, with compound eyes. In the successive stages, or *instars,* the wings appear externally as small wing pads that enlarge at successive molts to become functional in the adult, or *imago.* In the HOLOMETABOLA (MECOPTERA to HYMENOPTERA), the young emerge as small, worm-like, segmented *larvae* with the head, thorax, and abdomen much alike and often with short legs but no wings or compound eyes. The successive larval instars increase in size through several molts. Each then enters a "resting" stage as a *pupa,* within the last larval skin, in a special puparium, or in a *cocoon.* Many larval organs then break down and are reabsorbed by phagocytic cells, while new structures for the adult arise concurrently. These profound changes occur before the adult, or *imago,* emerges. This is complete metamorphosis (Fig. 23-16).

Both molt and metamorphosis are controlled by hormones secreted by the prothoracic gland and the corpus allatum, behind the brain. Removal of these glands at critical stages in nymphs of the bug *Rhodnius* prevents molt (par. 9-2). Like vertebrate hor-

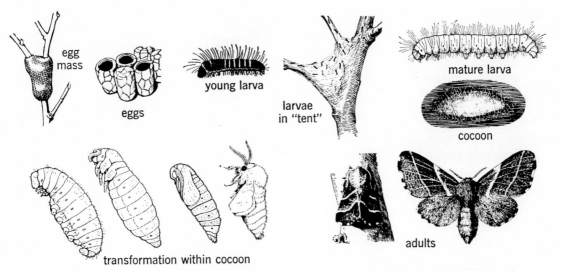

egg mass

eggs

young larva

larvae in "tent"

mature larva

cocoon

transformation within cocoon

adults

Fig. 23-16. Life history of the tent caterpillar (*Malacosoma americana;* adult 20 mm. long)—an insect having complete metamorphosis. Stages in the transformation take place inside the cocoon. Not to scale. *(After Snodgrass, Insects, 1930, Courtesy of Smithsonian Institution Series, Inc.)*

mones, the molting hormones are nonspecific; if transplanted, they will influence molt in insects of other genera.

23-28. Social insects. Most insects are *solitary,* each individual living unto itself; the sexes associate only to mate, and the female deserts her eggs or dies after laying. *Gregarious* species assemble in large numbers, as in swarms of locusts and hibernating ladybird beetles. With all such insects the parents usually never see or live coincidently with their offspring. About 6,000 species of insects, however, exhibit social instincts, the female or both parents living cooperatively with their offspring in a common shelter. These conditions begin with *subsocial relations,* as of a female earwig, which guards her eggs and later the young; cockroaches and crickets, some beetles and bugs, and other insects do likewise. A solitary wasp provisions individual egg cells with insects as food for the larvae, which later hatch out and grow independently. True *social life* occurs among all termites, all ants, and certain wasps and bees. The female lives, according to her species, protected within the soil, in cavities in wood, or in a manufactured nest, often in darkness

under a lowered temperature and regulated humidity where her muscular movements and metabolism are lessened. She has a lengthened life span, possibly because of these favorable conditions. Queens of some termites and ants may live for several years. In the more primitive types, the female merely remains with successive broods or feeds them daily. From this situation there is a graded series to the complex colonial life of termites, ants, and hive bees, which have division of labor between several castes (Fig. 23-17). The constant association of many individuals in a colony evidently leads to formation of useful new reflexes and instincts; with different kinds of food and possibly by the action of hormones, these may have brought on the origin of castes. The larger populations with social life require an enhanced food supply. The ants show a progression in food habits such as probably occurred in man's history. The lowest kinds hunt insects or flesh. Pastoral ants attend and shelter aphids ("ant cows") from which they obtain honeydew as food, and harvester ants gather and store seeds in summer to tide them through the winter. Finally, the fungus ants (*Atta*) grow their own pure crops of certain

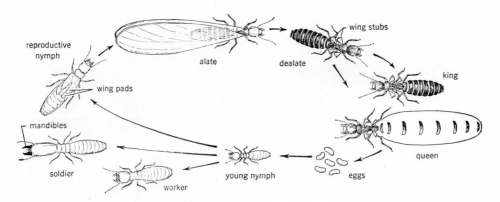

Fig. 23-17. Castes and life cycle of a termite. *(Modified from Kofoid, Termites and termite control, University of California Press.)*

fungi in underground gardens that are fertilized with organic debris; each young queen upon setting out to found a new colony carries a seed stock of fungal hyphae in an infrabuccal pouch.

23-29. Relations to man. Practically every person is affected by some insects, from the apartment dweller who eats honey, wears silk, and swats flies to the primitive tribesman who is plagued by lice, fleas, and flies and in extremity eats grasshoppers. Economic entomology deals with the several thousand species of insects of importance to agriculture, forestry, and the food industries, and medical entomology with those which affect the health of man and domestic animals.

There are many beneficial insects. The bees and other insects that go from flower to flower to gather pollen are essential in cross-fertilizing the blossoms of apples, cherries, blackberries, clover, and other crops, as these will not otherwise set fruit or seed. Hives of bees are placed in orchards or fields to ensure such fertilization. The Smyrna fig, which is grown in California, produces only female flowers; to set good fruit, these need "caprification" (pollination) by a small wasp (*Blastophaga*) that develops only in the small, nonedible caprifig, whence it brings pollen. The hive bees of the United States produce about 100,000 tons of honey annually, which serves as human food; they also yield over 1,000 tons of beeswax,

which is used in polishes, church candles, and modeling, and to wax thread. Raw silk is obtained in the Orient and Europe from the silkworm (*Bombyx mori*). The larvae are reared in domestication on a diet of white mulberry leaves, and each spins a cocoon of silk from its salivary secretions. A cocoon yields about 1,000 feet of fiber, and about 25,000 cocoons are unwound to spin one pound of silk thread. The shellac of commerce is obtained from waxy secretions of certain lac or scale insects (Coccidae) of India, and the dyes known as "cochineal" and "crimson lake" are derived from the dried bodies of some tropical cactus scale insects.

Many harmful plant-eating insects are devoured by a host of *predaceous insects,* such as ground beetles, syrphid flies, and wasps. The scale insects that feed on and damage citrus and other trees are eaten by the larvae of ladybird beetles, and the latter are a major factor in controlling such pests. Certain species of ladybird beetles have been imported, reared, and liberated in orchards in attempts to control scale insects. The *parasitic insects* that oviposit in the eggs or young of plant-feeding insects and whose larvae destroy the latter are another useful group; some of them are reared artificially and liberated to serve in "biological control" of harmful species. Unfortunately, some such parasites are themselves in turn subject to hyperparasites, which

Table 23-1. Examples of diseases transmitted by insects and ticks

Disease	Causative organism	Carried by	Order
Dutch elm disease ✓	*Ceratostomella* (fungus)	Bark beetles (*Scolytus*)	COLEOPTERA
Cucumber wilt	*Erwinia tracheiphila*	Cucumber beetles (*Diabrotica*)	COLEOPTERA
Curly top of sugar beets	Virus	Beet leafhopper (*Circulifer*)	HOMOPTERA
Human yellow fever	Virus	Mosquito (*Aëdes aegypti*)	DIPTERA
Bubonic plague of rats and ✓ man	*Pasteurella pestis*	Fleas (*Xenopsylla* and others)	SIPHONAPTERA
Tularemia	*Pasteurella tularensis*	Deer fly (*Chrysops*) and others	DIPTERA
Human typhus fever	*Rickettsia*	Body louse (*Pediculus*)	ANOPLURA
Human malaria ✓	*Plasmodium*	Mosquito (*Anopheles*)	DIPTERA
Chagas' disease	*Trypanosoma cruzi*	Bug (*Triatoma*)	HEMIPTERA
Filariasis ✓	*Wuchereria bancrofti*	Mosquitoes (*Culex* and others)	DIPTERA
Dog tapeworm	*Dipylidium caninum*	Louse (*Trichodectes*) and fleas	MALLOPHAGA SIPHONAPTERA
Rocky Mountain spotted ✓ fever of man	*Dermacentroxinus rickettsi*	Tick (*Dermacentor andersoni*)	ACARINA
Texas cattle fever	*Babesia bigemina*	Tick (*Boöphilus annulatus*)	ACARINA

cancel the benefits from the parasitic species.

Other useful insects are the scavenger beetles and flies that clean up the dung and dead bodies of animals. Flesh flies lay quantities of eggs in animal carcasses, which their voracious larvae soon reduce to skin and bone. Ants, termites, and beetles slowly reduce the remains of dead trees and other plants, but termites also do much damage to buildings and other wooden structures. Finally, many insects are indirectly useful as the food for fishes, game birds, fur mammals, and other wild vertebrates and at times for domestic poultry.

Many species of **harmful insects** injure farm crops, forests, flower and truck gardens, stored foods, and other property; and some affect the comfort and health of wild and domestic animals and man. The aggregate damage by such insects has been estimated at more than a billion dollars annually in the United States. Every cultivated plant has more than one insect pest, and each important crop such as corn, cotton, wheat, and tobacco has a hundred or more. These levy a steady toll in damage or loss of crops and in expenditures for control by poison sprays, dusts, and parasites. Some major **native pests** are the Colorado potato beetle, chinch bug, and grasshoppers; among the many **introduced pests** are the hessian fly of wheat, European corn borer, cotton

Fig. 23-18. Examples of Oligocene fossil insects. *Above.* A beetle (weevil), 7×, in shale rock at Florissant, Colorado. *Below.* Fungus gnat, 3½×, in amber (fossil resin), from Simojovel, Mexico.

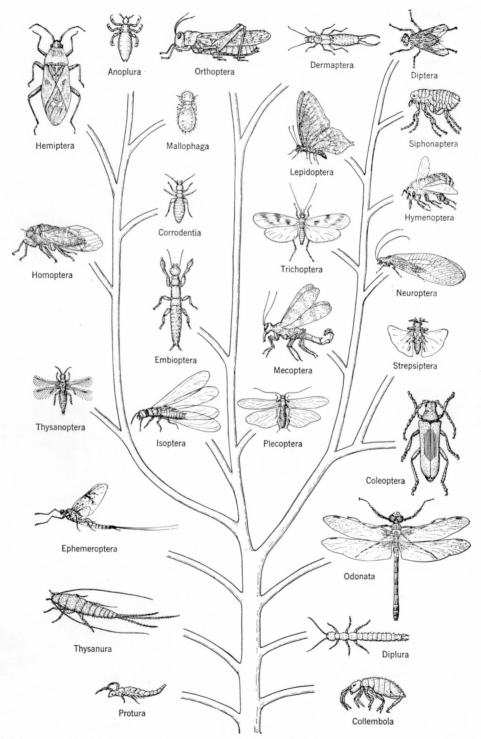

Fig. 23-19. The orders of insects. Examples of each in a presumed evolutionary sequence suggesting probable relationships between the various orders (compare Table 23-2).

Table 23-2. Orders of the Class Insecta

(*Characters of adults; exceptions as to wings or other features omitted*)

Subclass	Metamorphosis	Orders and common names	Mouth parts		Wings		Distinctive features
			Chewing	Sucking	Fore	Hind	
APTERYGOTA	AMETABOLA: no metamorphosis	1. **Protura**	C		None		No antennae
		2. **Collembola:** springtails	C		None		Spring (furcula) on abdomen
		3. **Diplura:** japygids	C		None		2 pincers or cerci on abdomen
		4. **Thysanura:** bristletails	C		None		Body fine-scaled; 3 "tails" on abdomen
PTERYGOTA typically winged; wings reduced or absent in some	HEMIMETABOLA: young are *nymphs* with compound eyes, and wings grow externally; metamorphosis gradual (incomplete)	(5) **Odonata:** dragon-flies	C		Filmy, not folded, nearly alike		Large; eyes big; no cerci
		6. **Ephemeroptera:** May-flies	C		Filmy, not folded Larger	Smaller	Mouth parts vestigial, "tails" 2 or 3
		7. **Orthoptera:** roaches, grasshoppers	C		4 or none Leathery	Thin	Usually with cerci
		8. **Dermaptera:** earwigs	C		Hard, short	Thin, fan-like	Forceps at end of abdomen
		9. **Plecoptera:** stone-flies	C		Filmy, narrower	Pleated, broader	2 long cerci
		10. **Isoptera:** termites	C		Sexual forms with like wings; others wingless		Sexual forms pigmented; others pale, uncolored
		11. **Embioptera:** embiids	C		♂ winged; ♀ wingless		Tarsi of forelegs enlarged for spinning
		12. **Mallophaga:** biting lice	C		None		Minute, flat; head wide
		(13.) **Anoplura:** sucking lice		S	None		Minute, flat; mouth parts retractile; head narrow
		14. **Corrodentia:** book lice	C		4, folded, roofed, or none		A maxillary "pick"
		15. **Hemiptera:** true bugs		S	Half leathery	Filmy	A triangular scutellum; base of beak far forward on head
		16. **Homoptera:** aphids, scale insects		S	Texture uniform; 4, 2, or none		Base of beak close to thorax
		17. **Thysanoptera:** thrips		S	Fringed with hairs		Tarsi bladder-like
	HOLOMETABOLA: young are *larvae* with no compound eyes; wings grow internally; metamorphosis complex (complete)	18. **Mecoptera:** scorpion-flies	C		Filmy, roofed, nearly alike		Head elongate as a beak; cerci short
		19. **Neuroptera:** ant lions, dobson-flies	C		Filmy, roofed, nearly alike		No cerci
		20. **Trichoptera:** caddis-flies	C		Filmy, roofed		Wings, hairy-coated
		(21) **Lepidoptera:** moths, butterflies		S	Covered by fine overlapped scales		Maxillae as coiled proboscis for feeding
		(22) **Diptera:** true flies		S	No hind wings		Halteres ("balancers") replace hind wings
		(23) **Siphonaptera:** fleas		S	None		Small; body laterally compressed
		(24) **Coleoptera:** beetles, weevils	C		Hard, veinless	Filmy, folded	Prothorax large, mesothorax reduced
		25. **Strepsiptera:** stylops	C		Hind wings only in ♂; none in ♀		♀ maggot-like, having head and thorax fused
		(26) **Hymenoptera:** ants, wasps, bees	C	S	Filmy; 2 pairs or none		Base of abdomen usually constricted

♂ = male   ♀ = female   filmy = membranous   roofed = wings at rest over abdomen, thus /\.

boll weevil, and codling moth of apples. Federal and state quarantines are maintained to limit the spread of some of these insects.

Human foods are eaten or ruined by ants, cockroaches, and weevils and are dirtied by house flies; stored cereals are damaged by grain weevils and moths; woolen clothing, carpets, furs, and feathers are riddled by clothes moths and carpet beetles; and books are damaged by silverfish, beetle larvae, and termites. Bedbugs, stable flies, mosquitoes, and the gnats bite man and his animals; attacks of biting lice cause poultry and livestock to become unthrifty; bloodsucking tabanid flies annoy horses, and horn flies do the same to cattle; the larvae of botflies are a source of irritation in the stomachs of horses; and the larvae of ox warble flies burrow in the backs of cattle, causing them to lose flesh and injuring the hides for leather.

Many insects and some ticks act as intermediate hosts for various diseases of man and the larger animals and plants; a few important examples are given in Table 23-1.

Control of injurious insects has become more efficient with the development of many new organic poisons, of which DDT and benzene hexachloride are conspicuous examples.

23-30. Fossil insects. Despite their fragile nature, remains of insects as fossils have been found in Australia, China, Russia, Europe, and the United States, and over 10,000 species have been described. The first primitive wingless insects (COLLEMBOLA) are recorded from the Devonian Period, about 350,000,000 years old. The earliest winged insects are in Upper Carboniferous rocks, about 300,000,000 years old, and include the primitive †PALEODICTY-OPTERA, which lasted into Permian time; others (BLATTARIA) are closely related to living cockroaches. The †PROTODONATA resembled dragonflies, and some (†Meganura) had a wingspread up to 28 inches! Six existing orders date from the Permian, and others appeared in the Mesozoic. The rising land, colder climates, and appearance of seasonal seed plants in those times evidently stimulated

the evolution of pupae to withstand adverse conditions, since the earliest scorpion-flies (MECOPTERA) are so much like existing species as to suggest that complete metamorphosis was an early achievement. The fossil remains indicate that the orders differed in relative abundance; the beetles (COLEOPTERA) comprise only 1 per cent of known Permian insects but nearly 40 per cent of all insect species today. The flies (DIPTERA) make up 0.3 per cent in the Permian, 5 per cent in Mesozoic, 27 per cent in Tertiary, and 10 per cent of Recent species.

The transparent amber (fossil resin) of Lower Oligocene, found along the Baltic coast of Europe, contains many insects with all external details beautifully preserved and easily seen. Existing families and genera are common, but extinct species also occur. Eight kinds of ants are structurally identical with living species, implying survival for 30,000,000 years. The ants show polymorphism, and some had learned to attend plant lice. One of the richest known fossil insect faunas is preserved at Florissant, Colorado, near Pikes Peak, in Oligocene lake deposits of volcanic sand and ash that later became shale (Fig. 23-18). Most of the genera of insects of Tertiary time still survive, others have disappeared, and some (such as the tsetse fly, *Glossina*) are now less widely distributed.

REVIEW

1. What are the most distinctive characters of a "typical" adult insect?
2. Which features of structure and function enable insects to live successfully on land?
3. Describe the chewing mouth parts of a grasshopper, giving the arrangement of parts and the function of each. Compare these with the sucking mouth parts of a honeybee.
4. How do insects fly? Are insects similar in flight or wing structure to any other animals? How do the wings develop?
5. How does blood circulate in the body of an insect? Is the system open or closed?
6. Compare the insect tracheal system with the

blood transport system of vertebrate respiration. How is each system adapted to life in the water?

7. What are the Malpighian tubules? Are there homologous structures in other animals?

8. With the nervous system of what other phylum does that of an insect compare most closely?

9. Describe and give an example of each of the following: growth without metamorphosis, incomplete metamorphosis, complete metamorphosis. Define nymph, pupa, instar, molt, cocoon.

10. Compare the parts of the male and female reproductive systems of a grasshopper. What is meant by diapause in the grasshopper egg?

11. How is sex determined in the honeybee? What special treatment is given to bee larvae destined to become queens as compared with workers?

12. Explain the physical and chemical basis for coloration in insects. What is mimicry?

13. Define parthenogenesis, paedogenesis, oviparous reproduction, polyembryony, hyperparasite.

14. In what ways are the following insects beneficial to man: honeybee, blastophaga wasp, parasitic braconid wasp, lac insect, ladybird beetle, flesh flies, termites?

24
Introduction to the chordates

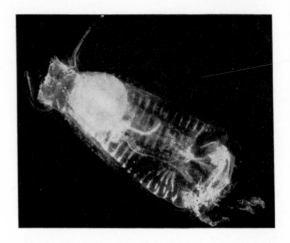

The Phylum CHORDATA (Gr. *chorda,* string) comprises the tunicates, lancelets, and the "vertebrates"—the lampreys, sharks and rays, bony fishes, amphibians, reptiles, birds and mammals. The lower chordates are mostly of small size, all are marine, and most tunicates are sessile. The vertebrates include practically all living animals of medium to large size, including some huge sharks and whales (Fig. 1-2). Vertebrates occupy all kinds of habitats in salt and fresh waters and on land, most of the reptiles, birds, and mammals being strictly terrestrial. The major divisions of the Phylum CHORDATA are given in Table 24-1.

24-1. Characteristics. The chordates are bilaterally symmetrical, with three germ layers, a basically segmented body, complete diges-

tive tract, and well-developed coelom. Three outstanding characteristics distinguish them from all other animals—a single dorsal, tubular nerve cord, a notochord, and gill slits in the pharynx (Fig. 24-2). These features all form in the early embryo of a chordate, and they persist, are altered, or may disappear in the adult.

The *notochord* is the first supporting structure of the chordate body. In the early embryo it forms above the primitive gut as a slender rod of cells containing a gelatinous matrix and is sheathed in fibrous connective tissue. In tunicates, it is present in the tail and only during the larval stages. In the lancelets and higher forms, it extends almost the length of the body. It persists throughout life as the

Illustration at top of page: A lowly chordate (*Salpa tilesii*). Internal organs visible through transparent tunic.

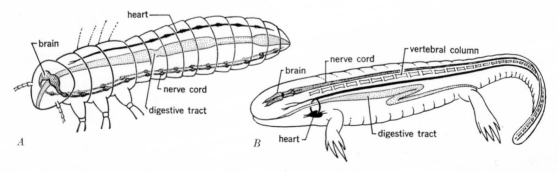

Fig. 24-1. Basic differences between (*A*) a nonchordate (insect) and (*B*) a chordate (salamander) as to location of the nervous system, digestive tract, and heart; diagrammatic.

Table 24-1. Major divisions of the Phylum Chordata *Skip*

(For other details, see classification scheme in Chap. 15)

Group	Subphyla	Classes and their principal characteristics	See Chapter
ACRANIA No cranium or brain, etc.	**TUNICATA** Notochord and nerve cord only in larva; adults contained in secreted tunic	*LARVACEA.* Minute, tadpole-like; tunic temporary, 2 gill slits	24
		ASCIDIACEA. Ascidians. Tunic with scattered muscles; many gill slits	
		THALIACEA. Chain Tunicates. Tunic with circular muscle bands	
	CEPHALOCHORDATA Notochord and nerve cord along entire body and persistent, as are the gill slits	*LEPTOCARDII.* Lancelets. Slender, fish-like, segmented; epidermis 1-layered, no scales; many gill slits	
CRANIATA (vertebrates) With cranium, visceral arches, vertebrae, and brain	**AGNATHA** No true jaws or paired appendages	†*OSTRACODERMI.* Ancient Armored Fishes. Scales large, often fused as cephalothoracic shield	25
		CYCLOSTOMATA. Cyclostomes. Skin without scales; mouth suctorial; gills 5 to 16 pairs	
	GNATHOSTOMATA With jaws and, usually, paired appendages — Superclass *PISCES* Paired fins, gills, and skin with scales	†*PLACODERMI.* Ancient Fishes. Jaws primitive; complete gill slit before hyoid	25
		CHONDRICHTHYES. Sharks and Rays. Skin with placoid scales; skeleton of cartilage; 5 to 7 pairs of gills in separate clefts	
		OSTEICHTHYES. Bony Fishes. Skin with cycloid or ctenoid scales; 4 pairs of gills in common cavity under opercula	
	Superclass *TETRAPODA* Paired limbs, lungs, cornified skin, and bony skeleton	*AMPHIBIA.* Amphibians. Skin moist, soft, no external scales	26
		REPTILIA. Reptiles. Skin dry, with scales or scutes	
		AVES. Birds. Skin with feathers; fore limbs are wings; warm-blooded	27
		MAMMALIA. Mammals. Skin with hair; warm-blooded; suckle young	28

main axial support in lancelets and lampreys, but in the fishes to mammals is later surrounded or replaced by the vertebral column.

The *nerve cord* forms on the dorsal surface of the early embryo soon after the gastrula stage. Infolding of the ectoderm produces a hollow tube (cord) that lies above the notochord. The anterior end becomes enlarged as a simple "cerebral vesicle" in tunicate larvae and in lancelets, but in all vertebrates, it thick-

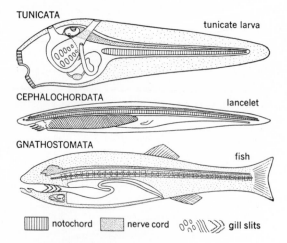

TUNICATA

tunicate larva

CEPHALOCHORDATA

lancelet

GNATHOSTOMATA

fish

‖‖‖ notochord   ▓ nerve cord   ⊙₀° \\\ ⫸ gill slits

Fig. 24-2. Phylum CHORDATA. Basic features of three subphyla; diagrammatic.

ens and differentiates as the brain, to become progressively more complex in higher forms. In tunicates the cord and vesicle degenerate to a ganglion at metamorphosis. From the lampreys onward the nerve cord later becomes surrounded by neural arches of the vertebrae that protect it from injury, and the brain is enclosed by a brain box, or cranium.

Paired *gill slits* develop on the sides of the embryonic pharynx (digestive tract). Each is formed by an outpocketing of endoderm in the pharynx and a corresponding inpocketing of ectoderm on the outside of the body; the intervening wall breaks through to form a gill slit. The characteristic development is seen in a shark or fish, where each slit is margined by many slender filaments containing blood vessels, to form a gill. Water containing dissolved oxygen passes into the mouth and pharynx and out over the filaments, where blood gives up its carbon dioxide and acquires oxygen, so that the gill serves the process of external respiration. All aquatic chordates from tunicates to amphibians respire by gills. In amphibians which transform from aquatic larvae to air-breathing adults, the gills are lost at metamorphosis. The reptiles, birds, and mammals all develop several pairs of gill slits during early embryonic life, but they are never functional and soon close; all these animals

later acquire lungs for breathing air when they hatch or are born.

A. THE LOWER CHORDATES

TUNICATES
SUBPHYLUM ~~TUNICATA~~ *Urochordata*

Tunicates inhabit the sea, from the polar oceans to the tropics and from the shallow beach waters to depths of 3 miles. Some are free-living, and others become attached (sessile) after a short free larval stage; some are solitary, others are colonial, and some are compound, the individuals being grouped in a common covering. They vary in size from nearly microscopic forms to others a foot in diameter. Their methods of reproduction are varied, some sexual, some asexual by budding. The group name refers to the self-secreted "tunic" or sac-like covering over the body. The best-known tunicates are the "sea squirts" or ascidians, which when touched suddenly squirt water from openings in the body covering.

Tunicates are best understood by considering first the free-living larva of an ascidian and then the adult. The larva shows chordate characteristics, but some of these are absent in the adult, and others are obscured by adaptations to the sessile mode of life.

24-2. The larval ascidian. The small fertilized egg segments to form a blastula and then a gastrula; the embryo lengthens and soon hatches as a free-swimming larva, somewhat like a frog tadpole (Fig. 24-3*A*). Its tail contains a supporting *notochord,* a dorsal tubular *nerve cord,* and pairs of lateral, segmental *muscles.* The other organs are confined to the anterior and larger head + body region. The anterior end bears three mucous or *adhesive glands.* The *digestive tract* is complete, with mouth, perforate *gill slits,* endostyle, intestine, and anus; there is a *circulatory system* with blood vessels, and a coelom. Besides the nerve cord, the *nervous system* and the sensory structures include (1) a *cerebral vesicle* and posterior to it (2) a *trunk ganglion,* (3) a median *optical organ* with retina, lens,

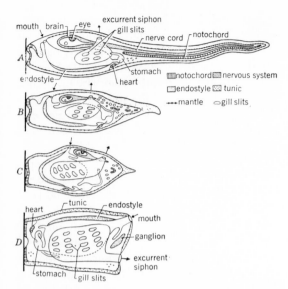

Fig. 24-3. Subphylum TUNICATA. Stages in the metamorphosis of a simple ascidian from the free-swimming larva to the sessile adult. Arrows indicate entrance and exit paths of water currents. *(Adapted from Kowalewsky; and Herdman.)* (A) Larva attaches to a solid object by anterior mucous suckers. (B) Tail reabsorbed, notochord and nerve cord reduced. (C) Notochord disappears, internal organs begin to rotate. (D) Metamorphosis complete, with rotation (90 to 180 degrees) of internal organs and external apertures; branchial sac enlarges, tunic (or test) is secreted, and nervous system reduced to a ganglion (see Fig. 24-4).

pigment, and cornea, and (4) a pigmented *otolith*, or ear, attached to delicate hair cells.

24-3. Metamorphosis. After a few hours or days of free life, the small larva attaches vertically by its adhesive glands to a rock or wharf pile (Fig. 24-3). A rapid transformation (retrograde metamorphosis) ensues during which most of the chordate features disappear. The tail is partly absorbed and partly cast off, its notochord, nerve cord, and muscles being withdrawn into the body and absorbed. Of the nervous system only the trunk ganglion persists. The branchial or "gill" sac enlarges, develops many apertures, and is invaded by blood vessels. The stomach and intestine grow.

That portion of the animal between the point of attachment and the mouth grows rapidly, causing the "body" within to rotate dorso-posteriorly nearly 180 degrees so that the "mouth" is at the upper or nonattached end. Finally the gonads and ducts form in mesoderm between the stomach and intestine. The adhesive glands disappear, and the tunic grows upward to enclose the entire animal.

24-4. The adult ascidian. A simple ascidian (*Ciona, Molgula*, etc.) is cylindrical or globose, attached by a *base* or stalk (Fig. 24-4). It is covered with a tough elastic layer, the *test* or *tunic*, of cellulose-like material (rare in animals). The test is lined by a membranous *mantle* containing muscle fibers and blood vessels. There are two external openings, the *incurrent siphon* (branchial aperture) at the top and the *excurrent siphon* (atrial aperture) at one side. Water drawn into the incurrent siphon brings minute organisms that

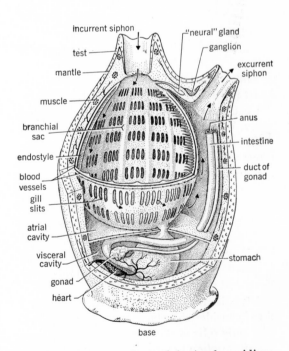

Fig. 24-4. Structure of an adult simple ascidian; diagrammatic. Tunic, mantle, and upper half of branchial sac removed on left side. Arrows indicate path of water currents through the animal.

serve as food and oxygen for respiration; water passed out the excurrent siphon removes wastes and the sex cells. Within the test and mantle is the *atrial cavity,* which contains a dilated *branchial sac* having many pores.

The digestive system begins with the *mouth* followed by a circle of hair-like sensory tentacles at the entrance to the branchial sac. Along the midventral wall of the latter is the *endostyle,* a vertical groove lined with both ciliated and mucous cells where food from the entering water is caught and moved downward. Feeding only on plankton, the ascidian needs no large appendages to handle food. From the base of the branchial sac the *esophagus* leads to the dilated *stomach,* which connects to the *intestine;* the latter two organs are outside the branchial sac. The intestine curves up to end at the *anus* below the excurrent siphon. A *digestive gland* ("liver") connects to the stomach.

The wall of the branchial sac has many pores margined by ciliated cells that beat to move water from within the sac to the atrial cavity, whence it flows to the excurrent siphon.

The circulatory system includes a tubular *heart* in the visceral cavity near the stomach. To each end is connected a large vessel or *aorta,* one distributing to the stomach, test wall, and one side of the branchial sac, the other vessel serving the opposite side of the sac. In the walls of the latter an intercommunicating series of small vessels around pores in the branchial sac serve as the respiratory mechanism. These "vessels" are spaces within the tissues and lack an endothelial lining. The tunicate is unique in that the path of blood flow reverses at short intervals. The heart and vessels lack valves.

Near the intestine is a structure, without a duct, considered to be excretory in function. The only relic of the nervous system is a long *trunk ganglion* in the mantle between the two siphons, with nerves to various parts. Close by is a neural gland, possibly of endocrine nature, and somewhat like a pituitary structure.

The ascidians are monoecious, but self-sterile. The *ovary* is a large hollow gland on the intestinal loop, and the *oviduct,* parallel to the intestine, opens in the atrial cavity near the anus. The *testes* comprise numerous branched tubules, on the surface of the ovary and intestine, that discharge into a *vas deferens* paralleling the oviduct. Some tunicates also reproduce asexually, by budding.

Simple ascidians, each individual in a separate test, are common in ocean shore waters, and others live down to depths of 2,900 fathoms. Many are pale white or yellowish, some more brilliantly colored. The compound ascidians (Fig. 24-5) grow as soft masses with many separate small individuals embedded in a common covering. Both types adhere to rocks, wood, and other materials in the water. The free-ranging salps (Class THALIACEA), with barrel-shaped bodies, live floating in the open sea. These organisms reproduce sexually, like ascidians; they also multiply asexually by forming long chains of individuals that later break apart and produce eggs and sperm.

LANCELETS

SUBPHYLUM CEPHALOCHORDATA

24-5. Amphioxus. Members of the Class LEPTOCARDII comprise about 30 species of fish-

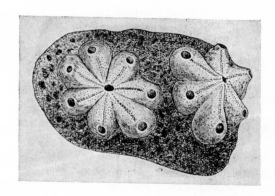

Fig. 24-5. A compound tunicate (*Botryllus*): individuals with separate incurrent siphons, but common excurrent siphon. (*After M. Edwards.*)

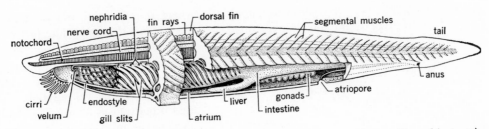

Fig. 24-6. Subphylum CEPHALOCHORDATA. The lancelet or amphioxus (*Branchiostoma*). Adult partly dissected from left side. Natural size about 2 inches long.

like animals (*Branchiostoma,* etc.), commonly called amphioxus, that inhabit tropical and temperate seacoasts. *Branchiostoma virginiae* occurs from Chesapeake Bay to Florida, and *B. californiense* from San Diego Bay southward. The latter grows to 100 mm. long, but most species are smaller. Amphioxus burrows in clean, shifting sand of shallow shore waters, leaving only its anterior end protruding. At times it emerges to swim by rapid lateral movements of the body. Amphioxus is of special zoological interest because it shows the three distinctive characteristics of the Phylum CHORDATA in simple form and is considered to resemble some ancient ancestor of the phylum containing the vertebrates.

The **body** is slender and laterally compressed, pointed at both ends; there is no distinct head (Fig. 24-6). The low median *dorsal fin* along most of the body and the **preanal fin** from atriopore to anus are made of chambers containing short *fin rays* of connective tissue. The **tail** has a membranous fin. Anterior to the ventral fin, the body is flattened on the lower surface with a **metapleural fold** along each side. The **mouth** is ventral at the anterior end, the **anus** is on the left side near the base of the tail fin, and the **atriopore** is an additional ventral opening forward of the anus.

The body covering is a single layer of soft **epidermis** with some cells bearing sensory processes. The **notochord,** chief support of the body, is a slender rod of tall gelatinous cells surrounded by a sheath of connective tissue. Other supportive structures include a circular reinforcement in the oral hood, the fin rays,

and delicate rods with cross connections in the gill bars. Along each side of the body and tail different species have 50 to 85 <-shaped **muscles** (myomeres), each of lengthwise muscle fibers and separated from one another by thin septa of connective tissue. Those on the two sides alternate in position—a unique feature. These muscles contract to produce the lateral bending for burrowing and swimming. Transverse muscles in the floor of the atrial cavity, between the metapleural folds, serve to compress that cavity and force water to the exterior.

The straight and simple **digestive tract** begins with the anterior **oral hood** (vestibule) surrounded by about 22 delicate, fleshy **buccal cirri;** behind the latter are several ciliated bars. The circular **mouth** opening is in a membrane (velum) posterior in the oral hood and is guarded by 12 **velar tentacles** that exclude large particles. Cilia in the hood, during life, produce a rotating effect and are called the "wheel organ." The cirri, tentacles, and hood bear sensory structures. Behind the mouth is the large, compressed **pharynx,** with many diagonal **gill slits** at the sides. There follows the narrow, straight **intestine,** which ends at the **anus.** A slender sac-like **liver,** thought to secrete digestive fluid, attaches ventrally to the anterior part of the intestine well forward in the coelom.

The pharynx is suspended dorsally, beneath the notochord, but hangs free in a cavity, the **atrium,** within the muscles of the body wall. The atrium is an external cavity, lined by ectoderm (hence not a coelom), and connects to the atriopore. The pharynx contains a mid-dorsal furrow (hyperbranchial groove) lined with ciliated cells, and midventrally is a corresponding groove, the **endostyle,** with both ciliated and gland cells (Fig. 24-7). Water containing minute organisms is drawn into the mouth by action of the cilia; the food is trapped by mucus in the endostyle and carried posteriorly to the intestine, while the water passes between the gill bars to the atrium and thence to the exterior through the atriopore.

The **circulatory system** is somewhat on the plan of that in higher chordates but lacks a heart. Besides the definite blood vessels there are open spaces where the colorless blood escapes into the tissues. Blood from the digestive tract flows anteriorly in a **subintestinal vein** to a **hepatic portal vein** entering the liver; thence it collects in a hepatic vein and with other blood from the posterior part of the body passes forward in a **ventral aorta** below the endostyle and into branches at each primary gill bar. Each branch has a small, pulsating bulb, and together these function as a heart, forcing blood upward in the gill bars,

where it is aerated and then collects in the paired **dorsal aortas.** The latter join behind the pharynx to form a single dorsal aorta in which the blood moves posteriorly to supply the body and intestine and finally through capillaries to the venous side. Some oxygenated blood passes forward in the right dorsal aorta to the anterior end of the body. The general course of blood movement in amphioxus is thus like that in higher chordates and opposite to that in invertebrates such as the annelids.

Respiration results from passage of water containing oxygen from the pharynx through 100 or more **gill slits** on each side and past the **gill bars,** which contain blood vessels. This water current is aided by cilia on the gill bars. The gill system of amphioxus is like that of higher chordates during early larval life, its inner surface being of endoderm and the exterior of ectoderm. Later the exterior surface of the gill region of amphioxus is enclosed by growth of the covering wall that forms the atrial cavity outside the gills.

The **coelom,** during development, is formed of five embryonic pouches as in hemichordates; in the adult amphioxus it becomes reduced and complicated, except around the intestine. The **excretory system** comprises about 100 pairs of small ciliated **nephridia** in dorsal relics of the coelom above the pharynx; they connect the coelom to the atrial cavity and show structural resemblance to the nephridia of some annelid worms. Two *"brown bodies,"* dorsal to the intestine, may also be excretory in function.

The **nervous system** lies above the notochord; it consists of a single dorsal **nerve cord** with a small central canal. The anterior end is slightly enlarged to form a median **cerebral vesicle,** with a middorsal **olfactory pit,** a small nonsensory **eyespot** of black pigment, and two pairs of cranial *"nerves."* The cord gives off to each myotome alternately a pair of nerves, the dorsal root being both sensory and motor, the ventral only motor in function. The epidermis of the body surface and the mouth

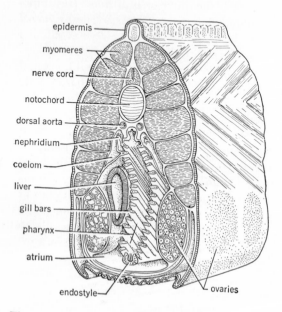

epidermis

myomeres

nerve cord

notochord

dorsal aorta

nephridium

coelom

liver

gill bars

pharynx

atrium

endostyle

ovaries

Fig. 24-7. Amphioxus. Enlarged section through pharynx. *(Adapted from Kükenthal.)*

region have ciliated cells, presumably sensory in function.

The sexes are separate; about 25 pairs of **gonads** (in two rows) bulge into the atrium. Eggs and sperm break into the atrial cavity to pass out through the atriopore, and fertilization is external. The egg is about 0.1 mm. in diameter, with little yolk, and segmentation is holoblastic (Fig. 11-9). During the breeding season eggs are set free about sunset, and by morning a free-swimming ciliated larva is hatched; this feeds and grows for up to 3 months, gradually assuming the adult form, and then takes to burrowing in the sand.

Amphioxus is mainly of zoological interest; but a local fishery for these animals has existed for centuries near Amoy (Fukien Province), southern China. The catch is over a ton per day; and an estimated one billion individuals are taken yearly and used for human food.

B. THE VERTEBRATES or CRANIATA

24-6. Characteristics. The Classes ~~Cyclo-stomata~~ *Agnatha* to Mammalia comprise the major part of the Phylum Chordata (Table 24-1; Fig. 24-8). All have an enlarged brain en-

closed in a brain case or cranium and a segmental spinal column of vertebrae that becomes the axial support of the body. Typically the body comprises a head, neck, trunk, and tail. These classes show a progressive series of structural and functional advances in all organ systems besides the features of the notochord, nerve cord, and gill slits mentioned earlier in this chapter.

1. The **body covering** becomes a stratified epithelium, of epidermis and dermis, with many mucous glands in aquatic species; most fishes are covered with protective scales; the exterior is cornified on land dwellers, with scales on reptiles, feathers on birds, and hair on mammals; feathers and hair form insulated body coverings.

2. The internal and jointed **skeleton** is of cartilage in lower vertebrates and of bone in higher groups; it supports and protects various organs; the cranium shelters the brain and has paired capsules to contain organs of special sense; a series of visceral arches supports the gill region, and certain arches become the jaws and other structures of the head region; the vertebral column extends from the base of the cranium to the end of the tail and has neural arches dorsally to house the nerve cord. Two pairs of appendages, the fins of fishes and limbs of tetra-

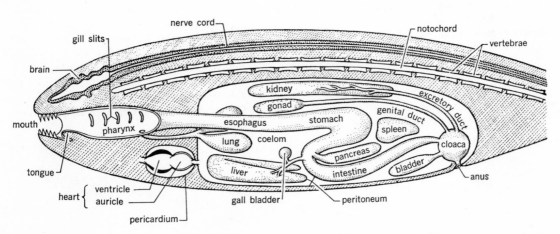

Fig. 24-8. Diagram of principal structures in a craniate or vertebrate (both lungs and gills are indicated but rarely occur together).

pods, with jointed skeletal supports, are joined to the vertebral column through limb girdles.

3. On the skeleton are *muscles* that move its parts and provide for locomotion.

4. The long *digestive tract* is ventral to the vertebral column; the mouth contains a tongue and usually teeth; the anus opens at the end of the trunk; the liver and pancreas are large digestive glands that pour their secretions through ducts joined to the intestine.

5. The *circulatory system* includes a well-developed muscular heart of 2, 3, or 4 chambers, located ventral to the digestive tract; its contractions force the blood through a closed system of arteries, capillaries, and veins, the flow being anteriorly on the ventral side and posteriorly in the dorsal arteries; the blood plasma contains both white and red corpuscles, the latter with hemoglobin as a respiratory pigment; a system of lymph vessels is present; paired aortic arches transport blood from the heart to the gills in the lower vertebrates; progressive separation of the respiratory (pulmonary) and systemic blood paths through the heart leads to regulated body temperature in the warm-blooded (homoiothermous) birds and mammals.

6. *Respiration* in the lower forms is by paired gills; terrestrial species have lungs.

7. The paired *excretory organs* (kidneys) discharge through ducts opening near or through the anus; in lower forms they are segmental and drain wastes from both coelom and blood; in higher forms they are nonsegmental and drain only from the blood; a bladder for storage of urine occurs in many.

8. The *brain* becomes regionally differentiated as to structure and function; the cerebral hemispheres and cerebellum enlarge, especially in higher forms; there are 10 or 12 pairs of cranial nerves in the head that serve both motor and sensory functions, including the paired organs of special sense (smell, sight, and hearing plus equilibration); from the *nerve cord* a pair of spinal nerves serves each primitive body somite; an autonomic nervous system regulates involuntary functions of internal organs.

9. A series of *endocrine glands* (thyroid, pituitary, etc.) provide internal secretions, or hormones, transported by the blood stream, that regulate bodily processes, growth, and reproduction.

10. With rare exceptions the sexes are separate. The *reproductive system* in each has a pair of gonads that discharge sex cells through ducts opening into or near the anus.

REVIEW

1. What are the 3 distinctive characteristics of the CHORDATA? Are the CHORDATA and VERTEBRATA identical in scope?

2. Why are lancelets considered as among the lowest members of the CHORDATA?

3. What chordate characteristics are seen in tunicates? In which stage of life history do they appear?

4. In what ways, anatomically, is amphioxus of special interest?

5. What is the significance of gill slits in the development of a chordate? Is there evidence of recapitulation in this character?

6. Where does the notochord originate in the embryo? How does it differ from the nerve cord? Trace the fate of the notochord through the main groups of chordates.

7. To what group does the name CRANIATA apply? On what characteristic is it based?

8. In which groups of the CHORDATA is the blood colorless? Which lack a heart?

9. Compare the life cycles of a simple tunicate and amphioxus.

25
Fishes

Many kinds of animals that live in the water are called fishes, but strictly the name applies only to the lower aquatic vertebrates (AGNATHA and PISCES), of which there are three classes living today. The Greeks called them *ichthyes*, and ichthyology is the scientific study of fishes. The common name derives from the Latin *pisces*. Lowest and simplest are the eel-like hagfishes and lampreys (Class CYCLOSTOMATA) with slender, cylindrical bodies, no appendages, jaws, or scales and a persistent notochord but no true vertebrae. They inhabit fresh or salt waters, and their nearest allies are the extinct armored ostracoderms of Silurian and Devonian times.

The cartilaginous sharks and rays (Class CHONDRICHTHYES) are the lowest vertebrates that have separate and complete vertebrae, paired appendages, scales in the skin, movable jaws, and multiple gill slits. Most species live in the sea, and all are predaceous. The shark is of special biological interest because many of its anatomical features appear in the embryonic stages of higher vertebrates.

The true or bony fishes (Class OSTEICHTHYES) have bony skeletons, scales of several types, and a single exit from the gills on each side. They are of many shapes and live in all sorts of waters—fresh, brackish, or salt, warm or cold.

A. LAMPREYS AND HAGFISHES
CLASS ~~CYCLOSTOMATA~~ Agnatha
Order

The cyclostomes (Gr. *cyklos,* circular + *stoma,* mouth) are the lowest forms with vertebrate features such as a differentiated brain and paired cranial nerves, eyes, internal ears, both red and white blood cells, and organ systems on the vertebrate pattern (Fig. 25-1).

25-1. Characteristics.

1. Body cylindrical, tail region compressed; median fins supported by cartilaginous fin rays; skin soft and smooth, many unicellular mucous glands; no scales, jaws, or paired fins.
2. Mouth anterior and ventral, suctorial, and margined by fleshy papillae, or tentacles; nasal sac single and median.
3. Skull and visceral arches (branchial basket) cartilaginous; notochord persistent; vertebrae represented by small, imperfect neural arches over notochord.
4. Heart with 1 auricle and 1 ventricle; multiple aortic arches in gill region; blood with leucocytes and nucleated circular erythrocytes.
5. Five to fifteen pairs of gills, in lateral pouches off pharynx.
6. Two kidneys with excretory ducts.
7. Brain with 10 (or 8) pairs of cranial nerves; each auditory organ with 1 or 2 semicircular canals.
8. Body temperature variable (poikilothermous).
9. Gonad single, large, without duct; fertilization external; development direct (hagfishes and slime eels) or with long larval stage (lampreys).

25-2. Structure of a lamprey (Fig. 25-2).
The slender, cylindrical *body* is a combined

Illustration at top of page: A fossil fish (†*Copeichthys dentatus*) from Eocene Green River shale, Wyoming.

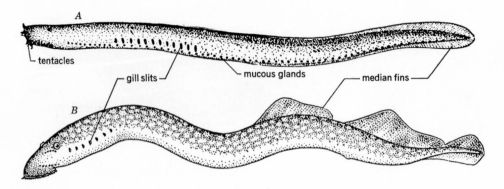

Fig. 25-1. Representative cyclostomes. (*A*) Hagfish (*Polistotrema*) with 12 pairs of gill slits. (*B*) Sea lamprey (*Petromyzon*), with buccal funnel and 7 pairs of gill slits. (*A, After Wolcott, Animal biology; B, after Norman, Guide to Fish Gallery, British Museum.*)

head and trunk, and the **tail** is laterally compressed. On the posterior dorsal region and tail are **median fins.** Ventrally on the head is a large, cup-like **buccal funnel,** margined by soft papillae and lined within by conical, yellow, horny **teeth.** The single **nasal aperture** is middorsal on the head, followed by thin skin over the pineal organ. The two large **eyes** are lateral and covered by transparent skin but lack lids. Behind each are seven rounded **gill apertures.** A row of small lateral **sense pits** extends segmentally along each side of the body and tail. The **anus** opens ventrally at the base of the tail, and close behind is a small **urogenital papilla,** pierced by a duct. The whole animal is covered by smooth epithelium containing many mucous glands, but the skin has no scales.

The slender gelatinous **notochord** is the axial skeleton. Other **skeletal elements,** all cartilaginous, are (1) the skull; (2) a stout rod in the tongue and ring around the buccal funnel; (3) an elaborate "branchial basket" supporting the gill region; and (4) small segmental bits of cartilage (arcualia) above the notochord, representing neural arches. The trunk muscles are ⋝-shaped. The small **mouth** is centered in the buccal funnel (Fig. 25-3) and closed or opened by the fore-and-aft piston-like movement of the **tongue,** which bears teeth. Beyond the pharynx the **digestive tract** divides into a dorsal esophagus and ventral respiratory tube. There is no stomach. The straight intestine contains a spiral valve. There is a liver but no bile duct.

The **circulatory system** has a heart with one auricle and one ventricle that pumps blood anteriorly in a ventral aorta to vessels in the gill filaments. Thence it collects in a dorsal aorta distributing to the body. The venous system has hepatic portal vessels but no renal portals.

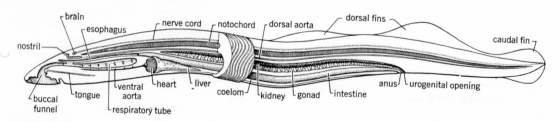

Fig. 25-2. Structure of an adult lamprey (*Entosphenus*); left side of body mostly removed.

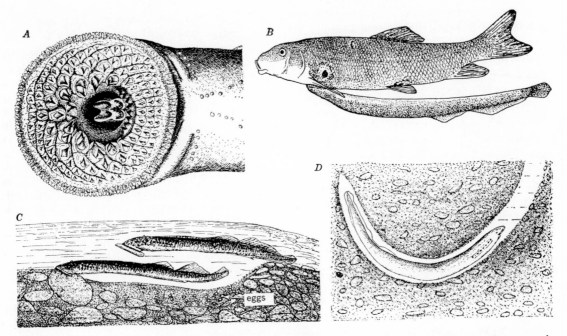

Fig. 25-3. Structure and life of lake lampreys. (*A*) Buccal funnel in ventral view with many horny teeth. (*B*) Lamprey attached to a fish. (*C*) Nest with female attached to a stone, male carrying another stone; small eggs in rear of nest. (*D*) Larval lamprey (ammocoetes) in its burrow under the water. (*After S. H. Gage, 1893, 1929.*)

There are seven pairs of **gill pouches** between the respiratory tube and the body wall. Each has many **gill filaments** with fine capillaries where blood is aerated by water in the pouches. In an adult lamprey the water currents for respiration pass both *in* and *out* of the gill openings; this method is necessary because the lamprey often attaches its buccal funnel to food or other objects, when passage of water through the mouth is impossible; the larval lamprey pumps in through the mouth and out the gill openings as in bony fishes.

The excretory system comprises two **kidneys** and a tubular **ureter** from each to the urogenital sinus and aperture. The **nervous system** includes a distinct brain with the subdivisions found in higher vertebrates, 10 pairs of cranial nerves, a flat, band-like nerve cord, and paired spinal nerves to each body segment.

The **sense organs** are a median olfactory sac, the paired eyes, and a median pineal eye with lens and retina behind the nasal aperture. Each internal ear (organ of equilibrium) has two semicircular canals. There are taste buds in the pharynx and lateral line sense organs on the sides of the body and on the under surface of the head. There is a pituitary structure under the brain, and the larva has a ventral endostyle like that in tunicates and amphioxus.

The immature **gonad** is hermaphroditic but later becomes either male or female in any one individual. At sexual maturity the one gonad fills much of the abdominal cavity. There is no genital duct; eggs or sperm discharge into the abdominal cavity and through paired genital pores into the urogenital sinus.

25-3. Hagfishes and slime eels. These parasitic forms differ from lampreys in several ways: they have (1) a soft suctorial mouth with a rasping tongue set with parallel rows of teeth; (2) three pairs of soft anterior tentacles; (3) one terminal nostril with a canal (and pituitary pouch) to the pharynx that carries water for aerating the gills; and (4) 5 or 15 pairs of gills, far posterior. There are three accessory hearts.

25-4. Natural history. Lampreys occur in both fresh and salt waters, and some adults are nonparasitic; the hagfishes are marine, some descending to depths of more than 300 fathoms. Parasitic species attach to fishes (Fig. 25-3B) by the funnel and use the lingual teeth to rasp a hole. An anticoagulant is injected, and the host's blood flows into the mouth of the lamprey. Healthy fishes are attacked and may be killed. Hagfishes and slime eels burrow into the bodies of dead or dying fishes and consume the flesh.

25-5. Reproduction. When lampreys become sexually mature in spring or early summer, the gonads swell and both sexes move into streams, sometimes "riding" a passing fish or boat. They seek clear water on riffles in streams and use the buccal funnel to move stones on the bottom until a shallow, rounded nest (Fig. 25-3C) is prepared. The female attaches to a stone upstream, and the male to the female, both by their funnels. They wiggle back and forth as eggs and sperm are discharged, fertilization being external. The small, adhesive eggs sink and are covered by silt and sand. A female brook lamprey may contain up to 65,000 eggs and a large sea lamprey up to 236,000 eggs. All adults die after spawning.

The young emerge in a month or so as small larvae and when 12 or 15 mm. long quit the nest to seek quiet water. There each constructs and inhabits a U-shaped tunnel in the sand and silt but emerges to feed on ooze covering the stream bottom (Fig. 25-3D). Water is drawn into the mouth by ciliary action and passes out through the gill apertures. Food is caught in mucus secreted by the endostyle on the floor of the pharynx, as in amphioxus.

The larvae, or "ammocoetes," are blind and toothless; they live and grow for 3 to 7 years.

At metamorphosis some retain a functional digestive tract and strong, sharp teeth develop; such lampreys feed on fishes. They live and grow in the sea or in large streams or lakes according to the species. After a year or more, they reascend small streams in the spring to spawn and then die. Other lampreys cease feeding and growth after metamorphosis; the alimentary tract and teeth partly degenerate, and after 4 to 11 months the animals breed and die. In the hagfish the same individual first produces sperm and then eggs. The eggs are large (10 by 30 mm.) and enclosed in a horny shell that may attach to seaweeds. Growth to the adult form is direct, without a larval stage.

25-6. Relations to man. Larval lampreys serve as bait for both commercial and sport fishing, and some adult sea lampreys are used as food. Lampreys injure or destroy fishes by taking blood and causing secondary infections. They have invaded the Great Lakes and have reduced the annual catch of lake trout from about 15 million pounds to less than one-tenth that amount. Control measures have been partly successful, using chemicals to poison the larvae in stream bottoms. Hagfishes often damage fishes caught on lines or in nets.

B. Cartilaginous Fishes
Class *CHONDRICHTHYES*

The sharks, rays, and chimaeras (Gr. *chondros*, cartilage + *ichthyes*, fish) are the lowest living vertebrates with complete and separate vertebrae, movable jaws, and paired appendages. All are predaceous, and practically all are ocean dwellers. The group dates from Devonian time and is represented by many fossil remains, especially teeth, fin spines, and scales (Fig. 25-4).

25-7. Characteristics.
1. Skin tough, with minute placoid scales and many mucous glands; both median and paired fins present, all supported by fin rays; pelvic fins with claspers in males.

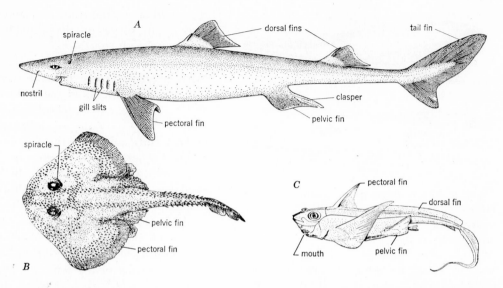

Fig. 25-4. Cartilaginous fishes. (*A*) Spiny dogfish or shark (*Squalus acanthias*). (*B*) Ray (*Raja*). (*C*) Chimaera (*Chimaera colliei*). (*A, after Goode; B, after General Biological Supply House; C, after Dean, Fishes living and fossil, The Macmillan Co.*)

2. Mouth ventral, with many enamel-capped teeth; olfactory sacs 2 (or 1), not connected to mouth cavity; with lower and upper jaws; intestine with spiral valve.

3. Skeleton cartilaginous, no true bone; cranium joined by paired sense capsules; notochord persistent; vertebrae are many, complete, and separate.

4. Heart 2-chambered (1 auricle, 1 ventricle), with sinus venosus and conus arteriosus, containing only venous blood; several pairs of aortic arches; red blood cells nucleated and oval.

5. Respiration by 5 to 7 pairs of gills, each in separate cleft (3 pairs in chimaeras).

6. Ten pairs of cranial nerves; each auditory organ with 3 semicircular canals.

7. Body temperature variable (poikilothermous).

8. Sexes separate; gonads typically paired; reproductive ducts discharging into cloaca; fertilization internal; oviparous or ovoviviparous; eggs large, with much yolk, segmentation meroblastic; no embryonic membranes; development direct, no metamorphosis.

The cartilaginous fishes show advances over the cyclostomes in having (1) scales covering the body; (2) two pairs of lateral fins; (3) movable jaws articulated to the cranium; (4) enamel-covered teeth on the jaws; (5) three semicircular canals in each ear; and (6) paired reproductive organs and ducts. They stand below the bony fishes in having (1) the skeleton of cartilage, with no true bone; (2) placoid scales; (3) separate gill clefts; (4) a pair of spiracles connecting to pharynx; and (5) no air bladder.

Several theories have been proposed on the origin of paired fins in fishes. That of Balfour and others would derive the paired fins from lengthwise lateroventral fin folds supported by parallel fin rays (Fig. 25-5) as seen in amphioxus.

Dogfishes (*Squalus*) grow to about 3 feet, and most sharks are under 8 feet long; the great white shark (*Carcharodon carcharias*) and the basking shark (*Cetorhinus maximus*) may exceed 40 feet, and the whale shark (*Rhineodon typus*) reaches 50 feet in length. These are the biggest living vertebrates except whales. Most rays are 1 to 3 feet in length, but the greater devil-fish (*Manta birostris*) grows

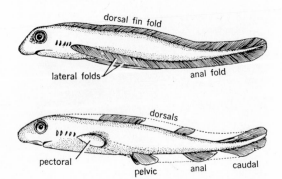

Fig. 25-5. Possible origin of fins on fishes from fin folds such as on amphioxus. Compare Fig. 24-8. (*After Wiedersheim.*)

to 17 feet in length and 20 feet across the pectoral fins. The chimaeras are less than 3 feet long.

STRUCTURE OF A DOGFISH or DOG SHARK

25-8. External features. The *head* is bluntly pointed, and the *trunk* is spindle-shaped, largest near the pectoral fins, and tapering behind. There are two separate median *dorsal fins* (each preceded by a spine in the spiny dogfish, *Squalus*), a median *caudal fin,* and two pairs of *lateral fins, pectoral* and *pelvic.* Between the latter on males is a pair of slender *claspers,* used in mating. The smooth dogfish (*Mustelus*) has also a median *anal fin* ventrally. The *tail* is heterocercal, with the vertebrae extending into the larger dorsal lobe.

Ventrally on the head are two *olfactory sacs* and the wide transverse *mouth;* the *eyes* are lateral and without lids. Five oval *gill slits* open anterior to each pectoral fin and there is a gill-like cleft, or *spiracle,* behind each eye. The *anus* is between the pelvic fins.

25-9. Body covering. The gray-colored skin is evenly covered with diagonal rows of minute *placoid scales* (Fig. 25-6), each with a backward-pointing spine covered by enamel and a basal plate of dentine in the dermis. At the mouth a gradual transition from scales to teeth occurs, suggesting the probable origin of vertebrate teeth.

25-10. Skeleton. The entire skeleton is of cartilage (gristle) more or less reinforced with limy deposits; the axial parts are the *skull* and the segmented *vertebral column.* Each vertebra has a spool-shaped *centrum,* concave on both ends, and above this a *neural arch* to house the nerve cord. In the tail each also bears ventrally a *hemal arch,* shielding the caudal aorta and vein; the *notochord* persists in the spaces between vertebrae. The skull is made up of (1) the cranium housing the brain; (2) paired capsules for the olfactory, optic, and auditory organs; and (3) the visceral skeleton, consisting of the jaws, the hyoid arch, and five pairs of branchial arches supporting the gill region. The appendicular skeleton includes (1) the U-shaped *pectoral girdle* supporting the pectoral fins; (2) the flatter *pelvic girdle,* to which the pelvic fins attach; and (3) the many small jointed cartilages within and supporting each lateral fin. The median fins are supported by dermal *fin rays.*

25-11. Muscular system. The body and tail muscles are of segmental character and serve to produce the lateral undulations of the trunk and tail necessary for swimming. More specialized muscles serve the paired fins, gill region, and structures of the head.

25-12. Digestive system. The broad *mouth* is margined with transverse rows of sharply pointed *teeth;* these are embedded in flesh on the jaws and frequently replaced by new rows

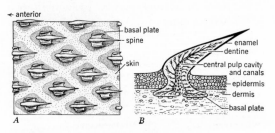

Fig. 25-6. Placoid scales (enlarged). (*A*) Skin with scales in surface view. (*B*) Median section through a scale. (*After Klaatsch.*)

of teeth from behind. A flat *tongue* adheres to the floor of the mouth. On the sides of the wide pharynx are openings leading to the separate *gill slits* and *spiracles*. The short *esophagus* leads to the ∪-shaped *stomach,* which ends at a circular sphincter muscle, the *pyloric valve.* The *intestine* follows and connects directly to the *cloaca* and *anus.* In the intestine is a spirally arranged partition, or *spiral valve,* covered with mucous membrane, that delays the passage of food and offers increased area for absorption. The large *liver* is of two long lobes, attached at the anterior end of the body cavity. Bile from the liver collects in the greenish *gall bladder* and thence passes through the *bile duct* to the anterior part of the intestine. The *pancreas* lies between the stomach and intestine, its duct joining the latter just below the bile duct. A slim *rectal gland* attaches dorsally where the intestine and cloaca join. It serves to dispose of excess salt received with food or from the seawater (Fig. 25-7).

25-13. Coelom. The stomach, intestine, and other internal organs lie in the large *body cavity,* or *coelom.* It is lined with a smooth, glistening membrane, the *peritoneum,* which also covers the organs. The latter are supported from the middorsal wall of the coelom by thin *mesenteries,* also formed of peritoneum. A transverse *septum* separates the coelom from the cavity containing the heart.

25-14. Circulatory system. The *heart* lies beneath the gill region in a sac, the pericardium; it consists of (1) a thin-walled *sinus venosus* that receives blood from various veins, followed by (2) the *auricle,* (3) the thick-walled *ventricle,* and (4) the *conus arteriosus.* From the latter, blood passes anteriorly into the *ventral aorta,* whence five pairs of *afferent branchial arteries* distribute to capillaries in the gills for aeration; four pairs of *efferent branchial arteries* then collect the blood into the *dorsal aorta,* which extends along the middorsal wall of the coelom. The principal arteries are (1) paired external and internal carotids to the head; (2) paired subclavians to the pectoral fins; (3) coeliac to the stomach, liver, and intestine; (4) anterior mesenteric to the large, tapered spleen and hind part of the intestine; (5) posterior mesenteric to the rectal gland; (6) several renal and gonadic (ovarian or spermatic) to the kidneys and reproductive organs; and (7) paired iliacs to the pelvic fins. Beyond the latter the caudal aorta continues in the tail.

In the *venous system,* blood in the caudal vein from the tail passes in (1) paired renal portal veins to the kidneys. Other blood from the posterior regions passes forward in (2) the

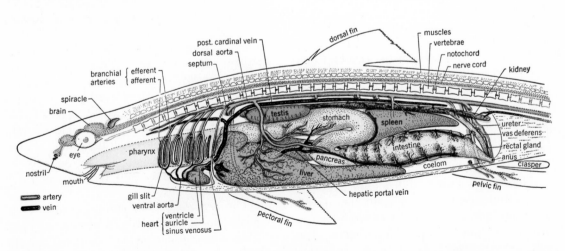

Fig. 25-7. Structure of spiny dogfish.

paired postcardinal veins paralleling the kidneys and in (3) paired lateral abdominal veins on either side of the body cavity. Paired (4) jugular and (5) anterior cardinal veins return blood from the head region. All these veins enter large sinuses connected to the sinus venosus. Blood from the digestive tract flows in (6) the hepatic portal vein to be filtered through capillary-like sinusoids in the liver, then is collected in (7) the hepatic veins joined to the sinus venosus. The blood passes through the heart but once in each circuit of the body, as in cyclostomes and most fishes, and the heart blood is all venous (unoxygenated).

25-15. Respiratory system. By opening and closing the mouth the shark draws water in and forces it out the gill clefts and spiracles (Fig. 25-13). The *gills* lining the five pairs of separate clefts (and the spiracles) are composed of numerous parallel, slender filaments that contain capillaries. Blood from the ventral aorta passes through these capillaries, discharges carbon dioxide and absorbs oxygen dissolved in the water, and then continues into the dorsal aorta.

25-16. Excretory system. The two slender *kidneys* lie immediately above the coelom along the dorsal aorta. Urine is collected in segmental tubules that join a longitudinal duct, the *ureter,* leading posteriorly, the two emptying through a single urogenital papilla dorsal in the cloaca.

25-17. Nervous system. The shark's *brain* (Fig. 10-2) is of a more advanced type than that of the lamprey. From the two olfactory sacs in the snout, large olfactory tracts extend to the *olfactory lobes,* which attach closely to the paired *cerebral hemispheres* on the *diencephalon.* Dorsally the latter bears a pineal stalk and *pineal body* and ventrally the *infundibulum,* to which is attached the *hypophysis.* All of these structures are part of the forebrain. Two rounded *optic lobes* lie dorsally on the midbrain. The hindbrain comprises the large median dorsal *cerebellum* over the open-topped *medulla oblongata.* Ten pairs of *cranial nerves* serve structures, chiefly of the head, in approximately the same

distribution as among other vertebrates (Table 10-1). The spinal *nerve cord* is fully protected by the neural arches of the vertebrae, an advance over the condition in cyclostomes. Paired *spinal nerves* to each body somite emerge between the neural arches of successive vertebrae.

25-18. Sense organs. Sharks receive olfactory stimuli from water passing through the two shallow *olfactory sacs* on the snout. The *eyes* are moved by three pairs of muscles attaching the eyeball to the eye socket. The *ears,* entirely within the head, serve two distinct functions: (1) receiving sound impressions and (2) orientation. Each ear has three semicircular canals at right angles to each other, as in all higher vertebrates. A slender endolymphatic duct extends from each ear to a small opening on the dorsal surface of the head.

The *lateral line* is a slight groove along each side of the body and tail that contains a minute longitudinal canal with many openings to the surface. Within the canal are sensory hair cells, segmentally arranged and connected to the tenth cranial nerve. On the head are many sensory canals opening in *pores* and containing *pit organs,* with sensory hairs connected to nerve fibers. These structures derive, embryologically, from the auditory organ and are equivalent to the inner ear of higher vertebrates; they respond to slow pressure stimuli of waves in the water.

25-19. Reproductive system. The sexes are separate. In a *male,* sperm develop in two long *testes* anterior in the body cavity; from each testis several *vasa efferentia* lead to a much convoluted *vas deferens* extending posteriorly on the ventral surface of the kidney and emptying into the urogenital papilla. At mating, sperm are transferred from the male, by aid of the claspers, into the cloaca of the female.

The *female* system comprises one large *ovary* attached dorsally by a stout membrane. Two large *oviducts* extend the length of the body cavity, each having at the anterior end a large funnel through which the eggs enter.

The anterior portion of each duct is dilated as a *shell gland,* and ovoviviparous species like the dogfish have the posterior part enlarged as a *"uterus"* to contain the young during development. The oviducts open separately into the cloaca.

OTHER CARTILAGINOUS FISHES

25-20. Structure. Most other sharks resemble the dogfish in general anatomy. The rays have much depressed bodies with large pectoral fins broadly joined to the head and trunk so that these fishes are diamond- or disc-shaped in outline. The gill openings are on the flat ventral surface, and the spiracles serve for entry of the respiratory currents of water. The tail is long and slender. Chimaeras are grotesque-appearing, the skin is scaleless, the four gill slits on either side are covered by a membranous operculum, and the teeth are fused.

25-21. Natural history. The sharks and rays are mostly marine, but a few inhabit rivers above salt water. Rays are mainly bottom dwellers and feed largely on invertebrates. Sharks live in open water and often congregate around schools of fishes. The biggest predaceous sharks may catch seals or sea lions, but the huge basking and whale sharks take only plankton.

25-22. Reproduction. The primitive sharks, some dogfishes and rays, and the chimaeras deposit each egg in a brown, horny capsule (mermaid purse). Most sharks, dogfishes, and rays, however, are ovoviviparous, retaining the eggs for development internally and giving birth to living young. The walls of the oviduct in the female produce numerous loops of blood vessels that lie against the yolk sac of the embryo and provide for the respiration of the latter. The large eggs develop slowly (16 to 25 months in the dogfish; 9 to 12 months in the chimaera). The young of all sharks and rays resemble their parents, and there is no metamorphosis.

25-23. Relations to man. Sharks are a nuisance to fishermen because they tear nets and steal netted fishes or remove bait or fishes from hooks. Large sharks may capsize small boats or injure fishermen, and some tropical and subtropical species menace bathers. The great white shark attacks human beings in Australian waters, where half of 40 earlier attacks were fatal. Around North America there were few attacks by sharks until recent years, when several persons were bitten and some died in the shore waters of California and Florida. Occasionally human deaths result from injuries by the spines of sting rays.

Sharks and rays are used for human food in many countries. Shark fins are gathered and dried in Ceylon, the Philippines, and California; they are boiled to yield a gelatinous material favored for soups. Sharkskin tanned with the scales in place (then termed shagreen) was used in the Old World for casing fine books, jewel boxes, and sword handles and as an abrasive for polishing wood and ivory. With the scales crushed, the skins make leather for shoes and bags.

Shark livers contain much oil, and there are fisheries for this product in Greenland, Iceland, and Norway; a large basking shark yields about 125 gallons of oil. The oil contains large amounts of vitamin A.

25-24. Fossil forms. The first CHONDRICHTHYES appear in mid-Devonian rocks (later than the first bony fishes) but already were well advanced in evolution of the jaws. The cartilaginous skeleton seems more likely to be a degenerate rather than a primitive character. Some early types inhabited fresh waters, but the group has been predominantly marine; they were abundant and often well armored in the Paleozoic era but later decreased in numbers and had less armor.

C. BONY FISHES
CLASS *OSTEICHTHYES*

The most typical fishes are those that have skeletons with bone, are covered by dermal scales, usually have spindle-shaped bodies, swim by fins, and breathe by gills. Various species inhabit waters that are fresh, brackish, or salt, and either warm or cold. Fishes have been a staple protein food of mankind since antiquity, and many species provide pleasant sporting recreation (Fig. 25-8).

25-25. Characteristics.

1. Skin with many mucous glands, usually with embedded dermal scales; some naked (scaleless), a few with enamel-covered scales; both median and paired fins present (some exceptions), supported by fin rays of cartilage or bone; no limbs.
2. Mouth usually terminal and with teeth; jaws well-developed, articulated to skull; olfactory sacs 2, dorsal; eyes large, no lids.

3. Skeleton chiefly of bone (cartilage in sturgeons and some others); vertebrae many, distinct; tail usually homocercal; relics of notochord often persist.
4. Heart 2-chambered (1 auricle, 1 ventricle), containing only venous blood; 4 pairs of aortic arches; red blood cells nucleated and oval.
5. Respiration by pairs of gills on gill arches in a common chamber at each side of pharynx, covered by an operculum; usually with an air (swim) bladder, sometimes with duct to the pharynx, and lung-like in DIPNOI and some others.
6. Ten pairs of cranial nerves.
7. Body temperature variable.
8. Gonads typically paired; usually oviparous; fertilization external (some exceptions), eggs minute to 12 mm., yolk various in amount; segmentation usually meroblastic; no embryonic membranes; early young (post larvae) sometimes quite unlike adults.

The head is encased in a true skull comprised of both cartilage or replacement bones and membrane or dermal bones. The fins in most bony fishes are supported by many parallel dermal rays; in crossopterygians each paired fin has a single, stout central lobe that articulates with the limb girdle—a possible source of the limb skeleton in land vertebrates. In some bony fishes the swim bladder is lung-like, and a few species have perforate nostrils and accessory structures that enable them to breathe air in shallow, mucky water.

The smallest fish is a Philippine goby only 10 mm. long; most fishes are under 3 feet in length. Some record large specimens are of halibut at 9 feet, swordfish at 12 feet, and Columbia River sturgeon at 12½ feet and 1,285 pounds.

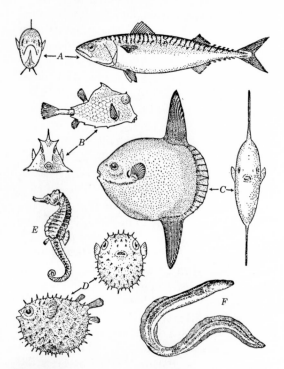

Fig. 25-8. Representative bony fishes, of different bodily form. (*A*) Mackerel (*Scomber*), streamlined and fast-swimming. (*B*) Trunkfish (*Ostracion*), body rigid, only fins movable. (*C*) Marine sunfish (*Mola*), huge, thin, deep-bodied. (*D*) Globefish (*Chilomycterus*), body spiny, swollen, fins small. (*E*) Sea horse (*Hippocampus*), swims erect by small dorsal fin, tail prehensile. (*F*) Common eel (*Anguilla*), long and highly flexible. (*After Norman, History of fishes, Ernest Benn, Ltd.*)

STRUCTURE OF A BONY FISH: THE YELLOW PERCH

25-26. External features (Fig. 25-9). The compressed and spindle-shaped body makes for easy passage through the water. The **head** is the portion from the snout to the hind edge

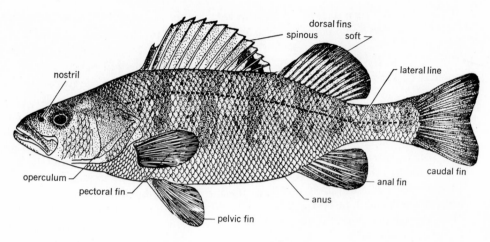

Fig. 25-9. Yellow perch (*Perca flavescens*); external features.

of the operculum, the **trunk** from that point to the anus, and the remainder is the **tail.** The large terminal **mouth** contains movable jaws bearing fine teeth; dorsal on the snout are two **olfactory sacs** (not connected to the mouth cavity), and the large **eyes** are lateral and lack lids. The **operculum** is a bony plate covering the gill chamber on each side. There are four median **fins** (2 dorsal, 1 caudal, 1 anal) and two lateral pairs, the pectorals and pelvics. The fins are membranous extensions of the integument and are supported by **fin rays.** All except the first dorsal are flexible, being supported by soft rays which are calcified but with many joints and usually branched. The first dorsal has 13 to 15 solid calcified **spines,** and there are 1 or 2 similar spines in the anterior edge of the other fins. The body is covered by soft, mucus-producing **epidermis** that facilitates easy movement in the water and is a protection against entry of disease organisms. The trunk and tail bear thin, rounded dermal **scales,** in lengthwise and diagonal rows, with their free posterior edges overlapping; each lies in a dermal pocket and grows throughout life. Along either side is the **lateral line,** a row of small pores connected to a lengthwise tubular canal under the scales, in which are sensory organs responsive to slow vibrations in the water (Fig. 25-10).

25-27. Skeleton. The scales, collectively, form an exoskeleton. The endoskeleton consists of the skull, vertebral column, ribs, pectoral girdle, and many small accessory bones supporting the fin rays. In the embryo and young the cranium is of cartilage, later replaced by separate **cartilage bones.** To these are added many **membrane bones** that result from ossifications in the embryonic connective tissue. The adult skull has about 40 bones. It is so closely affixed to the vertebral column

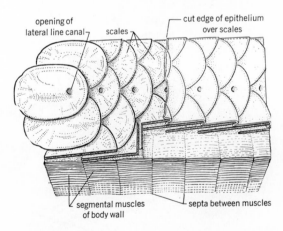

Fig. 25-10. Body wall of a bony fish (carp) near the lateral line, showing relations of the epidermis, scales, and muscles. (*Modified from Lankester, Treatise on zoology, A. & C. Black, Ltd.*)

that a fish cannot "turn its head." The ***visceral skeleton*** comprises seven paired arches, first of cartilage and later ossified; these correspond to the arches of sharks and rays, but not to the branchial basket of lampreys. The mandibular arch (No. 1) provides the jaws, No. 2 is the hyoid arch giving support for the tongue, and Nos. 3 to 6 are gill arches, each bearing a gill on the outer curvature and a row of small, spiny gill rakers on the inner border; the latter form a sieve to protect the gills from injury by food. The last arch, No. 7, is small, with pharyngeal teeth but no gill.

The vertebral column is of many similar and separate ***vertebrae,*** each with a dorsal ***neural arch*** over the spinal cord; in the tail region every vertebra also bears a ventral ***hemal arch*** sheltering the caudal artery and vein. Slender, paired, rib-like bones attach to each trunk vertebra, and delicate ***intramuscular bones*** extend lengthwise between some of the ribs. In the flesh between the spines of the vertebrae are interspinal bones that support and articulate the dorsal and anal fin rays.

25-28. Muscular system. The substance of the trunk and tail consists chiefly of ***segmen-*** ***tal muscles*** that alternate with the vertebrae and produce the swimming and turning movements. Fish muscles are broadly ⋜ -shaped, in four principal bands, and heaviest along the back. Between the successive muscles are delicate septa which dissolve upon cooking to leave the muscles as individual "flakes."

25-29. Digestive system. The jaws have many small conical ***teeth*** to grasp food, and the small ***tongue*** fixed in the floor of the mouth cavity may aid respiratory movements. The ***pharynx*** has gills on the sides and leads to a short ***esophagus*** followed by the recurved ***stomach.*** A ***pyloric valve*** separates the latter from the ***intestine.*** Three tubular ***pyloric caeca,*** secretory or absorptive in function, attach to the intestine. There is a large ***liver*** anterior in the body cavity with a ***gall bladder*** and duct to the intestine. The pancreas is usually indistinct (Fig. 25-11).

25-30. Circulatory system. The two-chambered ***heart*** lies below the pharynx in a ***pericardial cavity,*** an anterior portion of the coelom. Venous blood passes into the sinus venosus, to the thin-walled auricle, thence into the muscular ventricle, all separated by valves

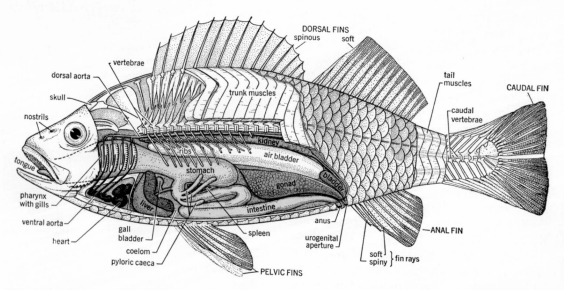

Fig. 25-11. Yellow perch, general structure. Operculum, pectoral fin, most of the skin and scales, and some trunk and tail muscles have been removed on the left side.

that prevent reverse flow. Rhythmic contractions of the ventricle force the blood through the conus arteriosus and short *ventral aorta* into four pairs of *afferent branchial arteries* distributing to capillaries in the gill filaments. After oxygenation there it collects in correspondingly paired *efferent branchial arteries* leading to the *dorsal aorta,* which distributes to the head and body. The principal veins are paired anterior cardinals and posterior cardinals and an unpaired hepatic portal circulation leading through the liver. The blood of fishes is pale and scanty as compared with that of terrestrial vertebrates. The plasma contains nucleated oval red cells (erythrocytes) and various types of white cells (leucocytes). The large red-colored *spleen* is near the stomach. A lymphatic system is also present.

25-31. Respiratory system (Figs. 25-12, 25-13). The perch respires by means of *gills,* of which there are four in a common gill chamber on each side of the pharynx, beneath the operculum. A gill consists of a double row of slender *gill filaments;* every filament bears many minute transverse plates covered with thin epithelium and containing capillaries between the afferent and efferent branchial arteries. Each gill is supported on a cartilaginous *gill arch,* and its inner border has expanded *gill rakers,* which protect against hard particles and keep food from passing out the gill slits. In "breathing," the opercula close against the body, and the gill arches bulge laterally, whereupon water flows into the opened mouth; then the oral valve closes, the gill arches contract, the opercula lift, and the water is forced out over the filaments. Blood in the filaments gives up its carbon dioxide and absorbs oxygen from the water. The fish needs a constant supply of oxygen-bearing water and soon dies of asphyxiation if removed from water or if the water is depleted of oxygen. The phrase "to drink like a fish" is a misconception; actually a fish "drinks to breathe" but takes little or no fluid into its stomach except with food.

A large thin-walled sac, the *air bladder* or *swim bladder,* occupies the dorsal portion of

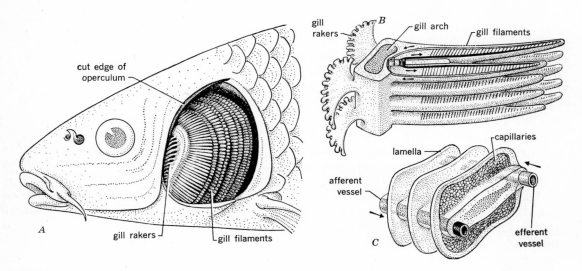

Fig. 25-12. Gills of a bony fish (carp). (*A*) Gills in the gill chamber with operculum cut away. (*B*) Part of a gill showing gill rakers and filaments, with path of blood in the latter; afferent vessels dark, efferent vessels light (in many fishes the gill rakers are slender). (*C*) Portion of one filament with thin lamellae containing capillaries where blood is aerated. (*Partly after Goldschmidt, Ascaris, Prentice-Hall, Inc.*)

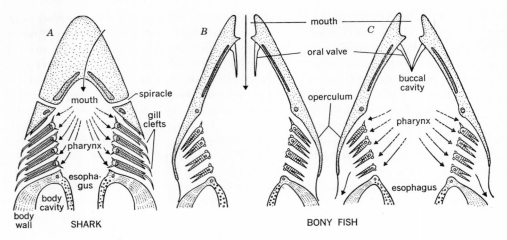

Fig. 25-13. The respiratory mechanism of fishes; diagrammatic frontal sections (lobes of oral valve actually are dorsal and ventral); arrows show paths of water currents. SHARK. (*A*) Water enters ventrally placed mouth, which then closes and floor of mouth region rises to force water over the gills and out the separate clefts. BONY FISH. (*B*) *Inhalent:* opercula closed, oral valve open, cavity dilated, and water enters. (*C*) *Exhalent:* oral valve closes, buccal cavity contracts, water passes over gills in common cavities at sides of pharynx and out beneath opercula. (*Modified from Boas.*)

the body cavity. It is connected to the pharynx by a pneumatic duct in some fishes, but not in the perch. The bladder is filled with gases (O_2, N_2, CO_2) and acts as a hydrostatic organ to adjust the specific gravity of the fish to that of the water at different depths. By secretion or absorption of the gases through blood vessels in the wall a fish makes this adjustment slowly as it moves from one depth to another; if a fish is suddenly hauled up from a considerable depth, the greater pressure within the air bladder may, upon reaching the surface, force the stomach out of the mouth.

25-32. Excretory system. The two slender, dark *kidneys* lie dorsally between the air bladder and vertebrae. Fluid nitrogenous waste removed from the blood is carried posteriorly from each in a tubular *ureter,* both emptying into a *urinary bladder,* which in turn discharges through the *urogenital sinus* to the exterior.

25-33. Nervous system and sense organs. The perch *brain* is short, the olfactory lobes, cerebral hemispheres, and diencephalon be-

ing smaller and the optic lobes and cerebellum larger than in a shark. There are 10 pairs of *cranial nerves.* The *nerve cord* is covered by the neural arches and gives off a pair of lateral spinal nerves to each body segment. The dorsal *olfactory sacs* on the snout contain cells sensitive to substances dissolved in water. *Taste buds* are present in and around the mouth. The large *eyes* probably focus clearly only on nearby objects but serve to detect moving objects above water, such as a person walking on the bank. The *internal ear* contains three semicircular canals and an *otolith* serving the sense of equilibrium; there is no eardrum or middle ear. The *lateral line system* has various extensions on the head and evidently detects slight changes in pressure or slow wave or current movements (not over six per second) such as might be experienced by a fish swimming close to some solid object from which water movements would be reflected.

25-34. Reproductive system. In a *male* the two *testes* enlarge greatly in the breeding season, and at mating the "milt," or sperm, passes in a *vas deferens* from each to emerge from the urogenital aperture. In a *female* the eggs pass from the two united *ovaries* through the *oviducts*.

STRUCTURE OF OTHER BONY FISHES

Many fishes have the general configuration of the perch; the flounders, soles, and some tropical reef fishes are thin-bodied, the eels are long and slender, and the porcupine fishes are globular (Fig. 25-8).

25-35. Scales (Fig. 25-14). The scales are separate and minute on eels, small and tuberculate on some flounders, and spiny on porcupine fishes. Those of tarpon are up to 2 inches in width, whereas some fishes are scaleless. On

the perch and many others the exposed hind part of each has many tiny spines, making a *ctenoid scale.* Others that lack such spines are termed *cycloid scales,* and still others have *ganoid scales* covered by enamel. The head and body are armor-plated with heavy scales on the trunkfish.

The scales grow throughout life, and there is no molt of the body covering. On many species growth results in a series of fine concentric ridges on each scale. After cessation of growth during winter, the first ridges of the next growth season form a definite "winter line" that makes age determination possible in salmon, trout, bass, and others.

Most fishes have fixed color patterns, but some change color by concentrating or spreading pigment in the chromatophores. Flounders and some others can simulate closely the bottom on which they rest. Fishes in the perennial darkness of the deep sea are often black.

25-36. Fins. The pectoral fins are usually near the gill apertures; the pelvic fins are on the abdomen in trout, near the gill openings in perch, on the throat in blennies, and lacking in eels. The dorsal fin may be single, multiple, or continuous along the back; salmonids and catfishes have, besides the single dorsal, a small fleshy or adipose fin posteriorly. In the top minnow and some other viviparous species the anterior part of the anal fin is modified as a copulatory organ.

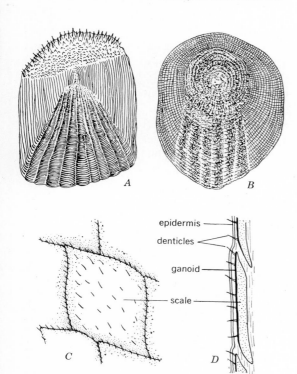

Fig. 25-14. Scales of bony fishes, enlarged. (*A*) Ctenoid (with fine teeth). (*B*) Cycloid. (*C, D*) Ganoid (*Lepidosteus*) in surface view and vertical section.

NATURAL HISTORY

25-37. Distribution. Fishes occur from the polar seas to the equator, from the surface to depths of more than 12,000 feet, and up to 14,000 feet in the Andes. They live variously in open water, on sandy or rocky or muddy bottoms, in the crannies of reefs, in saline bays and estuaries, in fresh or alkaline rivers and lakes, in cave waters, and even in hot springs up to 93°F. Most fishes are limited by a temperature range of about 12° to 15°F., but carp and goldfish survive wider extremes and carp, mud minnows, and some others can withstand temporary freezing.

Many fishes, like birds, perform seasonal *migrations.* The barracuda and swordfish move north in spring and south in autumn, in a latitudinal migration. The salmon, shad, striped bass, and some trout travel from salt water to fresh for spawning and are termed *anadromous;* the fresh-water eel, which reverses this process, is said to be **catadromous.** Cod and herring of the ocean perform an inshore migration to spawn on banks or shoals. Some deep-water (mesopelagic) fishes have a daily vertical migration.

25-38. Habits. Fishes of fresh-water streams habitually head against the current to maintain position, facilitate respiration, and catch food, as may be seen in a trout hatchery. Marine species are evidently active at all seasons, but many fresh-water species become inactive during the winter, descending to deeper water in lakes and rivers. Some fishes are solitary, whereas others are gregarious and live in schools of various sizes, those of herring numbering a few thousands to many millions of individuals.

Most fishes swim by lateral undulations of the tail and tail fin, produced by alternate contractions of the metameric muscles on the two sides. The action is comparable to that of a man sculling a boat, with one oar at the stern moved from side to side. The other fins serve chiefly to maintain balance and change direction. Trout and salmon and others may jump or leap from the water at times when in pursuit of prey; they swim rapidly up to the surface when momentum alone carries them into the less dense air. The flying fishes actually leave the water to "volplane." They swim rapidly, then "taxi" with the body above the surface while the submerged tail vibrates laterally—up to 70 times per second (the pectoral fins also may vibrate as a result of bodily movements); the speed may be up to 10 meters per second (22 miles per hour). Then the broad pectoral fins are instantaneously extended, and the fishes rise and glide for 3 to 8 seconds, traveling 35 to 100 yards. Flights may be repeated at short intervals.

25-39. Food. A few fresh-water fishes and some marine species feed on aquatic vegetation, and the carp and suckers draw up bottom materials containing algae and minute invertebrates. Most fishes, however, are entirely predaceous. They feed mainly on aquatic invertebrates or other fishes. Being "cold-blooded," most fishes require no energy to maintain a constant body temperature; yet their basic food intake is considerable.

25-40. Enemies. Fishes serve as staple food for other fishes, for water snakes, some turtles and alligators, many kinds of sea birds, herons, and kingfishers, and mammals such as seals, mink, otter, and bears. The eggs and young of fishes are devoured by a host of aquatic animals. Man is an important enemy of fishes.

25-41. Reproduction. The majority of fishes are oviparous, although many individual species and all members of some groups are viviparous. The top minnows and the viviparous perches bear but few young at a time, whereas most oviparous fishes produce many eggs. Brook trout lay 80 to more than 5,600 according to size, Atlantic salmon up to 17,000, the cod to over 6,000,000, and the ocean sunfish to 300,000,000. The bodies of females are often swollen with the maturing eggs just before laying. Changes in coloration or other features, such as the hooked jaws of salmon, may develop in males for the mating season. Courting performances precede actual spawning among various kinds of fishes. Eggs of some marine fishes hatch as small, transparent larvae within a few hours, and those of most tropical freshwater species hatch in 20 to 48 hours. By contrast, the eggs of brook trout need about 44 days at 50° to 52°F. and 90 days or more at below 40°F. The young of some viviparous fishes resemble their parents when hatched; other young are quite larval upon emergence, gradually assuming the form of the adult (Fig. 25-15).

Flounders and soles are bilaterally symmetrical when hatched, with an eye on each

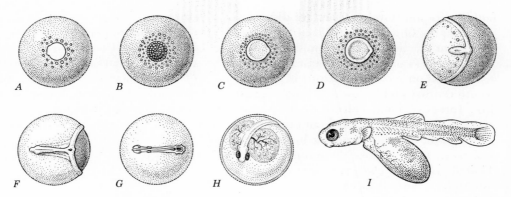

Fig. 25-15. Early development of the trout, a bony fish. (*A*) Germinal disc (white) concentrates after fertilization. (*B*) Meroblastic segmentation. (*C, D*) Gastrula forming, blastodisc elongates in axis of future embryo. (*E*) Primitive streak begins, blastodisc spreads. (*F*) Neural tube forms, blastoderm surrounds yolk. (*G*) Embryo with eye and ear vesicles and 18+ somites. (*H*) "Eyed egg"—embryo with large eyes; blood vessels spread over yolk. (*I*) "Yolk sac" stage of hatched young. (*A–G, after Henneguy,* 1888.)

side; but at an early age one eye begins to "migrate" to the opposite side which thenceforth is the upper surface as the fish lies on the bottom.

The period of growth until sexual maturity varies with the species and also with the local water temperature. Young of the top minnow (*Gambusia*) may mature and breed before four months of age, in the same summer that they are hatched. The king salmon of the Yukon River, by contrast, requires 5 or 6 years before spawning. Most fishes live to breed in several successive seasons, but individuals of the Pacific salmon (*Oncorhynchus*) grow to sexual maturity, breed once, and then die.

25-42. Relations to man. Fishes have been important as human food from the time of Paleolithic man, who left fishbones in his "kitchen middens," to the present day. The world fisheries take 35 billion pounds worth over $800,000,000 annually and employ thousands of persons. The flesh of most fishes is white (or reddish) and flaky in texture. It contains 13 to 20 per cent of protein and has a food value of 300 to 1600 calories per pound, depending on the oil content (to 17 per cent in

salmon). Fishes deteriorate rapidly after being caught and must either be consumed soon or preserved. In the fresh state they are iced or frozen. Fishes are preserved by salting, drying, smoking, and canning. Crude fish oils are used in paints and insecticidal sprays, and refined oils from livers of cod and other species comprise a concentrated source of vitamin D. The scraps from canneries as well as entire fishes of some species are ground and dried into meal, used for feeding poultry and for fertilizer. Liquid glues are rendered from heads and trimmings of fishes.

Sport fishing is an outdoor recreation for thousands of persons and also a source of food. Millions of dollars are spent each year by anglers in pursuit of trout, salmon, perch, bass, and other game fishes. In the United States the Federal and state governments rear millions of trout and some other fishes in hatcheries and plant them in streams and lakes to replace some of those taken by fishermen.

Captive fishes of many kinds in ponds and aquaria are kept and bred by fish fanciers and other persons, and many public institutions maintain large, glass-fronted aquaria where both native and foreign fishes are displayed. The keeping of fishes in artificial ponds was an ancient practice of the Orient, the Romans, and the Aztecs of Middle America. Artificial rearing was on record in Europe in the fourteenth century and is now a widespread practice. Intensive pond culture of fishes, especially carp in Central Europe and the Orient, supplies considerable protein to human populations in those regions. Experiments in the United States and elsewhere have shown that addition of natural or chemical fertilizers to fish ponds will increase the diatom-algae-invertebrate food chain upon which fishes depend, and 250 pounds or more of fish may be produced in an acre of water annually.

In recent years a "fish flour" or "FPC" (fish protein concentrate) has been developed to provide a cheap source of protein for the world's expanding human population.

The top minnow (*Gambusia affinis*) has been propagated and distributed widely to aid in control of mosquitoes and malaria, by devouring mosquito larvae.

25-43. Fossil fishes. Bony fishes probably arose from primitive fishes during Silurian time. There were many ancient types, as revealed by fossils, before the ancestors of modern fishes appeared. Some Mesozoic relics still living are the African bichir, the spoonbill (*Polyodon*) of the Mississippi Valley, and the sturgeons. The ancient Order COELACANTHINI ranged almost unchanged from Lower Carboniferous to Cretaceous; long considered extinct, it is remarkable that several individuals of a large species (*Latimeria chalumnae*) of this order have been taken off southeastern Africa in recent years.

REVIEW

1. What classes of living vertebrates are properly called "fishes"? Do they have any distinctive characteristics in common?
2. Why are the lampreys and hagfishes regarded as the lowest in the vertebrate line? When did the nearest related class become extinct?
3. How do cyclostomes differ from cartilaginous fishes as to fins and scales?
4. Describe the life history of a parasitic lamprey.
5. What characters distinguish the cartilaginous fishes from cyclostomes? From bony fishes?
6. To what class do each of the following belong: ray, slime eel, chimaera, perch?
7. How does the respiratory system differ as to structure and function in a lamprey, shark, and carp?
8. Give a plausible theory as to the origin of paired fins in fishes.
9. In what kinds of fishes do the following types of scales occur: cycloid, placoid, ctenoid? How does the scale grow on a bony fish?